Engineering Fluid Mechanics

ENGINEERING FLUID MECHANICS

DR. R.J. GARDE
Professor Emeritus
Department of Civil Engineering
Indian Institute of Technology
Roorkee

DR. A.G. MIRAJGAOKER
Retired Principal
National Institute of Technology
Jamshedpur

Publishing for future
SCITECH PUBLICATIONS (INDIA) PVT. LTD.
www.scitechpublications.com

SCITECH PUBLICATIONS (INDIA) PVT. LTD.
Old No: 3, New No: 5,
Bakthavachalam Street,
Tambaram West, Chennai - 600 045.
E-mail: scitechcorp@yahoo.co.in
Visit us at www.scitechpublications.com

Branches:

HYDERABAD: scitech_hyd@yahoo.co.in
KOLKATA: scitech_kol@yahoo.co.in
NEW DELHI: scitech_del@yahoo.co.in

Reprint, July 2019

978 81 8371 563 8

Published by M. R. Purushothaman for Scitech Publications (India) Pvt. Ltd., Old No: 3, New No Bakthavachalam Street, Tambaram West, Chennai - 600 045. Printed at Printed at AKL Pri Chennai.

PREFACE

The present text on Engineering Fluid Mechanics deals with the, basic aspects of fluid mechanics and fluid machinery, and is an outgrowth of the authors' experience in teaching fluid mechanics to the undergraduate and postgraduate students in engineering over four decades. It was first published in 1965 and over a period of years it has undergone changes based on authors' experience.

The contents of the text cover the fluid mechanics syllabus for undergraduate classes of most of the Indian Universities in the north as well as the south. Hence it can serve as the text for undergraduate classes in Civil, Mechanical and Chemical Engineering, and can also be useful to the diploma students and to the students who are preparing for competitive examinations.

Certain features of the book need to be mentioned. Firstly, the book is written in SI units. Secondly, the authors have departed from the accepted sequence of chapters on Fluid Statics and Equations of Motion. Since Fluid Statics can be considered as the special case of Fluid Dynamics when the external forces acting on the fluid are in equilibrium, and hence the fluid mass is either stationary or moves bodily at a constant velocity, the presentation of fluid statics after equations of motions seems more logical and has been adopted here. Also to make the maximum use of the technique of Dimensional Analysis, this chapter is introduced at an earlier stage so that the functional relationships for various flow phenomena discussed later can be explored. Further, the text contains an extended chapter on Open Channel Flow for the benefit of Civil Engineering students, and three chapters on Fluid Machinery. Lastly a number of objective questions for all the chapters are given at the end of the text. It is hoped that answering these questions will improve students' understanding of fluid mechanics principles.

Over a period of years, several of authors' colleagues and former students have given valuable assistance through discussion, review of the manuscript and solution of the problems. Among them mention may be made of Professors K.G. Ranga Raju, P.K. Pande, R.C. Malhotra, R.L.Misri, M.K. Magazine, V.P. Gupta, U.C. Kothyari and late Sri. S.N.P.Sharma. Authors greatly appreciate their assistance. Authors are also thankful to SCITECH Publications (India) Pvt Ltd., Chennai for the excellent co-operation they have given in the publication of this text.

PUNE
February: 2003

R.J. GARDE
A.G. MIRAJGAOKER

PREFACE

The present text on Engineering Fluid Mechanics deals with the basic aspects of fluid mechanics and fluid machinery and is an outgrowth of the authors' experience in teaching fluid mechanics to the undergraduate and postgraduate students in engineering over four decades. It was first published in 1965 and over a period of years it has undergone changes based on authors' experience.

The contents of the text cover the fluid mechanics syllabi for undergraduate classes of most of the Indian Universities in the north as well as the south. Hence it can serve as the text for undergraduate classes in Civil, Mechanical and Chemical Engineering and can also be useful to the diploma students and to the students who are preparing for competitive examinations.

Certain features of the book need to be mentioned. Firstly, the book is written in SI units. Secondly, the authors have departed from the accepted sequence of chapters on Fluid Statics and Equations of Motion. Since Fluid Statics can be considered as the special case of Fluid Dynamics when the acceleration forces acting on the fluid are in equilibrium and hence the fluid mass is either stationary or moving bodily at a constant velocity, the presentation of fluid statics after equations of motion seems more logical and has been adopted here. Also, to make the maximum use of the technique of dimensional analysis, the chapter is taken up at an earlier stage so that the functional relationships for various flow phenomena discussed later can be explored. Further, the text comprises an extended chapter on open channel flow for the benefit of Civil Engineering students, and three chapters on Fluid Machinery. Lastly a number of objective questions for all the chapters have been included in the text. It is hoped that answering these questions will improve understanding and thinking of fluid mechanics principles.

Over a period of years, several of authors' colleagues and former students have [illegible] [illegible] critical review of the manuscript and [illegible] the [illegible]. Among them mention may be made of Professors [illegible] R.K. [illegible], [illegible], [illegible], R.C. Mishra, [illegible], V.P. Gupta, [illegible] and late Shri S.N.P. Sharma. Authors greatly appreciate their assistance. Authors are also thankful to [illegible] Publishers [illegible] for the excellent cooperation they have given in the publication of this text.

[illegible] R.J. GARDE

[illegible] 2003 A.G. MIRAJGAONKAR

Contents

CHAPTER ONE

PROPERTIES OF FLUIDS

1.1 Introduction

Matter exists in two states – the solid state and the fluid state. The fluid state is further divided into liquid state and gaseous state. This classification of matter is based on the spacing between different molecules of matter as well as on the behaviour of matter when subjected to stresses. Because molecules in solid state are spaced very closely, solids possess compactness and rigidity of form. The molecules in a liquid can move more freely within the liquid mass and therefore the liquids do not possess any rigidity of form. The molecules in a gas are spaced farther apart and as such they have greater freedom of movement. Due to the difference in molecular spacing, the solids and the fluids behave differently when subjected to stresses. A solid when subjected to a shearing stress deforms until the internal shear resistance is equal to the externally applied stress. This is not so in the case of fluids. As soon as a small shearing stress is applied to a fluid it starts deforming and continues to do so as long as the applied stress exists. In other words, fluids tend to flow when they are subjected to a shear stress. On the basis of this property, fluids can be defined as substances which deform or yield continuously due to application of shear stress, no matter how small it is.

It must be remembered that there is no clear line of demarcation between solids, liquids and gases. Under appropriate conditions a solid can be melted to a liquid state and a liquid can be vapourised into a gas and vice versa.

Similarly, there are certain solids which exhibit characteristics of fluids with a slight increase in temperature. Solids as well as liquids are reduced in volume when they are subjected to compressive stresses. Solids are the least compressible while gases are the most compressible. For all practical purposes, liquids are considered incompressible even though they can be compressed slightly. Due to this, liquids and gases exhibit properties which are different from those of solids. Liquids occupy a certain volume and they have a free surface. On the other hand, gases have a tendency to expand and fill the container in which they are kept; they cannot have a free surface.

Fluid Mechanics is a science which deals with the behaviour of fluids when subjected to a system of forces. In general, it involves the study of kinematics, dynamics and statics. Kinematics deals with the space-time relationships for fluid flow. In other words, it deals with displacements, velocities, accelerations and rotations of fluid mass. Dynamics deals with certain aspects of fluid flow concerning acceleration, forces, energy losses and their variation. Statics deals with the cases in which the forces on a fluid mass are in equilibrium. Study of kinematics, dynamics, and statics is developed on the basis of Newtonian mechanics. In its generalised form, fluid mechanics serves as a basis for the study of various fields in engineering, e.g. hydraulics, irrigation engineering, environmental engineering, hydraulic machinery, lubrication, chemical engineering, aeronautics, meteorology, oceanography, biomedicine, plasma physics, etc.

In the present text the basic laws of fluid mechanics which are applicable to the class of fluids known as Newtonian fluids (see Sect. 1.5) will be discussed. Commonly encountered fluids such as water, air, kerosene, glycerine, and thin lubricating oils fall under this category.

1.2 Development of Fluid Mechanics

The earlier development in the science of fluid flow has been influenced by two basic schools of thought, one dealing with the theoretical aspect and the other with the practical aspect of fluid flow. In the 17th century, mathematicians and mathematical physicists studied the behaviour of the so called *ideal fluid* in which the shearing stresses were assumed to be nonexistent. An ideal fluid is supposed to have no viscosity (inviscid), surface tension and compressibility. This branch of fluid mechanics which deals with ideal fluids is known as *classical hydrodynamics*. Notable contributions to this field have been those of Euler, Lagrange, D'Alembert, Kelvin, Bernoulli, and many others. Although hydrodynamics gives considerable insight into several problems of fluid flow, the assumption of no viscosity leads to unrealistic solutions for many practical problems.

Realising the limitations of hydrodynamics, engineers felt the need for some empirical relationships for fluid flow which could be used in solving every day problems. These efforts resulted in a branch of engineering known as *hydraulics* the main basis for which has been experimental observations. Hydraulics supplied answers to practical problems in water supply, irrigation engineering, and water power. In a broad sense, experimental hydraulics is the study of flow of water in pipes and open channels. Many engineers have contributed to the development of hydraulics, notable amongst them being Chezy, Dubuat, Venturi, Bazin, Hagen, Poiseuille, Darcy and Weisbach. Even though the equations in hydraulics have found practical utility in several problems, it is not possible to extend these to cope with the more challenging problems in aerodynamics and the flow of fluids other than water, Hence, there was a definite need for a new approach to the problems of fluid flow-an approach which relied on hydrodynamics for its logical development and at the same time on experimental means for checking the validity of the theoretical analysis. Such a need is fulfilled by Fluid Mechanics.

Fluid Mechanics takes a balanced view of both the theorists and the experimentalists. As is the case with Mechanics of Solids, Fluid Mechanics also is based on the fundamental laws of motion with the theoretical results being checked by experimental studies. Since all fluids and their properties are considered in fluid mechanics, its scope is very wide embracing the fields of hydraulic machinery, aeronautics, chemical engineering, etc. Some of the foremost contributors to fluid mechanics are Prandtl, Blasius, Karman, Nikuradse, Schlichting, Taylor, and Rouse. Fluid Mechanics is relatively a new science; it began taking shape around the beginning of. the 20th century. Some leaders in Hydraulics and Fluid mechanics and their contributions are listed below.

287 – 212B.C. Archimedes : Principles of buoyancy and flotation

1452 – 1519 Leonardo Da Vinci : Continuity equation, flow visualization, hydraulic machinery

1623 – 1662 Blaise Pascal : Pascal's law about pressure, barometer

1642 – 1727 Issac Newton : Newton's laws of motion, resistance

1695 – 1771 Henri de Pi.ot : Velocity measurement through differential head

1700 – 1782 Daniel Bernoulli : Energy principle in fluid motion

1707 – 1783 Leonhard Euler : Equations of Motion

1718 – 1798 Antoine Chezy : Flow resistance in channels

1733 – 1799 Jean Charles Borda : Efflux through tubes, expansion loss formulation

1736 – 1813 Joseph Louis Lagrange : Velocity potential and stream function concepts

1746 – 1822 Giovanni Batista Venturi : Venturimeter and mouth pieces

1785 – 1836 L.M Henri Navier : Equations of motion for laminar flow

1797 – 1886 Jean – Claude Barre de Saint – Venant : Generalised equations of motion for laminar and turbulent flow.

1799 – 1860 Jean Louis Poiseuille : Flow through capillary tubes

1803 – 1858 Henry Darcy : Experiments on filtration, pipe and open channel resistance

1806 – 1871 Julius Weisbach : Weir and resistance equations

1810 – 1879 William Froude : Towing tank experiments, waves, resistance prediction from scale models

1815 – 1892 James B. Francis : Tests on Turbines and diffusers

1816 – 1897 Robert Manning : Open channel resistance

1818 – 1888 G.G.Stokes : Navier – Stokes' equations, flow past sphere

1824 – 1907 Lord W.H. Kelvin : Vortex motion, stability of flows, waves

1829 – 1908 Lester Allen Pelton : Design of Pellon wheel

1842 – 1929 Joseph Boussinesq : Velocity distribution and turbulence

1857 – 1959 Franz Prasil : Flow-net

1857 – 1953 Ludwig Prandtl : Boundary layer Theory

1881 – 1963 Theodor Von Karman : Turbulent flow, velocity distribution

(source: History of Hydraulics by Hunter Rouse and Simon Ince, 1957)

In the more complex application of fluid mechanics one has to utilise the theories of thermodynamics, mass transfer, electromagnetism, etc. in addition to the principles of fluid mechanics. Man's quest for outer space and journey to the moon have given an added stimulus to the study of fluid mechanics.

The scope of fluid mechanics is so vast that one can find innumerable problems in every day life which require application of fluid mechanics for their solution. Flow of water and oil through soil-strata, design of efficient hydraulic structures in river valley projects, dynamics of aeroplanes, rockets and missiles, analysis of cyclones, surges and waves, design of lubricators and chemical engineering plants, resistance to flow of fluids in conduits and open channels, flow around immersed bodies, and flow of blood in veins are a few of the applications.

In the most generalised form, one must study the behaviour of individual molecules which make up the fluid. However this is not necessary if the number of molecules per unit volume is quite large, because in such a case one can consider the behaviour of the fluid as a continuous mass. This condition is satisfied by liquids and also by gases at moderate and high pressure. At very low pressures this is not the case. When liquids and gases can be treated as a continuous mass of fluid, they are called *continuum*.

Whether a gas can be treated as continuum or not depends primarily on the mean free path between molecules in comparison with characteristic length of flow and the time elapsed between collisions of the molecules. The former should be less than about one precent of characteristic length to consider a gas as a continuum.

1.3 Units of Measurement (SI Units)

The units of measurement used in mechanics are based on Newton's second law of motion, viz. $F = (M \times a)$ in which F is the force, M is the mass and a is the acceleration. There are two basic systems of measurement; these are known as the absolute or physicist's system, and the gravitational system. The primary unit in the absolute system is the unit of mass, whereas in the gravitational system the primary unit is the unit of force. The absolute metric system of units in which kilogramme is the unit of mass, metre is the unit of length and second is the unit time, forms the basis of an internationally agreed system of units since 1960. This system is known as SI units (Systeme Internationale d'unites). In SI units the basic units are the following:

TABLE 1.1

SI Base Units

Quantity	SI Units	Abbreviation in SI
Length	metre	m
Mass	kilogramme	kg
Time	second	s
Electric current	ampere	A
Luminance	candela	cd
Thermodynamic temperature	kelvin	K
Temperature	celsius	G

In SI units, force is a derived quantity. A force which produces an acceleration of 1.0 m/s² in a mass of 1.0 kg is known as one newton (N). Therefore,

$$1.0\ \text{N} = 1.0\ \text{kg} \times 1.0\ \text{m/s}^2$$

Such other derived units commonly used in mechanics pertain to the physical quantities work or energy, power and frequency. Since work equals force multiplied by distance, one joule (J) of work is done when 1.0 newton (N) force acts through 1.0 m. Power, which is work done per second, has SI name of watt (W);

$1\ \text{W} = \frac{1\text{J}}{1\text{s}} = 1\ \frac{\text{N m}}{\text{s}}$. The name for frequency in SI units is hertz (Hz) and has the dimension s^{-1}. Certain rules and conventions are to be followed in using SI units; these include the following :

1. Names of units, even when they are named after persons, are not written with first letter capital, e.g. joule, kelvin, and newton.
2. The symbol for the unit, named after the persons, has a capital initial letter, e.g. W for watt. J for joule, etc.
3. Other symbols are written in lower case. e.g. m, s, kg, etc.
4. Symbols for units do not take plural form e.g. 100 m and not 100 ms.
5. A space is left between the symbols for compound units. e.g. N m, kW h.
6. Numerals with more than three digits should be written in groups of three with narrow space in between consecutive groups. However, a sequence of four figures is not usually broken, e.g.

40000 should be written as	40 000
81235.876 should be written as	81 235.876
0.12468 should be written its	0.12 468

7. Prefixes indicating multiplying factors can be used, such as

tera	T	12^{12}	centi	c	10^{-2}
giga	G	10^{9}	milli	m	10^{-3}
mega	M	10^{6}	micro	μ	10^{-6}
kilo	10^{3}	nano	n	10^{-9}	
deci	d	10^{-1}	Pico	p	10^{-12}

However, the prefix should be attached to the quantity in numerator and not in the denominator.

1.4 Mass Density, Specific Weight, Specific Volume and Relative Density

Since fluid mechanics treats fluid in general, one does not deal with individual fluid but deals with fluid properties which affect the motion. Thus while studying fluid motion, only the variation of these properties and the manner in which they influence the motion need be studied.

Amongst the fluid properties density or *mass density* is probably the most important property. The mass density of a fluid, designated by a symbol ρ(Rho), is the fluid mass per unit volume. Mathematically the mass density at a point is given as

$$\rho = \lim_{\Delta V \to 0} (\Delta F / \Delta V) \quad (1.1$$

where ΔM is an incremental mass is an incremental volume ΔV surrounding the point. In SI units ρ is expressed in kilogramme per cubic metre (kg/m³). The mass density of a fluid depends on the space co-ordinates and the temperature. In other words,

$$\rho = \rho\ (x, y, z, T),$$

where x, y and z are the co-ordinates of a point at which the mass density is considered and T is the temperature at that point. In several engineering problems the mass density can be assumed constant. However, the spatial variation in mass density becomes important when large changes in elevation are encountered and also in heat transfer problems. The mass density is an index of the inertial characteristics. The greater the mass density, the more difficult it is to set the fluid in motion.

Specific weight, designated by γ (Gamma), is the weight of fluid per unit volume. It represents the force exerted by gravity on a unit volume of fluid and therefore, it has units of force per unit volume. It is expressed as newtons per cubic metre (N/m³). The specific weight depends on the mass density and the gravitational acceleration; hence it varies from place to place due to changes in density and gravitational acceleration.

The mass density ρ and the specific weight γ are related as follows

$$\gamma = \rho g \qquad \text{or} \qquad \rho = \frac{\gamma}{g} \quad (1.2$$

Value of g equal to 9.806 m/s² should be used.

Specific volume v is the volume of the fluid per unit weight. It is the reciprocal of specific weight, i.e., $v = 1/\gamma$, having dimensions of m³/N. Specific volume is commonly used in problems involving gas flows.

Relative density (sometimes known as specific gravity) of a fluid is the ratio of its mass density to that of pure water at a standard temperature and pressure, i.e. at 4°C and 101.325 kN/m². For gases the standard mass density is that of air or hydrogen at specified temperature and pressure. Being a pure number, the relative density is independent of the system of units used.

1.5 Viscosity

Earlier, while defining fluids, it was mentioned that fluids cannot resist shearing stresses. Nevertheless, there is still cohesion and interaction between fluid molecules. As a consequence all fluids possess *viscosity*. The viscosity of a fluid is a very important property in the analysis of motion of real fluids near a solid boundary. When two layers of fluid, a distance dy apart, move one over the other at different velocities, say u and (u + du), see Fig. 1.1, the viscosity together with relative velocity causes a shear stress acting between the fluid layers. The fast moving upper layer causes a shear stress on the slow moving lower layer in the positive u direction. Similarly the lower layer causes a shear stress in the opposite direction on the upper layer. This shearing stress designated as τ (Tau) between layers of nonturbulent fluid moving in straight parallel lines is proportional to the rate of change of velocity with respect to y. This can be written as

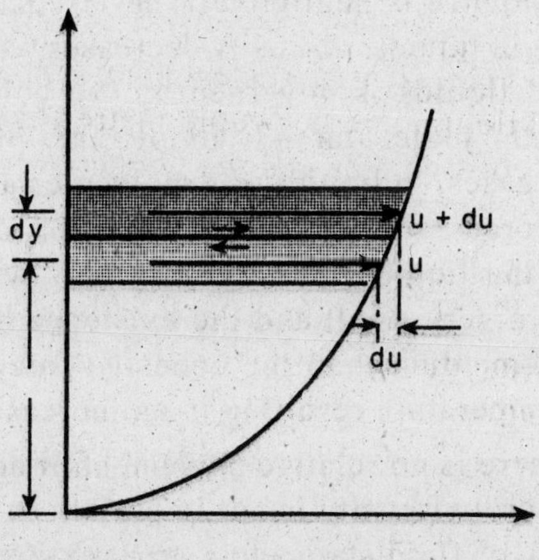

Fig.1.1 Variation of velocity near a boundary

$$\tau \propto \frac{du}{dy} \tag{1.3}$$

Introducing the constant of proportionality μ (Mu), the relation 1.3 can be written as

$$\tau = \mu \frac{du}{dy} \tag{1.4}$$

This equation is called Newton's law of viscosity and fluids which follow this law are known as *Newtonian fluids*. The constant of proportionality μ is known as the *coefficient of dynamic viscosity* or only viscosity. In transposed form Eq. 1.4 becomes

$$\mu = \frac{\tau}{du/dy} \tag{1.5}$$

If one considers a vertical element dy, its upper end will move a distance du with respect to the lower end in one second. Hence, du/dy will represent rate of angular deformation. Thus the dynamic viscosity can be defined as the shear stress required to produce unit rate of angular deformation. Because of the property of viscosity, the fluid sticks to the boundary; therefore if the boundary is stationary, the fluid velocity there is zero.

In mechanics of solids a shear modulus of elasticity, which is analogous to the coefficient of dynamic viscosity of fluids, is defined as the shear stress required to produce unit (one radian) angular deformation. There is a distinct difference between a solid and a Newtonian fluid in the manner in which they behave when subjected to a shear stress. Under the application of shear stress, a solid deforms until the internal shear resistance is equal to the externally applied shear stress; it is then in equilibrium. A fluid on the other hand, continues to deform as long as the shear stress is applied. Therefore, while the total deformation is important in solids, the rate of deformation is important in fluids. Common fluids such as air. water, glycerine and kerosene follow Eq. 1.4.

The viscosity of a fluid is a function of temperature primarily and pressure very slightly. In most cases pressure dependence is negligible. The viscosity of a gas increases with increase in temperature while in liquids, viscosity decreases with increase in temperature. This is because viscosity of liquids is governed by the cohesive forces between the molecules of liquid whereas the molecular activity of gases plays a dominant role in the existence of the viscosity of gases. In liquids, the molecules are very closely spaced and consequently the cohesive forces are also large. Cohesion decreases with increase in temperature and, therefore, the liquid viscosity decreases with rise in temperature. In gases, the cohesive forces are very small and the existence of viscosity is more due to the transfer of molecular momentum than the cohesive forces. The molecular activity increases with increase in temperature resulting in an increase in viscosity.

When fluids are at rest, there is no relative movement of adjacent layers and so shear stresses do not exist. Therefore, viscosity is not important in the study of fluids at rest. This fact simplifies the study of fluid statics to a great extent. It is only when there is a relative motion between different fluid layers that viscosity comes into the picture.

The dimensions of viscosity can be found from Eq. 1.5.

$$[\mu] = \left[\frac{\tau}{du/dy}\right] = \frac{N/m^2}{(m/s)/m} = \frac{N\,s}{m^2}$$

Alternately, it can be shown that dimensions of μ can be expressed as kg/m s. The dynamic viscosity can also be expressed in the units of *poise*; one poise equals 0.10 N s/m^2. As most fluids have low viscosities, a unit *centipoise* which is one hundredth of a poise is commonly used. It has another advantage; water has a viscosity of one centipoise a 20°C and viscosity of any liquid in centipoise at 20°C is an indication of the viscosity of that fluid relative to water.

In many problems of fluid flow, the ratio of viscosity to mass density appears very frequently which is called *kinematic viscosity* and is expressed by a symbol ν (Nu). Kinematic viscosity has dimensions of length and time as in kinematics viz

$$[\nu] = \left[\frac{\mu}{\rho}\right] = \frac{\text{kg/m s}}{\text{kg/m}^3} = \text{m}^2/\text{s}$$

Other unit of kinematic viscosity is *stoke* [cm²/s]. *Centistoke* which is one hundredth of a stoke is often a more convenient unit of kinematic viscosity. Viscosity of fluid is important in many practical problems such as lubrication, flow through soil mass, fall of small particles in liquids, flow through channels and pipes, and wherever a flowing fluid comes in contact with boundary.

Viscosity of pure liquids is affected by suspension of particles (such as silt, clays, red blood cells, etc.) and by dissolved materials such as electrolytes and organic compounds.

When fine material is suspended in a liquid causing a stable suspension, the dynamic viscosity of the liquid is found to increase. For low concentrations of suspended material, the resulting suspension acts as a Newtonian fluid, its viscosity μ_m being given by Einstein's equation

$$\frac{\mu_m}{\mu} = 1.0 + 2.5\, C_v \qquad (1.6\text{ a})$$

where C_v is absolute volume concentration of suspended matter and μ is viscosity of clear liquid. For higher concentrations one can use Ward's equation

$$\frac{\mu_m}{\mu} = 1.0 + 4.5\, C_v \qquad (1.6\text{ b})$$

Whereas Einstein's equation is recommended to be used upto 0.3 concentration, Ward's can be used for higher values. With dilute solution of electroytes (molar concentrations C_m below 0.10 moles/m³) the dynamic viscosity varies according to the empirical relation

$$\frac{\mu_m}{\mu} = 1 + A\sqrt{C_m} + B\, C_m \qquad (1.6\text{ c})$$

where A is found to vary from 0.005 to 0.02 and B is smaller than 0.50. At high concentrations and/or when the suspended particles are flexible (e.g. long chain molecules, red blood cells) the fluid does not behave as Newtonian.

However, there are some fluids which do not follow Newton's law of viscosity. These are classified according to the relationship between shear and rate of deformation du/dy. *Ideal plastics* or *Bingham plastics* are characterised by the fact that they have a definite yield stress beyond which the shear stress is linearly related to du/dy; or

$$\tau = \tau_y + \mu\left(\frac{du}{dy}\right)$$

Drilling mud, sewage sludge, cement rock slurry, oil paints, tooth paste and suspension of granular solids at high concentrations behave as Bingham plastics. *Thyxotropic* liquids are those in which the relationship between shear and rate of deformation is nonlinear beyond a certain yield stress. Printer's ink falls in this category. In general Non-Newtonian fluids are those in which there is no yield stress and the relationship between τ and du/dy is nonlinear, viz.

$$\tau = k\left(\frac{du}{dy}\right)^n$$

where k is a proportionality constant and index n may vary between zero and greater than unity. Fluids with n less than unity are called *pseudoplastics*. Liquids such as milk, blood, paper pulp in water and colloids such as clay and gelatin behave as pseudoplastics. *Dilatant fluids* have n greater than unity. A common feature of dilatant fluids is that at low shear stress (low velocity) they behave as Newtonian fluids but like a solid at higher values. Aqueous solution of fine grained quartz and concentrated sugar solution, are a few examples of dilatant fluids. Fluid which does not possess viscosity, compressibility and surface tension is known as *ideal fluid*. Ideal fluid is a subject of discussion in classical hydrodynamics. Even though no fluid exists which can be really called as an ideal fluid, fluids having small viscosity can be treated as ideal fluids and analysis of flow of such fluids can be simplified in a certain class of problems. All fluids which have viscosity are known as *real fluids*. Figure. 1.2 gives diagramatic representation of different fluids.

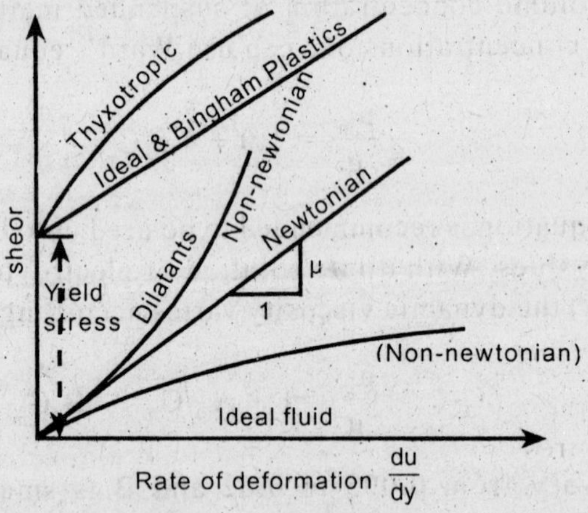

Fig.1.2 Rheological definition of differnt fluids

1.6 Pressure

As mentioned earlier, liquids and gases require a container to store them whereas solids do not require any container. Solids can be supported by a platform which resists its weight. On the other hand fluids exert a force on the walls of the container in which they are stored (otherwise they should have been able to retain shape). If ΔF represents this force over an area ΔA, the *pressure* p is defined as

$$p = \lim_{\Delta A \to 0} (\Delta F/\Delta A)$$

The pressure p can be expressed in N//m² or kN/m². One Newton per metre square pressure is sometimes called *pascal* (P_a). A more useful unit is *bar* which is equal to *100 000 N/m²*. Since the pressure force F is proportional to the area it is known as a surface force. If there is no relative motion between fluid layers, it can be shown that this force is always perpendicular to the surface. In general, the pressure (or pressure intensity) p varies with space and time, i.e.,

$$p = f(x, y, z, t)$$

Further, the pressure in a fluid, in a state of equilibrium is everywhere normal to the surface on which it acts and is the same in all directions at a point. A more detailed discussion on pressure will be presented in Chapter 4.

1.7 Compressibility and Elasticity

Fluids can be compressed by the application of external pressure; they will expand to their original volume once this external pressure is removed. This is known as the elastic property of fluid. Because of compressibility, the fluid density changes with pressure. This change in mass density due to change in pressure is very small in liquids and therefore, liquids are ordinarily considered incompressible. For instance water is generally considered to be incompressible, but in special problems like water hammer involving the travel of a pressure wave, the elastic properties of water come into play and have to be considered in the analysis. On the other hand, the mass density of gases changes appreciably with a variation in pressure and hence all gases are compressible. In some cases, such as air flowing in a ventilating system, the gas may be treated as incompressible because the pressure variation is so small that the change in air density is of little significance. But in most problems, for instance in the case of a gas flowing through a pipe line at high velocity, density changes are involved, if the drop in pressure is high. Similarly, when an airplane moves with a velocity greater than that of sound, the pressure of air adjacent to the body of airplane is different from that of the air some distance away and therefore, the air near the airplane is treated as a compressible fluid.

For analysing problems involving elastic characteristics of fluids, compressible fluids are characteristics by the property of modulus of elasticity. In the case of solids, the bulk modulus is defined as stress divided by volumetric strain. In an analogous manner, the modulus of elasticity for fluids is defined on the basis of volume change under a pressure increase of Δp.

Consider a cylinder containing a compressible fluid which is being compressed by a piston, as shown in Fig. 1.3 (a). The cylinder and the piston are assumed to be inelastic. Let the original volume of fluid be V_1. Suppose that due to the application of an additional force F of various magnitudes over area A, the pressure intensity p is increased thereby decreasing the volume to V.

If the ratio of V/V_1 is plotted against the pressure intensity p, (which corresponds to an increase in stress), a curve of negative slope, as shown in Fig. 1.3 (b) results. The *bulk modulus of elasticity* can be written as,

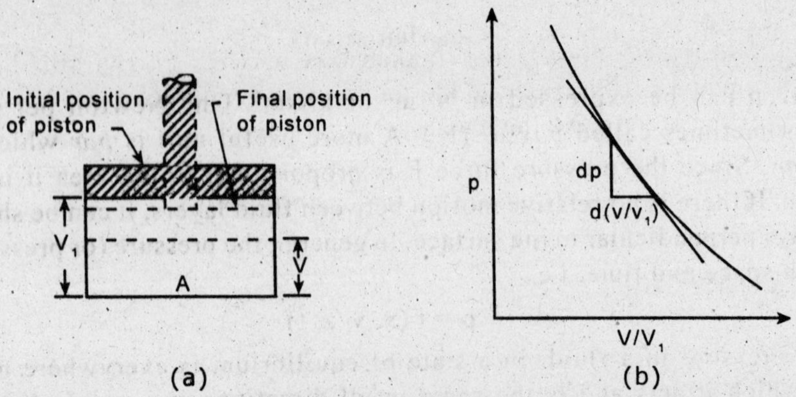

Fig.1.3 Definition sketch

$$E = \frac{\text{Stress}}{\text{Strain}} = -\frac{dp}{d(V/V_1)} = -v\frac{dp}{dv} \tag{1.7}$$

The negative sign implies that with an increase in p there is a decrease in the value of V/V_1. Here v is the specific volume.

The bulk modulus of elasticity is not constant for a fluid but necessarily depends on the pressure p. Since for gases, there is an intimate relationship between pressure and temperature, E depends on temperature also. For all practical purposes, however, it is sufficient to use the value of E at standard atmospheric pressure and temperature. The bulk modulus has the dimensions of (force/area); hence it is expressed either in N/m^2 or kN/m^2.

In the case of liquids the effect of compressibility can be neglected in most of the problems. However, there are some problems such as the rapid closure of valves, etc. where compressibility must be taken into account. If there is no appreciable change in pressure or elevation, gases can also be treated as incompressible without loss of much accuracy. In problems of gas flow where large changes in elevation, velocity and temperature are involved, compressibility must be considered.

Example 1.1

If the relative density of a liquid is 0.79 determine its mass, density and specific weight.

(Mass density of liquid) (Mass density of water) = 0.79

$$\therefore \quad \text{Mass density of liquid} = 998.0 \times 0.79 = 788.42 \text{ kg/m}^3$$

$$\text{Specific weight of liquid} = 788.42 \times 9.806 = 7731.25 \text{ N/m}^3 = 7.731 \text{ kN/m}^3$$

Example 1.2

Crude oil at 20°C (μ = 1.6 kg/m s) fills the space between two parallel horizontal plates which are 8 mm apart. If the upper plate moves with a velocity of 1.50 m/s, and the lower plate is stationary, determine the shear stress.

$$\frac{du}{dy} = \frac{1.50}{8\times10^{-3}} = 187.5\ s^{-1}$$

$$\tau = \mu\frac{du}{dy} = 1.6 \times 187.5$$

$$= 300.0\ N/m^2$$

1.8 Thermodynamic Properties

In the flow of a fluid the temperature is an important property since the viscosity of fluid is significantly affected by the temperature. The vapour pressure of liquids (see Sect. 1.10) is also affected by changes in temperature. In the case of gases the pressure, temperature and volume of the gas are related by the equation of state (see Sect. 1.9).

When the fluid comes in contact with a body with different temperature, such as cool air flowing over a warm land surface or vice versa, there is a transfer of heat from the warmer to cooler body. Therefore, temperature, is an important property in heat transfer phenomena. In connection with conductive heat transfer, one can define the thermal conductivity K as the ratio of conductive heat flow per unit area to the temperature decrease per unit length in direction normal to the area. In other words

$$H = -K\frac{\partial T}{\partial n}$$

where H is heat flow per unit area expressed in W/m^2 and $\partial T/\partial n$ is the temperature gradient K/m. The negative sign implies that the heat flow is in the direction of decreasing temperature. Here K is the coefficient of thermal conductivity, the units of which are W/m K.

Other thermodynamic properties which one must consider are specific heat at constant pressure, specific heat at constant volume, and entropy. These properties are discussed in Chapter 14.

1.9 Gas Laws

Unlike liquids, gases can be compressed into a very small volume by the application of suitable pressure, and on the other hand, if more space is given, they can fill it uniformly.

A large volume change under change in pressure is the distinguishing property between gases and liquids ; otherwise the properties of gases are similar to those of liquids. As in the case of liquids, the resistance to deformation for the gases vanishes, when they are at rest and they exhibit a definite viscosity if relative displacement occurs. The most important gas is the atmospheric air. The average atmospheric pressure at sea level is taken as equal to pressure of 0.760 m high column of mercury or 101.325 kN/m^2.

Compression and expansion in gases take place in accordance with the various laws of thermodynamics. According to Boyle's law, the product of absolute pressure and specific volume is constant provided the temperature remains the same. Such a process, taking place at constant temperature, is known as an *isothemal* process. If p and v represent the pressure intensity and specific volume for given mass of gas respectively, Boyle's law states that,

$$p\,v = \text{constant } C_1 \qquad (1.8)$$

On the other hand, if changes in volume take place in a manner such that the total amount of heat in the system remains unchanged, the *adiabatic* case is obtained. This case is governed by the law,

$$p\,v^k = \text{constant} \qquad (1.9)$$

In which k is known as the *adiabatic constant* and is the ratio of the specific heat at constant pressure to that at constant volume. If the adiabatic process is reversible, it is known as *isentropic* process. Values of k for various gases are given in Table 14.1. For air and other diatomic gases at standard temperature, k is taken to be 1.4.

Expressions for the modulus of elasticity E for gases can be obtained from Eqs. 1.8 and 1.9. Writing Eq. 1.8 in differential form, one obtains

$$v\,dp + p\,dv = 0$$

or
$$p = -\frac{dp}{dv/v} = E \qquad (1.10)$$

which is the same as Eq. 1.7 obtained earlier. Likewise, from Eq. 1.9 one can write,

$$kpv^{k-1}\,dv + v^k\,dp = 0$$

or
$$kp = -\frac{dp}{dv/v} = E \qquad (1.11)$$

for an isentropic process.

Another important gas law of thermodynamics is the Charles' law which expresses the variation of pressure p with absolute temperature T for a constant volume as

$$p/T = \text{constant } C_2 \qquad (1.12)$$

When one considers the general case in which pressure depends both on volume and temperature, one can write,

$$p = f(v.\,T)$$

and
$$dp = \frac{\partial p}{\partial v}dv + \frac{\partial p}{\partial T}dT$$

However, values of $\frac{\partial p}{\partial v}$ and $\frac{\partial p}{\partial T}$ can be obtained from Eqs. 1.8 and 1.12 as $-\frac{p}{v}$ and $\frac{p}{T}$ respectively. Hence

$$dp = -\frac{p}{v}dv + \frac{p}{T}dT$$

or
$$\frac{dp}{p} + \frac{dv}{v} = \frac{dT}{T}$$

Integration of this equation yields

$$\frac{pv}{T} = \text{constant} = R \qquad (1.3)$$

which is known as the *Equation of State* of gas, and R is called the gas constant having the dimensions of m/K. Introducing $\gamma = 1/v$, the above equations can be written as,

$$\gamma = \frac{p}{RT} \qquad (1.14)$$

The specific weight of gases can be readily calculated, at any temperature, from known values of R and Eq. 1.14.

Avogadro's law states that all gases at the same temperature and pressure have the same number of molecules per unit volume. The law leads to the result that the specific weight of a gas γ, is proportional to its molecular weight m. Hence,

$$\frac{\gamma_2}{\gamma_1} = \frac{m_2}{m_1} = \frac{R_1}{R_2}$$

or
$$m_1 R_1 = m_2 R_2$$

In other words, the product of the molecular weight m, and the gas constant R is the same for all gases. The product mR is known as the *Universal Gas Constant.* The value of the Gas Constant R, for air is 29.57 m/K. It is assumed that the equation of state is valid when the gas is in motion as well as at rest. Experimental results have amply supported this assumption.

1.10 Vapour Pressure

All liquids have a tendency to evaporate when exposed to the atmosphere. The rate of evaporation depends on the nature of the liquid, its temperature (i.e. molecular energy of the liquid) and condition of atmosphere just above the liquid surface. Consider a closed container partly filled with a liquid and maintained at a constant temperature. As the liquid evaporates, the number of vapour molecules in the air above the liquid increases. Simultaneously a small number of vapour molecules re-enter the liquid. With the passage of time the concentration of vapour molecules above the liquid surface increases to such an extent that the rate at which molecules enter the liquid is equal to the rate at which molecules leave the liquid. Thus a condition of equilibrium is reached, in which case the air above the liquid surface is saturated with vapour molecules. The pressure on the liquid surface exerted by the vapour molecules is called *vapour pressure* (or saturated vapour pressure), It can be seen that vapour pressure is dependent on temperature. A liquid having very high vapour pressure will evaporate more easily than a liquid having low vapour pressure. When the vapour pressure of a liquid is slightly greater than the pressure impressed on the surface, the liquid will boil.

Depending on the flow conditions, the pressure at any point can vary over a large range. If the pressure at any point in the liquid approaches the vapour pressure, the liquid starts vapourising and creates pockets or bubbles of dissolved gases and vapours. This phenomenon is known as *cavitation* and because of its destructive characteristics, every attempt is made to avoid the occurrence of cavitation in liquid flow problems.

1.11 Surface Tension and Capillarity

Two types of forces act between molecules of matter. The first one is directly proportional to the product of the masses of two molecules and inversely proportional to the square of the distance between their mass centres. This force can be called mass attraction. The second one is an electro-chemical attractive force between molecules which gives rise to the properties of *cohesion* and *adhesion*. This electro-chemical attractive force is effective over a very minute distance. The electro-chemical attractive force between two liquid molecules is known as cohesion.

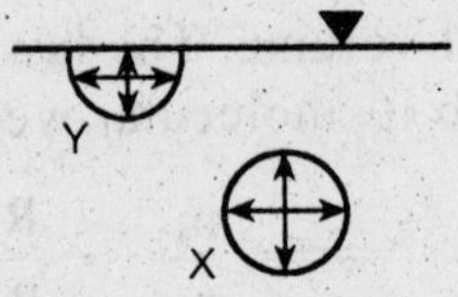

Fig.1.4 Intermolecular forces near liquid surface

Consider a molecule X (see Fig. 1.4) well below the liquid surface; it will be attracted equally on all sides by the neighbouring molecules and will therefore be stable. However, the molecule Y near the surface will have a resultant force acting in the downward direction and perpendicular to the surface. As a result the surface will be pulled down causing a curvature to the surface. This in turn develops a tension in the surface which is similar to the tension in a stretched membrane. This is known as *surface tension* σ which is a force per unit length with dimensions N/m. Presence of surface tension can be demonstrated by a simple experiment. A thin loop of thread is attached to a wire ring and is dipped in a soap solution so that it is covered with a thin film, see Fig. 1.5. The loop of thread does not take any particular position. Now if part of the film inside the thread is pierced, the thread loop is pulled out into a circular shape due to surface tension effect.

The downward force acting on the free surface in Fig. 1.4 depends not only on the attractive forces between liquid molecules but also on the attractive force between liquid molecules and those of medium above it (e.g. air molecules, or molecules of other liquid above it). Since the gas molecules are farther apart than liquid molecules, the cohesion between gas molecules or between gas and liquid molecules is negligible. Therefore, presence of gas in the case of liquid-gas interface has negligible effect on surface curvature. However, in the case of two immiscible liquids the presence of top liquid reduces the surface tension of lower one and hence has effect on surface curvature.

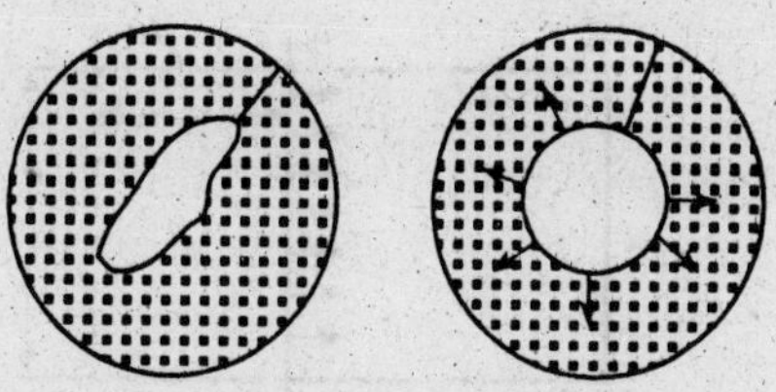

Fig.1.5 Effect of surface tension in a thin liquid film

Once the surface becomes curved, the existence of a normal force requires that an equal and opposite force must act in the fluid to maintain static equilibrium. Thus a pressure difference p must exist between the two sides of the curved surface. This can be evaluated by cutting a spherical droplet of radius r into two halves as shown in Fig. 1.6.

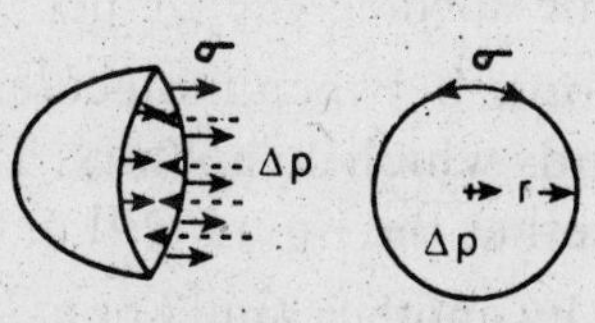

Fig.1.6 Definition sketch

The force due to surface tension σ acting along the circumference will be $2\pi r\sigma$ which will be balanced by pressure force acting on the area πr^2 viz $\pi r^2 \Delta p$. Hence

$$\pi r^2 \Delta p = 2\pi r\sigma$$

or

$$\Delta p = \frac{2\sigma}{r} \quad (1.15)$$

This shows that the pressure difference increases with the decrease in the size of droplet.

As mentioned earlier, the molecules on the free surface are acted upon by a net downward force and the surface is pulled down. In doing this, certain amount of work is done. The energy required to create the surface in this manner is known as *surface energy*. Expression for surface energy can be obtained in the following manner. A rectangular frame ABCD, in which the arm AD is not fixed but is capable of sliding, is taken (see Fig. 1.7). The frame is dipped in soap solution so that a film. ABCD is formed. The surface tension force acting on the wire AD of length l is

$$F = 2\, l\, \sigma$$

where σ is surface tension of the soap solution. The factor 2 appears because the soap film has two faces. If AD is now slid to new position A′ D′ through distance x, the work done W will be

$$W = F \times x$$
$$= 2\, l\, \sigma\, x$$

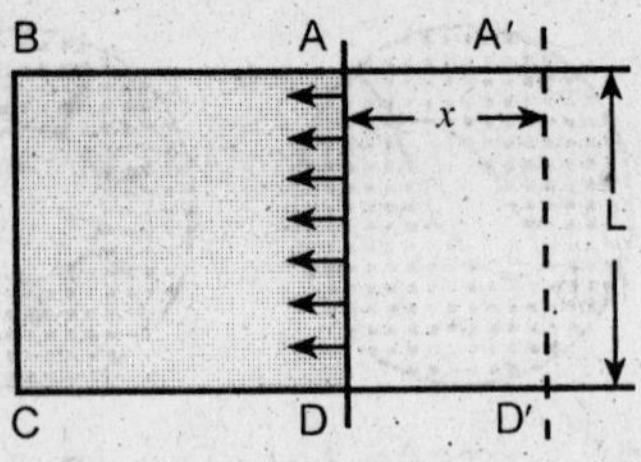

Fig.1.7 Work done by surface tension

But $2lx$ = increase in surface area ΔA. Thus

$$\frac{W}{2lx} = \text{work done per unit area} = \sigma$$

Therefore σ is also called the surface energy per unit area.

Adhesion is the attractive force between molecules of solids and liquids or between molecules of two different liquids which do not mix. The relative magnitudes of cohesive and adhesive forces decide whether the liquid will or will not wet the given surface.

When a liquid is surrounded by another liquid or gas and a solid, the condition becomes different as shown in Fig. 1.8. Here two fluids meet the solid surface at an angle θ. For equilibrium, the summation of horizontal components of surface tension and adhesive stresses must be zero. Hence

$$\sigma_{23} - \sigma_{13} = \sigma_{12} \cos\theta \qquad (1.16)$$

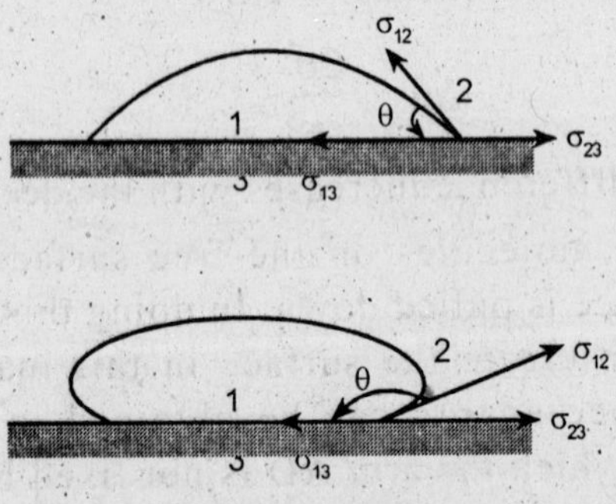

Fig.1.8 Liquid drop wetting the surface ($\theta < \pi/2$) and not wetting the surface ($\theta > \pi/2$)

where σ_{12} is surface tension of liquid 1 in contact with fluid 2, σ_{13} is the adhesive stress between liquid 1 and solid, and σ_{23} is the adhesive stress between fluid 2 and solid. If $(\sigma_{23} - \sigma_{13})$ is positive and less than σ_{12}, θ will be less than 90° and the liquid wets the surface. If $(\sigma_{23} - \sigma_{12})$ is negative and $|(\sigma_{23} - \sigma_{13})| < \sigma_{12}$, θ is greater than 90° and liquid does not wet the surface. If $(\sigma_{23} - \sigma_{13})$ is greater than σ_{12}, the above equation will not be satisfied at any angle which means that there will not be any equilibrium. In such cases the liquid creeps along the surface continuously. Such a phenomenon is shown by certain oils on glass or by oil drops on water. The angle θ is known as angle of contact. If surface is clean, θ is zero for water and about 140° for mercury.

One of the important applications of cohesion and adhesion is concerning *capillary rise* or *capillary depression* in small diameter tubes and in interstices of porous material. If adhesive stress predominates, a liquid such as water wets the glass surface and liquid will rise in a vertical capillary tube dipped in a liquid. On the contrary, if the surface tension predominates over adhesion then the liquid does not wet the surface and will tend to depress the point of contact resulting in capillary depression, see Fig. 1.9. For example if a glass tube of small diameter is inserted in water, the water will wet the surface of glass tube and rise to some height above the normal water surface. If the same tube is inserted in mercury, the level inside the tube will be lower than the adjacent mercury level.

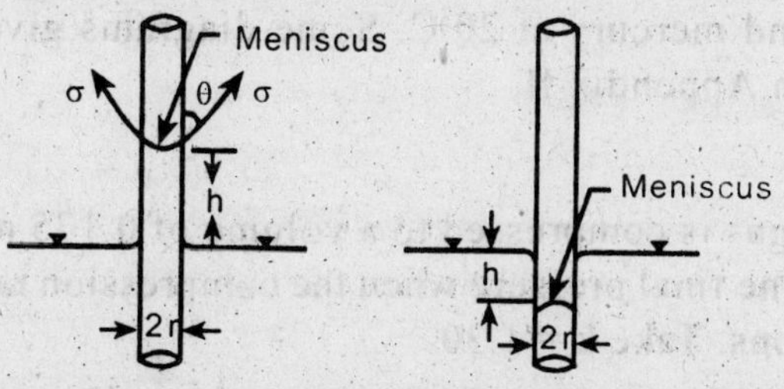

(a) Capillary rise in water (b) Capillary depression in mercury

Fig.1.9 Capillary rise and depression

Capillary rise or depression can be determined by considering the equilibrium condition in the tube. Let h be the capillary rise in a tube of radius r, see Fig. 1.9 (a). Under the state of equilibrium the weight of liquid column h is balanced by the force at the surface of the liquid due to surface tension σ.

Equating the two forces one gets

$$h\,\pi r^2\gamma = 2\,\pi r\,\sigma\cos\theta$$

in which γ is the specific weight of the liquid. This gives

$$h = \frac{2\sigma\cos\theta}{\gamma r}$$

As θ is approximately zero for water in glass, cos θ = 1 and expression for h becomes

$$h = 2\,\sigma/\gamma\,r \qquad (1.17)$$

Equation 1.17 shows that smaller the radius of tube, greater will be the capillary rise. The curved surface of liquid in the tube is known as *meniscus*. Fig. 1.9 (b) shows the capillary depression for mercury. When a needle is carefully placed lengthwise on the water surface, it floats even though it is heavier than water. This happens because component of surface tension force on two sides of needles balances the weight of the needle.

Capillary rise also takes place in soil mass. A soil mass can be considered to be made of innumerable small interstices which are interconnected. The average size of the opening depends on the characteristic diameter of the soil and its gradation. In general the average size of the pore is about 1/5 to 1/10 times the average size of soil particles. If such a soil mass is submerged in water upto a certain level, the water will rise above this level due to capillary action. This rise can be of the order of 2 to 3 m or more; the rise takes place gradually and may take a few days to weeks to attain the equilibrium height. The capillary rise can be calculated using Eq. 1.17 if one estimates the average size of the pore diameter.

For tubes of diameter 6 mm or more, the capillary rise is negligible for water. In general, the surface tension forces are important if the length dimension, such as the depth of flow or the diameter of opening is smaller than 6 mm. For most of the everyday problems in fluid mechanics, surface tension forces can be neglected.

In Table 1.2, are listed the properties of some of the common liquids such as water glycerinc, kerosene and mercury at 20°C. Some diagrams giving properties of common fluids are presented in Appendix II.

Example 1.3

0.5 cubic meters of a gas is compressed to a volume of 0.175 m³. If the initial pressure is 150 kN/m² determine the final pressure when the compression takes place under isothermal and adiabatic conditions. Take k = 1.30.

When compression takes place under isothermal condition

$$p_1 v_1 = p_2 v_2 \text{ or } p_2 = \frac{p_1 v_1}{v_2}$$

$$p_2 = \frac{0.5 \times 150}{0.175} = 428.571 \text{ kN/m}^2$$

Under adiabatic conditions,

$$p_1 v_1^k = p_2 v_2^k$$

$$p_2 = p_1 \left(\frac{v_1}{v_2}\right)^k$$

$$p_2 = 150 \times \left(\frac{0.5}{0.175}\right)^{1.3}$$

$$= 587.223 \text{ kN/m}^2$$

Example 1.4

Determine the depression of mercury level in a capillary tube of 1 mm diameter when is immersed in it.

Since σ = 0.51 N/m and γ = 132.800 kN/m³ for mercury,

$$h = \frac{2\sigma}{\gamma r} = \frac{2 \times 0.51}{132\,800 \times 1 \times 10^{-3}}$$

$$= 0.00\,768 \text{ m or } 7.68 \text{ mm}$$

1.12 Regimes in Fluid Mechanics

The flow of a fluid can be classified into various types depending upon the fluid properties which are important in a particular situation. The governing factors such as velocity, depth or diameter and the fluid properties are combined to give dimensionless parameters whose magnitude characterises the type of flow.

(a) Ideal Fluids, Newtonian Fluids, Non-Newtonian Fluids

In the case of ideal fluids one deals with a hypothetical fluid having no viscosity, no compressibility and no surface tension. Flow of such fluids can be dealt with analytically using methods of hydrodynamics. Such analysis yields valuable results in problems of flow of real fluids that are rapidly accelerating and also in the analysis of lift, waves, etc.

The flow of Newtonian fluids can be classified into *Laminar* and *Turbulent* flows. Laminar flows are characterised by low velocities, small length dimensions and large kinematic viscosities. Flow of water in capillary tubes, problems in lubrication, fall of small particles in fluid, etc. fail in this category. Turbulent flow is characterised by high velocities, large length dimensions and small kinematic viscosities. Such flow is a more common occurrence as in the case of river flows, pipe flow, flow of air over land surfaces, etc. Flow is classified into laminar or turbulent flow depending on the magnitude of nondimensional parameter called *Reynolds Number* (see Chapter 7).

Flow of Non-Newtonian fluids is dealt with separately since in such cases the analysis becomes more complicated due to nonlinear dependence of shear stress on velocity gradient.

(b) Compressible Flows, Magneto-Fluid Mechanics

In the case of gas flows the fluid compressibility has to be taken into account unless the variation in mass density is so small that it can be neglected. Flow of compressible fluids is also subdivided into *subsonic, transonic, supersonic* and *hypersonic* flows. This classification is based on the magnitude of *Mach Number* which is the ratio of characteristic velocity to velocity of sound. The ranges of Mach number for these flows are

Subsonic	0.40 to 1.00
Transonic	Slightly less than unity to slightly greater than unity.
Supersonic	1.00 to 6.00
Hypersonic	6.00 to 40.00

Furthermore, these flows can be divided into laminar or turbulent flows depending on whether viscosity is important or not. In addition, if gas at high temperature is to interact with magnetic field, one must take into account the fact that the gas, because of ionization, becomes conducting. Such a gas is called *plasma*. The science which deals with problems involving plasma and magnetic field is called *Magneto-fluid mechanics*. Such problems are encountered in re-entry of missiles, satellites, etc.

(c) Continuum and Free Molecular Flow

This classification is based on the fact that the mean free path of the molecules divided by the characteristic length of flow–which is called *Knudsen Number*–is an important parameter in determining whether the fluid behaves as continuum or not. If Knudsen number is less than 0.01, the compressible fluid acts as a continuum. In such case the velocity of fluid at the sationary boundary is zero. On the other hand if Knudsen number is greater than 10, the molecules are very wide apart and hence molecular interaction can be neglected. Such flow is known as *Free Molecular Flow.* In between these limits of Knudsen number one has what are known as *Slip Flows* and *Transition Flows.*

1.13 Fluid Properties and Analysis of Fluid Flow

The analysis of fluid flow with an assumption of ideal fluids-having no viscosity, surface tension and compressibility is amenable to a rigorous mathematical analysis. Considerable insight and information about the problem is obtained by such a simplification. For many problems, the solutions thus obtained by neglecting the effects of viscosity, compressibility and surface tension, are quite adequate. Hence more emphasis is placed on the results obtained using such simplifications. However, once such an approximate analysis is carried out, it is necessary to study how the flow characteristics are affected by these properties. In the latter part of the book, consideration is given to such effects. The analytical techniques in Fluids Mechanics are not adequately developed to consider the effects of gravity, surface tension and compressibility simultaneously. Thus their effects on the flow characteristics are to be considered individually as far as possible.

PROBLEMS

1.1. A liquid has a mass density of 1029.70 kg/m^3. Calculate its specific weight and specific volume.

1.2. If the mass density of a fluid is 799.23 kg/m^3 find its specific weight.

1.3. If a force of 100 N acts on an area of 4.0 cm^2, find the pressure intensity in kN/m^2.

1.4. If the kinematic viscosity of a fluid is 10^{-6} m^2/s and its density is 998 kg/m^3, find its dynamic viscosity.

1.5. Determine the specific volume of ethyl alcohol whose mass density is 788.45 kg/m^3.

1.6. Give two examples where fluid viscosity is an important property.

1.7. A liquid has a viscosity of 0.075 P and relative density of 0.85. Calculate the kinematic viscosity in stokes and m^2/s and dynamic viscosity in N s/m^2.

1.8. Air weighs 0.01179 kN/m^3. Find the kinematic viscosity of air if the viscosity is given as 1.78×10^{-4} P.

1.9. If the velocity distribution over a plate is given by

$$u = \frac{2}{3}y - y^2$$

in which u is the velocity in m/s at a distance y metres above the plate, determine the shear stress in N/m^2 at y = 0 and y = 0.15 metres. Take μ = 8.63 P.

1.10. At a certain point in a fluid the shear stress is 0.216 N/m^2 and the velocity gradient 0.267s^{-1}. If the mass density of the fluid is 1268 kg/m^3, find the kinematic viscosity.

1.11 A rectangular plate 1 m × 0.5 m weighing 980.7 N slides down a 30° inclined surface at a uniform velocity of 2.0 m/s. If the 2.0 mm gap between the plate and the inclined surface is filled with castor oil, determine the viscosity of the oil.

1.12 Assuming blood to consist of water with 50 percent by volume of red cells, compute its dynamic viscosity at 35°C using Ward's equation.

1.13 During an exceptional flood in the Ganga river the concentration of fine sediment in the Ganga canal was found to be 15 percent by volume. What will be the viscosity of water-sediment complex at 20°C ?

1.14 By increasing the pressure of a liquid from 7950 kN/m^2 to 11 470 kN/m^2 the volume of the liquid decreases by 1.5 percent. Determine the bulk modulus of the liquid.

1.15 The bulk modulus of a fluid is defined as E = –v dp/dv. Find an expression for E in terms of the pressure and mass density.

1.16 A cylinder contains 0.132 kN of gas and has a volume of 56.6 litres. It is under an absolute pressure of 0.1440 kN/m^2. If the gas is compressed to half of its volume isothermally, what will be the pressure?

1.17 A gas occupying a volume of 300 litres at a certain temperature and 340 kN/m^2 pressure, is compressed isothermally to 150 litres. Determine the final pressure and the initial and final volume moduli of elasticity.

1.18 The air in an automobile tyre is at 2940 kN/m^2 absolute pressure and 26.6°C. Assuming no change in the volume of air, what will be the pressure if its temperature rose to 65.5°C ?

1.19 In Problem 1.17, if the gas is compressed adiabatically determine the final pressure. Take k to be 1.40.

1.20 What should be the diameter of a droplet of water in mm if the pressure inside is to be 170 N/m^2 greater than the outside pressure ?

1.21 Assuming sap in trees rises purely due to capillary phenomenon, find the diameter of the tube in mm which can carry it to a height of 15.0 m? Assume the sap to have the same characteristics as those of water.

1.22 Two vertical parallel plates distance t apart are partially immersed in a liquid of surface rension σ and specific weight γ. Obtain an expression for the capillary rise h.

1.23 Assuming the depth of sea to be 11 000 m find the mass density of sea water at this depth if its relative density at sea level is 1.026. Take a constant value of $E = 2.113 \times 10^9$ N/m^2

1.24 Determine the capillary rise of water in a clay soil of average diameter 0.06 mm. Assume the average size of pores to be one fifth of the soil diameter.

1.25 Wollny conducted experiment on sand of average size 0.12 mm and obtained a capillary rise of 0.90 m at the end of 20 days. Find the ratio of average size of pores to the diameter of material.

1.26. Calculate the work done in blowing the soap bubble from a radius of 100 mm to 150 mm if σ for soap solution is 0.035 N/m.

TABLE 1.2

Properties of Some Common Fluids at 20°C and Atmospheric Pressure

			Dynamic viscosity μ		Kinematic viscosity ν				
Fluid	Mass density ρ kg/m²	Specific weight γ kN/m³	poise P	kg/m s	stoke St	m²/s	Modulus of Elasticity E N/m²	Surface tension in contact with air σ N/m	Vapour Pressure N/m²
Water	998	9.787	0.010	1.00×10^{-3}	1.00×10^{-2}	1.00×10^{-6}	2.075×10^{9}	0.0735	0.239×10^{4}
Glycerine	1260	12.356	8.350	8.35×10^{-1}	6.63	6.63×10^{-4}	4.354×10^{9}	0.0637	1.373×10^{-2}
Carbon Te-trachloride	1594	15.632	0.010	1.00×10^{-3}	6.04×10^{-3}	6.04×10^{-7}	1.104×10^{9}	0.0265	1.275×10^{4}
Kerosene	800	7.845	0.020	2.00×10^{-3}	2.50×10^{-2}	2.50×10^{-6}	-	0.0235	-
Benzene	860	8.434	0.007	7.00×10^{-4}	8.14×10^{-3}	8.14×10^{-7}	1.0356×10^{9}	0.0255	1.000×10^{4}
Caster Oil	960	9.414	9.800	9.80×10^{-1}	1.00×10^{1}	1.00×10^{-3}	1.441×10^{9}	0.0392	-
Ethyl Alcohol	789	7.737	0.012	1.20×10^{-3}	1.52×10^{-2}	1.52×10^{-6}	1.118×10^{9}	0.0216	5.786×10^{3}
Mercury	13 550	132.800	0.016	1.60×10^{-3}	1.18×10^{-7}	1.18×10^{-7}	2.431×10^{10}	0.510	1.726×10^{-1}
Air	1.208	0.011 85	1.85×10^{-4}	1.85×10^{-5}	1.53×10^{-1}	1.53×10^{-5}	-	-	-

Chapter Two

Kinematics of Fluid Flow

2.1 Introduction

The fluid motion can be analysed on lines similar to the ones used in mechanics of solids. However, there is one essential difference between motion of a solid and motion of a fluid. When a solid body is moving, it moves as a single entity; hence it is not necessary to consider the motion of individual particles in the solids. This is not so in the case of fluids. Because of extreme mobility of the fluid particles, each particle can move differently from the other, even though there may be some inter-relationship between motion of neighbouring fluid particles. For this reason, when one deals with fluid motion one must study the motion of individual fluid particles. The study of fluid flow begins with description of the motion of a fluid particle. The present chapter deals primarily with space-time relationship for fluids; this is known as the *Kinematics* of fluid flow.

There are two methods by which the motion of a fluid can be described. In the first method, the observer focusses his attention on a single fluid particle and deals with the history of this particle i.e. his primary interest is to find out what happens to these individual fluid particles with the passage of time. What paths do they trace ? What are their velocities and accelerations ? This is known as *Lagrangian* method of describing the fluid motion. In the second method-known as *Eulerian* method-the observer's concern is to know what happens at any given point in the space which is filled by the fluid. The questions that are answered are-what are the velocities, accelerations, pressures, etc. at various points in space at a given time ? Of these two methods, the Eulerian method is used in the following analysis, because this is more useful in the analysis of problems in fluid mechanics which are dealt within this text. Eulerian approach is also known is control volume approach. A control volume is defined as a volume fixed with respect to co-ordinate system in fluid flow system,

2.2 Visualisation of Flow Pattern

Since the fluids under consideration are homogeneous, it is impossible to distinguish between various fluid particles and follow the paths traced by certain fluid particles. Hence it is not possible to visualise the flow pattern unless some special means are used to label the fluid particles. Such means include introduction of a dye in the flowing liquid, introduction of foreign fluid bubbles in the flowing liquid, or introduction of smoke in the flowing gas. These and similar means make visible the fluid particles which are moving and the flow pattern can be easily photographed. Such flow patterns when predicted or observed give a variety of information about the flow phenomenon and hence the study of the methods of obtaining flow patterns becomes very important. The present chapter ultimately gives techniques of obtaining flow patterns for a certain class of flows. However, before discussing such methods some basic concepts in fluid mechanics must be developed.

2.3 Velocity

As mentioned earlier, in any particular flow phenomenon, each fluid particle can have different characteristics of motion. This motion of the fluid particles is expressed in terms of a quantity known as *velocity*. Velocity is a vector quantity and hence it has a magnitude as well as direction. If Δs is the distance travelled by the fluid particle in time Δt, then

$\lim\limits_{\Delta t \to 0} \frac{\Delta s}{\Delta t}$ is called the velocity V_S. The direction of velocity is along the tangent as shown in Fig. 2.1. However the distance Δs can be resolved into distances Δx, Δy and Δz in the x, y and z directions respectively. Hence the velocity vector V_S can also be resolved into u, v and w components, which represent velocities in the x, y, and z directions respectively. The magnitudes of u, v and w will in general depend on x, y and z viz. the location of point under consideration and the time t. The time t is introduced to take into consideration the fact that the velocity at any given point can change from time to time. Hence the velocity V_S and its components u, v, w are functions of x, y, z and t; or

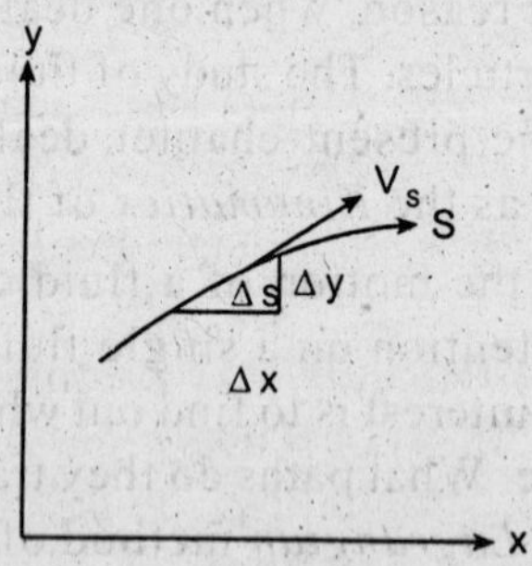

Fig.2.1 Definition sketch

$$\left.\begin{aligned} V_S &= f_1 (x, y, z, t) \\ u &= f_2 (x, y, z, t) \\ v &= f_3 (x, y, z, t) \\ w &= f_4 (x, y, z, t) \end{aligned}\right\} \qquad (2.1)$$

In the vector notation one can write

$$\overline{V} = u\,i + v\,j + w\,k \qquad (2.1\ a)$$

where i, j and k are unit vectors in x, y and z directions respectively. For different problems the functional relationships in Eq. 2.1 will be different and finding out the forms of these functional relationships is the primary aim in the solution of the problem.

2.4 Types of Flow

If the fluid or the flow property–such as density, velocity, and pressure at any given point does not change with the passage of time i.e., if it has the same magnitude (and direction if it is a vector quantity) for various times, the flow is termed as *steady flow*. On the other hand, if these characteristics at a given point x_0, y_0, z_0, change with time, the flow is termed *unsteady flow*. For incompressible fluids the mass density does not change; however for compressible fluids i.e. gases, the density can change from point to point and from time to time. Considering velocity as one of the characteristics of the flow (which is a function of x, y, z, and t), the above condition for steady and unsteady flows can be stated as follows : If partial derivative of V_s with respect to t is zero, the flow is steady and if partial derivative is not zero, the flow is unsteady. or

$$\left.\begin{aligned} \left(\frac{\partial V_s}{\partial t}\right)_{x_0,y_0,z_0} &= 0 \text{ for steady flow} \\ \left(\frac{\partial V_s}{\partial t}\right)_{x_0,y_0,z_0} &\neq 0 \text{ for unsteady flow} \end{aligned}\right\} \qquad (2.2)$$

If a water faucet is kept half open and left untouched and if other conditions remain the same, then the velocity at any point in the pipe or the quantity of water coming out of the pipe will remain unchanged and hence the flow is steady. On the other hand if the faucet is slowly opened, the velocity will also change accordingly and the flow will be unsteady. However, it must be remembered that the velocity at any point can change either in magnitude or in direction. Therefore, a change in the direction of velocity vector can also make the flow unsteady.

If the fluid or the flow characteristics at any given time remain the same at different points in the direction of flow, the flow is known as *uniform flow*. If, however, the characteristics, at any given time, change with distance, the flow is called *non-uniform flow*. Thus, along the s direction

$$\left.\begin{aligned} \left(\frac{\partial V_s}{\partial s}\right)_{t_0} &= 0 \text{ for uniform flow} \\ \left(\frac{\partial V_s}{\partial s}\right)_{t_0} &\neq 0 \text{ for non-uniform flow} \end{aligned}\right\} \qquad (2.3)$$

Thus in the case of a pipe whose diameter gradually increases from D_1 to D_2, the velocity decreases in the direction of flow even if the quantity of flow flowing per unit time remains unchanged. As such the flow is non-uniform. On the other hand if the diameter remains same and quantity of fluid flowing remains the same, the flow will be uniform. Similarly, for the condition of the constant flow, if the depth in a river either increases or decreases along the length, the flow is non-uniform. The change in direction can also make the flow non-uniform. Hence for a constant quantity of fluid flowing, the flow in a pipe bend is non-uniform.

It is possible to have flows that are

(i) steady, uniform;

(ii) steady, non-uniform;

(iii) unsteady, uniform; and

(iv) unsteady, non-uniform.

Since the flow and the fluid characteristics such as velocity, pressure, density, temperature, can vary with space and time i.e. with x, y, z and t, the problems involving such variations are quite complicated to solve. On the other hand, the solution is considerably simplified if these quantities do not vary in one or more directions. Thus, if the flow conditions do not vary in the direction of the z axis i.e., if the flow conditions are identical in planes perpendicular to the z axis, the flow is called *two dimensional flow*. Consider a river which is straight and very wide ; in such a case the conditions of flow do not vary in the direction of the width i.e., in the lateral direction. Similarly, flow of a fluid between parallel plates, when the width of the plates is large, can be considered two dimensional. In many other problems a further simplification can also be made by assuming that the flow characteristics vary only in one direction i.e. in the direction of flow. Such a flow is called *one dimensional flow.* Two or one dimensional flows can be either unsteady or steady depending on whether quantities such as pressure or velocity vary with time or not. Thus considering the velocity as one of the flow characteristics, the following expressions can be written :

	Unsteady	*Steady*
Three dimensional	$u = f(x, y, z, t)$,	$u = f(x, y, z)$
Two dimensional	$u = f(x, y, t)$,	$u = f(x, y)$
One dimensional	$u = f(x, t)$,	$u = f(x)$

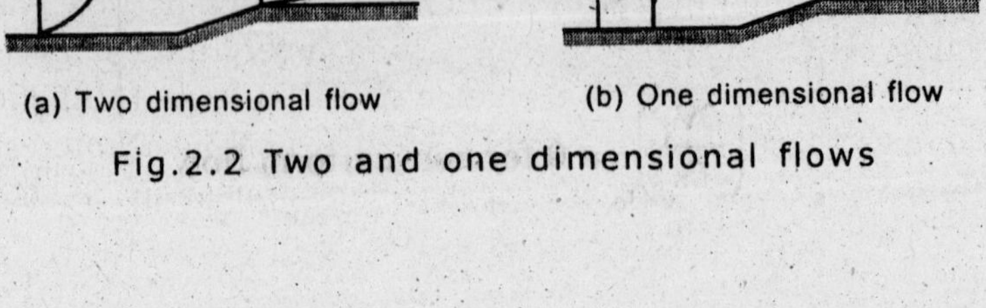

(a) Two dimensional flow (b) One dimensional flow

Fig.2.2 Two and one dimensional flows

Similar relations can be written for other flow or fluid characteristics. Figure 2.2 shows examples of two dimensional and one dimensional flows.

2.5 Stream Lines, Path Lines, Streak Lines and Stream Tubes

Suppose it were possible to know the direction and the magnitude of the velocity at any instant at every point in the space in which the fluid flow occurs. Then at every point in this space (see Fig. 2.3) arrow can be drawn whose direction indicates the direction of velocity at that point. If curved lines such as AB, CD, etc. are drawn such that the velocity vectors at all the points lying on the curves are tangent to the curve, such curves are called *stream lines*. The series of stream lines drawn in this manner will represent the flow pattern at that instant. If the flow is unsteady, the streamline pattern may or may not remain the same at the next instant. If the unsteadiness is due to a change in the magnitude of the velocity, then the stream line pattern still remains the same at different times. On the other hand, if the unsteadiness is due to change in the direction of the velocity, the pattern will change from time to time.

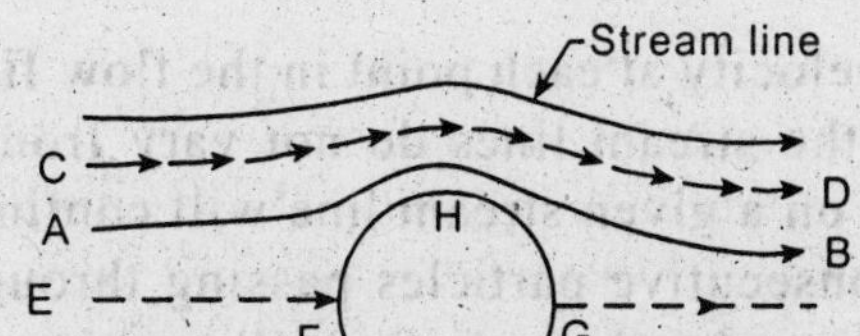

Fig. 2.3 Steady flow past a circular cylinder

Consider two dimensional flow. Since at any point along a stream line, the tangential velocity V_s will have u and v as the components in x and y directions and since the slope of the stream line at the same point is dy/dx, one can write

$$\left.\begin{aligned} \frac{dy}{dx} &= \frac{v}{u} \\ \text{or} \quad u\,dy - v\,dx &= 0 \end{aligned}\right\} \qquad (2.4)$$

Equation 2.4 is the differential equation for stream line. If the velocity components are known as functions of space coordinates, Eq. 2.4 can be integrated to give the equation of the stream line.

Further, consider that attention is focussed on a certain fluid particle by making it visible and a line is traced along which this fluid particle travels. The line traced in this way is known as a *path line.* Such a path line for the case of a body moving in a fluid at a uniform velocity is shown in Fig. 2.4. If the motion of a fluid particle A is considered at successive time intervals Δt, the particle will be found every time in a new position with respect to the body and hence will have a velocity in a different direction. When such paths are joined, one gets the path line. Further, suppose that one is interested in the locus of all fluid particles which pass through a particular point in space. This can be easily by inserting dye or smoke in the fluid at that point. The resulting line obtained is known as *streak line.* Figure 2.4 also shows a typical streak line passing through point B. The figure also shows unsteady state stream lines.

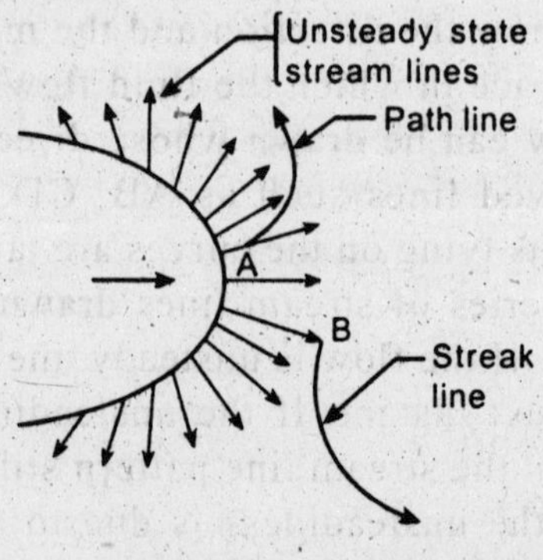

Fig.2.4 Path line

If the flow is steady, the velocity at each point in the flow field remains constant with respect to time and, hence, the stream lines do not vary from one instant to the next. Therefore, a particle located on a given stream line will continue to remain on the same stream line. Furthermore, consecutive particles passing through a fixed point in space will be on the same stream line and, subsequently, will remain on this stream line. Thus in a steady flow, path lines, streak lines and stream lines are identical lines. In unsteady flow, path lines, streak lines and stream lines do not coincide.

Another concept which is of considerable use in analysing the fluid flow problems is that of a *stream tube,* Stream tube can be defined as a group of stream lines. The bounding surface of the stream tube is made up of several stream lines as shown in Fig. 2.5. The properties of the stream lines make the concept of stream tube quite useful. Since at any point along a streamline the velocity is tangential to the streamline, the component of velocity at right angles to the streamline is always zero ; i.e. there is no flow across the stream line. As the surface of a stream tube is made up of numerous stream lines, one can conclude that there is no flow across the surface of a stream tube. In the case of flow through pipes or flow between fixed boundaries (see Fig. 2.2) there is no flow across the boundary surface. Therefore, the stream tube surface behaves like a boundary as far as the condition of "no flow at right angles to the surface" is concerned. If one considers two dimensional flow, a stream tube will be bounded by only two stream lines. The concept of a stream tube is very helpful in discussing the principle of the conservation of mass.

2.6 Principle of Conservation of Mass

There are three basic principles for analysing the problems in mechanics of solids. These are

(i) Principle of the conservation of matter.

(ii) Principle of the conservation of energy.

(iii) Principle of the conservation of momentum.

Fig.2.5 Stream tube

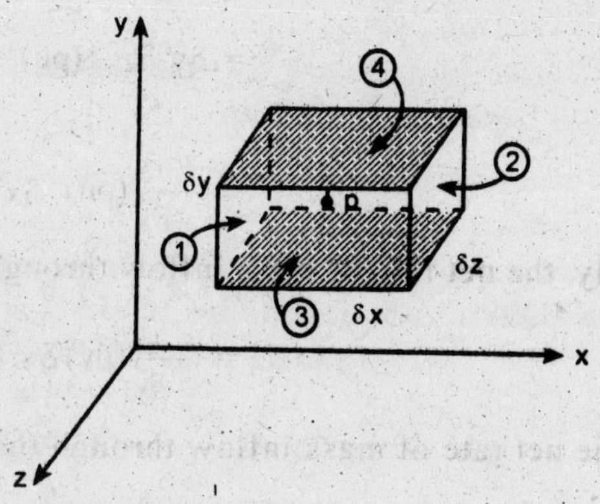

Fig.2.6 Elementary parallelopiped

The counterparts of the above principles in fluid mechanics are the *continuity equation*, the *energy equation* and the *momentum equation* respectively. The continuity equation, which expresses the principle of conservation of mass or matter-is derived in this chapter. The energy equation as well as the momentum equation are derived from the Newton's second law of motion. Energy equation is derived and its applications studied in Chapters 3 and 5 while the momentum equation is dealt with in Chapter 6.

Continuity equation expresses the fact that matter can neither be created nor destroyed. In order to develop the continuity equation consider an elementary parallelopiped with sides δx, δy and δz, see Fig. 2.6. Let P (x, y, z) be the centre of parallelopiped and let u, v and w represent the velocities in the x, y and z directions respectively at the point P. Let ρ represent the mass density of the fluid. Then the mass of fluid passing through area δy δz through point P is (ρu δy δz). Because (ρu), in general varies in x direction (for given y and z values) the mass flowing in through face (1) per unit time will be

$$= (\rho u\, \delta y\, \delta z) - \frac{\partial}{\partial x}(\rho u\, \delta y\, \delta z)\,\frac{\delta x}{2}$$

$$= \delta y\, \delta z \left\{(\rho u) - \frac{\partial}{\partial x}(\rho u)\frac{\delta x}{2}\right\} \qquad (2.5)$$

Similarly the mass flowing out through face (2) per unit time due to the u component of velocity is

$$= (\rho u\, \delta y\, \delta z) + \frac{\partial}{\partial x}(\rho u\, \delta y\, \delta z)\,\frac{\delta x}{2}$$

$$= \delta z\, \delta y \left\{(\rho u) + \frac{\partial}{\partial x}(\rho u)\frac{\delta x}{2}\right\} \qquad (2.6)$$

Hence the net rate of inflow of mass through faces (1) and (2) is obtained by subtracting Eq. 2.6.from Eq. 2.5 i.e.

$$= \delta y\ \delta z \left\{(\rho u) - \frac{\partial}{\partial x}(\rho u)\frac{\delta x}{2} - (\rho u) - \frac{\partial}{\partial x}(\rho u)\frac{\delta x}{2}\right\}$$

$$= -\frac{\partial}{\partial x}(\rho u)\ \delta x\ \delta y\ \delta z \quad (2.7)$$

Similarly, the net rate of mass inflow through faces (3) and (4) is

$$= -\frac{\partial}{\partial y}(\rho v)\ \delta x\ \delta y\ \delta z \quad (2.8)$$

Also, the net rate of mass inflow through the other two faces perpendicular to z axis is

$$= -\frac{\partial}{\partial z}(\rho w)\ \delta x\ \delta y\ \delta z \quad (2.9)$$

Since ($\rho\ \delta x\ \delta y\ \delta z$) represents the mass of fluid in the parallelopiped, $\frac{\partial}{\partial t}$ ($\rho\ \delta x\ \delta y\ \delta z$) i.e. $\frac{\partial \rho}{\partial t}\ \delta x\ \delta y\ \delta z$ represents the rate of change of mass of the parallelopiped. Evidently the total rate of mass inflow into the parallelopiped through all the faces must be equal to the rate of change of mass of the parallelopiped. Or

$$\delta x\ \delta y\ \delta z\ \frac{\partial \rho}{\partial t} = -\frac{\partial(\rho u)}{\partial x}\ \delta x\ \delta y\ \delta z - \frac{\partial(\rho v)}{\partial y}\ \delta x\ \delta y\ \delta z - \frac{\partial(\rho w)}{\partial z}\ \delta x\ \delta y\ \delta z \quad (2.10)$$

Dividing both sides of Eq. 2.10 by the volume of the parallelopiped, ($\delta x\ \delta y\ \delta z$), Eq. 2. 10 becomes

$$\frac{\partial \rho}{\partial t} + \frac{\partial(\rho u)}{\partial x} + \frac{\partial(\rho v)}{\partial y} + \frac{\partial(\rho w)}{\partial z} = 0 \quad (2.11)$$

In the vector notation Eq. 2.11 can be written as

$$\frac{\partial \rho}{\partial t} + \text{div}\,(\rho\,\overline{V}) = 0 \quad (2.11a)$$

in which $\overline{V}$ is the velocity vector. This is known as the continuity equation in a cartesian coordinate system. This equation is applicable for

(i) Steady as well as unsteady flows.

(ii) Uniform and nonuniform flows.

(iii) Compressible as well as incompressible fluids.

If the fluid is incompressible (homogeneous or nonhomogeneous), the mass density ρ is constant with respect to time. Also ρ of a unit volume will not change as it moves through δx, δy and δz. Therefore, for incompressible fluids, Eq.2.11 reduces to the form

$$\frac{\partial u}{\partial x} + \frac{\partial v}{\partial y} + \frac{\partial w}{\partial z} = 0 \qquad (2.12)$$

For several practical purposes, the continuity equation can be greatly simplified on the basis of stream tube concept. Equation 2.11 is derived for a unit volume since it has been obtained from Eq. 2.10 by dividing all terms by δx δy δz. Consider a stream tube in Fig. 2.5. Since the flow is always in the tangential direction and there is no component of velocity in the normal direction, both the velocity V_S and the cross-sectional area A will depend on s–the distance along the axis of stream tube. Hence

$$\frac{\partial}{\partial t}(\rho A\ \delta s) + \frac{\partial}{\partial s}(\rho\ V_S\ A)\ \delta s = 0$$

in which the distance along the s–axis is taken as δs. Dividing all terms by the volume of the element (A δs), one gets

$$\frac{\partial \rho}{\partial s} + \frac{1}{A}\frac{\partial}{\partial s}(\rho\ V_S\ A)\ \delta s = 0$$

If the fluid is incompressible, $\frac{\partial \rho}{\partial t} = 0$ and therefore

$$\frac{\partial}{\partial s}(\rho\ A\ V_S) = 0 \qquad \text{or} \qquad V_S\ A = \text{constant},$$

since ρ is constant. But V_S A = q which is the rate of flow of fluid or discharge. Hence

$$q = V_{S1}\ A_1 = V_{S2}\ A_2 = V_{S3}\ A_3 \qquad (2.13)$$

in which A_1 A_2, A_3 are the elementary areas of the stream tube and V_{S1}, V_{S2}, V_{S3} are the velocities at the centres of areas A_1, A_2, A_3. If the fluid is compressible and flow is steady,

$$\frac{\partial}{\partial s}(\rho\ V_S\ A) = 0$$

or

$$\rho\ V_S\ A = \text{constant}$$

i.e.

$$\rho_1\ V_{S1}\ A_1 = \rho_2\ V_{S2}\ A_2 = \rho_3\ V_{S3}\ A_3 \qquad (2.14)$$

Thus for compressible fluids one must take into account the variation of mass density along s direction.

If the areas A_1, A_2, A_3 are of very small magnitude, Eqs. 2.13 and 2.14 give accurate results. However, when the areas are large, the above equations are only approximately true. The reason is that, it has been implicitly assumed that V_S represents the velocity over the cross-sectional area A. If the areas are large this may not be true. Hence in the case of large areas, if the above equations are to give correct results, the velocity variation over the cross-sectional area must be taken into consideration. Otherwise the area A must be subdivided into smaller areas a_1, a_2, a_3, a_4, see Fig. 2.7 (a). By considering the actual tangential velocities over these areas as V_{S1}, V_{S2}, V_{S3}, etc., one can write

Total discharge $\qquad Q = q_1 + q_2 + q_3 + \ldots$

$$= V_{S1}a_1 + V_{S2}a_2 + V_{S3}a_3 + \ldots$$

Or, if V_1 is the average velocity over the area A_1 then

$$Q = V_1\,(a_1 + a_2 + a_3 + \ldots)$$

or $$Q = V_1\,A_1$$

The expression for the *average velocity* V can therefore be written as

$$V = \frac{Q}{A} = \frac{1}{A}\int_A V_S\,da$$

It can also be seen that since no flow enters or leaves the stream tube through its bounding surface and since matter is neither created nor destroyed in the stream tube,

$$Q = V_1\,A_1 = V_2A_2 = V_3\,A_3$$

Hence if the area increases, the velocity of flow must reduce and if the area decreases velocity must increase. In other words, the velocity is inversely proportional to the cross sectional area. If the flow is two dimensional and if Δn_1, Δn_2, Δn_3 etc. represent the spacing between two stream lines, see Fig.2.7(b), then according to the continuity equation

$$V_{s1}\,\Delta n_1 = V_{S2}\,\Delta n_2 = V_{S3}\,\Delta n_3$$

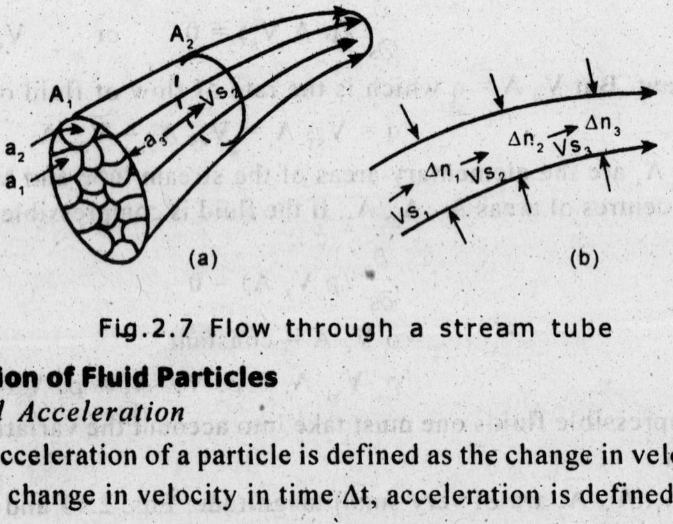

Fig.2.7 Flow through a stream tube

2.7 Acceleration of Fluid Particles

(a) *Tangential Acceleration*

In mechanics the acceleration of a particle is defined as the change in velocity per second. Thus if ΔV_S is the change in velocity in time Δt, acceleration is defined as

$$\lim_{\Delta t \to 0} \frac{\Delta V_S}{\Delta t} = \frac{dV_S}{dt} = a_S$$

Since acceleration is a vector, it has magnitude as well as direction and as is the case with the velocity vector, the acceleration vector can be resolved into three components along x, y and z directions respectively. However, there is an essential difference between the velocity vector and the acceleration vector. As described earlier, the velocity is always tangential to the curve along which the particle travels irrespective of whether the velocity changes in its magnitude or direction. The velocity can vary as the particle moves from one place to another if the flow is non-uniform (in such case the spacing between streamlines must vary). The acceleration, because of this change in velocity, is necessarily in the direction of velocity. The velocity at a point can also vary in its magnitude if the flow is unsteady. Both these accelerations are in the tangential direction, the first is known as *convective acceleration* and the second is known as *local acceleration*. For unidirectional flow, convective acceleration can be obtained as follows:

$$\frac{\Delta V_S}{\Delta t} = \frac{\Delta V_S}{\Delta s} \cdot \frac{\Delta s}{\Delta t}; \text{ but } \frac{\Delta s}{\Delta t} = V_s$$

Hence,

$$\frac{dV_S}{dt} = V_S \frac{\partial V_S}{\partial s} \qquad (2.15)$$

This is convective tangential acceleration.

Example 2.1

The velocity distribution for laminar flow between parallel plates is given by

$$u = K\,(Dy - y^2)$$

where u is the velocity at a distance y from the bottom plate, D is the spacing between the plates and K is constant. Determine the average velocity of flow.

The average velocity will be given by

$$U = \frac{1}{D}\int_0^D u\,dy = \frac{1}{D}\int_0^D K\,(Dy - y^2)\,dy$$

$$= \frac{K}{D}\left[\frac{Dy^2}{2} - \frac{y^3}{3}\right]_0^D = \frac{KD^2}{6}$$

It may be mentioned that K has the dimensions $L^{-1}\,T^{-1}$ and is a function of viscosity and the pressure gradient.

Example 2.2

In a two dimensional steady flow, the spacing between two stream lines is 3 cm at A and 1.5 cm at B, AB being 10 cm. If the velocity for steady flow is 0.50 m/s at A, determine the convective accelerations at A and B.

$$(V_S)_B \times 1.5 = 0.5 \times 3 \qquad \therefore (V_S)_B = 1.0 \text{ m/s}$$

$$\therefore \frac{\partial Vs}{\partial s} = \frac{1.0 - 0.50}{0.10} = 5.0 \text{ s}^{-1}$$

$$\therefore \text{Acceleration at A} = (V_S)_A \frac{\partial Vs}{\partial s} = 0.50 \times 5 = 2.50 \text{ m/s}^2$$

$$\text{Acceleration at B} = (V_S)_B \frac{\partial Vs}{\partial s} = 1.0 \times 5 = 5.0 \text{ m/s}^2$$

The characteristics of the convective acceleration are that it is due to non-uniformity of flow and it is in the tangential direction. This type of acceleration is therefore more appropriately known as *convective tangential acceleration*.

If in the Example 2.2 the discharge is suddenly increased, then the velocity at any point say A will also increase. Therefore there will be acceleration at any point due to unsteadiness.

Let original discharge be 150 cm³/s cm. Let the new discharge at the end of 2 seconds be 300 cm³/s cm.

∴ Initial velocity at A = 50 cm/s or 0.50 m/s

Final velocity at A = 100 cm/s or 1.0 m/s

Hence the velocity at A changed by 0.50 m/s in 2 seconds. Therefore the local acceleration at A will be 0.25 m/s².

The two characteristics of this *local acceleration* are that it is due to unsteadiness of flow and it is in the tangential direction. This is, therefore, more appropriately known as *local tangential acceleration*. Thus, the total tangential acceleration is

$$\frac{dV_S}{dt} = \frac{\partial V_S}{\partial t} + V_s \frac{\partial V_S}{\partial s} \tag{2.16}$$

(b) *Normal Acceleration*

In the above discussion, variation in the magnitude of the velocity vector has been considered. The velocity, however, can change in its magnitude as well as in its direction. The change in the direction and the acceleration produced by it are now considered.

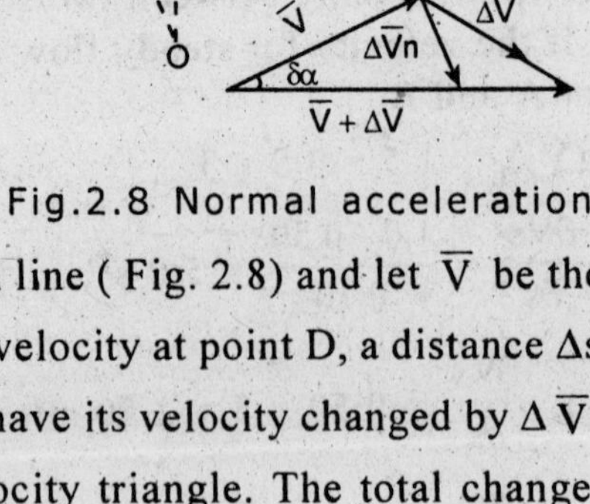

Fig.2.8 Normal acceleration

Consider a curved stream line (Fig. 2.8) and let $\overline{V}$ be the tangential velocity at point A and let ($\overline{V} + \Delta\overline{V}$) be the velocity at point D, a distance Δs apart. Thus, a fluid particle travelling from A to D will have its velocity changed by $\Delta\overline{V}$. This change in the velocity is shown by drawing a velocity triangle. The total change in the velocity $\Delta\overline{V}$ can be resolved into two components ΔV_s and ΔV_n. It is true that at point A there is no normal velocity component. However, as the fluid particle travels from A to D, there is a small component in the direction perpendicular to the stream line at A. Thus, since the velocity s always tangential to the streamlines, ΔV_n must represent velocity in the normal direction at A. Considering the similarity of two triangles one can write,

$$\frac{\Delta V_n}{V} = \frac{\Delta S}{R}$$

$$\therefore \quad \frac{\Delta V_n}{\Delta S} = \frac{V}{R} \qquad (2.17)$$

n which R is the radius of curvature of the streamline. Hence, acceleration in the normal irection will be

$$\frac{\Delta V_n}{\Delta t} = \frac{\Delta V_n}{\Delta S}\frac{\Delta S}{\Delta t} = \frac{V}{R}V = \frac{V^2}{R} \text{ or } \frac{V_S^2}{R}$$

This is the normal acceleration caused by the fact that the fluid particle is moving long a curved path. This acceleration is, therefore, known as *convective normal* cceleration. It can also happen that because the flow conditions change with time, the irection of the velocity at a point can also change with time. The normal acceleration aused by the unsteadiness of flow is known as *local normal acceleration.* It is presented by $\frac{\partial V_n}{\partial t}$. Hence the total normal at acceleration at a point is given by

$$\frac{dV_n}{dt} = \left(\frac{\partial V_n}{\partial t} + \frac{V_S^2}{R}\right)$$

hus for steady flow :

convective tangential acceleration is present, if the normal spacing between the stream lines changes;

) the convective normal acceleration is present, if the stream lines are curved, and

i) if the normal spacing between stream lines changes, and if the stream lines are curved, both the tangential and normal accelerations are present.

Figure 2.9 schematically shows the stream line patterns and the type of accelerations the case of steady flow.

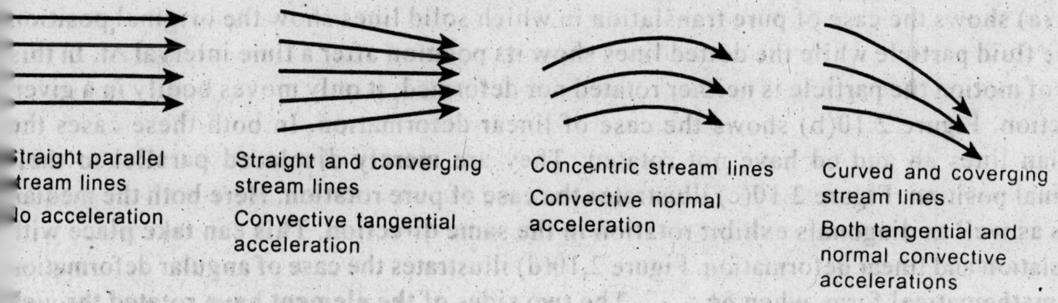

Fig.2.9 Streamline patterns and convective accelerations

The general expressions for acceleration can be obtained by taking the total differentials of expressions for u, v and w as given in Eq. 2. 1. Thus since u = u (x, y, z, t) one can write the expression for total change in u as

$$du = \frac{\partial u}{\partial x} dx + \frac{\partial u}{\partial y} dy + \frac{\partial u}{\partial z} dz + \frac{\partial u}{\partial t} dt$$

However dx = u dt, dy = vdt and dz = wdt. Hence

$$du = u\frac{\partial u}{\partial x} dt + v\frac{\partial u}{\partial y} dt + w\frac{\partial u}{\partial z} dt + \frac{\partial u}{\partial t} dt$$

Or

$$a_x = \frac{du}{dt} = u\frac{\partial u}{\partial x} + v\frac{\partial u}{\partial y} + w\frac{\partial u}{\partial z} + \frac{\partial u}{\partial t} \quad (2.19a)$$

where a_x is the total acceleration in the x direction. Similarly following expressions can be obtained for a_y and a_z,

$$a_y = \frac{dv}{dt} = u\frac{\partial v}{\partial x} + v\frac{\partial v}{\partial y} + w\frac{\partial v}{\partial z} + \frac{\partial v}{\partial t} \quad (2.19b)$$

$$a_z = \frac{dw}{dt} = u\frac{\partial w}{\partial x} + v\frac{\partial w}{\partial y} + w\frac{\partial w}{\partial z} + \frac{\partial w}{\partial t} \quad (2.19c)$$

The first three terms on R.H.S. of Eqs. 2.19 a, b and c represent convective acceleration while the last term represents local acceleration in that direction. It can be seen that Eq. 2.16 is a simplified form of Eq. 2.19 (a) when v = w = 0.

2.8 Rotational and Irrotational Motions

While considering the kinematics of fluid flow it is necessary to study another characteristic of the flow which is the angular velocity of the fluid elements about their mass centres. Fluid motion in which the fluid particles do not rotate about their own axes is known as *irrotational motion* or *irrotational flow*. On the other hand, fluid motion in which the fluid particles rotate about their own axes is known as *rotational motion*.

In general, a fluid particle can undergo the following basic types of displacements: (i) pure translation (ii) linear deformation (iii) angular deformation and (iv) rotation. Figure 2.10 (a) shows the case of pure translation in which solid lines show the original position of the fluid particle while the dotted lines show its position after a time interval Δt. In this type of motion the particle is neither rotated nor deformed; it only moves bodily in a given direction. Figure 2.10(b) shows the case of linear deformation. In both these cases the median lines ab and cd have not rotated. They are merely displaced parallel to their original position. Figure 2.10(c) illustrates the case of pure rotation. Here both the median lines as well as diagonals exhibit rotation in the same direction. This can take place with translation and linear deformation. Figure 2.10(d) illustrates the case of angular deformation in a mathematical form when $\delta\phi = \delta\theta$. The two sides of the element have rotated through equal angle but in oppsite directions.

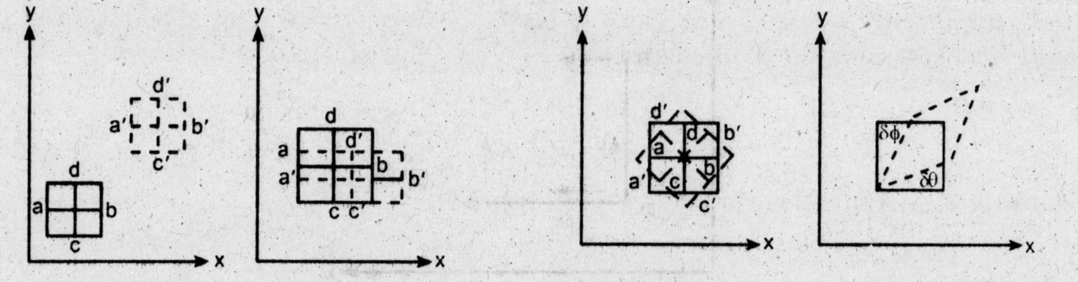

(a) Pure translation (b) Linear deformation (c) Pure rotation (d) Angular deformation

Fig.2.10 Displacements of fluid particle

Consider two elementary lengths in the fluid, such as OA and OB of lengths δx and δy respectively, as shown in Fig. 2.11. Let u and v represent the velocities at O in the x and y directions respectively. For two dimensional steady flow, both u and v depend on x and y. Hence the velocity in the y direction at A will be

$$\left(v+\frac{\partial v}{\partial x}\delta x\right)$$

and the velocity in the x direction at B will be

$$\left(u+\frac{\partial u}{\partial y}\delta y\right)$$

Since the velocities at O and at A in the y direction are different, OA will rotate in the anticlockwise direction (+ve) and its angular velocity will be

$$\frac{\left(v+\frac{\partial v}{\partial x}\delta x\right)-v}{\delta x}=\frac{\partial v}{\partial x}$$

Similarly, since the velocities at O and at B in the x direction are different, OB will rotate in a clockwise direction (–ve) with an angular velocity

$$\frac{u-\left(u+\frac{\partial u}{\partial y}\delta y\right)}{\delta y}=-\frac{\partial u}{\partial y}$$

If the rotation about the z axis (in the x y plane) ω_z is defined as the average rotation of two elements OA and OB, then

$$\omega_z=\frac{1}{2}\left(\frac{\partial v}{\partial x}-\frac{\partial u}{\partial y}\right) \qquad (2.20\text{ a})$$

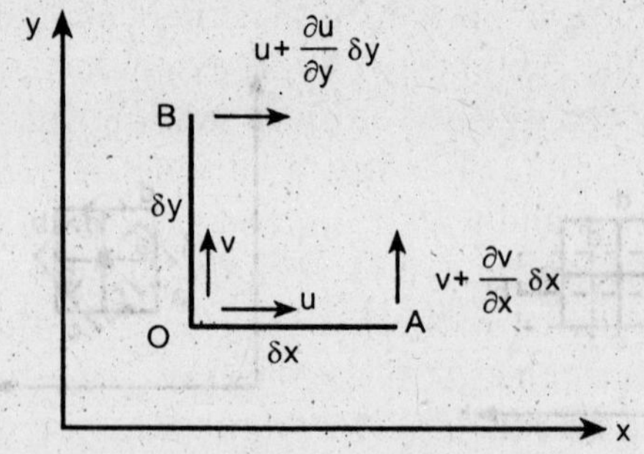

Fig.2.11 Rotation

In the same way the rotations about the x and the y axes will be

$$\omega_x = \frac{1}{2}\left(\frac{\partial w}{\partial y} - \frac{\partial v}{\partial z}\right) \quad (2.20\ b$$

$$\omega_y = \frac{1}{2}\left(\frac{\partial u}{\partial z} - \frac{\partial w}{\partial x}\right) \quad (2.20\ c$$

The rotation vector can be expressed as

$$\omega = \omega_x\, i + \omega_y\, j + \omega_z\, k$$

It may further be mentioned that

$$\omega = \frac{1}{2}\text{curl } \overline{V}$$

If at every point in the flow field ω_x, ω_y and ω_z are zero then the flow is known a *irrotational flow*. Otherwise the flow is *rotational*. In the light of above discussion, i can be seen that in Fig. 2.10 (d), if $\delta\phi = \delta\theta$, the motion will be irrotational; however eve then the angular deformation takes place. If $\delta\phi \neq \delta\theta$ for two elements, there will be ne rotation. Figure 2.12 shows the occurrence of the four types of fluid displacements translation, linear deformation, angular deformation and rotation.

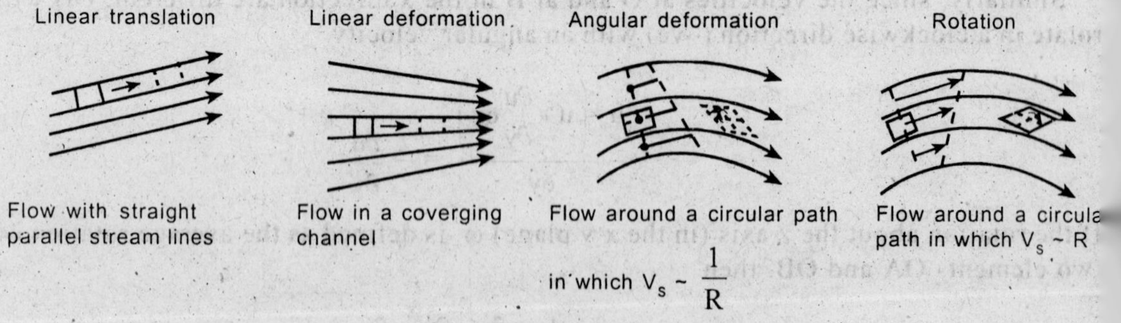

Fig.2.12 Examples, of fluid displacements

The irrotational flows are important in that their characteristics can be very neatly studied with the help of the methods of hydrodynamics. As can be better appreciated after studying the effects of viscosity on fluid motion, the concept of irrotational flow implies no viscosity or negligible viscosity. As discussed in Section 1.5, a fluid having no viscosity and surface tension and which is incompressible is called an ideal fluid; fluids such as air and water can be considered ideal fluids. However, this is not always possible. As a general principle, in the case of rapidly converging flows the velocity distribution has a strong tendency to be such as to make the flow irrotational. Thus flow from a large tank towards a conduit can be considered irrotational; whereas the reverse flow i.e. from a conduit into a tank cannot be considered so. This aspect will be again discussed at a later stage.

2.9 Circulation

Another concept which can be logically introduced at this stage and which will be used in studying the forces acting on immersed bodies is *circulation*. Consider a stream line pattern as shown in Fig. 2.13, and any closed curve C. Let $\overline{V}$ be the velocity vector whose magnitude $V_S = \sqrt{u^2 + v^2 + w^2}$ and $\overline{\Delta S}$ be the vector of C whose length is

$\Delta S = \sqrt{dx^2 + dy^2 + dz^2}$. Then the circulation Γ is defined as

$$\Gamma = \int_C \overline{V} \cdot \overline{\Delta S} \tag{2.21}$$

$$= \int_C (ui + vj + wk).(dx\, i + dy\, j + dz\, k)$$

$$= \int_C (u\, dx + v\, dy + w\, dz)$$

in which $\int_C$ denotes that the line integral is to be evaluated over the complete length of closed path. As the name implies, circulation means flow along a closed curve. If Γ is zero, it would imply an irrotational flow.

As an illustration let us find the circulation around a rectangular closed curve ABCD of sides δx and δy, see Fig. 2.14. Let $\hat{u}$ and v represent the x and y components of velocity at A then,

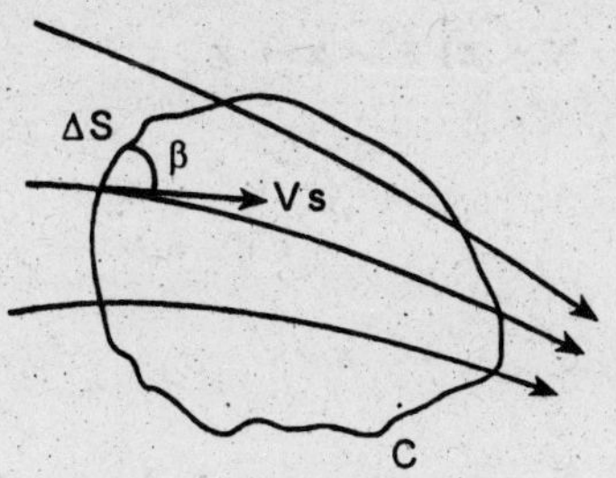

Fig.2.13 Circulation

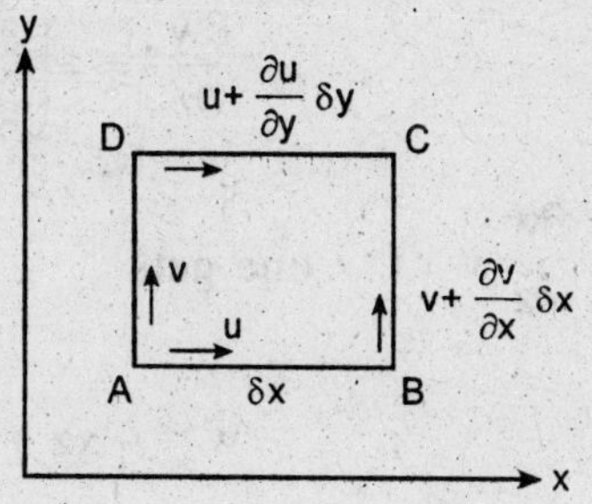

Fig.2.14 Circulation around a rectangular curve

circulation along AB = $u\ \delta x$

circulation along BC = $\left(v + \frac{\partial v}{\partial x}\delta x\right)\delta y$

circulation along CD = $-\left(u + \frac{\partial u}{\partial y}\delta y\right)\delta x$

circulation along DA = $-\ v\ \delta y$

Hence, $\Gamma = \int_C V_s \cos\beta\ \Delta s = \Gamma_{AB} + \Gamma_{BC} + \Gamma_{CD} + \Gamma_{DA}$

$$= u\ \delta x + v\ \delta y + \frac{\partial v}{\partial x}\delta x\ \delta y - u\ \delta x - \frac{\partial u}{\partial y}\delta y\ \delta x - v\ \delta y$$

$$\Gamma = \left(\frac{\partial v}{\partial x} - \frac{\partial u}{\partial y}\right)\delta y\ \delta x \qquad (2.22)$$

Circulation per unit area will be given by

$$\frac{\Gamma}{\delta x\ \delta y} = \left(\frac{\partial v}{\partial x} - \frac{\partial u}{\partial y}\right) = 2\omega_z \qquad (2.23)$$

In the above case a rectangular curve is chosen for simplicity. However, the results obtained in Eq. 2.22 and 2.23 are independent of the shape of the closed curve considered. Hence an important conclusion can be drawn. Circulation per unit area is equal to twice the rotation about an axis perpendicular to the plane of the area enclosed by the curve.

The limiting value of circulation per unit area is also known as *vorticity* about the axis perpendicular to the area.

Example 2.3

If $u = x^2 + y^2 + z^2$ and $v = -\ xy - yz - xz$, determine the velocity component w which will satisfy continuity equation for incompressible fluid.

$$\frac{\partial u}{\partial x} = 2x \text{ and } \frac{\partial v}{\partial y} = -\ x - z$$

or

$$\frac{\partial w}{\partial z} = -\left(\frac{\partial u}{\partial x} + \frac{\partial v}{\partial y}\right) = -\ (2x - x - z) = -\ x + z$$

Integrating $\frac{\partial w}{\partial z}$ w.r.t. z one gets

$$w = -\ xz + \frac{z^2}{2} + f(x, y, t)$$

Thus it can seen that the solution is not unique,

Example 2.4

If u = yz + t, v = xz – t and w = xy, determine the acceleration a_x at the point (2, 1, 3) at t = 0.5 s.

$$\frac{\partial u}{\partial t} = 1, \quad \frac{\partial u}{\partial x} = 0, \quad \frac{\partial u}{\partial y} = z, \quad \frac{\partial u}{\partial z} = y$$

$$\therefore \quad a_x = 1 + (yz + t) \times 0 + (xz - t)\, z + xy\,(y)$$

$$= 1 + xz^2 - tz + xy^2$$

Substituting the values of x, y, z and t

$$a_x = 1 + 18 - 1.5 + 2$$

$$= 19.5 \text{ m/s}^2$$

Example 2.5

Obtain the rotation for two dimensional flow given by V=C.r where V is the tangential velocity at a distance r from the centre and C is a constant. (Such a flow is obtained by rotating a container filled with liquid about a vertical axis at a constant angular velocity in the clockwise direction).

At any point $\quad u = -V \sin\theta = -C\, r \sin\theta = -C\, y$

and $\quad v = V \cos\theta = C\, r \cos\theta = Cx$

$$\therefore \quad \omega_z = \frac{1}{2}\left(\frac{\partial v}{\partial x} - \frac{\partial u}{\partial y}\right) = \frac{1}{2}(C + C) = C$$

Hence the flow is rotational.

2.10 Velocity Potential

In electromagnetic theory as well as in mechanics, the concept of potential is many times used. In electrostatics one has electrostatic potential such that, its derivative with respect to space gives a force experienced by a unit charge. In magnetism one has the magnetic potential such that, its derivative with respect to a given direction yields a magnetic force acting on a unit pole in that direction. And in mechanics the gravitational potential is defined in such a way that its derivative with respect to a direction gives the force acting on a unit mass in that direction. These are all force potentials since their derivatives yield corresponding forces.

In an analogous manner a *velocity potential* is defined in fluid mechanics. The velocity potential ϕ (phi) is a scalar function of space and time (i.e. x, y, z and t for cartesian coordinate system) such that its negative derivative with respect to any direction gives the velocity in that direction. Thus, $\phi = \phi$ (x, y, z, t) is such that

$$-\frac{\partial \phi}{\partial x} = u, \quad -\frac{\partial \phi}{\partial y} = v \quad \text{and} \quad -\frac{\partial \phi}{\partial z} = w \qquad (2.24)$$

The negative sign signifies that ϕ decreases with an increase in the values of x, y or z. In other words the flow is always in the direction of decreasing ϕ.

It is interesting to use the concept of velocity potential in conjunction with the continuity equation, Eq. 2.12, and conditions for irrotational flow (Eq. 2.20 a, b, c). For this, consider incompressible fluids only. By substituting expressions for u, v, w from Eq. 2.24 in Eq. 2.12 one gets

$$\frac{\partial}{\partial x}\left(-\frac{\partial \phi}{\partial x}\right)+\frac{\partial}{\partial y}\left(-\frac{\partial \phi}{\partial y}\right)+\frac{\partial}{\partial z}\left(-\frac{\partial \phi}{\partial z}\right)=0$$

or
$$\frac{\partial^2 \phi}{\partial x^2}+\frac{\partial^2 \phi}{\partial y^2}+\frac{\partial^2 \phi}{\partial z^2}=0 \tag{2.25}$$

This equation is known as *Laplace equation.* Laplace equation is linear second order partial differential equation and this equation has many important applications in physics. This equation is satisfied by the electrostatic, the magnetic and the gravitational potentials also. As can be seen from the above, any solution of Laplace equation automatically satisfy Eq. 2.24 i.e. $-\partial\phi/\partial x = u$, $-\partial\phi/\partial y = v$ and $-\partial\phi/\partial z = w$, and hence it corresponds to some case of fluid flow. Further consider the conditions for rotational flow and substitute expression for u, v and w from Eq. 2.24; then

$$\omega_x=\frac{1}{2}\left(\frac{\partial w}{\partial y}-\frac{\partial v}{\partial z}\right)=\frac{1}{2}\left\{\frac{\partial}{\partial y}\left(-\frac{\partial \varphi}{\partial z}\right)-\frac{\partial}{\partial z}\left(-\frac{\partial \varphi}{\partial y}\right)\right\}$$

$$=\frac{1}{2}\left(-\frac{\partial^2 \varphi}{\partial y\,\partial z}+\frac{\partial^2 \varphi}{\partial z\,\partial y}\right)$$

$$\omega_y=\frac{1}{2}\left(\frac{\partial u}{\partial z}-\frac{\partial w}{\partial x}\right)=\frac{1}{2}\left\{\frac{\partial}{\partial z}\left(-\frac{\partial \phi}{\partial x}\right)-\frac{\partial}{\partial x}\left(-\frac{\partial \phi}{\partial z}\right)\right\}$$

$$=\frac{1}{2}\left(-\frac{\partial^2 \phi}{\partial z\,\partial x}+\frac{\partial^2 \phi}{\partial x\,\partial z}\right)$$

$$\omega_z=\frac{1}{2}\left(\frac{\partial v}{\partial x}-\frac{\partial u}{\partial y}\right)=\frac{1}{2}\left\{\frac{\partial}{\partial x}\left(-\frac{\partial \phi}{\partial y}\right)-\frac{\partial}{\partial y}\left(-\frac{\partial \phi}{\partial x}\right)\right\}$$

$$=\frac{1}{2}\left(-\frac{\partial^2 \varphi}{\partial x\,\partial y}+\frac{\partial^2 \varphi}{\partial y\,\partial x}\right)$$

However if ϕ is a continuous function and its second derivatives exist,

$$\frac{\partial^2 \phi}{\partial y\,\partial z}=\frac{\partial^2 \phi}{\partial z\,\partial y},\quad \frac{\partial^2 \phi}{\partial z\,\partial x}=\frac{\partial^2 \phi}{\partial x\,\partial z}\ \text{and}\ \frac{\partial^2 \phi}{\partial x\,\partial y}=\frac{\partial^2 \phi}{\partial y\,\partial x}$$

Hence $\omega_x = \omega_y = \omega_z = 0$, i.e. the flow must be irrotational. Therefore, it can be stated that the existence of velocity potential also implies irrotational flow. In other words, velocity potential exists only for those fluid flow cases in which the motion is irrotational. Thus

(i) velocity potential is such that

$$-\frac{\partial \phi}{\partial x} = u, \; -\frac{\partial \phi}{\partial y} = v \text{ and } -\frac{\partial \phi}{\partial z} = w,$$

(ii) it exists for irrotational flows; and

(iii) it satisfies Laplace equation.

2.11 Stream Function

Along with the concept of the velocity potential ϕ, another concept that of stream function ψ is also useful in studying the flow patterns. The *stream function* ψ is defined as a function of space and time such that

$$\frac{\partial \psi}{\partial x} = v \text{ and } -\frac{\partial \psi}{\partial y} = u \qquad (2.26)$$

It must be remembered that while the velocity potential has been defined for the three dimensional case, the stream function is defined only for a two dimensional case. The stream function concept can be utilised in some special cases of three dimensional flows. Furthermore, while the velocity potential exists only for irrotational flows, stream function exists for irrotational as well as rotational flows.

Consider two points A and B with co-ordinates (x, y) and (x + δx, y + δy) respectively, see Fig. 2.15. Join A and B by any two arbitrary curves such as ACB and ADB. Let u and v represent the velocities in x and y directions respectively. Then the flow across ACB is $(-u\,\delta y + v\,\delta x)$

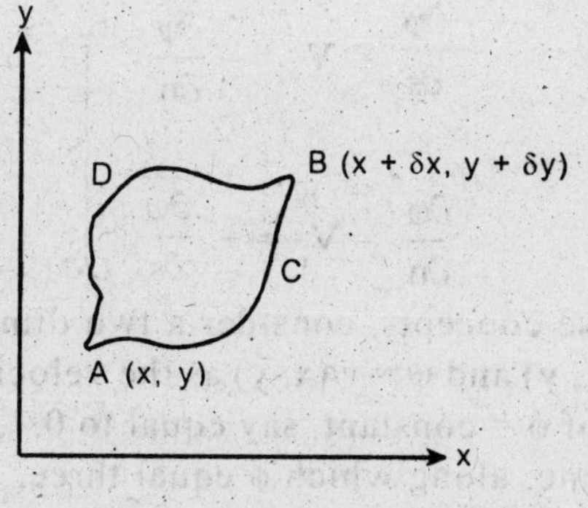

Fig.2.15 Definition sketch

In writing this, it is assumed that as one looks from A towards B, the flow from right to left is + ve. However, if the fluid is homogeneous and incompressible, the flow across ADB or any such curve must be the same. Let this flow be represented by dψ. Then

$$d\psi = -u\,\delta y + v\,\delta x \tag{2.27}$$

For steady flow ψ is a function of x and y. Hence the total differential dψ for steady flow can also be written as

$$d\psi = \frac{\partial \psi}{\partial x}dx + \frac{\partial \psi}{\partial y}dy \tag{2.28}$$

Comparing Eqs. 2.27 and 2.28 one gets

$$v = \frac{\partial \psi}{\partial x} \text{ and } u = -\frac{\partial \psi}{\partial y}$$

These velocity components satisfy the continuity equation. If these values are substituted into the condition for irrotational flow, it can be seen that the stream function ψ also satisfies Laplace equation. However for rotational flow it can be seen that

$$\frac{\partial^2 \psi}{\partial x^2} + \frac{\partial^2 \psi}{\partial y^2} = 2\omega_z$$

Thus ψ satisfies Laplace equation only if the flow is irrotational. The relationship between u, v and ϕ and ψ therefore are,

$$\left.\begin{aligned} -\frac{\partial \varphi}{\partial x} &= u = -\frac{\partial \psi}{\partial y} \\ -\frac{\partial \varphi}{\partial y} &= v = +\frac{\partial \psi}{\partial x} \end{aligned}\right\} \tag{2.29}$$

or, considering the tangential and the normal directions,

$$\left.\begin{aligned} -\frac{\partial \varphi}{\partial s} &= V_s = -\frac{\partial \psi}{\partial n} \\ -\frac{\partial \varphi}{\partial n} &= V_n = +\frac{\partial \psi}{\partial s} \end{aligned}\right\} \tag{2.30}$$

In order to apply these concepts, consider a two dimensional steady and irrotational flow patten, with $\phi = \phi(x, y)$ and $\psi = \psi(x, y)$ as the velocity potential and stream function to be known. The lines of ϕ = constant, say equal to 0,1,2,3 etc. can be drawn, as shown in Fig, 2.16. One such line, along which ϕ equal three, is AB. Since ϕ = constant along such a line, $-\partial\phi/\partial n = 0$; i.e. the velocity tangential to such a line is zero. However, ϕ is varying along the s direction, hence $-\partial\phi/\partial s$, velocity normal to such a line exists. Such lines along which ϕ is constant are known as *equipotential lines* and their property is that the flow is always at right angles to such lines.

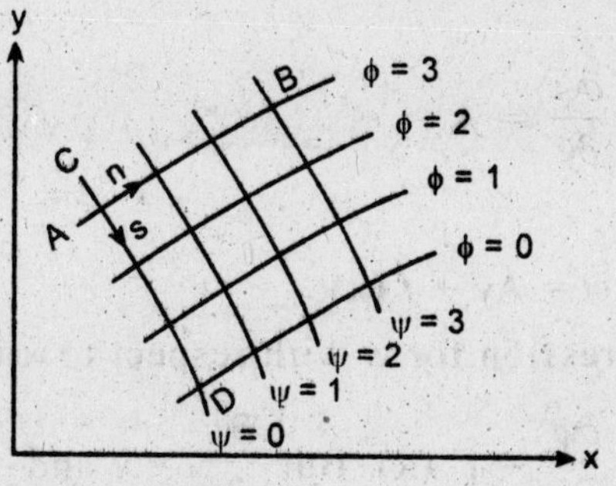

Fig.2.16 Stream lines and equipotential lines

Similarly lines with ψ = constant can also be drawn, such as CD. Since ψ = constant along CD, $\partial\psi/\partial s = V_n = 0$; i.e. there is no flow at right angles to the ψ = constant lines. But $-\partial\psi/\partial n = V_s$, exist. Therefore, the flow is always tangential to ψ = constant lines. It can be recalled that this is exactly the property of the stream line i.e. at every point along the stream line, the velocity is always tangential to it. Hence ψ = constant give a series of stream lines. Similarly ϕ = constant, gives a series of equipotential lines. It can be proved that the angle between tangents to the stream line and equipotential line at their point of intersection is 90°. For any given problem the combination of equipotential lines and stream lines is known as the *Flow Net*.

The *stagnation* point can be defined as the point where the fluid is at rest, i.e. $u = v = 0$ for two dimensional flow. Therefore at such a point $\frac{\partial\psi}{\partial x} = 0$ and $\frac{\partial\psi}{\partial y} = 0$. In Fig. 2.3 F and G are the stagnation points. It can be seen that at the stagnation point the stream line crosses itself. For irrotational flow the two branches cut at the right angles.

Example 2.6

Consider $\phi = Ax$ where A is constant. Determine ψ and draw a set of stream lines and equipotential lines and idenify the flow pattern.

First check that $\phi = Ax$ satisfies Laplace equation.

$$\frac{\partial\phi}{\partial x} = A \text{ and } \frac{\partial^2\phi}{\partial x^2}\ 0; \quad \frac{\partial\phi}{\partial y} = \frac{\partial^2\phi}{\partial y^2} = 0$$

$$\therefore \quad \frac{\partial^2\varphi}{\partial x^2} + \frac{\partial^2\phi}{\partial y^2} = 0$$

Hence $\phi = Ax$ can represent fluid flow case. Next find the stream function ψ. Since

$$-\frac{\partial\varphi}{\partial x} = -A = u, \text{ and } u = -\frac{\partial\psi}{\partial y}$$

$$\therefore \quad \frac{\partial \psi}{\partial y} = A$$

Integrating

$$\psi = Ay + f(x)$$

Differentiating the above expression for ψ with respect to x one gets

$$\frac{\partial \psi}{\partial x} = f'(x). \text{ But } \frac{\partial \psi}{\partial x} = v \text{ and } -\frac{\partial \phi}{\partial y} = v = 0$$

Therefore,

$$f'(x) = v = 0, \text{ Hence } f(x) = \text{constant}$$

Therefore the stream function is $\psi = Ay + C$ in which C is a constant. The sign of A will decide the direction of flow. The corresponding stream lines and equipotential lines are shown in Figure 2.17. Thus, this represents the case of parallel flow in which stream lines are parallel to x axis, and flow is in x direction.

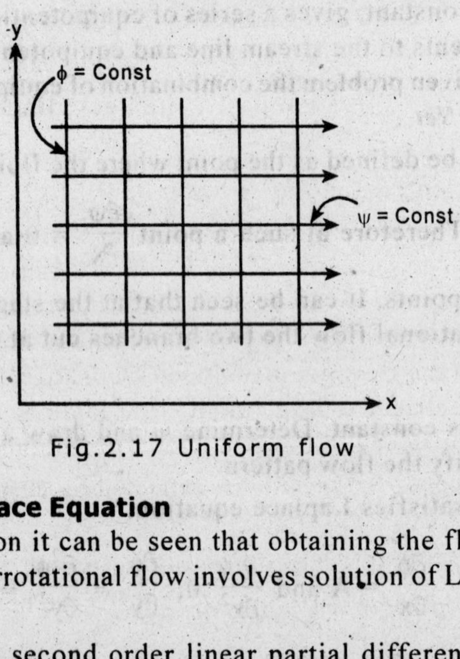

Fig.2.17 Uniform flow

2.12 Solution of Laplace Equation

From the above discussion it can be seen that obtaining the flow pattern or flow net for steady two dimensional irrotational flow involves solution of Laplace equation with given boundary conditions.

Laplace equation is a second order linear partial differential equation. It is second order because the highest derivative in the equation is second derivative. The equation is linear because the derivatives of φ or ψ occur to the first power. The linear equations are characterised by the fact that their solutions follow the principle of superposition, i.e. if ψ_1 and ψ_2 are two independent particular solutions of the equation, $(c_1 \psi_1 + c_2 \psi_2)$, where c_1 and c_2 are constants, is the general solution. This means that a complicated flow pattern can be interpreted as a result of combination of two or more flows which are relatively simple.

Simple flow patterns considered are, for example, the following :

Rectilinear flow:	$\phi = -Ux,$	$\psi = -Uy$
Source:	$\phi = \frac{A}{2\pi}\log_e r$	$\psi = -\frac{A\theta}{2\pi}$
Sink:	$\phi = \frac{A}{2\pi}\log_e r$	$\psi = \frac{A\theta}{2\pi}$
Doublet:	$\phi = -\frac{A\cos\theta}{2\pi r}$	$\psi = \frac{A\sin\theta}{2\pi r}$
Irrotational Vortex :	$\phi = \frac{B\theta}{2\pi}$	$\psi = -\frac{B\theta}{2\pi}\log_e r$

By superposition of these flows the following flow patterns can be generated

Source + sink	= Flow past a rankine body
Rectilinear flow + source	= Flow past two-dimensional long bluff body
Rectilinear flow + Doublet	= Flow past two dimensional circular cylinder
Rectilinear flow + doublet + irrotational vortex	= Flow past a circular cylinder with circulation

These are discussed by Vallentine, and by Streeter.

There are also other analytical methods available such as that using complex variables, method of separation of variables, etc for solving Laplace equation. However there are several cases of fluid flow which are of considerable interest to engineers and which are so complex that above mentioned analytical methods become too involved. In such cases a fairly good approximation of the flow net is obtained by using relaxation techniques or by using graphical method, electrical analogy method, or laminar flow analogy method. Out of these, the graphical, electrical analogy and relaxation methods are described here.

The flow net can be constructed for the flows restricted by certain conditions. These conditions are

i. The flow must be steady. If this condition is not satisfied, the flow net obtained represents the flow conditions at a particular instant. At the next instant the flow net may change.

ii. The fluid must be ideal, or the fluid should have negligble viscosity. However, if the flow is rapidly accelerating even for fluids of low viscosity, the flow nets give good results.

iii. Fluid weight should not govern the flow phenomenon. This condition is fulfilled by light fluids and in the case of flows which are confined within two dimensional boundaries.

Thus for practical purposes, for flow cases of ordinary fluids where flow is rapidly accelerating (i.e., where the streamlines are converging) and completely confined flows such as flows between fixed boundaries, flow net can be drawn. It must be remembered that in the case of diverging flows of real fluids, the fluid particle motion is not guided by the boundary very efficiently. Hence the flow separates away from the boundary as shown in Fig. 2.18. In such case even the approximate position of the surface of separation is not known and furthermore the flow is oscillating; hence a stream line pattern cannot be drawn.

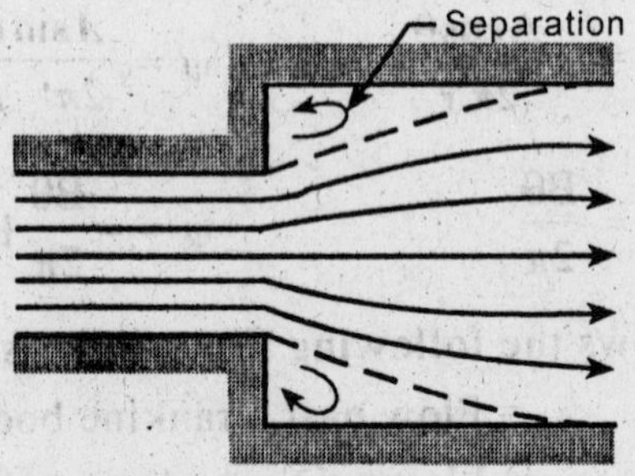

Fig.2.18 Separation in sudden expansion

iv. The flow net analysis can be adopted for flows with free surface e.g. flow over a weir; but to do this, one must have information about the shape of free surface. The reason for this is that the free surface itself is a stream line. Figure 2.19 shows flow nets for a rounded inlet, two dimensional circular cylinder, an asymmetric constriction and a two dimensional sluice gate.

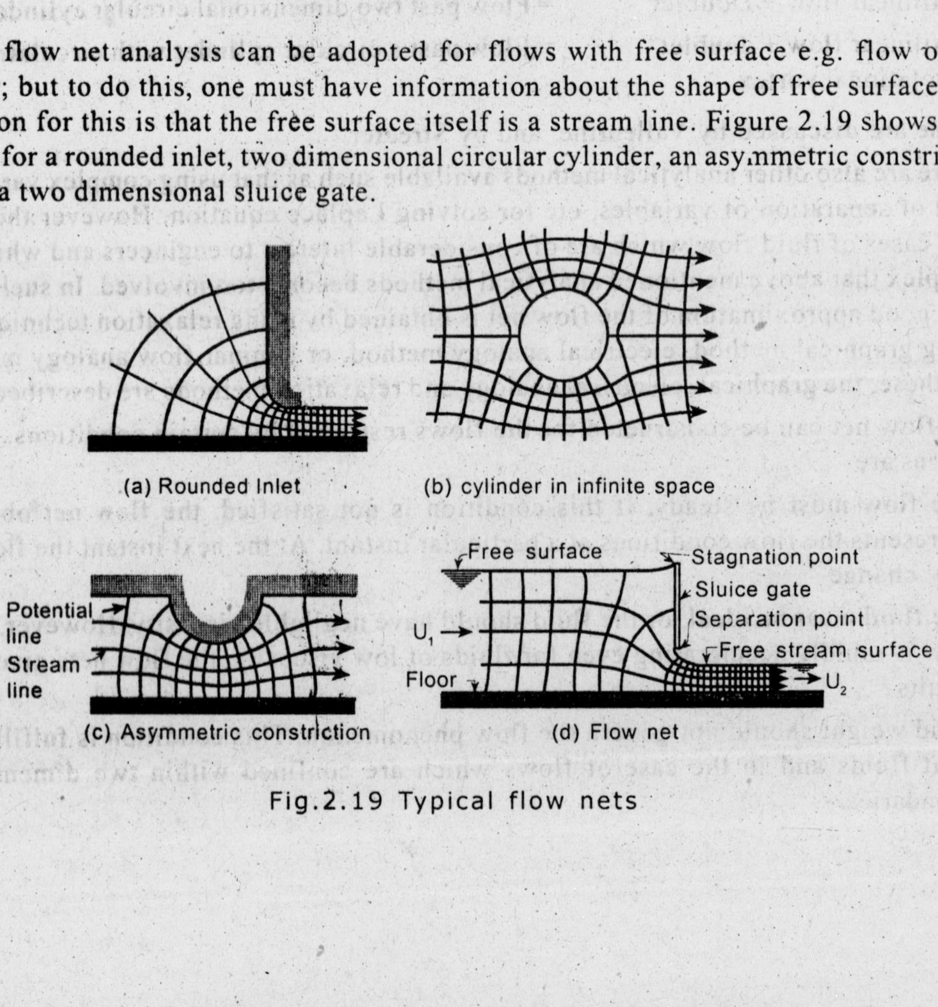

Fig.2.19 Typical flow nets

(a) Graphical Method

The graphical method of drawing a flownet is illustrated by considering flow through a transition shown in Fig. 2.20. There is no flow at right angles to be boundary anywhere and hence, the fixed boundaries AB and CD, coincide with stream lines. Far to the left and right of the transition the width of the channel is uniform and hence stream lines will be equally spaced in these regions and parallel to the boundary. Hence, deciding about the number of stream lines required, one can draw equal number of equally spaced stream lines to the left and to the right of transition. Between AC and BD, these stream lines can be joined by smooth curves. According to Eq. 2.30, $(\partial\psi/\partial n) = (\partial\phi/\partial s)$: therefore if $\delta\phi$ is made equal to $\delta\psi$ then δn will be equal to δs. It is also known that stream lines and equipotential lines intersect at right angles. Hence a set of equipotential lines can now be drawn such that:

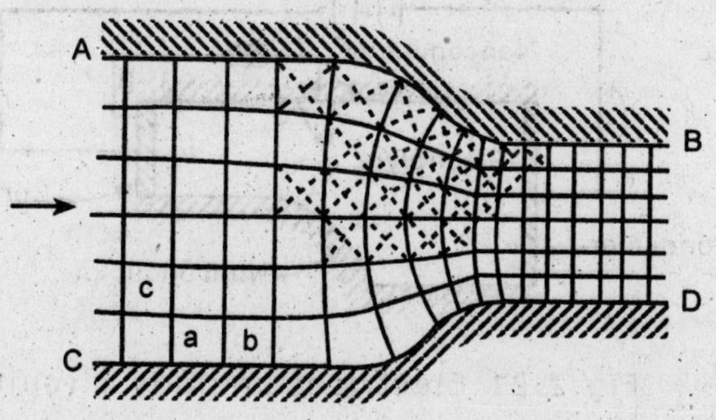

Fig.2.20 Graphical construction of flow net

- they intersect the boundary and other stream lines at right angles ;
- at any point the distance between consecutive stream lines is equal to that between consecutive equipotential lines. In other words, equipotential lines and streamlines form squares
- the diagonals of the squares form smooth curves which intersect each other normally.

In the region of extreme nonuniformity (at the curved boundaries) the latter two conditions may not be completely satisfied unless streamlines and equipotential lines are drawn very closely, i.e. meshes are infinitely small. Also, in the region where boundary curves sharply towards the flow (known as stagnation region), instead of a square, a five sided figure will result.

After drawing the equipotential lines, it may be necessary to modify the stream line pattern which in turn will require modification in equipotential lines. Thus by successive modifications in stream lines and equipotential lines one can improve the accuracy of the flow net drawn. The student will require a certain amount of practice in drawing flow nets; however with some practice it will be possible to sketch the flow net in three to four trials.

It can be seen that with the restrictions listed above, the flow net is a function only of the boundary geometry and hence there is a unique flow net for a given geometry of the boundary. In other words the flow net drawn in Figure. 2.20 will be the same for various discharges and for geometrically similar transitions of different sizes.

(b) Electrical Analogy Method

The word *analogous* means similar and hence electrical analogy method of drawing flow nets is based on the fact that flow of fluids and flow of electricity are analogous. The similarity between the two is as follows:

i. The electric potential is analogous to the velocity potential,

ii. The electric curent is analogous to the velocity of flow, and

iii. The homogenous conductor is analogous to homogenous fluid.

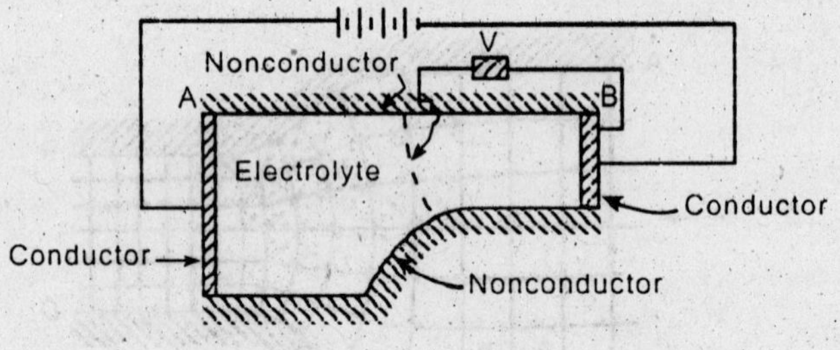

Fig.2.21 Electrical analogy circuit

Figure 2.21 shows a simple arrangement for an electrical analogy study. The fixed boundaries in the hydraulic model are replaced by non-conductors and conductors are fixed in the direction of flow. The tank thus formed is filled with an electrolyte such as salt-water. Electric current is passed through this by using a battery system. There is a drop in the voltage along AB. The probe connected to B through a voltmeter is moved in the electrolyte and a curve is traced along which voltage is constant. This gives one equipotential line. In a similar way other equipotential lines can be drawn. Once the pattern of equipotential lines is known, the stream lines can be sketched. A little thought will show that, if the conductors are replaced by nonconductors and the nonconductors are made conductors, this will give another set of equipontential lines. Both together give the flow net. A special conducting paper under the trade name Teledeltos can also be used in place of tank with an electrolyte. Silver ink is used to form a conducting strip or line having constant voltage. The paper is cut to the size and shape needed. Other procedure remains the same.

(c) Relaxation Method

In the relaxation method a network of ϕ or ψ values are estimated in a grid with given boundary form. These values are then systematically adjusted so as to satisfy Laplace equation and the boundary conditions.

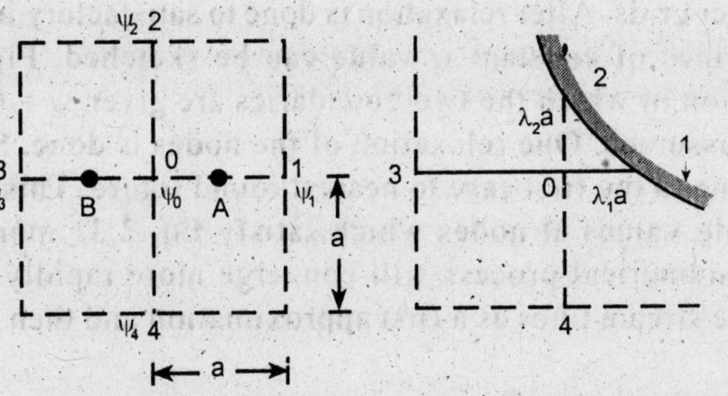

Fig.2.22 Symmetrical and unsymmetrical grid

Consider the symmetrical grid in Fig. 2.22. For small values of "a" one can write

$$\left(\frac{\partial\psi}{\partial x}\right)_A = \frac{\psi_1-\psi_0}{a}, \quad \left(\frac{\partial\psi}{\partial x}\right)_B = \frac{\psi_0-\psi_3}{a}$$

and

$$\left(\frac{\partial^2\psi}{\partial x^2}\right)_O = \frac{\left(\frac{\partial\psi}{\partial x}\right)_A - \left(\frac{\partial\psi}{\partial x}\right)_B}{a} = \frac{\psi_1+\psi_3-2\psi_0}{a^2}$$

Similarly

$$\left(\frac{\partial^2\psi}{\partial y^2}\right)_O = \frac{\psi_2+\psi_4-2\psi_0}{a^2}$$

$$\therefore \quad \frac{\partial^2\psi}{\partial x^2}+\frac{\partial^2\psi}{\partial y^2} = \frac{\psi_1+\psi_2+\psi_3+\psi_4-4\psi_0}{a^2}$$

If the assumed values of ψ at these points are correct, since $\Delta^2\psi = 0$

$$\psi_1+\psi_2+\psi_3+\psi_4 = 4\psi_0 \tag{2.31}$$

Since the initial values at grid points are approximate, relationship in Eq. 2.31 will not be satisfied. Hence at each node cross out the assumed ψ value and enter the new value which equals $\frac{\psi_1+\psi_2+\psi_3+\psi_4}{4}$. This is known as relaxing the node. Start from one direction and complete the relaxation. Near the curved boundary, the grid may have unequal arms. In such a case use the formula (see Fig. 2.22)

$$\psi_0 = \frac{\frac{\psi_1}{\lambda_1}+\frac{\psi_2}{\lambda_2}+\psi_3+\psi_4}{\frac{1}{\lambda_1}+\frac{1}{\lambda_2}+2} \tag{2.32}$$

After all nodal values are relaxed, repeat the relaxation through the grids until the adjustment due to relaxing becomes insignificant. The accuracy of the procedure can be increased by using finer grids. After relaxation is done to satisfactory level, lines of constant ψ value i.e. stream lines of constant ψ value can be sketched. Fig. 2.23 shows a two dimensional contraction in which the two boundaries are given $\psi = 0$ and 100 values and the nodal values are assumed. One relaxation of the nodes is done. Since relaxation is to be done again it is done in the first case to nearest round figure. This needs to be repeated to get more acceptable values at nodes which satisfy Eq. 2.31 more closely. It may be mentioned that such numerical process will converge more rapidly if one were to draw the grid, then draw the stream lines as a first approximation and then assign modal values.

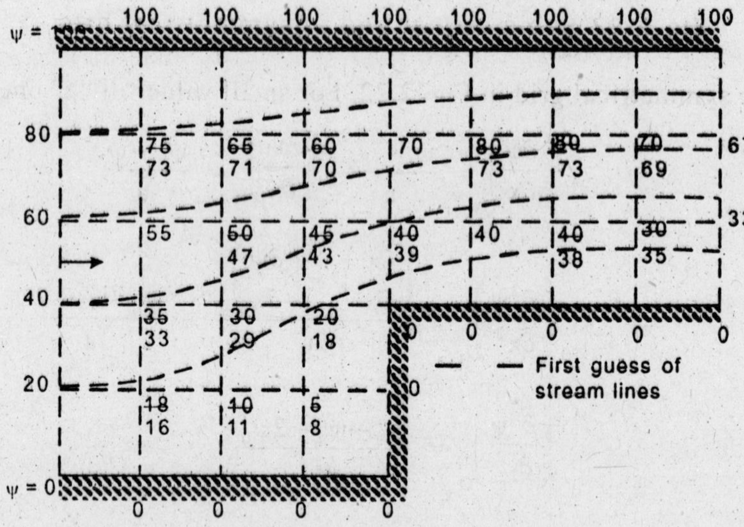

Fig.2.23 Relaxation method of drawing flow-net

Example 2.7

Examine the two dimensional flow pattern obtained by superposition of rectilinear flow and a source. Rectilinear flow in x direction is represented by $\phi = -Ux$ and $\psi = -Uy$, and source by $\phi = -\dfrac{A}{2\pi}\log_e r$ and $\psi = -\dfrac{A\theta}{2\pi}$. The velocity potential and stream function for resulting flow will be given by

$$\phi = -Ux - \frac{A}{2\pi}\log_e r = -Ur\cos\theta - \frac{A}{2\pi}\log_e r$$

$$\psi = -Uy - \frac{A\theta}{2\pi} = -Ur\sin\theta - \frac{A\theta}{2\pi}$$

since $y = r\sin\theta$ and $x = r\cos\theta$. At the stagnation point $V_r = V_\theta = 0$. In polar co-ordinate system.

$$-\frac{\partial\phi}{\partial r} = V_r = -\frac{1}{r}\frac{\partial\psi}{\partial\theta} \text{ and } -\frac{\partial\phi}{r\partial\theta} = V_\theta = \frac{\partial\psi}{\partial r}$$

$$V_r = 0 \text{ implies } -\frac{\partial \psi}{r \partial \theta} = \frac{A}{2\pi r} + U \cos\theta = 0$$

$$V_\theta = 0 \text{ implies } \frac{\partial \psi}{\partial r} = -U \sin\theta = 0 .$$

These conditions will be satisfied when $\theta = \pi$, $r = \frac{A}{2\pi U}$.

Substitution of these values in equation for ψ gives $\psi = -\frac{A}{2}$.

Hence equation of streamline passing through the stagnation point is (see Fig. 2.24)

$$-\frac{A}{2} = -U r \sin\theta - \frac{A\theta}{2\pi}$$

or

$$\frac{A}{2}\left(1 - \frac{\theta}{\pi}\right) = U r \sin\theta$$

$\therefore$

$$y = r \sin\theta = \frac{A}{2U}\left(1 - \frac{\theta}{\pi}\right)$$

y will be maximum when $x \to \infty$ i.e $\theta = 0$

$$y_{max} = \frac{A}{2U}; \text{ when } \theta = \frac{\pi}{2}, y = \frac{A}{4U}$$

and when $\theta = \pi$, $y = 0$ at which time $x = -\frac{A}{2\pi U}$. Hence $\psi = 0$ will plot as a two dimensional bluff body. See Fig. 2.24.

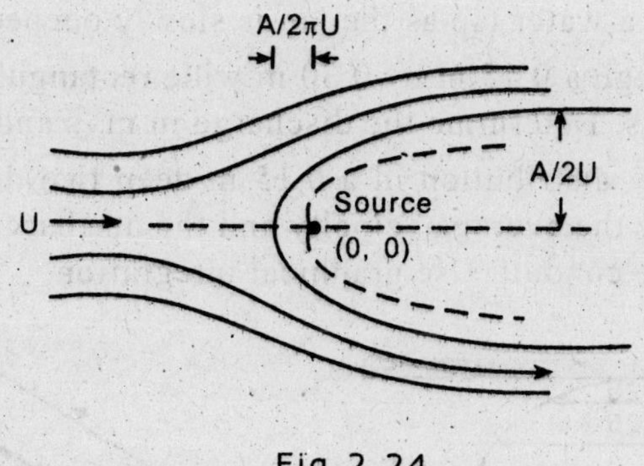

Fig.2.24

2.13 Utility of Flow Net Analysis

It can be seen that once a flow net is constructed, the same one applies to flows at different discharges. Since flow net for a given boundary geometry can be drawn to any desired scale, it can be seen that the same flownet applies to all geometrically similar boundaries. Once the flow net is drawn, the application of continuity equation gives the velocity at any point in terms of reference velocity. In Chapter 5 this information will be utilised to study other characteristics of flow.

A flow net analysis also yields important information about the design of efficient boundary profiles. The flow nets give a good idea about the smooth boundary profiles that can be substituted for boundaries with sharp corners. Corners such as 'a' in Fig. 2.25 create points of *stagnation* where there is almost dead water. Since such area cannot be useful for flow, it can be replaced by a smooth curve shown by the dotted line. A sharp corner such as 'b' causes flow to separate. The phenomenon of separation and its effects are discussed later. However, it may be mentioned that separation as well as stagnation are undesirable and therefore boundary shapes should be so chosen as to avoid both as far as possible.

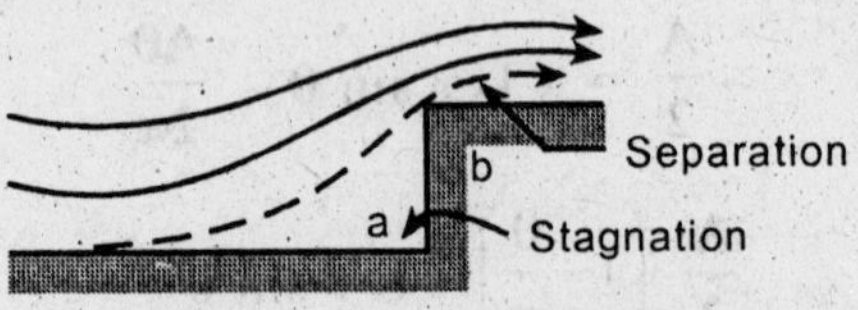

Fig.2.25 Stagnation and separation zones

PROBLEMS

2.1 In each of the following cases determine whether the flow is steady, unsteady, uniform or nonuniform

i. flow in a river during flood,

ii. flow through a pipe bend with constant discharge,

iii. flow through a pipe bend whose diameter reduces in the direction of flow, and in which the discharge slowly decreases,

iv. $u = ax + 2\,bx^2$ in which a and b are constants,

v. flow through a water tap as the tap is slowly opened.

2.2 Water flows through a 0.15 m by 0.30 m wide rectangular conduit at an average velocity of 1.0 m/s. Determine the discharge in m^3/s and l/s.

2.3 Measured velocity distribution in a 0.15 m deep two dimensional conduit is as shown. Determine the average velocity and the discharge in litres per second per metre width of the conduit. Use graphical integration.

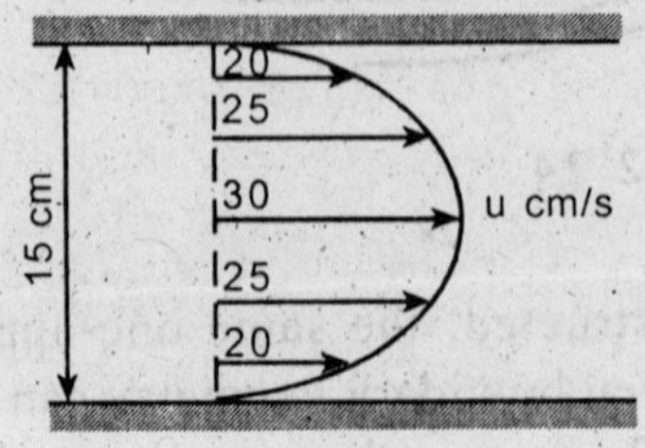

Problem 2.3

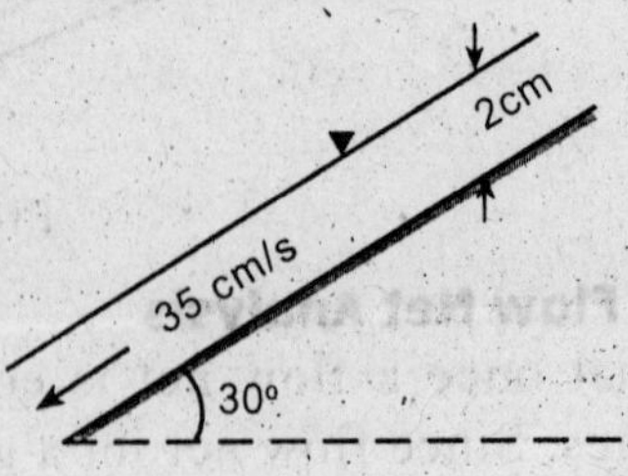

Problem 2.4

2.4 During a storm the depth of water (measured vertically) over a 30° inclined paved surface was found to be 2 cm. If the average velocity of flow was 35 cm/s determine the rate of flow in *l*/s per cm width.

2.5 Determine whether the continuity equation is satisfied in the following cases

i. $u = 2x^2 + 3y$, $v = -2xy + 3y^3 + 3zy$,

$w = -3z^2/2 - 2xz - 9y^2z$

ii. $u = x^2 + y^2 + z^2$, $v = x^2 - 2xy - 3yz^2$,

$w = x^3 + y^3 + z^3$

iii. For two dimensional flow :

$u = 6xy + 2x^2$, $v = -2y^2 + xy$

2.6 In the following cases determine the missing component of velocity such that they satisfy continuity equation :

i. $u = 3x^2$, $v = 4xyz$, $w = ?$

ii. $u = 2x^2 + 2xy$, $v = 2yz^2 + 3z^2$, $w = ?$

2.7 In cylindrical polar co-ordinate system consider an elementary volume with sides δx, δr, $r\delta\theta$, taking V_x V_r and V_θ as the velocity components in the x, r and θ directions respectively, show that the continuity equation takes the form

$$\frac{\partial \rho}{\partial t} + \frac{\partial}{\partial x}(\rho V_x) + \frac{1}{r}\frac{\partial}{\partial r}(\rho V_r . r) + \frac{1}{r}\frac{\partial}{\partial \theta}(\rho V_\theta) = 0$$

2.8 If $u = A(x^2 - y^2)/(x^2 + y^2)^2$ and $v = 2Axy/(x^2 - y^2)^2$ for two dimensional flow of an incompressible fluid, show that u and v satisfy the continuity equation. Here A is a non-zero constant.

2.9 If $u = -3y^2$ and $v = -6x$ for two dimensional flow of an incompressible fluid, determine the equation of the stream line passing through the point (2, 5).

2.10 A 7.5 cm diameter pipe carries carbon dioxide gas at a velocity of 4.0 m/s. The specific weight of the gas varies with temperature as well as pressure. At section A the specific weight is 54.92 N/m³, while at section B it is 40.89 N/m³. Determine the velocity at section B,

2.11 A pipe line of 30 cm diameter and having an average velocity of 4.5 m/s branches into two pipes–one of 15 cm in diameter and other 20 cm in diameter. If the average velocity in the 15 cm diameter pipe is 3.0 m/s determine the average velocity of flow in the 20 cm diameter pipe.

2.12 A 30 cm diameter pipe is gradually reduced to 15 cm diameter pipe in a transition length of 1.0 m. If the steady water discharge flowing through the transition is 325 *l*/s, determine the average velocity of flow in the transition at 30 cm from the 30 cm diameter pipe.

2.13 In problem 2.12 determine the accelerations 15 cm and 30 cm from 30 cm diameter pipe. Also obtain a general expression for acceleration at a distance x from the 30 cm pipe.

2.14 A 90 cm diameter pipe is reduced to 30 cm diameter in a length of 1.5 m. Wate flows through the pipe at a rate of 280 l/s. If the discharge increases at the rate o 60 l/s, determine the total acceleration at 0.5 m and 1.0 m from the beginning o the reducer.

2.15 The local velocity at the inside of a bend is 5.0 m/s. If the bend radius is 5.0 m determine the ratio of gravitational acceleration to the normal acceleration.

2.16 If $u = x^2 - y^2$, $v = y^2 - z^2$ and $w = -2xz - 2yz$ for an incompressible fluid determine the acceleration a_y at the point (1, 2, 1).

2.17 Determine the normal acceleration at the bucket spillway shown.

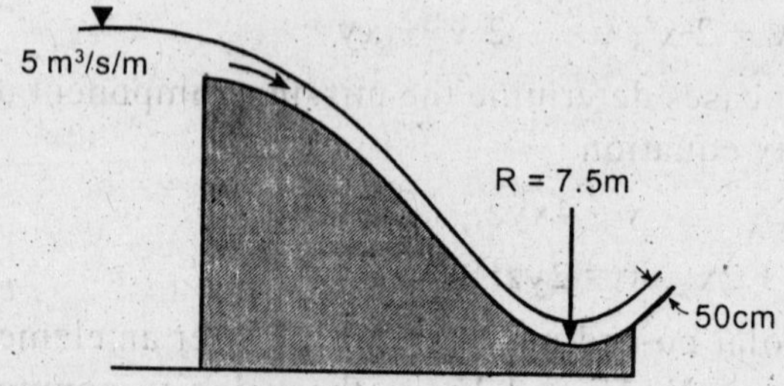

Problem 2.17

2.18 If $u = A(x + y)$ and $v = -A(x + y)$ determine the rotation of fluid motion abou z axis.

2.19 In a parallel two dimensional flow in the positive x direction the velocity varies linearly from zero at y = 0 to 2.0 m/s at y = 4.0 m. Determine the expression for ψ Is the flow irrotational ?

2.20 Find the circulation about the square enclosed by the lines $x = \pm 2$ and $y = \pm 2$ fo the flow with $u = x + y$ and $v = x^2 - y$.

2.21 Show that equipotential lines and stream lines intersect at right angles.

2.22 Check whether the following functions represent the possible irrotational flow phenomenon :

(i) $\phi = A(x^2 - y^2)$ (iii) $\phi = \dfrac{Ax}{(x^2 + y^2)}$

(ii) $\phi = Bxy$ (iv) $\phi = \tan^{-1} \dfrac{y}{x}$

2.23 If $\psi = 5x - (10/\sqrt{2})\, y$, determine the magnitude and direction of velocity at any point.

2.24 If $x^2 - y^2$ = constant, is the equation of a stream line, determine the magnitude and direction of the velocity at (2, 3).

2.25 For two dimensional flow of incompressible fluid, the flow consists of parallel stream lines making an angle θ with the x axis and the velocity is V. Obtain ψ and ϕ functions.

2.26 If $\phi = A\,(x^2-y^2)$ represents a possible flow phenomenon, determine the stream function ψ.

2.27 If $V = A.R$ represents the variation of tangential velocity with the radius R, A being a constant, determine the circulation per unit area about an axis perpendicular to the plane containing the velocity vector

2.28 If $\phi = 3xy$ and $\psi = 3\,(y^2-x^2)/2$, determine the x and y components of velocity at (1, 3) and (3, 3). Determine the discharge passing between stream lines through these points.

2.29 If $V = A/R$ represents the variation of tangential velocity with radius R, A being a constant find the circulation,

i. around any closed curve;

ii. around a closed curve formed by two stream-lines with $R = R_1$ and $R = R_2$ and the two radius vectors with an angle θ between them.

2.30 If $\psi = 3xy$, determine the location of the point where the velocity is 5 units and it makes an angle of 128° 45' with positive x axis.

2.31 If $\phi_1 = -Ax$ and $\phi_2 = -B\log_e(x^2+y^2)$ satisfy Laplace equation (A and B being nonzero constants), show that $\phi_1 + \phi_2$ is also a solution of Laplace equation.

2.32 If $\psi_1 = -Ay$ and $\psi_2 = B\tan^{-1} y/x$ satisfy Laplace equation (A and B being nonzero constants) show that $\psi_1 + \psi_2$ is also a solution of Laplace equation.

2.33 Draw flow nets for the following cases :

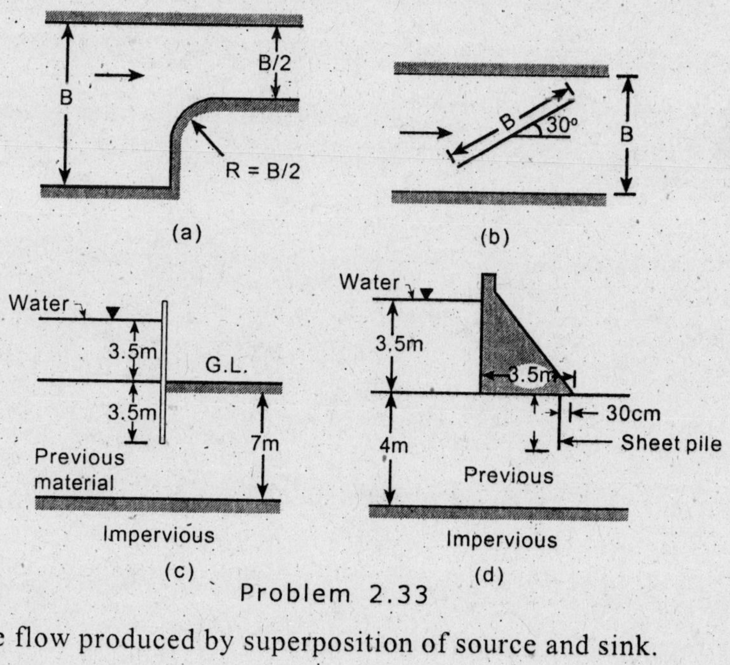

Problem 2.33

2.34 Examine the flow produced by superposition of source and sink.

2.35 Prepare a graph of V/V_0 versus distance along the curved boundary for case (a) in problem 2.33.

[illegible]

2.27 If [illegible] AB represents [illegible] velocity [illegible] with [illegible] radius [illegible] about [illegible] constant angular velocity [illegible] plane [illegible]

[illegible] determine [illegible] components [illegible]

2.29 [illegible] represents [illegible] rotation of [illegible] vortex with radius [illegible] constant [illegible] circulation.

(i) [illegible] around a closed curve

(ii) [illegible] closed curve formed by two streamlines with [illegible] and the two radius vectors with an angle [illegible] between them.

2.31 [illegible] Determine the location of the point where the velocity [illegible] makes an angle of [illegible] with positive x-axis.

2.32 [illegible] A and B [illegible] satisfy Laplace equation (A and B being arbitrary constants) show that [illegible] is also a solution of Laplace equation.

2.33 [illegible] satisfy Laplace equation (A and B being arbitrary constants) show that [illegible] is also a solution of Laplace equation.

2.34 [illegible] the following cases:

[illegible]

2.35 [illegible]

2.36 [illegible] [illegible] for each of [illegible]

CHAPTER THREE

EQUATIONS OF MOTION AND ENERGY THEOREM

3.1 Introduction

In the previous chapter the space-time relationships of fluid motion have been discussed. The present chapter deals with the forces responsible for fluid motion, the resulting accelerations and the energy change involved in the flow phenomenon. This aspect of fluid motion is known as the *dynamics of fluid flow.* Similar to the mechanics of solids, the Mechanics of Fluids also is governed by Newton's second law of motion which states that

$$\text{Force} = \text{Mass} \times \text{Acceleration} \tag{3.1}$$

Since force and acceleration are both vectors. Eq. 3.1 is a vector equation and therefore, in order to study the motion of a body in a particular direction, one has to consider the components of all forces acting on the body in that direction. In the case of a solid body, the motion indicated by the above equation refers to its mass centre because solids have a rigidity of form. In a fluid mass, on the other hand, the particles are engaged in continuously changing their relative position and form, so that the motion of a particle at the mass centre does not necessarily represent the mean motion of the fluid as a whole. Hence, it becomes necessary to investigate the forces producing motion at each point of a given flow and so mass per unit volume is of greater significance than the total mass. Thus along the direction of x axis, Newton's equation of motion will be

$$\Sigma f_x = \rho\ a_x \tag{3.2}$$

where Σf_x is the summation of the components, in the x direction, of all the forces per unit volume acting on the fluid mass, a_x is the total acceleration in the x direction and ρ is the mass density of the fluid under consideration. Similar equations can be written in y and z directions. In order to study the dynamics of fluid motion, one must study the types of forces which influence the fluid motion.

3.2 Forces Influencing Motion

The forces that influence the fluid motion can be of various types. These are forces due to gravity, pressure, viscosity, surface tension, compressibility and turbulence.

The gravity force F_g is due to the weight of the fluid; its component in the direction of motion causes an acceleration in problems where gravity is important such as in open channel flow. The gravity force is proportional to the volume of the fluid under consideration. The gravity force per unit volume is designated by f_g and is equal to ρg acting in the vertically downward direction.

Fluid pressure is defined as a force exerted by a fluid on any surface in a direction normal to the surface. The pressure intensity *p* is the force per unit area indicating a local intensity of pressure force. Fluid pressure can produce acceleration in a given direction only if the pressure changes in that direction. In order to determine the magnitude of the pressure force per unit volume f_p, consider a small fluid element of area da and length dx as shown in Fig. 3.1. On the left face of the element the pressure is p. Since p, in general, varies with x, y and z, the pressure on the right face will be $\left(p+\frac{\partial p}{\partial x}dx\right)$, $(\partial p/\partial x)$ being the rate of change of pressure in the x direction. As there is a difference in pressure between the two faces of the element, there exists a pressure force F_{px} in the direction which can cause acceleration in the x direction.

$$F_{px} = p\,da - \left(p+\frac{\partial p}{\partial x}dx\right) da = -\frac{\partial p}{\partial x}\,dx\,da$$

Thus the pressure force per unit volume is $f_{px} = -\partial p/\partial x$, the volume of the element being (da. dx). The negative sign indicates that the force f_{px} will act in the direction of decreasing value of p. In the same way, a negative gradient of pressure in any given direction gives a pressure force acting on a unit volume of the fluid in that direction.

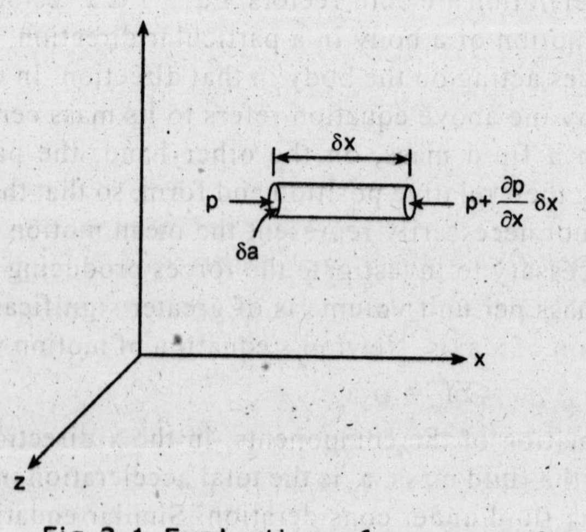

Fig.3.1 Evaluation of pressure force

The force per unit volume f_v, due to viscosity, exists in all real fluids. When there is relative motion between two layers of a fluid, a tangential force is created due to the effects of viscosity. The shear resistance f_v is in a direction opposite to that of motion. In other words the viscous force f_v retards the flow. The details about this force are given in Chapter 8.

The force per unit volume due to surface tension f_σ is important when the depths of flow or the related length dimensions are extremely small. The force due to compressibility, f_e, for incompressible fluids, becomes significant in problems of unsteady flow like water hammer, in which the elastic properties of fluids come into the picture. In most problems the force due to surface tension f_σ and the force due to compressibility f_e are neglected.

In highly turbulent flow, the velocity fluctuates with time at all points and varies in an irregular manner from point to point at any instant. There is, therefore, a continuous momentum transfer between adjacent layers which causes additional normal and shear stresses due to turbulence; these are known as Reynolds stresses. These stresses designated by f_t must be taken into consideration in the case of turbulent flow.

3.3 Equations of Motion

Fluid motion is influenced by all the forces mentioned above and motion in any direction is caused by the components of all the forces in that direction. For the x direction, Newton's equation can be written as

$$f_{gx} + f_{px} + f_{vx} + f_{\sigma x} + f_{ex} + f_{tx} = \rho\, a_x \tag{3.3}$$

The second subscript x indicates that the component of each force per unit volume in the x direction is considered. Similar equations can be written along other two co-ordinate directions.

As mentioned earlier, the forces due to surface tension f_σ and compressibility f_e are extremely small and can therefore be neglected unless the problem specially calls for the consideration of these forces. Viscous forces f_v are predominant in the study of real fluids at extremely low velocities. The forces due to turbulence f_t play an important part when turbulent flow is studied. For ideal fluids, which have no viscosity, Eq. 3.3 can be written neglecting all the forces except that of gravity and that due to the pressure gradient. Thus, one can write,

$$f_{gx} + f_{px} = \rho\, a_x \tag{3.4}$$

When proper expression for f_{gx}, f_{px} and a_x are substituted in Eq. 3.4, one gets what is known as *Euler's equation of motion* in the x-direction.

When the viscous forces are considered, Eq. 3.4 may be written as

$$f_{gx} + f_{px} + f_{vx} = \rho\, a_x \tag{3.5}$$

This equation gives the *Navier-Stokes' equation* in the x-direction when the proper expressions for the forces and the acceleration are substituted into it.

For a turbulent flow the force due to turbulence must be considered in addition to that due to viscosity and Eq. 3.5 can be written as

$$f_{gx} + f_{px} + f_{vx} + f_{tx} = \rho\, a_x \tag{3.6}$$

Equation 3.6 gives the *Reynolds equation of motion in* the x direction. This equation differs from the Navier Stokes' equation in the addition of the turbulence forces resulting from the velocity fluctuations. A detailed study of the Navier-Stokes' equations and the Reynolds equations is beyond the scope of this book. The Euler's equation of motion, however, will be discussed here to some extent.

Introducing the term $(-\partial p/\partial x)$ in Eq. 3.4, in place of the pressure force per unit volume f_{px} and letting f_{gx} represent the gravity force per unit volume, Eq. 3.4 can be rewritten as

$$f_{gx} - \frac{\partial p}{\partial x} = \rho \left(\frac{\partial u}{\partial t} + u \frac{\partial u}{\partial x} \right) \tag{3.7}$$

which is Euler's equation for one dimensional flow. Here $\partial u/\partial t$ is the local acceleration in the x direction and $u\,(\partial u/\partial x)$ is the convective acceleration in the x direction.

The general three dimensicnal form of the Euler's equations of motion can be written as:

$$\left.\begin{aligned}
\frac{\partial u}{\partial t} + u\frac{\partial u}{\partial x} + v\frac{\partial u}{\partial y} + w\frac{\partial u}{\partial z} &= X - \frac{1}{\rho}\frac{\partial p}{\partial x} \\
\frac{\partial v}{\partial t} + u\frac{\partial v}{\partial x} + v\frac{\partial v}{\partial y} + w\frac{\partial v}{\partial z} &= Y - \frac{1}{\rho}\frac{\partial p}{\partial y} \\
\frac{\partial w}{\partial t} + u\frac{\partial w}{\partial x} + v\frac{\partial w}{\partial y} + w\frac{\partial w}{\partial z} &= Z - \frac{1}{\rho}\frac{\partial p}{\partial z}
\end{aligned}\right\} \tag{3.8}$$

where u, v and w are components of velocity in the x, and z direction, and X, Y and Z are the components of fluid weight per unit mass in the three co-ordinate directions. The components X, Y. Z are sometimes called the components *of body force.*

3.4 Integration of Euler's Equation Along Stream Line

Integration of Euler's equation along any streamline results in an important equation in fluid mechanics known as Bernoulli's equation. Consider the forces acting on an element of cross-sectional area da and length ds along a streamline, as shown in Fig. 3.2. The forces acting on the element are those due to gravity and due to the pressure gradient. It is assumed that fluid is frictionless and that the other forces mentioned in section 3.2 are nonexistant.

The gravity force is $(\rho g \, da \, ds \cos\theta)$ in the direction of motion. The force due to the pressure is $-(\partial p/\partial s)\, da\, ds$. If the velocity in the direction of motion is V, then Euler's equation can be written as

$$\rho g \, da \, ds \cos\theta - \frac{\partial p}{\partial s} \, da \, ds = \rho \, da \, ds \left(\frac{\partial V}{\partial t} + V\frac{\partial V}{\partial s} \right) \tag{3.9}$$

in which da ds is the volume of the element. Dividing Eq. 3.9 by ρda ds one gets,

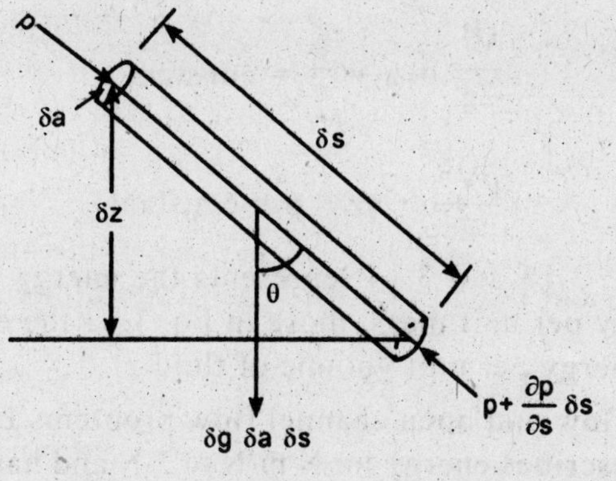

Fig.3.2 Forces acting on a stream tube

$$g \cos \theta - \frac{1}{\rho} \frac{\partial p}{\partial s} = \left(\frac{\partial V}{\partial t} + V \frac{\partial V}{\partial s} \right)$$

Considering a steady flow i.e. $\frac{\partial V}{\partial t} = 0$, and replacing $\cos \theta = -\frac{\partial z}{\partial s}$ the above equation may be written as

$$-g \frac{\partial z}{\partial s} - \frac{1}{\rho} \frac{\partial p}{\partial s} = V \frac{\partial V}{\partial s} \qquad (3.10)$$

Equation 3.10 can also be written as

$$\rho V \frac{\partial V}{\partial s} = -\frac{\partial}{\partial s} (p + \gamma z) \qquad (3.10a)$$

Equation 3.10 can be integrated along a stream line, after multiplying each term by ds. Hence,

$$-\int g \, dz - \int \frac{dp}{\rho} = \int V \, dV$$

or

$$\frac{V^2}{2} + g z + \int \frac{dp}{\rho} = \text{constant} \qquad (3.11)$$

Equation 3.11 is Bernoulli's equation for fluids which are compressible as well as incompressible. However, for an incompressible fluid ρ is independent of pressure, i.e. ρ is constant. Hence,

$$\frac{V^2}{2} + gz + \frac{p}{\rho} = \text{constant} \qquad (3.12)$$

Equation 3.12 is Bernoulli's equation along a stream line for incompressible fluids. This equation can be written in the following two alternate forms,

$$\frac{V^2}{2g} + z + \frac{p}{\gamma} = \text{constant} \tag{3.13}$$

$$\frac{\rho V^2}{2} + \gamma z + p = \text{constant} \tag{3.14}$$

Each term in Eqs. 3.12, 3.13 and 3.14 represents the energy of the fluid. Terms in Eq. 3.12 describe the energy per unit mass, those in Eq. 3.13 the energy per unit weight and those in Eq. 3.14 the energy per unit volume of fluid.

In most of the pipe flow and open channel flow problems Eq. 3.13 is employed. Each term in that equation describes energy in: N m/N or J/N and has the dimensions of length. The term $V^2/2g$ is known as the *velocity head,* p/γ is known as the *pressure head* and z is known as the *potential head.* Thus Bernoulli's equation (Eq. 3.13) states that in a steady flow of an ideal fluid the sum of velocity head, the pressure head and the potential head, along a stream line is constant. One more observation concerning Eq. 3.13 can be made at this stage. Applying Eq. 3.13 between two sections one gets,

$$\frac{V_1^2}{2g} + \left(z_1 + \frac{p_1}{\gamma}\right) = \frac{V_2^2}{2g} + \left(z_2 + \frac{p_2}{\gamma}\right)$$

Hence if V_2 is greater than V_1, $(z_1 + p_1/\gamma)$ must be greater than $(z_2 + p_2/\gamma)$. In other words, any increase in velocity will cause a corresponding reduction in the quantity $(z+p/\gamma)$. Similarly a reduction in velocity will cause an increase in $(z + p/\gamma)$. In case the flow is in a horizontal plane or when the fluid is a gas, the term z drops out and hence changes in velocity cause corresponding changes in the pressure. The quantity $(p/\gamma + z)$ is known as the *piezometric head.*

The velocity head $V^2/2g$ is the kinetic energy of the fluid per unit weight, the pressure head is the pressure energy per unit weight and z is the potential energy per unit weight. Bernoulli's equation can also be stated in other words as total energy per unit weight for a steady flow of an ideal fluid remains constant along a stream line. Some explanation is needed regarding interpretation of pressure head as energy per unit weight of fluid. Consider a cylindrical tube attached to a reservoir on one side ; the other side has a piston. If the piston is moved through a distance dx against pressure p, volume of fluid displaced is $A\delta x$ and work done is $pA\delta x$ where A is cross-sectional area of cylinder. Hence work done per unit weight of fluid is $(pA\delta x/\gamma A\delta x)$ or p/γ.

In real fluids some energy is converted into heat due to the viscous shear and consequently there is a certain amount of energy loss. Hence for real fluids Eq. 3.13 can be written as

$$\frac{V_1^2}{2g} + \frac{p_1}{\gamma} + z_1 = \frac{V_2^2}{2g} + \frac{p_2}{\gamma} + z_2 + h_L \tag{3.15}$$

in which the subscripts 1 and 2 refer to the two sections under consideration and h_L is the energy loss per unit weight of fluid between the two sections.

Example 3.1

Water flows down a 2.3 m long vertical pipe. The top of the pipe is 10.0 cm in diameter which tapers down to 5.0 cm at the bottom. Find the pressure difference between the two ends if the flow is 25 *l*/s. Assume no energy loss.

Area of pipe at upper end $= \frac{\pi}{4} \times 0.10^2 = 0.007\ 85\ m^2$

The velocity U_1 at upper end $= \frac{25 \times 10^{-3}}{0.00785}$

$= 3.185$ m/s

Area of pipe at lower end $= \frac{\pi}{4} \times 0.05^2 = 0.001\ 963\ m^2$

The velocity U_2 at lower end $= \frac{25 \times 10^{-3}}{0.001963}$

$= 12.739$ m/s

Taking the datum through the lower end, Bernoulli's equation can be written as

$$\frac{3.185^2}{2 \times 9.81} + \frac{p_1}{\gamma} + 2.3 = \frac{12.739^2}{2 \times 9.81} + \frac{p_2}{\gamma} + 0$$

$$\therefore \quad \frac{p_1 - p_2}{\gamma} = 5.454 \text{ m}$$

$$p_1 - p_2 = 5.454 \times 9.787 = 53.308 \text{ kN/m}^2$$

3.5 Bernoulli's Equation for Compressible Fluids

For the case of compressible fluids, Bernoulli's equation takes a different form because of the fact that the mass density does not remain constant but varies with the pressure. As such, the term (dp/ρ) in Eq. 3.11 needs to be evaluated from the relation between p and ρ. Such a relationship can be obtained from Eq. 1.9 for adiabatic conditions in the following form,

$$\frac{p}{\rho^k} = C_1 \qquad (3.16)$$

in which C_1 is a constant. Differentiating Eq. 3.16

$$\frac{dp}{d\rho} = C_1\ k\ \rho^{k-1}$$

or

$$\frac{dp}{\rho} = C_1\ k\ \rho^{k-2}\ d\rho \qquad (3.17)$$

Substituting this value in Eq. 3.11

$$\frac{V^2}{2} + g\,z + C_1\,k \int \rho^{k-2}\,d\rho = \text{constant}$$

or

$$\frac{V^2}{2} + g\,z + C_1 \frac{k}{k-1} \rho^{k-1} = \text{constant}$$

However, from Eq. 3.16, $C_1\,\rho^{k-1} = p/\rho$. therefore,

$$\frac{V^2}{2} + g\,z + \frac{k}{k-1}\frac{p}{\rho} = \text{constant} \quad (3.18)$$

For gases the potential head term gz does not have much importance for moderate variations in z. Therefore, neglecting the term gz from Eq. 3.18 the following counterpart of Eq. 3.13 can be obtained,

$$\frac{V^2}{2} + \frac{k}{k-1}\frac{p}{\rho} = \text{constant} \quad (3.19)$$

This is Bernoulli's equation for non-viscous compressible fluids under adiabatic condition.

3.6 Measurement of Pressure and Velocity Head

The sum $(p/\gamma + z)$ is known as *piezometric head.* A piezometer is a simple device for measuring pressures in liquids. It consists of a glass tube in which the liquid can rise freely without over-flowing. The height of the liquid in the tube above a given datum gives the value of the piezometric head directly. To reduce the capillary error, the tube diameter should be greater than 6 mm. Special precautions should be taken in connecting the piezometer tube to the pipe in which the pressure measurement is desired. The hole must be absolutely normal to the interior surface of the wall and the piezometer tube must not project beyond the surface. Such protrusion or the obliquity of the piezometer tube causes either an acceleration or deceleration of the fluid in the tube that affects the piezometric head. To minimize turbulence it is desirable to round off the edge of the hole. The piezometer opening in the wall surface should be 1 to 4 mm in diameter and should extend to at least twice the diameter before it is connected to the glass tube. Fig. 3.3 shows the correct and incorrect forms of piezometer opening and the type of error that is caused. The velocity head can be measured by inserting a tube having a short right angled limb facing the flow. This causes stagnation at the entrance to the tube. At this point the velocity is reduced to zero and velocity head is converted into the pressure head. Such a tube for measuring the velocity head is known as a *pitot tube* or total head tube. The liquid surface in the pitot tube indicates the total head at the point. In order to know velocity head, one must know the piezometric head at the same section which can be measured with the help of piezometer. If H_S is the reading of total head tube and h that of piezometric head, then $(H_S - h) = u^2/2g$. Figure 3.4 explains the use of a piezometer and pitot tube. Another form of the pitot tube, known as Prandtl-Pitot tube, is shown in Fig. 3.5.

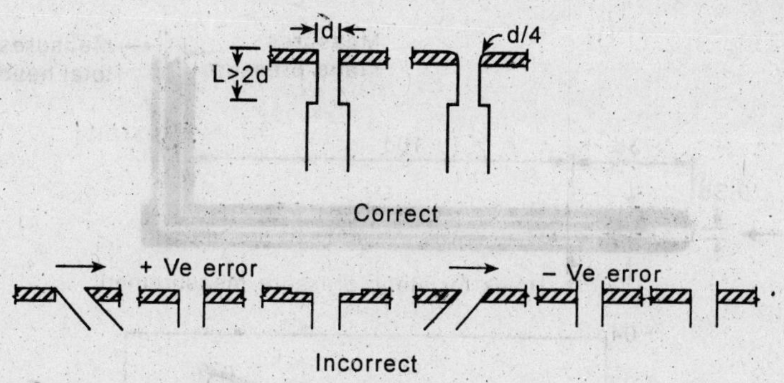

Fig.3.3 Correct and incorrect piezometer openings

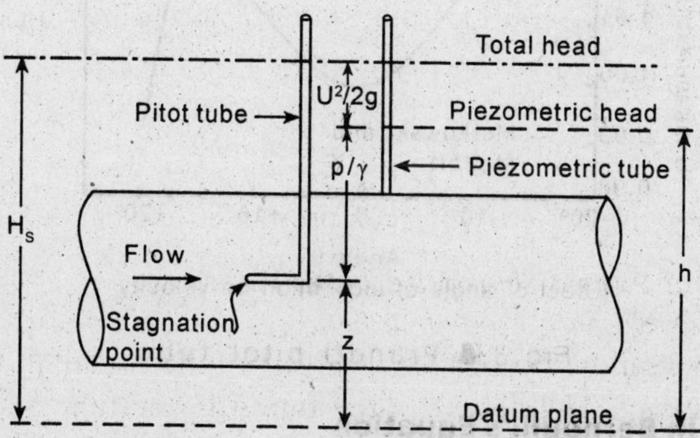

Fig.3.4 Measurement of piezometric head and total head

Prandtl-Pitot tube is a combination of a total head tube and a static pressure tube, the latter measuring the piezometric head at the given point. The front portion of the tube i.e. its head is well rounded so as to avoid separation of the flow and on its shaft are provided holes at such a place that static pressure prevails there. The two tubes are enclosed in the same tube and are then connected to a differential menometer which measures $(H_S–h)$. Because of slight imperfection in the fabrication, etc. the actual velocity at a given point is slightly smaller than the velocity calculated as $\sqrt{2g(H_S - h)}$. Therefore Prandtl tube is calibrated to determine C_d in the equation,

$$u_{actual} = C_d \sqrt{2g(H_S - h)} = C_d \sqrt{\frac{2\Delta p}{\rho}} \qquad (3.20)$$

The usual values of C_d range from 0.95 to 0.99. Prandtl tube is used to determine velocity at any elevation in a pipe or in open channel. Prandtl's pitot tube gives accurate results of course only when it is perfectly aligned in the direction of flow. Fortunately however, small deviations from this direction do not cause large errors. Experimental data giving pitot tube readings as a function of the angular position of the tube are also shown in Fig. 3.5. It can be seen that even when pitot tube is aligned with direction of flow with an angle of 20°, the error in velocity is only 2.0 percent.

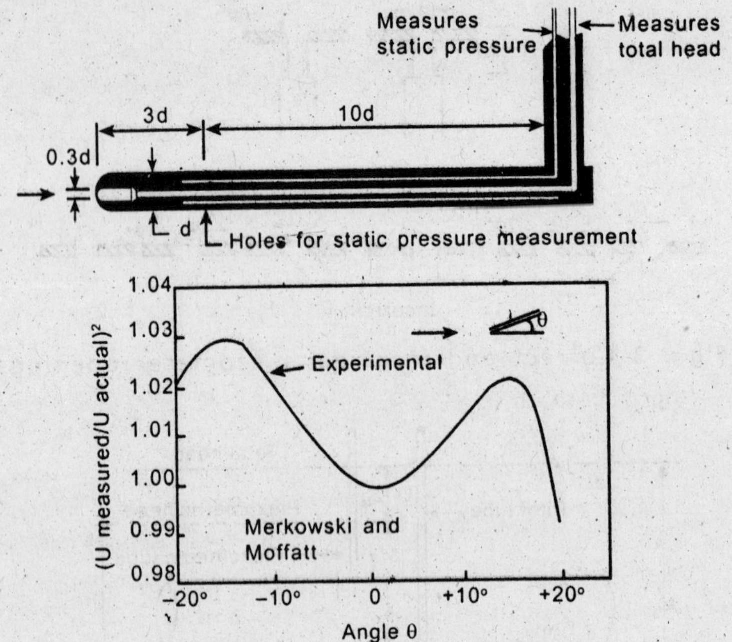

Effect of angle of inclination on velocity

Fig.3.[illegible] Prandtl pitot tube

3.7 Assumptions in Bernoulli's Equation

Before applying Bernoulli's equation for solving fluid flow problems one must carefully understand the assumptions and limitations of the equation. These assumptions are discussed below :

(i) The flow is assumed to be steady, i.e. there is no change in the pressure, the velocity and the density of the fluid at any point with respect to time. However, in problems of unsteady flow with gradually changing conditions, Bernoulli's equation can be applied without appreciable error. Provided the liquid surface level does not drop too rapidly, a problem of emptying a large reservoir can be solved by applying Bernoulli's equation for steady flow, inspite of the fact that it is strictly an unsteady flow case.

(ii) It should be noted that Bernoulli's equation has been derived by integrating Euler's equation of motion along a streamline and therefore, it holds good only along a streamline. Since in its derivation, no mention was made as to whether the flow is rotational or irrotational, it holds good for both these cases. For rotational flow the constant has different value for different streamlines whereas for irrotational flow the constant has the same value for all streamlines. If Euler's equation written for Fig. 3.2 is considered in a direction normal to the streamline, it will be

$$-\frac{\partial}{\partial n}(p + \gamma z) = \rho\, a_n$$

where a_n is the total acceleration normal to the stream line (compare this equation with Eq. 3.10 a). This could be written as

$$-\frac{\partial}{\partial n}(p+\gamma z)=\rho\left[\frac{\partial V_n}{\partial t}+V\frac{\partial V_n}{\partial s}\right]$$

The local component of acceleration ($\partial V_n/\partial t$) is zero for the case of steady flow. Adding the term $-\frac{\partial}{\partial n}\left(\frac{\rho V^2}{2}\right)$ to both the sides of the above equation one gets,

$$-\frac{\partial}{\partial n}\left[p+\gamma z+\rho\frac{V^2}{2}\right]=\rho V\left[\frac{\partial V_n}{\partial s}-\frac{\partial V}{\partial n}\right] \qquad (3.21)$$

Equation 3.21 can be integrated to yield Eq. 3.14 only if ($\partial V_n/\partial s$) = ($\partial V/\partial n$), i.e. if the flow is irrotational. In the case of rotational flows, ($\partial V/\partial n$) ≠ ($\partial V_n/\partial s$) and as such integration of Eq. 3.21 will show that ($p + \gamma z + \rho V^2/2$) or ($p/\rho + gz + V^2/2$) varies in the normal direction. Thus the constant in Bernoulli's equations Eqs. 3.12, 3.13 and 3.14 will be different for each streamline. In other words, the total head in rotational flow will change in the normal direction; this is shown in Fig. 3.6 for rotational flow. The velocity variation in the vertical is also shown in the figure. It can be seen that in steady uniform rotational flow there is no acceleration in the vertical direction and hence the piezometric

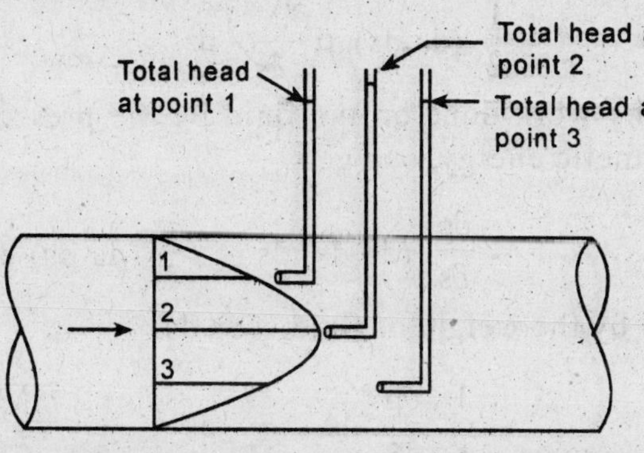

Fig.3.6 Variation of total head in rotational flow

head in any vertical is constant. The variation in total head for each streamline is because of variation in the velocity head as indicated.

(iii) The fluid is assumed to be incompressible. The liquids are incompressible and hence Bernoulli's equation in the form of Eqs. 3.12, 3.13 and 3.14, is applicable for all liquid. However, Bernoulli's equation in these particular forms can also be applied to problems of gas flow when there is small variation in pressure, velocity and temperature so that mass density can be assumed to be constant. Gases under such conditions can be treated as incompressible.

(iv) Since this equation is derived for ideal fluids, the loss of energy due to friction is assumed to be zero. For real fluids, in which energy loss occurs due to friction, one must consider this loss as is done in Eq. 3.15. However for rapidly converging flows of real fluids, the energy loss can be neglected if the two sections are close to each other.

3.8 Bernoulli's Equation as Energy Equation

Bernoulli's equation can also be studied in the light of energy considerations. It has been shown in sections 3.1 and 3.3 that the pressure force for unit volume and the gravity force per unit volume, both in the direction of motion, can be expressed as $-\frac{\partial p}{\partial s}$ and $-\gamma\frac{\partial z}{\partial s}$ respectively. These forces will perform work on the fluid as it flows through a distance ds. Under steady flow conditions, the work done will be

$$\left(-\frac{\partial p}{\partial s}\,da\,ds\right)ds - \left(\gamma\frac{\partial z}{\partial s}\,da\,ds\right)ds,$$

in which da is the cross-sectional area of tube and ds is the distance travelled. As a result of this work done on the fluid, according to the principle of conservation of energy, the kinetic energy of the fluid must increase. The increase in kinetic energy can be expressed as

$$\frac{1}{2}\text{(mass) (change in } V^2 \text{ over distance ds)}$$

i.e. $$\frac{1}{2}\,(da\,ds)\;\rho\frac{\partial(V^2)}{\partial s}\,ds$$

Therefore, equating the work done on the fluid by the pressure and the gravity forces with the increase in kinetic energy, one gets

$$-\frac{\partial p}{\partial s}\,(da\,ds)\,ds - \gamma\frac{\partial z}{\partial s}(da\,ds)\,ds = \frac{1}{2}\,(da\,ds)\;\rho\frac{\partial(V^2)}{\partial s}\,ds$$

or, dividing each term by the weight of fluid, γ da ds,

$$-\frac{1}{\gamma}\frac{\partial p}{\partial s}\,ds - \frac{\partial z}{\partial s}\,ds = \frac{1}{2g}\frac{\partial(V^2)}{\partial s}\,ds$$

Integrating this equation along the direction of flow between two sections 1 and 2, the following equation is obtained

$$\left(\frac{p_1 - p_2}{\gamma}\right) + (z_1 - z_2) = \frac{V_2^2 - V_1^2}{2g}$$

or $$\frac{p_1}{\gamma} + z_1 + \frac{V_1^2}{2g} = \frac{p_2}{\gamma} + z_2 + \frac{V_2^2}{2g}$$

Thus it can be seen that in its simplified form the energy equation and Bernoulli's equation are identical. In some problems mechanical energy is either added or extracted from the flow system between sections 1 and 2; then the energy equation becomes

$$\frac{p_1}{\gamma} + z_1 + \frac{V_1^2}{2g} + E_m = \frac{p_2}{\gamma} + z_2 + \frac{V_2^2}{2g} \tag{3.22}$$

Here E_m represents the mechanical energy added per unit weight of the fluid. Such energy can be added to the flow system by a pump while energy can be extracted from the system by a turbine.

In a similar way, the scope of the energy equation can be enlarged by considering addition or subtraction of heat to the flow system. This is discussed in chapter 14.

Example 3.2

Water enters a hydraulic machine through a pipe of 60 cm diameter under a pressure of 147.1 kN/m². It leaves the machine through a 90 cm diameter pipe under a pressure of 34.32 kN/m². A vertical distance of 2.0 m separates the centres of two pipes. If the flow of 450 *l*/s passes through the machine, how much power is supplied to the machine ?

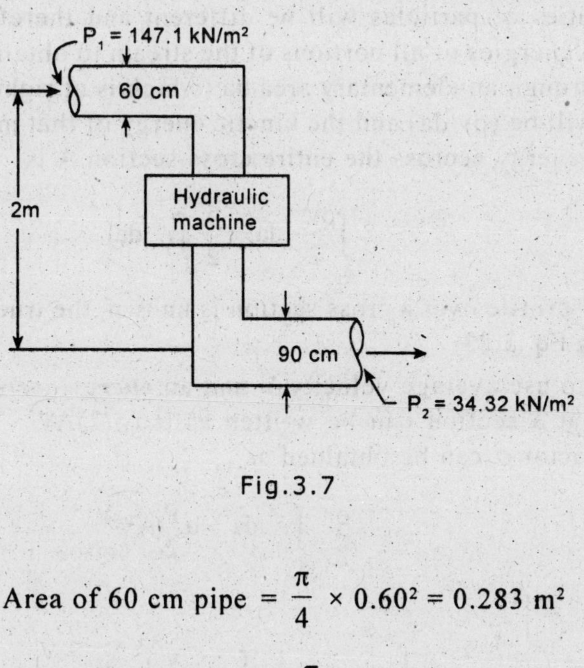

Fig.3.7

$$\text{Area of 60 cm pipe} = \frac{\pi}{4} \times 0.60^2 = 0.283 \text{ m}^2$$

$$\text{Area of 90 cm pipe} = \frac{\pi}{4} \times 0.90^2 = 0.636 \text{ m}^2$$

$$\text{Velocity in 60 cm pipe, } V_1 = \frac{0.45}{0.283} = 1.590 \text{ m/s}$$

$$\text{Velocity in 60 cm pipe, } V_2 = \frac{0.45}{0.636} = 0.708 \text{ m/s}$$

Applying the energy equation between sections 1 and 2

$$\frac{V_1^2}{2g} + \frac{p_1}{\gamma} + z_1 = \frac{V_2^2}{2g} + \frac{p_2}{\gamma} + z_2 + E_m$$

$$\frac{1.590^2}{2 \times 9.81} + \frac{147.1}{9.787} + 2 = \frac{0.708^2}{2 \times 9.81} + \frac{34.32}{9.787} + 0 + E_m$$

Solving for E_m one gets, $E_m = 13.672$ m

$$= \frac{13.626 \times 0.45 \times 9787}{1000} = 60.011 \text{ kW}$$

This energy is supplied to the machine.

3.9 Energy Correction Factor

The term velocity head in the energy equation considers velocity to be uniform over a cross-section of the conduit or stream tube which is seldom true in real fluids. In any cross-section velocities of particles will be different and therefore it is necessary to integrate the kinetic energies of all portions of the stream to obtain its total value. If v is the local velocity through an elementary area da (which is at right angles to v) the mass flow per unit time will be (ρv da) and the kinetic energy of that mass will be (ρv da) $v^2/2$. The total kinetic energy accross the entire cross-section A is

$$\int_A \frac{\rho v^3}{2} da = \frac{\rho}{2} \int_A v^3 \, da \qquad (3.23)$$

If the exact velocity profile over a cross section is known, the true kinetic energy can be determined by using Eq. 3.23.

It is convenient to use average velocity V and an *energy correction factor* α; hence the kinetic energy at a section can be written as α (ρ/2)AV^3. Thus the value of the energy correction factor α can be obtained as

$$\frac{\rho}{2} \int_A v^3 \, da = \alpha \frac{\rho}{2} A V^3$$

Solving for α one gets,

$$\alpha = \frac{1}{A} \int_A \left(\frac{v}{V} \right)^3 da \qquad (3.24)$$

in which v is the local velocity over the area da and V is the average velocity over the cross sectional area A. The value of α depends on the velocity variation across the area which in turn depends on effects of the viscous shear. Hence α is a measure of effects of the viscous shear on a flow pattern.

While applying the energy equation between two sections, one must see whether the velocities at the two sections are uniform or nonuniform. If the velocity varies over the cross section, the kinetic energy term needs correction and therefore the energy equation takes the form

$$\frac{p_1}{\gamma} + z_1 + \frac{\alpha_1 V_1^2}{2g} = \frac{p_2}{\gamma} + z_2 + \frac{\alpha_2 V_2^2}{2g} \qquad (3.25)$$

in which α_1 and α_2 are the energy correction factors at sections 1 and 2 respectively.

The value of α will always be greater than unity. The greater the variation in the velocity over a cross section, the greater will be the value of α. For laminar flow in circular pipes, in which the velocity distribution is parabolic, the energy correction factor α has a value of 2.0. For turbulent flow, the value of α varies between 1.01 to 1.15, the normal values being between 1.03 and 1.06. Most fluid flow problems are in the turbulent range of flow for which the value of α is only slightly greater than unity. Assuming α to be unity will not, therefore, result in any appreciable error.

Example 3.3

The velocity distribution in a pipe is given by the equation

$$u = u_{max}\left(\frac{R-r}{R}\right)^{1/7}$$

where R is the radius of the pipe and r is any radius at which the velocity u is described by the equation. Find the energy correction factor for such a velocity distribution.

The discharge through a small annular ring of width dr will be $2\pi r\, u\, dr$. The total flow will be the integral of that expression, integrated between limits from r = 0 to r = R. If the average velocity is U, then

$$\pi R^2 U = \int_0^R 2\pi r\, u_{max}\left(1-\frac{r}{R}\right)^{1/7} dr$$

$$= \pi R^2 u_{max} \frac{98}{120}$$

$$\therefore \quad U = \frac{98}{120} u_{max}$$

$$\frac{u}{U} = \frac{u_{max}\left(\frac{R-r}{R}\right)^{1/7}}{\frac{98}{120}u_{max}} = \frac{120}{98}\left(\frac{R-r}{R}\right)^{1/7}$$

From Eq. 3.24

$$\alpha = \frac{1}{\pi R^2}\int_0^R 2\pi r\left(\frac{120}{98}\right)^3\left(1-\frac{r}{R}\right)^{3/7} dr$$

Simplifying and solving the integral one gets

$$\alpha = 1.06$$

Example 3.4

A pitot tube connected to a sail boat is used to determine its velocity. When the water level in the tube is 0.60 m above the surface, how fast is the sail boat going ?

$$U = \sqrt{2g(H_S - h)} = (2.0 \times 9.81 \times 0.60)^{1/2}$$

$$= 3.431 \text{ m/s}$$

Here it is assumed that $C_d = 1.0$

Example 3.5

In order to calibrate Prandtl's Pilot tube, velocity distribution was measured in a 5 cm diameter pipe using a vertical inverted U-tube manometer. The difference of head at various sections is given below. Volumetric measurement yielded 0.249 m³ of discharge in 100 seconds. Find discharge coefficient C_d of the Pitot tube.

y cm	0.50	1.0	1.5	2.0	2.5	3.0	3.5	4.0	4.5
Δh cm	1.83	4.13	4.60	4.89	5.10	4.89	4.22	3.95	2.02

Initially assume C_d to be unity and compute $u = \sqrt{2g\Delta h}$ as the theoretical velocity at each section. Velocity at y = 0 and 5.0 cm will be zero. Divide the cross-sectional area into rings as shown in Fig. 3.8. The velocities at the extremities of each ring are shown in the figure. Taking the average of these velocities as the mean velocity for that ring, the discharge theoretical δQ_T flowing through that ring can be calculated. $\Sigma\delta Q_T$ will give the theoretical discharge Q_T flowing through the pipe. Calculation of Q_T can be done in the tabular form shown below

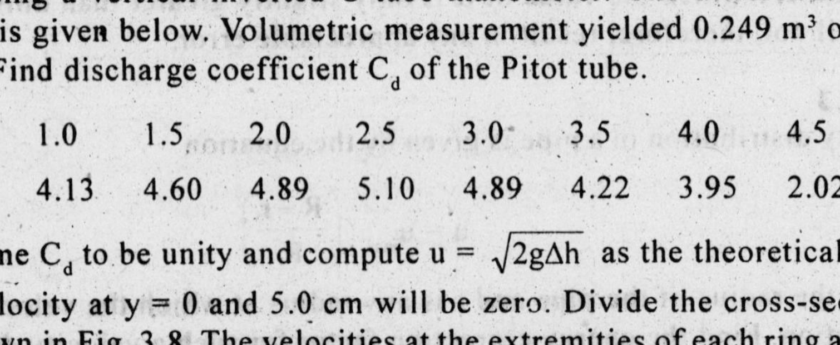

Fig.3.8 Velocity distribution in the pipe

Ring	Outer radius r_1 cm	Inner radius r_2 cm	dA = $\pi\,(r_1^2 - r_2^2)$ m^2	u m/s	dQ_T = udA
1	2.5	2.0	0.001 964	0.3057	0.0006 039
2	2.0	1.5	0.001 257	0.7503	0.0009 431
3	1.5	1.0	0.000 707	0.9100	0.0006 433
4	1.0	0.5	0.000 314	0.9550	0.0002 988
5	0.50	0	0.000 079	0.9870	0.0000 799
					Q_T = 0.002 569 m^3/s

Actual discharge $= \dfrac{0.249}{100} = 0.002\ 49\ m^3/s$

$$C_d = \frac{\text{Actual discharge}}{\text{Theoretical discharge}}$$

$$= \frac{0.002\ 49}{0.002\ 569} = 0.97$$

PROBLEMS

3.1 A section of convergent pipe is so shaped that the velocity of flow along the centre line varies linearly from 1.0 m/s to 10.0 m/s in a distance of one metre. The pipe is inclined downwards at an angle of 30° with the horizontal. Determine the difference in pressure between the sections assuming the relative density of the liquid to be 0.80.

3.2 A pipe line enlarges from a diameter of 10 cm at A to 20 cm at B which is 2 m higher than A. With a pressure of 68.65 kN/m² at A, water flows at the rate of 15.0 *l*/s. Find the pressure at B.

3.3 A vertical cylinder is placed in a horizontal air stream of velocity 30.0 m/s and pressure of 101.0 kN/m². Calculate the stagnation pressure and pressure at a point 90° from the flow direction on the surface of the cylinder if the local velocity at that point is 60.0 m/s. Assume ρ to be 1.226 kg/m³.

3.4 Air (ρ = 1.226 kg/m³) flows through a horizontal pipe line. At section A the diameter is 9.0 cm, pressure is 176.5 kN/m² and velocity is 25.0 m/s. Calculate the discharge through the pipe and the velocity and the pressure at section B, if the diameter of the pipe at that section is 18.0 cm. Assume air to be incompressible and no loss of energy between the two sections

3.5 Show that the dimensions of each term in Eq. 3.13 are energy per unit weight of the fluid.

3.6 Find the average velocity and energy correction factor for the following velocity profiles in a pipe (Note : u_m is the maximum velocity, u is velocity at distance r from the pipe centre and R is the pipe radius)

a. $u = u_{max}\left(1 - \frac{r}{R}\right)$

b. $u = u_{max}\left[1 - \left(\frac{r}{R}\right)^2\right]$

c. $u = u_{max}\left[1 - \left(\frac{r}{R}\right)^{2/3}\right]$

3.7 The velocity distribution in a wide 2.5 m deep river is found to vary from 0.6 m/s at the bottom to 2.0 m/s at surface according to an expression $u = 0.6 + 1.4\,(y/y_0)^{1/2}$, in which y_0 is the depth of flow and u is the velocity at any distance y from channel bottom. Find the kinetic energy correction factor.

3.8 Determine the value of energy correction factor in the following cases of two dimensional flows :

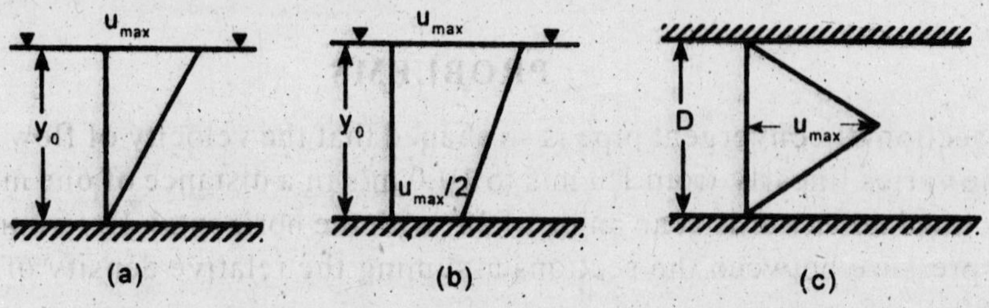

Problem.3.8

3.9 What will be the discharge through a turbine if 44.1 kW energy is extracted when the pressure gauges at points A and B read 112.78 kN/m² and – 27.46 kN/m² respectively.

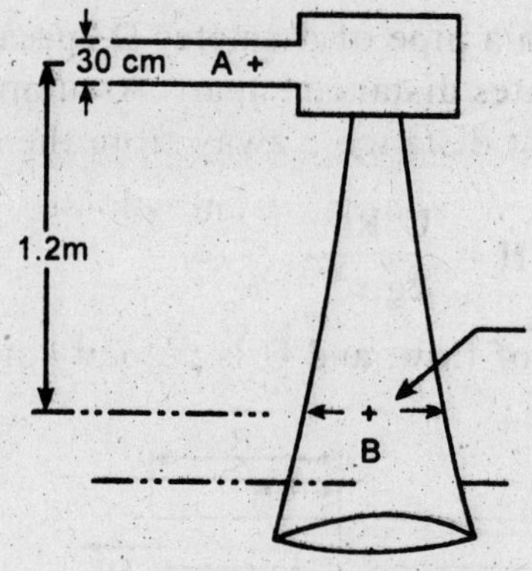

Problem.3.9

3.10 In the above problem, if the discharge is 400 l/s and the pressures at A and B are 147 kN/m^2 and 29.42 kN/m^2 respectively, determine the energy extracted by the turbine.

3.11 If 115 l/s of water is pumped from the reservoir shown in figure, what will be the pressures at points m and n when the pump supplied 17.65 kW energy ?

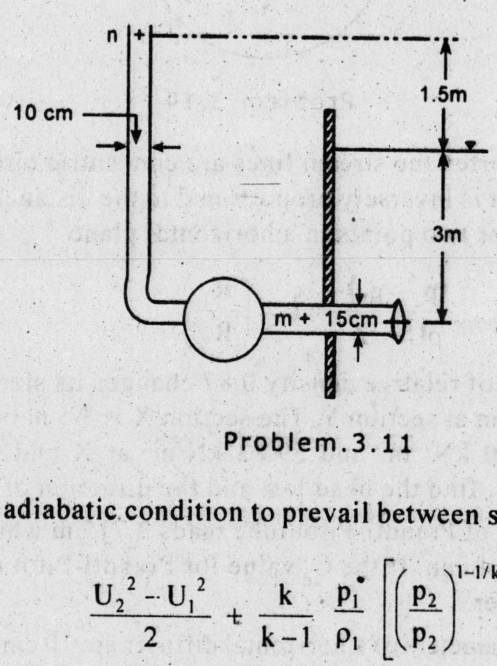

Problem.3.11

3.12 Considering the adiabatic condition to prevail between sections 1 and 2, show that

$$\frac{U_2^2 - U_1^2}{2} + \frac{k}{k-1} \cdot \frac{p_1}{\rho_1}\left[\left(\frac{p_2}{p_2}\right)^{1-1/k} - 1\right] = 0$$

3.13 A body is immersed in an air stream with the ambient velocity of 40 m/s, at pressure of 98.07 kN/m^2 and ρ = 1.206 kg/m^2. If the velocity at some point on the immersed body is 80 m/s determine the pressure at that point ?

3.14 Liquid after flowing through a pipe of diameter D spreads out radially outwards between parallel circular plates distance t apart. Assuming no loss to occur, show that the pressure at any point distance x away from the centre is given by

$$\frac{p}{\gamma} = H - \frac{U^2 R^2}{2g\,x^2}$$

where H is the total energy of flow, and U is velocity at the end of the plate.

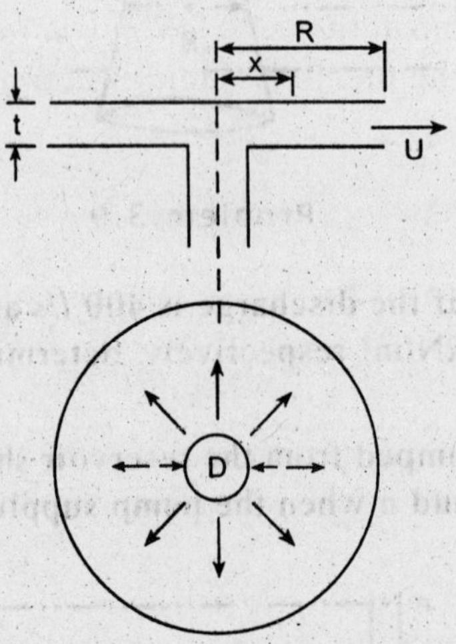

Problem.3.14

3.15 In an irrotational vortex the stream lines are concentric circles and the tangential velocity at any point is inversely proportional to the distance of that point from the centre. Show that for two points in a horizontal plane

$$\frac{(p_2 - p_1)}{\rho U_1^2/2} = 1 - \left(\frac{R_1}{R_2}\right)$$

3.16 A pipe carrying oil of relative density 0.87 changes its size gradually from 15 cm at section X to 45 cm at section Y. The section X is 3.5 m below section Y and the pressures are 91.20 kN/ m² and 59.82 kN/m² at X and Y respectively. If the discharge is 145 l/s, find the head lost and the direction of flow.

3.17 The total head tube of Prandtl-Pitot tube reads 2.715 m while the static tube reads 2.570 m of water column. If the C_d value for Prandtl-Pitot tube is 0.98, determine the velocity of water.

3.18 The inlet and exit diameters of a horizontal diffuser are 10 cm and 30 cm respectively. For a discharge of 20 l/s of water the pressure at the inlet is 200 kN/m² and head lost in friction and expansion is 0.15 m of water. Determine the pressure at the exit.

3.19 The cross-section of a pipe is divided into ten equal areas by means of concentric circles. The mean velocities in the areas beginning at the centre of the pipe are found as follows (in m/s):

1.713, 1.700, 1.676, 1.640, 1.579, 1494, 1.384, 1.231, 1.024, 0.768

Compute α.

3.20 The suction and delivery pipe diameters of a pump are 200 mm and 100 mm respectively. If the inlet and outlet pressures are 70 kN/m^2 and 210 kN/m^2 respectively and the pump delivers 40 kW power to the fluid, find the discharge of water flowing through the pump. Assume exit to be 0.5 m above inlet.

CHAPTER FOUR

FLUID STATICS

4.1 Introduction

When a fluid mass is subjected to acceleration, the relation between the forces acting and the resulting acceleration gives equations of motion. These have been developed and discussed in detail in Chapter 3. It is of interest to simplify the equations of motion to a case in which there is no acceleration in x, y and z directions. In other words, the fluid mass is either stationary or is moving bodily at a uniform velocity. Such a simplification leads to the study of *Fluid Statics*. Principles of Fluid Statics find important applications in engineering related to forces acting on submerged bodies such as gates, submarines, dams, etc., and in the analysis of stability of floating bodies such as pontoons, ships, etc. For understanding Fluid Statics, one must get a clear concept of the nature of fluid pressure, which has been briefly discussed in Chapter 1.

4.2 Fluid Pressure

Consider a small area ΔA in a large mass of fluid. The fluid surrounding this area exerts a force on that area. If the fluid is stationary, this force is always perpendicular to the surface ΔA. If ΔF is the elemental force acting on area ΔA in the normal direction, $\lim_{\Delta A \to 0} (\Delta F/\Delta A)$ is known as intensity of force or *intensity of pressure* of simply *pressure*. In other words

$$p = \lim_{\Delta A \to 0} (\Delta F/\Delta A) \tag{4.1}$$

The pressure p has the units of N/m². If the force ΔF is not perpendicular to ΔA, it will have a component parallel to area ΔA, i.e., a shear stress. However, it is known that a shear stress cannot exist unless there is relative motion between different fluid layers.

fluid layers. Therefore, one must conclude that p acts normal to the surface. It must be remembered that since the fluid is stationary, it is immaterial whether the fluid is ideal or real.

A fluid is said to be in static equilibrium when each fluid particle is at rest i.e. it has no velocity with respect to the reference axis. Under such condition, according to the principles of mechanics, summation of the components of forces along each of the three directions must be zero. Since individual fluid particles have no velocity with respect to the reference axis, there is no relative motion between various fluid layers; as such no tangential force exists. Therefore, in considering the equilibrium of a fluid mass, only the pressure force and the gravity force need to be considered. It can be shown that in the case of stationary fluid in equilibrium, the pressure at any point is independent of the surface on which it acts; in other words, the pressure at a point is the same in all directions.

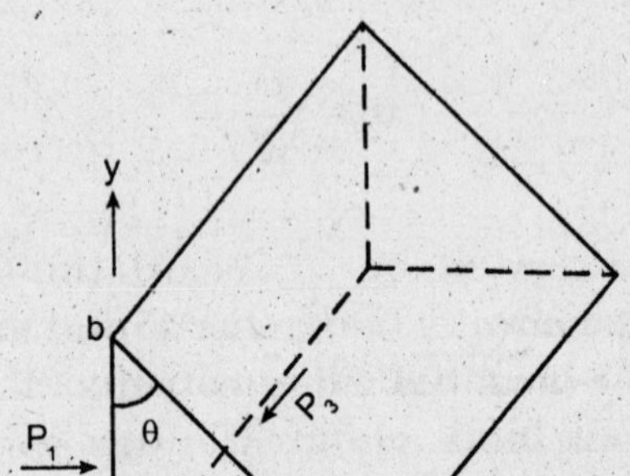

Fig.4.1 Equilibrium of a fluid element

Consider a triangular prism of unit width as in Fig. 4.1. Let p_1, p_2 and p_3 be the intensities of pressures acting on the faces ab, ac and bc with unit widths. Writing equations for equilibrium along x any y directions, one gets

$$p_1\,(ab \times 1) - p_3\,(bc \times 1)\cos\theta = 0$$

and $$p_2\,(ac \times 1) - p_3\,(bc \times 1)\sin\theta - \frac{ab \times ac}{2} \times 1 \times \gamma = 0 \qquad (4.2$$

However, $bc\cos\theta = ab$ and $bc\sin\theta = ac$.

Hence, Eq. 4.2 becomes

$$p_1\,ab - p_3\,ab = 0$$

or $$p_1 = p_3$$

and $$p_2\,ac - p_3\,ac - \frac{ab \times ac}{2} \times 1 \times \gamma = 0$$

Now, as the prism is shrunk to very small dimensions, ab and bc become infinitesimally small and hence the product (ab × ac) tends to zero. As such

$$p_2 = p_3 \text{ and } p_1 = p_3 \quad (4.3)$$

Since the choice of prism was completely arbitrary, it can be seen that pressure at any point is the same in all directions. This is known as *Pascal's law*.

Example 4.1

Find the force required to lift a weight of 19.6 kN by means of a hydraulic press which has a ram of 15 cm diameter and a plunger of 2 cm diameter. If the plunger has a stroke of 30 cm and if it makes 96 strokes per minute, through what distance is the weight lifted per minute ? Find the power required at the plunger.

A hydraulic press is a machine which works on the principle that liquids transmit pressures equally in all directions. It has a ram and a plunger as shown in Fig. 4.2.

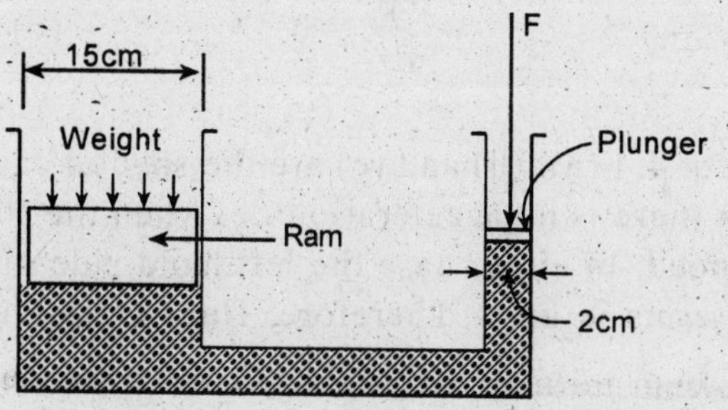

Fig.4.2 Hydraulic press

Pressure intensity p developed due to plunger = F/a.

The same is transmitted to the ram and therefore p = W/A where a and A are the areas of plunger and ram respectively and W is the weight to be lifted. Thus,

$$F = \frac{a}{A}W = \frac{\frac{\pi}{4}\times 0.02^2}{\frac{\pi}{4}\times 0.15^2} \times 19.6 = 0.348 \text{ kN}$$

Distance moved by the plunger per minute

$$= 96 \times 30 = 2880 \text{ cm} = 28.8 \text{ m}$$

Distance through which the weight of 19.6 kN is lifted is

$$\frac{28.8\times 2^2}{15^2} = 0.512 \text{ m}$$

$$\therefore \text{Power required} = \frac{19.6\times 0.512}{60} = 0.167 \text{ kW}$$

It has been already mentioned that, just like any other flow characteristics, the pressure can vary from one point to other and from time to time. In other words, $p = f(x, y, z, t)$. It has also been shown that $-\partial p/\partial x$, $-\partial p/\partial y$ and $-\partial p/\partial z$ represent the pressure force per unit volume in the x, y, and z directions respectively. While considering the equilibrium one must consider, in addition to the above pressure force, components of gravity force per unit volume in the three directions. If x and z axes are in horizontal plane and y axis is vertically upwards, then the components of gravity force per unit volume in x, y and z directions are 0, $-\gamma$ and 0 respectively. Hence the conditions for equilibrium become,

$$\left.\begin{aligned} -\frac{\partial p}{\partial x} &= 0 \quad &\text{(a)}\\ -\frac{\partial p}{\partial y} - \gamma &= 0 \quad &\text{(b)}\\ -\frac{\partial p}{\partial z} &= 0 \quad &\text{(c)} \end{aligned}\right\} \tag{4.4}$$

It can be seen that Eq. 4.4 (a), (b) and (c) are the special case of Euler's equations of motion (Eq. 3.8), when there is no acceleration i.e. when the fluid either is stationary or moving at a uniform speed. In either case the left hand side of Euler's equations which represent the inertial terms is zero. Therefore, fluid statics is a special case of fluid dynamics.

Integration of Eq. 4.4 yields important results. Since $\partial p/\partial x = 0$ and $\partial p/\partial z = 0$, p must be a function of y alone. Equation 4.4 (b) gives,

$$\int_{p_1}^{p_2} dp = -\int_{y_1}^{y_2} \gamma \, dy \tag{4.5}$$

Assuming γ to be independent of y i.e. if specific weight does not change with change in y, one gets

$$(p_2 - p_1) = \gamma (y_1 - y_2) \tag{4.6}$$

This integration is possible only for incompressible fluids. From this one can conclude that pressure depends only on y and it remains constant in xz plane where y remains constant. Thus pressure difference between any two points depends only on the difference between their elevations, if fluid is stationary.

Consider free surface of the liquid in Fig. 4.3, along which the pressure intensity must be constant and is equal to the atmospheric pressure p_a. Since from Eq. 4.5

$$p = -\gamma y + C \tag{4.7}$$

and $\quad p = p_a$ when $y = y_o$,

$$p_a = -\gamma y_o + C$$

Therefore

$$\left.\begin{aligned} p - p_a &= \gamma (y_o - y)\\ p - p_a &= \gamma h \end{aligned}\right\} \tag{4.8}$$

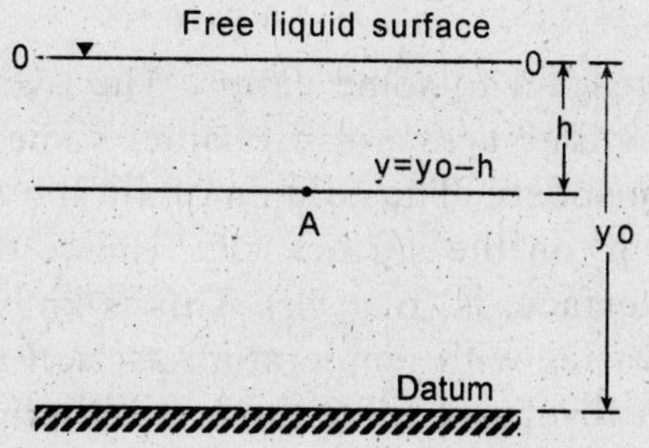

Fig.4.3 Definition sketch

In most of the problems the pressure above the atmospheric pressure is considered and therefore, Eq. 4.8 becomes

$$p = \gamma h \qquad (4.9)$$

Equation 4.9 can be written as $(p/\gamma) = h$ and hence pressure can also be expressed as equivalent pressure head of the liquid. It represents the column of liquid that gives a pressure p at its base. Such a concept is evidently valid only as long as there is a free surface. Hence in the case of gases, equivalent pressure head has no physical significance.

Equation 4.7 can also be written in the form $(p/\gamma) + y = \text{constant}$, meaning thereby that any increase in the elevation is compensated by the corresponding decrease in the pressure head. The term $(p/\gamma) + y$ is known as *piezometric head* which is a sum of pressure head and elevation. This has been discussed earlier in section 3.5. Such a variation in pressure is known as *hydrostatic pressure variation*. If the fluid is at rest, pressure distribution is hydrostatic in all directions.

It can be seen from the above discussion that pressure varies linearly with the elevation for incompressible fluids (i.e. liquids) and evidently does not depend on the shape of the bounding container. This is illustrated in Fig. 4.4 in which containers of various shapes are interconnected and hence have the same height of liquid. The pressure on the bottom of each container is γh. It can also be seen that this pressure is due to the column of liquid over the bottom.

Fig.4.4 Interconnected containers

Pressure Datum

Pressure is measured with respect to some datum. The two most common datums used are known as *absolute* and *gauge pressure*. Consider some container filled with liquid and kept exposed to the atmosphere. The column of air above the liquid surface OO (see Fig. 4.3) exerts a pressure p_a on the surface OO. Hence the pressure at any point A, distant h below the liquid surface, is $(p_a + \gamma h)$. This is known as the *absolute pressure*. The atmospheric pressure varies with temperature as well as the elevation of the place under consideration. At sea level and 15°C the atmospheric pressure is 101.325 kN/m² and it is known as *standard atmospheric pressure*.

In order to simplify the problem, the pressure is many times referred with respect to the local atmospheric pressure. This is known as *gauge pressure*. If the pressure is greater than the atmospheric pressure, the gauge pressure is positive. If the pressure is smaller than the atmospheric pressure, the gauge pressure is negative and is known as *vacuum pressure*. The concept of pressure datum is aptly illustrated in Fig. 4.5 which is self explanatory.

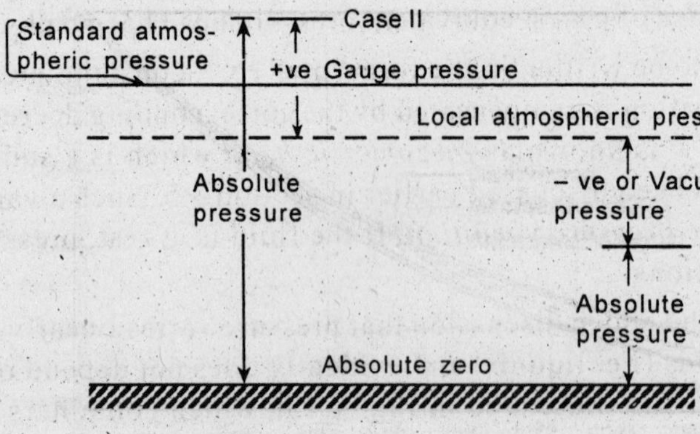

Fig.4.5 Various pressure datums

Example 4.2

Determine the pressure at a point which is 2.5 m below the surface of clear water. Express it as N/m² both in absolute and gauge units. Take atmospheric pressure as 101.325 kN/m².

Gauge pressure $= 2.5 \times 9787 = 24\ 467.5$ N/m²

Since atmospheric pressure is 101.325 kN/m² or 101 325 N/m² the corresponding absolute pressure will be

Absolute pressure $= 24\ 467.5 + 101\ 325.0$

$= 125\ 792.5$ N/m²

$= 125.703$ kN/m²

4.3 Pressure Variation in Static Compressible Fluids

It may be appreciated that Eq. 4.4 (b) can be integrated easily only if the specific weight of the fluid is constant as in the case of a liquid. However this is not true with gases. In such a case integration of Eq. 4.4 (b) gives

$$p = -\int \gamma \, dy + C \tag{4.10}$$

If the gas is ideal and the temperature remains constant, (i.e. for isothermal process) Boyle's law, Eq. 1.8 is applicable. This can also be written in the form

$$\frac{p}{\gamma} = \frac{p_o}{\gamma_o} \tag{4.11}$$

in which p and γ are the pressure and specific weight at any point and p_o and γ_o are pressure and specific weight at reference level. Hence Eq. 4.4 (b) becomes

$$dp = -p\frac{\gamma_o}{p_o}\, dy$$

or

$$\frac{dp}{p} = -\frac{\gamma_o}{p_o}\, dy \tag{4.12}$$

Integrating Eq. 4.12 one gets,

$$\log_e p = -\frac{\gamma_o}{p_o}\, y + C \tag{4.13}$$

The value of constant C can be found from the condition that when $y = y_o$, $p = p_o$.

$$C = \log_e p_o + \frac{\gamma_o}{p_o}\, y_o$$

or

$$\log_e \frac{p}{p_o} = -\frac{\gamma_o}{p_o}\,(y - y_o) \tag{4.14}$$

Hence,

$$\frac{p}{p_o} = e^{-(\gamma_0/p_0)(y-y_0)} \tag{4.15}$$

If the reference point is on the surface of earth and if y is measured vertically above earth's surface, $y_o = 0$ and Eq. 4.15 becomes

$$p = p_o\, e^{-(\gamma_0/p_0)y} \tag{4.16}$$

In the same way an expression can be obtained for variation of pressure with height in an adiabatic process. In the case of atmosphere, when one considers large variations in the altitude, the assumption of constant temperature is not valid. In fact there is a decrease in temperature with increasing elevation. As a result, Eq. 4.11 takes a different form and can be written as

$$\frac{p}{\gamma^k} = \frac{p_o}{\gamma_o^k}$$

in which k = 1.40 for adiabatic process. For atmospheric conditions, k is approximately 1.20. For such a case the pressure is given by

.write as

$$\frac{p}{p_o} = \left\{1 - \frac{k-1}{k}\frac{r_o y}{p_o}\right\}^{\frac{k}{k-1}} \qquad p = p_o\left\{1 - \frac{k-1}{k}\frac{y}{\left(\frac{p_o}{\gamma_o}\right)}\right\}^{\frac{k}{k-1}} \tag{4.18}$$

in which p_o and γ_o represent pressure and specific weight at the earth's surface where y is equal to zero. Figure 4.6 shows variation of (p/p_o) with $y/(p_o/\gamma_o)$ for isothermal and adiabatic processes and also for k = 1.20.

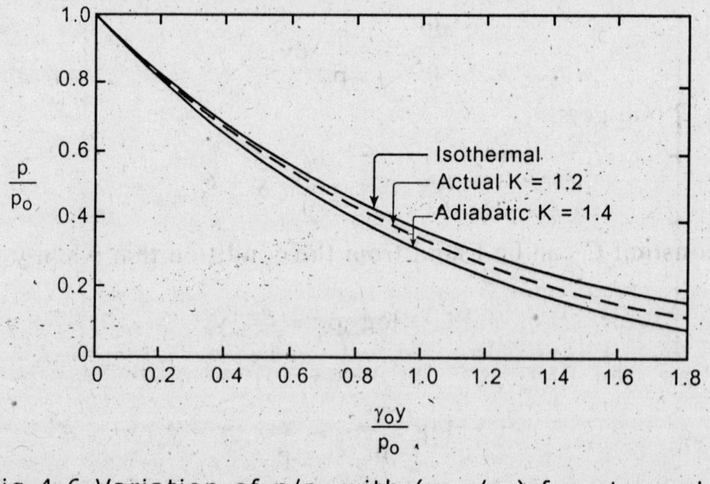

Fig.4.6 Variation of p/p_o with $(y\ \gamma_o/p_o)$ for atmosphere

4.4 Manometers

Manometers are devices used for measuring the fluid pressure by balancing the pressure against a column of liquid in static equilibrium. Figure 4.7 shows various types of simple manometers. Figure 4.7 (a) illustrates a simple vertical tube attached to a container where pressure is to be measured. This is useful if the container is filled with liquid because, in that case, the liquid rises in the tube to such a level that the liquid column of height h balances the pressure inside. Figure 4.7 (b) shows a U-tube manometer which is used to measure negative pressure with liquid in the container. If the pressure at A were equal to the outside pressure, the liquid in other limb would have risen to a level of A. Figure 4.7 (c) depicts a similar U-tube manometer indicating positive pressure in the container which is filled with a gas. The same arrangement can be used for measuring the negative pressure also.

In all the above three cases, the pressure within the container is measured with respect to the pressure that prevails over free surface in the open tube i.e. atmospheric pressure. If this open tube is connected to another container, a U-tube manometer can be used to determine the pressure difference between the two, see Figure. 4.7(d). This is some times known as a *differential manometer*. If the two containers or pipes carry gas, any liquid can be used in the U-tube for measuring the pressure difference. However, if the two containers carry one or more liquids, the liquid in the manometer must be immiscible with the liquid or liquids in the containers.

Accuracy of pressure measurement can be increased by inclining the measuring limb of the manometer in Fig. 4.7 (a) as shown in Fig. 4.7 (e). The original pressure head now gives a reading $h_1 = h/\sin\theta$ and is thus magnified. An inclined U-tube as shown in Fig. 4.7 (f) can be used in the same way to measure the difference of pressure. However in such a case, care must be taken to ensure that the diameters of the two tubes are equal since a difference in the diameters introduces an error because of different capillary rise in each tube. Another device commonly used for accurate measurement of pressure difference is a two liquid manometer as shown in Fig. 4.7 (g).

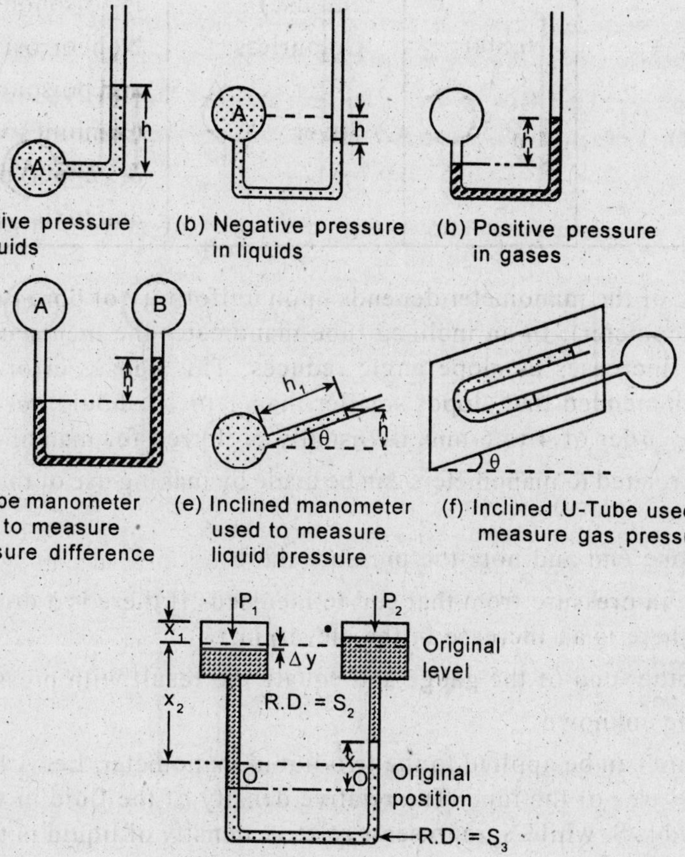

(a) Positive pressure in liquids
(b) Negative pressure in liquids
(b) Positive pressure in gases
(d) U-Tube manometer used to measure pressure difference
(e) Inclined manometer used to measure liquid pressure
(f) Inclined U-Tube used to measure gas pressure
(e) Two liquid manometer

Fig.4.7 Different types of manometers

The liquid or liquids to be used in the manometer depend on the range of pressure differential to be measured and fluid in the conduit or container. Table 4.1 gives the characteristics of common liquids used in the manometers.

Table 4.1

Common Liquids Used in the Manometer

Manometric Liquid	*Relative Density*	*Colour*	*Remarks*
Water	1.0	Colourless	Corrodes iron & steel
Ethyl Alcohol	0.794	Colourless	Corrodes iron & steel
Methyl Alcohol	0.797	Colourless	Corrodes iron & steel Poisonous and toxic
Acetylene Tetrabromide	2.964	Yellow (red for commercial use)	Corrodes iron & steel, weaknes rubber, and is poisonous.
Kerosene	0.800	Colourless	Noncorrosive, toxic and poisonous
Mercury	13.55	Silver	Combines with brass & copper, poisonous and toxic

The accuracy of the manometer depends upon uniformity of bore of the tube's (mainly for inclined manometer). In an inclined tube manometer the meniscus is elongated and the elongation increases as slope angle reduces. This causes errors in measurement; hence it is recommended that slopes smaller than 1 in 10 should not be used. The tube diameters of the order of 4 to 6 mm are usually preferred for manometers.

Calculations related to manometers can be made by making use of the following general procedure:

1. Start from one end and note the pressure there.
2. Add change in pressure from that end to meniscus if there is a drop in elevation and subtract if there is an increase in the elevation.
3. Reach the other end of the gauge and equate the result with pressure at that point.
4. Solve for the unknown.

This procedure can be applied to the two liquid manometer. Let A be the area of each tank and "a" the area of the tube. The relative density of the fluid in which the pressure is to be measured is S_1 while S_2 represents relative density of liquid in the tanks. Let S_3 be relative density of heavier liquid which fills the U-tube. When the pressure p_1 is greater than p_2, the following relationships can be written,

$$\left.\begin{aligned} &\Delta y\ A = a\frac{x}{2} \\ \text{and} \quad & p_1 + \gamma\ S_1(x_1 + \Delta y) + \left(x_2 - \Delta y + \frac{x}{2}\right) S_2\gamma - x\ S_3\gamma \\ & - \left(x_2 + \Delta y - \frac{x}{2}\right) S_2\ \gamma - (x_1 - \Delta y)\ S_1\ \gamma = p_2 \end{aligned}\right\} \tag{4.19}$$

or

$$\frac{p_1 - p_2}{\gamma} = S_2\ (x_1 - \Delta y) - S_1\ (x_1 + \Delta y) + S_2\left(x_2 + \Delta y - \frac{x}{2}\right)$$

$$- S_2\left(x_2 - \Delta y + \frac{x}{2}\right) + xS_3$$

$$\therefore \quad \frac{p_1 - p_2}{\gamma} = -2\ \Delta y\ S_1 + 2\ \Delta y\ S_2 - x\ S_2 + xS_3 \tag{4.20}$$

Substituting $\Delta y = \frac{a}{A} \cdot \frac{x}{2}$, Eq. 4.20 can be written as

$$\frac{p_1 - p_2}{\gamma} = x\ (S_2 - S_1)\ \frac{a}{A} + x\ (S_3 - S_2)$$

or

$$\frac{p_1 - p_2}{\gamma} = x\left[S_3 - S_2\left(1 - \frac{a}{A}\right) - S_1\ \frac{a}{A}\right] \tag{4.21}$$

In most of the cases, since a/A is extremely small, Eq. 4.21 can be approximated to

$$\frac{p_1 - p_2}{\gamma} = x\ (S_3 - S_2) \tag{4.22}$$

in which γ is specific weight of water.

Example 4.3

Determine the pressure difference between A and B for conditions shown in Fig. 4.8.

As discussed above, the following equation can be written:

$$\frac{p_A}{\gamma} + (0.60 + 0.45) - 0.20 \times 13.55 - (0.45 - 0.20) \times 0.80 = \frac{p_B}{\gamma}$$

$$\therefore \quad \frac{p_A - p_B}{\gamma} = (2.71 + 0.20 - 1.05)$$

$$= 1.86 \text{ m of water}$$

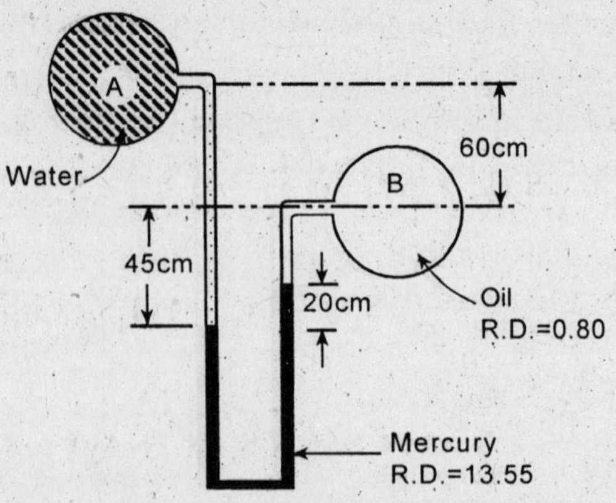

Fig.4.8

Example 4.4

In Figure. 4.9 determine the difference of pressure $(p_b - p_a)$.

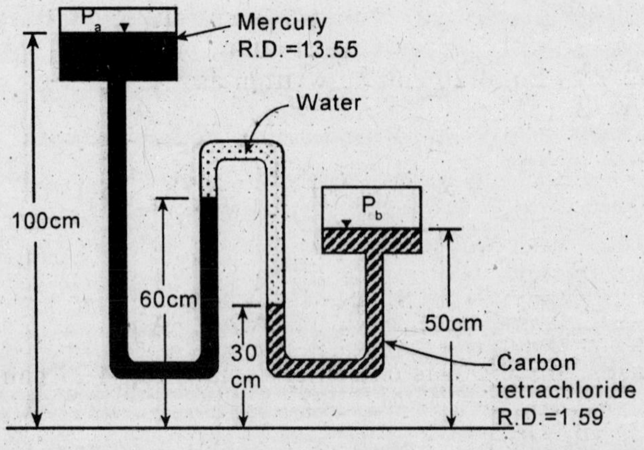

Fig.4.9

Following the same procedure as in Example 4.3, one can write

$$p_a + (0.40 \times 13.55 \times 9.787) + (0.30 \times 9.787)$$
$$- (0.20 \times 1.59 \times 9.787) = p_b$$

or
$$(p_b - p_a) = 53.046 + 2.936 - 3.112$$
$$= 52.87 \text{ kN/m}^2$$

4.5 Forces Acting on Immersed Plane Surfaces

It has been shown earlier that, in the case of a static fluid or fluid moving bodily at uniform velocity, the pressure acting on any immersed surface is perpendicular to the surface. Furthermore, when this pressure is referred to the atmospheric pressure, the pressure at a point is given by γh, in which h is the depth below the free surface of the liquid. In the case of gases, γ being extremely small, moderate variations in elevation h do not change the pressure appreciably.

(a) *Total force on Immersed Surfaces*

In several engineering problems it is required to estimate the magnitude and direction of the force on surface immersed in liquids, as well as to determine the location of the total force. Such information is useful in the design of tanks, gates, dams, submarines, etc. In the case of gases, since the pressure does not vary appreciably with change in elevation, the pressure remains constant at various points on the immersed surface. However, in the case of liquids the pressure varies appreciably.

Consider a plane area xy (see Fig. 4.10) immersed in a liquid and let θ be the angle between plane xy and the free surface.

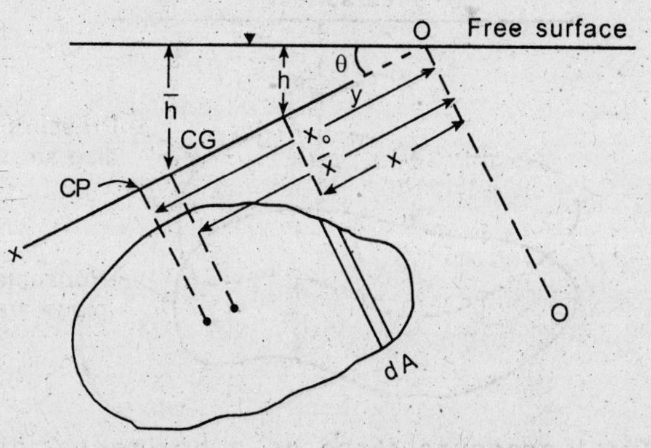

Fig.4.10 Centre of pressure for immersed plane surface

Pressure on elementary area dA = $\gamma\, x \sin\theta$

Hence, force dF on elementary area dA = $\gamma\, x \sin\theta\, dA$

The resultant force F on the total area is obtained by integrating dF over the area. In other words,

$$F = \int_A dF = \int_A \gamma\, x \sin\theta\, dA \qquad (4.23)$$

However, it is known that x dA gives the first moment of area A about an axis passing through O, at right angles to plane of paper. Therefore, it can be written as

$$\int_A x\, dA = A\bar{x} \qquad (4.24)$$

in which $\bar{x}$ is the distance of centroid CG from O

Hence
$$F = \gamma A \bar{x} \sin\theta$$

or
$$F = \gamma A \bar{h} \qquad (4.25)$$

where h is depth of the centroid. Since $\gamma\bar{h}$ is the intensity of pressure at the centroid, it can be said that the total force on a plane area (inclined or otherwise) is equal to the area multiplied by the pressure at the centroid.

The derivation of the expression for total force, as given by Eq. 4.25 is quite general and hence it can give total pressure (or total force) for vertical as well as the horizontal plane areas. When the surface is horizontal, each portion of the surface is exposed to the same depth of liquid, say h, see Fig. 4.11. Hence the total force on the horizontal surface becomes $F = \gamma Ah$. In the case of a vertical plane area immersed in a liquid as shown in Figure. 4.12 the pressure intensity at the top area is γh_1 while, at the lowest portion the pressure intensity is γh_2. The pressure diagrams for horizontal and vertical surfaces are also shown in these figures.

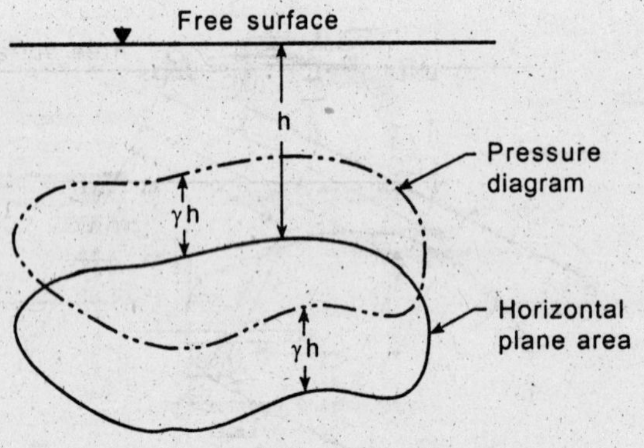

Fig.4.11 Total pressure force on a horizontal plane area

(b) *Centre of Pressure*

In addition to the direction and magnitude of total force, one must also know the point of application of this force. If the pressure distribution on the plane area were uniform as in the case of a plane area immersed horizontally in a liquid or as in the case of plane area immersed in a gas-the resultant pressure force would pass through the centroid of the area. However, if the area is inclined, the centroid and the point of application of the resultant pressure force do not coincide. Since the pressure increases with increase in depth, one would expect the point of application of resultant pressure force to lie below the centroid of the area.

In Fig. 4.10, (γx dA sin θ) is the pressure force on area dA, and (γx^2 dA sin θ) is the moment of this force about an axis OO. Let x_o be the distance of point CP from OO such that if resultant pressure force were acting at CP, it would produce the same moment about OO as the moment produced by the pressure forces on elementary areas. This point CP is known as the *centre of pressure.* From the definition of centre of pressure one can write,

$$Fx_o = \int_A \gamma x^2 \, dA \sin\theta \tag{4.26}$$

However

$$F = \int_A \gamma x \, dA \sin\theta \tag{4.23}$$

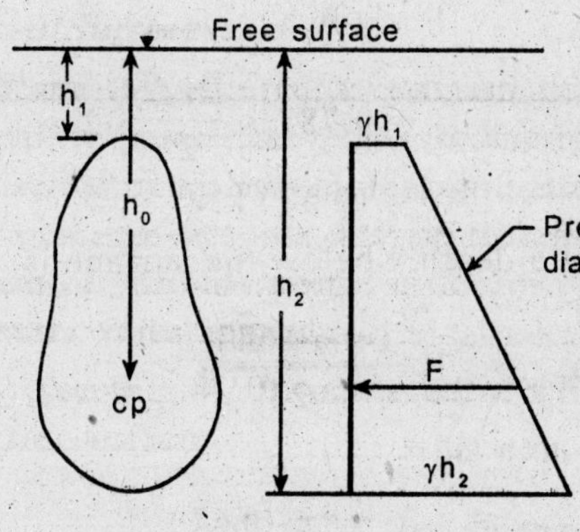

Fig.4.12 Total pressure force on a plane vertical area

hence $$x_o \gamma \sin\theta \int_A x\, dA = \gamma \sin\theta \int_A x^2\, dA$$

or $$x_o = \frac{\int_A x^2\, dA}{\int_A x\, dA} \tag{4.27}$$

But $\int_A x^2\, dA$ represents the summation of second moment of elementary areas dA and as such , it is equal to I_{oo} the moment of inertia of area A about OO. Similarly $\int_A x\, dA$ represents the summation of first moment of elementary area dA, and as such it is equal to $A\bar{x}$.

Therefore $$x_o = \frac{I_{oo}}{A\bar{x}} \tag{4.28}$$

Substituting $I_{oo} = I_{gg} + A\bar{x}^2$ in which I_{gg} is the moment of inertia about an axis passing through CG and parallel to OO, Eq. 4.28 becomes

$$x_o = \frac{I_{gg} + A\bar{x}^2}{A\bar{x}} = \bar{x} + \frac{I_{gg}}{A\bar{x}} \tag{4.29}$$

Equation 4.29 gives the position of centre of pressure.

Example 4.5

Find the total pressure and the position of centre of pressure for a triangular area immersed in water as shown in Fig. 4.13.

$$F = \gamma A h$$

$$= 9.787 \times \frac{2 \times 1}{2} \times 2$$

$$= 19.574 \text{ kN}$$

The width of the triangle at a depth x below the surface is

$$b = \frac{x - 0.67}{2}$$

and therefore the elementary area is

$$dA = \left(\frac{x - 0.67}{2}\right) dx$$

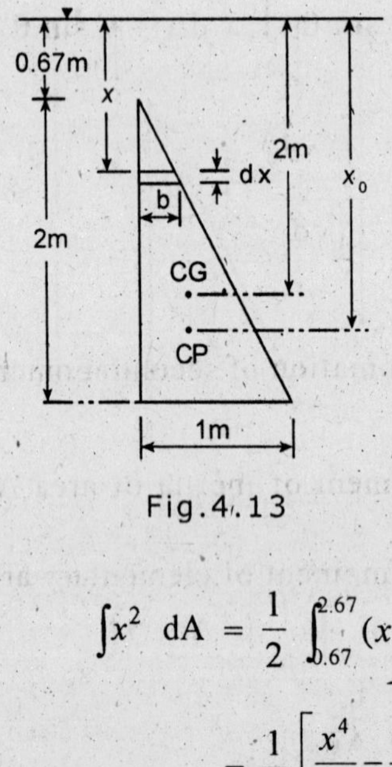

Fig.4.13

Hence $$\int x^2 \, dA = \frac{1}{2} \int_{0.67}^{2.67} (x^3 - 0.67\,x^2)\, dx$$

$$= \frac{1}{2}\left[\frac{x^4}{4} - \frac{0.67\,x^2}{3}\right]_{0.67}^{2.67}$$

$$= 4.236 \text{ m}^4$$

Also $$\int x \, dA = \frac{1}{2} \int_{0.67}^{2.67} (x^2 - 0.67\,x)\, dx$$

$$= \frac{1}{2}\left[\frac{x^3}{3} - \frac{0.67}{3} x^2\right]_{0.67}^{2.67}$$

$$= 2.003 \text{ m}^3$$

$\therefore$ $$x_o = \frac{4.236}{2.003} = 2.115 \text{ m}$$

4.6 Total Force on Immersed Curved Surfaces

The analysis of the total force on a plane area is relatively simple because the pressure forces on a elementary areas act in the same direction viz. perpendicular to the area. As a result, one can deal with the total force without much difficulty. In the case of a curved surface immersed in a liquid, however, the forces on elementary areas do not act in the same direction. In addition, the elementary areas dA cannot be easily described mathematically there by, making the analytical integration difficult. For these reasons, it is desirable to work with the components of total force rather than the total force itself as indicated below. For simplicity only a two dimensional case is considered.

Suppose it is required to find the total force acting on the curved surface ACB immersed in water as shown in Fig. 4.14. In order to find this force consider the equilibrium of the body of liquid ACB with unit width perpendicular to the plane ACBO. Let F_x and F_y represent the total forces on areas OB and OA respectively, the magnitudes and points of applications of which can be easily known by using the methods described previously. Let R_x and R_y represent the components of unknown total force on the curved surface ACB, and W be the weight of the liquid in ACBO which acts through the centroid of the area. Equations for the equilibrium will be obtained from the conditions that :

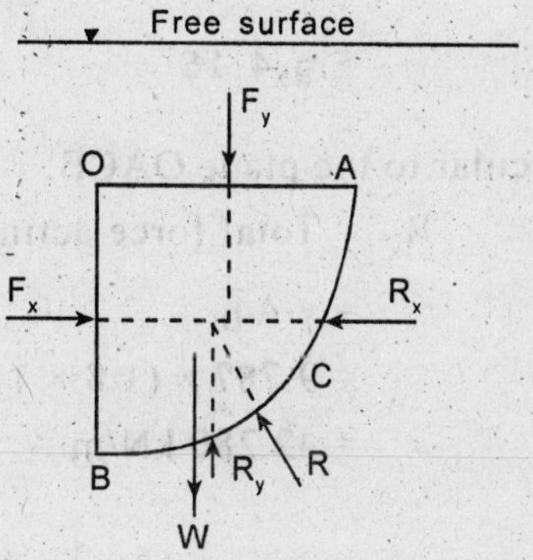

Fig.4.14 Force acting on a curved surface

i. Summation of all horizontal force components is equal to zero.
ii. Summation of all vertical force component is equal to zero.
iii. Summation of moments of all forces about any axis, such as the one passing through 0 and perpendicular to ACBO is zero.

Hence,
$$F_x - R_x = 0 \tag{4.30}$$
or
$$R_x = F_x$$

Evidently F_x and R_x must act along the same horizontal line.

Similarly,
$$F_y + W - R_y = 0$$
$$R_y = F_y + W \tag{4.31}$$

Knowing actual values of F_y and W and their points of application, the point of application of R_y can be obtained by equating moments of these forces about O.

Example 4.6

Compute the horizontal and vertical components of the total force acting on a curved surface in the form of a quadrant of a circle as shown in Fig. 4.15. Take γ to be 9.787 kN/m³.

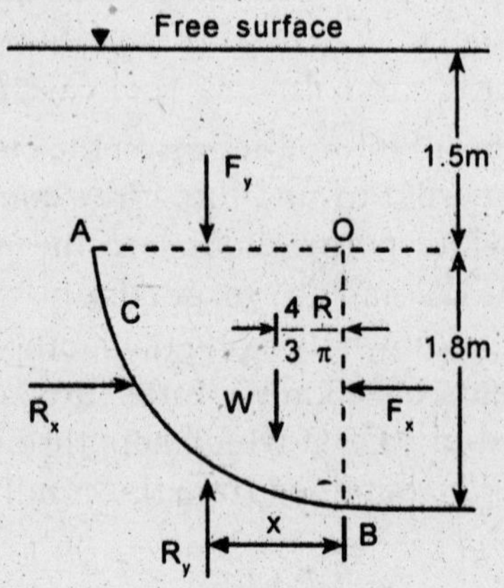

Fig.4.15

Consider unit width perpendicular to the plane OACB.

$$R_x = \text{Total force acting on ACB}$$
$$= \gamma A \bar{h}$$
$$= 9.787 \times (1.8 \times 1) \times 2.4$$
$$= 42.280 \text{ kN/m}$$

and it will act at

$$h_o = \bar{h} + \frac{I_{gg}}{A\bar{h}} = 2.4 + \frac{0.485}{(1.8 \times 1) \times 2.4} = 2.512 \text{ m}$$

below the free surface.

$$R_y = 9.787 \times (1.8 \times 1) \times 1.5 + \frac{\pi}{4} \times 1.8^2 \times 1 \times 9.787$$
$$= 26.425 + 24.892 == 51.317 \text{ kN/m}$$

To find the point of application of R_y take moments about OB

$$51.317x = 26.425 \times 0.9 + 24.892 \times \left(\frac{4}{3} \times \frac{1.8}{3.142}\right)$$

$$x = \frac{23.783 + 19.104}{51.317} = \frac{42.887}{51.317}$$
$$= 0.836 \text{ m from OB}$$

4.7 Floating Bodies

When a body is submerged in a fluid, various parts of the surface of the body are exposed to varying pressures. As a result of this, the body is acted upon by a resultant vertical upward force called the *buoyant force*.

Consider a body submerged in a fluid of constant mass density, as shown in Fig. 4.16. In order to determine the resultant force acting on the body, divide the body into small vertical cylinders such as AB.

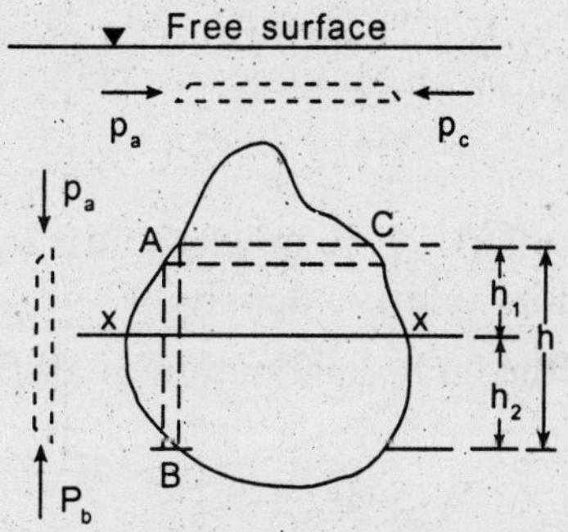

Fig.4.16 Buoyant force on a submerged body

Vertically upward force on cylinder AB $= (p_b - p_a)\,dA$

Hence total vertical force on the body $= \int_A (p_b - p_a)\,dA$

However $(p_b - p_a) = \gamma h$

Hence vertical force $F_v = \int_A \gamma h\,dA$

$= \gamma \int_A h\,dA$

or $F_v = \gamma V$

in which V is the volume of the body. But γV is weight of fluid displaced. Hence

F_v = Weight of fluid displaced by the body

Horizontal force on cylinder AC $= (p_a - p_c)\,dA$

But since A and C are at the same elevation, $p_a = p_c$. Therefore, total horizontal force on the elementary cylinder AC (and hence on the whole body) is zero. Hence one can conclude that the buoyant force has no horizontal component and the vertical force acts in the upward direction, its magnitude being equal to the weight of fluid displaced by the body. Since the body is in equilibrium, the buoyant force must act through the centre of gravity of the displaced volume of the fluid. This principle is known as *Archimedes principle*.

Suppose the body in Fig. 4.16 is floating in between the plane of separation of two fluids having γ_1 and γ_2 as their specific weights. In such case $(p_b - p_a) = h_1\gamma_1 + h_2\gamma_2$ and hence

$$F_v = \int_A (h_1\gamma_1 + h_2\gamma_2)\,dA$$

$$F_v = \gamma_1 V_1 + \gamma_2 V_2 \tag{4.32}$$

in which V_1 and V_2 are volumes of two fluids displaced. Further assume the top fluid is air and the lower one liquid. In such case γ_1 being extremely small compared to γ_2, $\gamma_1 V_1$ can be neglected and hence $F_v = \gamma_2 V_2$. Therefore for a body floating in a liquid $\gamma_2 V_2$ must evidently be equal to the weight of the body.

Example 4.7

A body of dimensions 1.00 m × 0.60 m × 1.50 m when immersed in water weighs 1765 N. What will be its weight in air and its relative density ?

Considering the equilibrium of the body, summation of all forces in the vertical direction must be zero. Hence

$$W_a - F_v = W_w$$

But $F_v = 1.0 \times 0.60 \times 1.50 \times 9.787 = 8.808 \text{ kN}$

∴ $W_a = 8.808 + 1.765 = 10.573 \text{ kN}$

Relative density $= \dfrac{\text{Weight of body}}{\text{Weight of equal vol. of water}} = \dfrac{10.573}{8.808}$

$= 1.20$

Example 4.8

An odd shaped body when immersed in water weighs 980 N and when immersed in kerosene (rel. density 0.80) weighs 1127.76 N. Determine its volume and weight in air.

Writing conditions of equilibrium for the forces in vertical direction, for both the cases one gets :

$$W_w = W_a - (F_v)_w$$

or $W_w = W_a - 9787\,V$

and $W_k = W_a - (9787 \times 0.8)\,V$

Substituting $W_w = 980$ N and $W_k = 1127.76$ N and solving the two equations, following values are obtained

$$W_a = 1718.920 \text{ N and } V = 0.0755 \text{ m}^3$$

Example 4.9

A glass test tube of cross-sectional area A is made heavier by keeping some lead at its bottom and it is proposed to use this as a device for measuring the relative density of liquids. When immersed in water, it displaces a volume V. Obtain a relation between change in height of immersion and relative density of liquid (This device is commonly known as *hydrometer*).

Let γ be specific weight of water. Then

$$W = \gamma \forall$$

in which W is the weight of hydrometer. When the hydrometer is kept in other liquid of specific weight γ_1 and if it moves up through height Δh (see Fig. 4.17) then

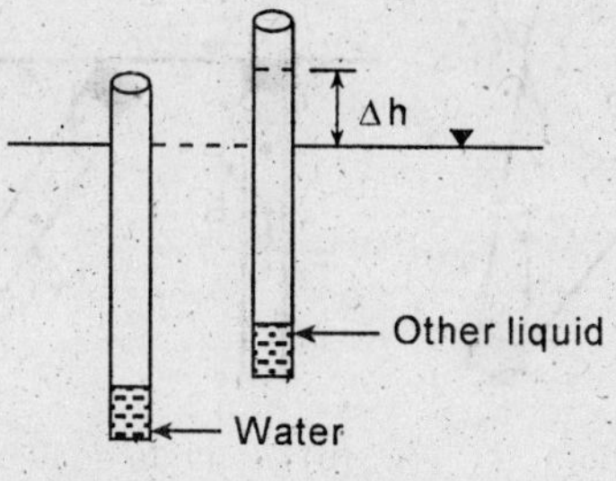

Fig.4.17 Hydrometer

$$(\forall - A\,\Delta h)\,\gamma_1 = W$$

Hence $$(\forall - A\,\Delta h)\,\gamma_1 = \forall\gamma$$

$\therefore$ $$\frac{\forall\gamma_1 - \forall\gamma}{A\gamma_1} = \Delta h$$

or $$\Delta h = \frac{\forall}{A}\left(1 - \frac{1}{S}\right)$$

in which S is the relative density of liquid.

4.8 Stability of Floating and Submerged Bodies

Consider a body which is either completely submerged in a fluid or is partly in one fluid and partly in another fluid. Under such a case two forces act on the body, namely the weight of the body acting in a vertically downward direction and the buoyant force acting in a vertically upward direction. If the body is at rest, the summation of these two forces must be zero. Furthermore, they must act along the same vertical line so that their moment about any axis is zero. It has been already mentioned that the weight of the body acts through its centre of gravity while the buoyant force acts through the centre of gravity of the displaced fluid volume.

By stability of such a floating or submerged body is meant the tendency of the body either to come back to its original position or to go away from the original position when disturbed slightly. If a floating body is displaced vertically, it comes back to its original stable position. If it is displaced upwards, the volume of displaced fluid and hence the buoyant force is decreased causing an unbalanced downward force. This unbalanced downward force brings the body down to its original position. Since any slight horizontal displacement does not change either the magnitude or the location of buoyant force, the body is still in equilibrium.

Just as a body can be given a small vertical or horizontal displacement, it can also be given a small angular displacement. When such a small angular displacement is given, the body can be either *stable, unstable* or *neutral* in its equilibrium. Figure 4.18 (a), (b) and (c) give the examples of stable, unstable and neutral equilibrium.

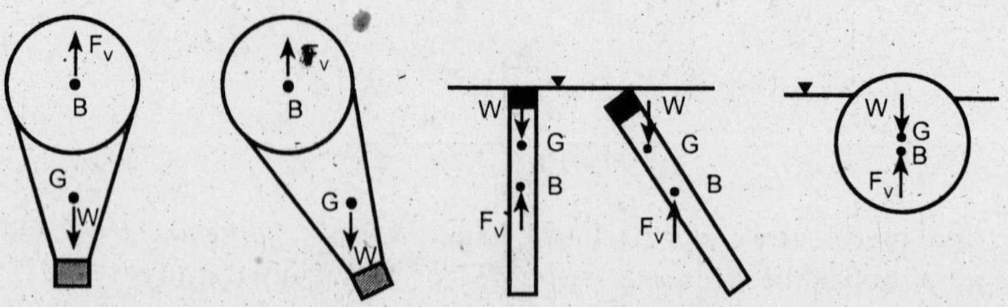

(a) Stable equilibrium (b) Unstable equilibrium (c) Natural equilibrium

Fig.4.18 Types of equilibium

Figure 4.18 (a) shows a balloon as an example of stable equilibrium. The centre of gravity G of the body is below the centre of buoyancy B. As a result, when a small angular displacement is given, it causes a restoring couple and brings the body to its original position. In the unstable equilibrium for the submerged body, the centre of gravity lies above the centre of buoyancy, see Fig. 4.18 (b). When a small angular displacement is given, it causes a couple which increases the displacement. A sphere which has its centre of gravity on its geometrical axis floats in neutral equilibrium. Any angular displacement does not shift the positions of G and B and as a result neutral equilibrium occurs, see Fig. 4.18 (c).

4.9 Metacentre

It has been stated above that for the condition of stable equilibrium the centre of gravity of the body must be below the centre of buoyancy. This is so if the body is completely submerged. However, if the body is floating, this need not be the case, because with slight rotation the shape of the displaced liquid can change thereby causing a shift in the centre of buoyancy.

Consider a body in Fig. 4.19 for which G lies above B. When a small angular displacement is given to the body, the shape of displaced liquid is no longer the same. Portion OXY has been added while portion OWZ has been taken away. The centre of buoyancy of the new area is B_1. A vertical through B_1 intersects the line BG produced at M. The point M is in fact the centre of curvature of a curve giving the locus of centres of buoyancy obtained for various small angular displacements. The point M is known as the *metacentre.*

It can be seen from Fig. 4.19 that as long as metacentre M lies above B and G any small angular displacement causes a restoring moment of magnitude Wx ; hence the floating body comes back to its original position. On the other hand if M lies below G, the couple Wx is no longer a restoring couple but it increases the displacement and therefore causes instability. Hence, it can be concluded that M must be above G and in no case fall below G. The distance MG is known as *metacentric height.*

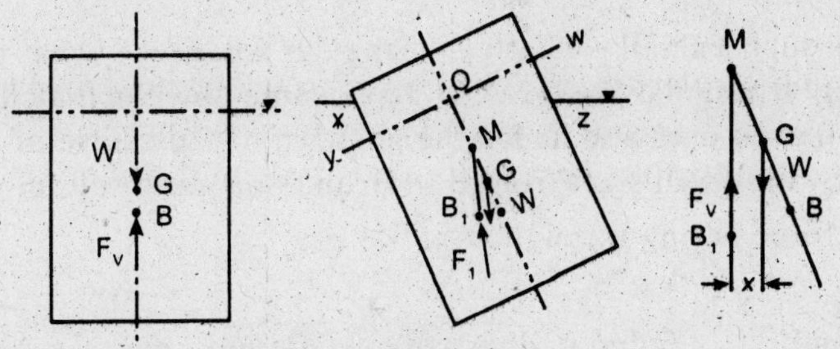

Fig.4.19

The concept of metacentre and metacentric height is useful in the design of ship profiles and navel architects make accurate estimates of metacentric height under various conditions of loading to ensure the stability of the vessel.

Determination of Metacentric Height

It is known that the cross-sectional shape and area of the ship varies from one place to another along the longitudinal axis. As a result, the positions of B_1 and M cannot be easily determined. The section of the ship taken through its centre of gravity is shown in Fig. 4.20. Let AA′ be the original water line and CD be the new waterline when the ship experiences a small rotation through an angle α.

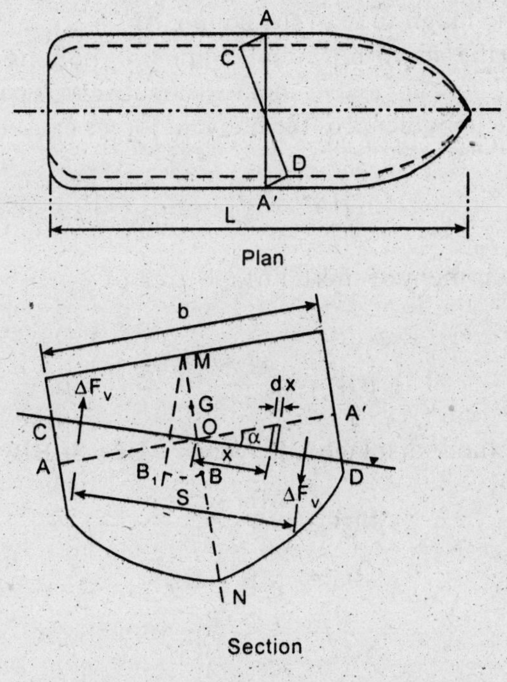

Fig.4.20 Stability of a ship

In undergoing such a small rotation, a triangular wedge ACO has gone inside the liquid while an identical triangular wedge A'DO has come out. Such a change naturally alters the shape of immersed area and hence the position of the centre of buoyancy. Therefore the centre of buoyancy will shift from B to B_1 and one must determine the position of B_1.

The buoyant force acting through B_1 is

$$F_{v1} = \underbrace{F_v}_{\text{original buoyant force}} + \underbrace{\Delta F_v}_{\text{due to displacement of wedge area ACO and length L}} - \underbrace{\Delta F_v}_{\text{due to decrease in displacement of wedge of area A'DO and length L}}$$

$$= F_v + \Delta F_v - \Delta F_v$$

$$= F_v$$

Hence taking moment about an axis through B, perpendicular to plane of paper, one gets

$$F_{v1} \times BB_1 = (F_v \times 0) + (\Delta F_v \times S)$$

or

$$BB_1 = \frac{\Delta F_v}{F_{v1}} S = \frac{\Delta F_v}{F_v} S$$

Since $F_v = F_{v1}$. The magnitude of the couple $\Delta F_v \times S$ can be more conveniently written as follows. Considering an infinitesimal element of volume $(\alpha\, x\, dx)$ L, the buoyant force associated with it is $(L\gamma\alpha\, x\, dx)$ and its moment about an axis passing through O is $(L\gamma\alpha\, x^2 dx)$. The summation of such moments of the buoyant forces caused by displacement is therefore

$$\int_{-b/2}^{+b/2} L\gamma\alpha\, x^2\, dx = \gamma\,\alpha \int_{-b/2}^{+b/2} L\, x^2\, dx = \gamma\,\alpha\, I$$

in which I is the moment of inertia of the area of water section about the axis passing through O. Hence

$$BB_1 = \frac{\Delta F_v S}{F_v} = \frac{\gamma\alpha I}{\gamma \forall} = \alpha\,\frac{I}{\forall}$$

in which $\forall$ is the volume displaced However MB $\alpha = BB_1$

or

$$MB = \frac{BB_1}{\alpha}$$

and

$$MG = MB - BG$$

or

$$MG = \frac{I}{\forall} - BG \tag{4.34}$$

Since the position of centre of gravity is usually known, the above equation can be used to determine the metacentric height of ships. The metacentric height of large ships is of the order of 0.5 to 2.0 m. It must be remembered that since $BB_1 = MB \times \alpha$, is true only for small values of α, the relationship for MG is also true under this condition. The period of oscillation of the ship is given by

$$T = 2\pi \sqrt{\frac{K^2}{g \times MG}}$$

where K = radius of gyration from the axis of rotation $\left(I = \frac{\text{weight of ship}}{g} K^2 \right)$. Hence large MG also means smaller period of oscillation. This produces discomfort to passangers and excessive stresses on the ship.

4.10 Relative Equilibrium

Consider a fluid mass M which is acted upon by a system of forces. As a result, uniform acceleration is associated with this mass; then according to Newton's second law of motion,

$$\left.\begin{aligned} \Sigma F_x &= M a_x \\ \Sigma F_y &= M a_y \\ \Sigma F_z &= M a_z \end{aligned}\right\}$$

in which ΣF_x, ΣF_y and ΣF_z represent the summation of components of external forces acting on M and a_x, a_y and a_z are the components of acceleration. The above equations can be rewritten in the form,

$$\left.\begin{aligned} \Sigma F_x - M a_x &= 0 \\ \Sigma F_y - M a_y &= 0 \\ \Sigma F_z - M a_z &= 0 \end{aligned}\right\} \qquad (4.35)$$

Since $-M a_x$, $-M a_y$ and $-M a_z$ have the dimensions of force they can be considered as fictitious forces in x, y and z directions respectively such that, their summation with ΣF_x, ΣF_y and ΣF_z yields zero. It may be recalled that the condition for static equilibrium is that the summation of force components along the x, y and z directions must be zero. Hence Eqs. 4.35 represent similar condition and can be compared with Eq. 4.4 which is valid for static equilibrium. However, in the present case the fluid mass is not stationary but moving. Therefore, the above equations give conditions of dynamic equilibrium. The fictitious forces $-M a_x$, $-M a_y$ and $-M a_z$ are known as *inertial forces* which are in dynamic equilibrium with the external forces ΣF_x, ΣF_y and ΣF_z respectively. Once the system is brought into dynamic equilibrium by taking into account the inertial forces, one can apply the laws of statics to such a system. This principle is known as *d'Alembert's principle*.

This principle can be applied to analyse the cases of fluid mass subjected to uniform horizontal and vertical acceleration, and uniform rotation.

(a) ***Uniform Horizontal Acceleration***

Figure 4.21 shows a tank filled with liquid and given a constant horizontal acceleration a_x as shown. According to d' Alembert's principle this can be changed into a problem of statics by considering inertial force in condition of equilibrium. Take the co-ordinate axes as shown in the figure. Considering an inertial force ρa_x acting towards left, one can write

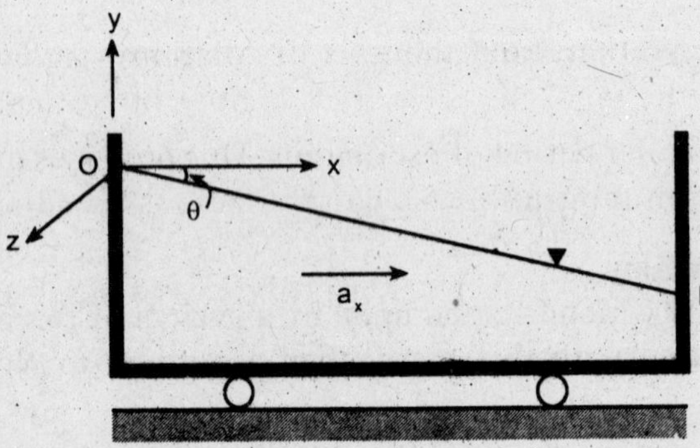

Fig.4.21

$$\left.\begin{aligned} -\frac{\partial p}{\partial x} - \rho a_x &= 0 \quad (a)\\ -\frac{\partial p}{\partial y} - \rho g &= 0 \quad (b)\\ -\frac{\partial p}{\partial z} &= 0 \quad (c)\end{aligned}\right\} \qquad (4.36)$$

Integration of 4.36(c) yields p = p (x, y) i.e. p is not a function of z. Integration of 4.36 (b) gives

$$p = -\rho gy + f(x, z)$$

However, since p is not a function of z, f will be a function of x alone; or

$$p = -\rho gy + f(x)$$

Differentiating this expression with respect to x and comparing the results with Eq. 4.36 (a),

$$\frac{\partial p}{\partial x} = f'(x) = -\rho a_x$$

Therefore $f(x) = -x\rho a_x + C$ where C is a numerical constant of integration. The expression for p becomes

$$p = -x\rho a_x - \rho gy + C$$

The constant of integration can be found from the condition that at $x = 0$ and $y = 0$, $p = p_a$ the atmospheric pressure.

Hence $\qquad C = p_a \quad$ and $\quad (p - p_a) = -x \rho a_x - \rho g y$

Water surface will be characterised by the fact that $(p - p_a) = 0$,

or
$$\tan\theta = \frac{-y}{x} = \frac{a_x}{g}$$

The liquid surface will therefore slope in the direction shown. Since no vertical acceleration is given to the tank, the pressure variation in vertical is unaffected and is therefore hydrostatic.

If the tank is filled with a liquid and is closed, there is no adjustment in the surface elevation. Hence in such cases there is a higher pressure at the rear and lower pressure at the front end, the relation $a_x/g = \tan\theta$ still giving the slope of planes of constant pressure intensity.

Example 4.10

The tank in Fig. 4.21 is 3.0 in wide, 2.5 m deep and 10 m long. If oil stands 1.0 m from the top of the tank, determine the maximum horizontal acceleration that can be given to the tank without spilling the oil.

The maximum slope of oil surface $= \frac{1}{5} = 0.20$

$$\therefore \quad \frac{a_x}{g} = 0.20$$

or
$$a_x = 9.81 \times 0.20 = 1.962 \text{ m/s}^2$$

Example 4.11

If the tank car in the above example is closed at the top and is completely filled with crude oil, find the pressure difference between the front and rear top corners if $a_x = 3.0$ m/s² and relative density of crude oil is 0.92.

Since the top is closed, there cannot be any slope to the oil surface. Hence pressure at rear end will build up and will be greater than that at front end :

$$\frac{p_b - p_a}{\gamma} \times \frac{1}{10} = \frac{a_x}{g}$$

or
$$p_b - b_a = \left(\frac{3}{9.81} \times 10 \times 9.787 \times 0.92\right)$$

$$= 27.535 \text{ kN/m}^2$$

(b) *Uniform Vertical Acceleration*

Figure 4.22 shows a container filled with liquid. Assume that the container is given a uniform acceleration a_y in the vertically upward direction. According to d'Alembert's principle, the whole or part of this body can be in equilibrium after taking into consideration the inertial forces. Hence for a cylindrical body such as ab,

$$(p_b - p_a)\,da - \rho h\,(g + a_y)\,da = 0$$

or
$$(p_b - p_a) = \rho h\,(g + a_y) = \gamma h\left(1 + \frac{a_y}{g}\right) \qquad (4.37)$$

in which da is cross-sectional area of the cylindrical body. Since there is no horizontal acceleration, the pressure along any horizontal plane remains the same. Hence it follows that given only a uniform vertical acceleration, the free surface in the container will always remain horizontal.

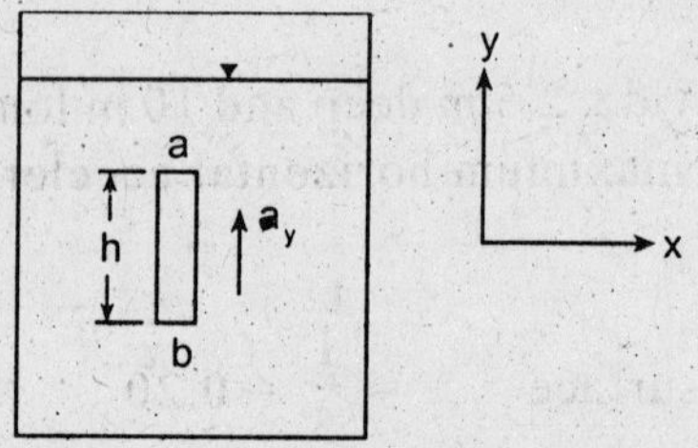

Fig.4.22

It can be seen that when $a_y = -g$ i.e., the container is coming down at an acceleration g,

$$(p_b - p_a) = \gamma h\left(1 - \frac{g}{g}\right) = 0$$

and hence there will be no pressure difference between any two points such as a and b. In other words the pressure throughout the liquid will be same.

When the container is subjected to uniform acceleration both in horizontal and vertical directions, the above principle can be easily extended to cover such a case too.

Example 4.12

A water tank is given an acceleration of 7.0 m/s² along a 30° inclined plane in the upward direction. Find what angle the water surface will make with the horizontal and also find the pressure at "a".

Resolve the acceleration a, into the horizontal and vertical components :

$$a_x = 7\cos 30° = 6.062\ \text{m/s}^2$$
$$a_y = 7\sin 30° = 3.500\ \text{m/s}^2$$

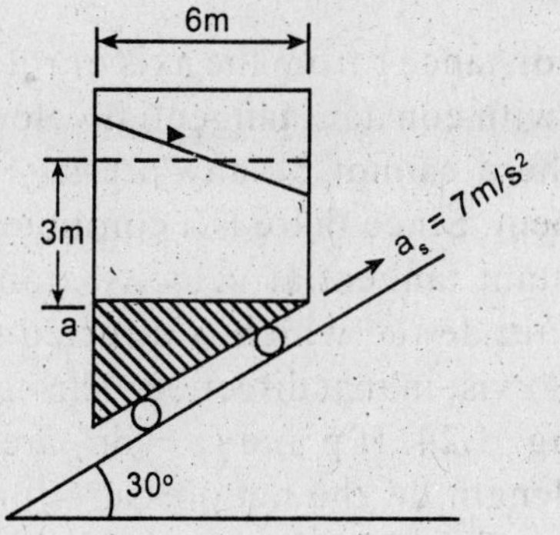

Fig.4.23

Hence the water surface slope is given by

$$\tan\theta = \frac{a_x}{(a_y+g)} = \frac{6.062}{(3.50+9.81)} = \frac{6.062}{13.31} = 0.455$$

$$\therefore \qquad \theta = 24.42° \text{ with the horizontal}$$

The depth at "a" = 3 + 3 tan θ = 4.365 m

$$\therefore \qquad \frac{p_a}{\gamma} = h_a\left(1+\frac{a_y}{g}\right) = 4.365\left(1+\frac{3.5}{9.81}\right)$$

$$= 4.365 \times 1.357 = 5.922 \text{ m}$$

$$p_a = 57.962 \text{ kN/m}^2$$

(c) *Uniform Rotation*

Consider a cylindrical container partly filled with liquid and rotated at a constant angular velocity ω about a vertical axis, see Fig. 4.24. The rotational motion is transmitted to different parts of the liquid through the action of viscosity. Short time after the motion is started the whole liquid moves with the same angular velocity and hence as a single body. Such a motion can be analysed by making use of d'Alembert's principle.

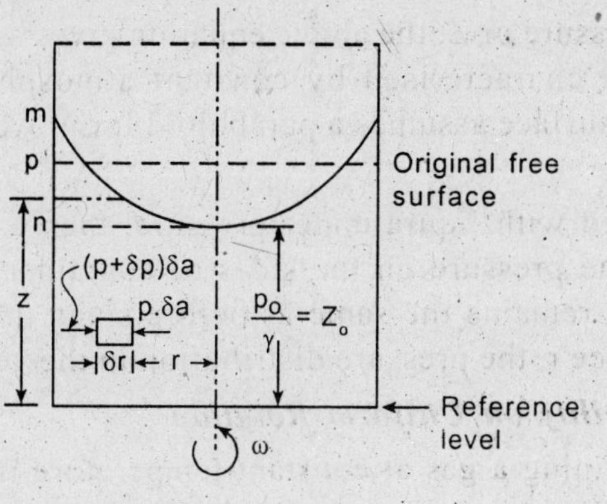

Fig.4.24 Motion with uniform rotation

Consider a fluid element at a distance r from the axis of rotation. Since the fluid element is moving along a circular path with constant tangential velocity $r\omega$, there is no tangential acceleration. For this reason there cannot be any pressure gradient along the circular path traversed by the fluid element. Since there is a continuous change of direction as the fluid element moves with constant tangential velocity along the circular path, there is centripetal acceleration of magnitude $r\omega^2$ which is directed towards the centre. To cause such an acceleration a force must exist in that direction. This is provided by rise in elevation of liquid surface as shown in Fig. 4.24. If p and (p + dp) are the pressures at two ends of a fluid element of area da and length dr, the net pressure force is – (p + dp) da + p da = – dp da acting towards the centre. This must be in equilibrium with inertial force (da dr ρ $r\omega^2$) acting outwards; or

$$da\ dr\ \rho\ r\omega^2 - dp\ da = 0$$

or

$$dp = \rho\ r\omega^2\ dr \tag{4.38}$$

Integration of this expression yields

$$p = \frac{\rho\omega^2 r^2}{2} + C$$

Considering the bottom of the container as reference level and introducing the boundary condition $p = p_o$ at $r = 0$, one gets $C = p_o$. Hence

$$p = \frac{\rho\omega^2 r^2}{2} + p_o \tag{4.39}$$

$$\frac{p}{\gamma} = \frac{\omega^2 r^2}{2g} + \frac{p_o}{\gamma} \tag{4.40}$$

It may be recalled that since there is no vertical acceleration, the pressure distribution in the vertical is hydrostatic.

Letting $p/\gamma = Z$ and $p_o/\gamma = Z_o$, Eq. 4.40 becomes

$$Z = \frac{\omega^2 r^2}{2g} + Z_o$$

for a constant value of pressure or Z, the above equation gives a paraboloid of revolution. Since the free surface is characterised by constant atmospheric pressure, it can be concluded that the liquid surface assumes a paraboloid form. According to the properties of paraboloid, mn = 2np.

If the container is filled with liquid under pressure, then as the container is rotated about the vertical axis, the pressure on the sides of container increases. However, the pressure at the top centre remains the same as before since there is no velocity at that point. At any radial distance r, the pressure distribution in the vertical is still hydrostatic.

(d) *Effect of Compressibility on Uniform Rotation*

If a closed cylinder containing a gas at constant temperature is rotated about a vertical axis at a constant angular velocity, one must consider the variation in ρ that can occur with pressure.

Since $\frac{p_o}{\rho_o} = \frac{p}{\rho} = C_1$. Eq. 4.38 becomes

$$dp = \frac{p}{C_1}\,\omega^2 r\,dr \tag{4.42}$$

and the integration of Eq. 4.42 gives

$$\log_e p = \frac{\omega^2 r^2}{2C_1} + \log_e C$$

in which C is a constant of integration. Value of C can be found from the fact that when $r = 0$, $p = p_o$.

Hence $\log_e C = \log_e p_o$

$$\log_e \frac{p}{p_o} = \frac{\omega^2 r^2}{2C_1}$$

$$p = p_o\, e^{\omega^2 r^2/2C_1} \tag{4.43}$$

Therefore, this relation gives variation of pressure in the container for different values of r.

PROBLEMS

4.1 Find the gauge pressure in N/m^2, kN/m^2 and bars at a depth of 40 m below the water surface in the sea. The relative density of sea water may be taken as 1.04.

4.2 A hydraulic press has a ram of 12 cm and a plunger of 2.0 cm in diameter. What force would be required on the plunger to lift a weight of 14.71 kN through 3.0 m? If the plunger has a stroke of 24 cm and the time required to lift the weight is 10 minutes, what power will be required to drive the plunger ?

4.3 At what pressure in the air tank shown in the figure will the piston be in equilibrium if friction and leakage are neglected ?

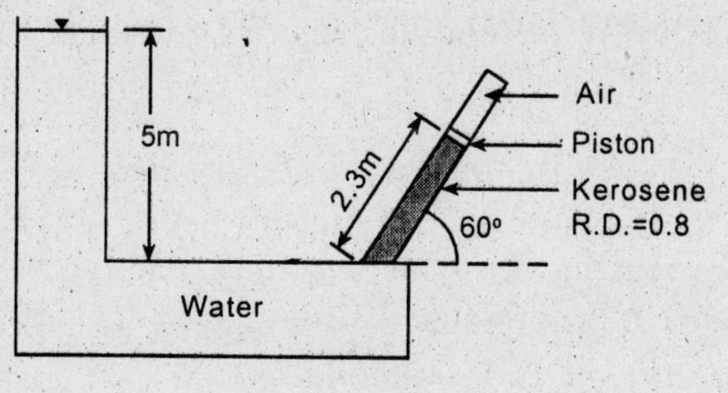

Prob.4.3

4.4 Find the gauge pressure and the absolute pressure at point A and B as shown in figure. Take the relative densities of kerosene and mercury as 0.80 and 13.55 respectively.

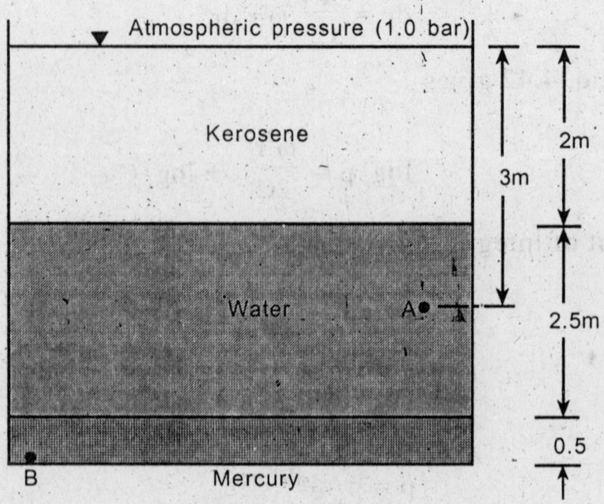

Prob.4.4

4.5 If the atmospheric pressure at sea level is 101.325 kN/m² determine the pressure at a height of 2000 m assuming the pressure variation to follow (i) hydrostatic law and (ii), isothermal process. Take the density of air at sea level as 1.208 kg/m³.

4.6 A pressure of 101.325 kN/m² is maintained inside the cabin of a jet plane flying at an altitude of 10 000 m above mean sea level. If the atmospheric pressure follows the adiabatic law with $k = 1.2$, determine the difference of pressure between inside and outside of the jet plane.

4.7 A *barometer* is a device for measuring atmospheric pressure. If mercury having a relative density of 13.55 is used and a glass tube full of mercury is inverted as shown in the figure, determine to value of h if atmospheric pressure is 101.00 kN/m². Neglect the effects of vapour pressure.

4.8 Find gauge pressure at A if the relative densities of mercury and oil are 13.55 and 0.80 respectively.

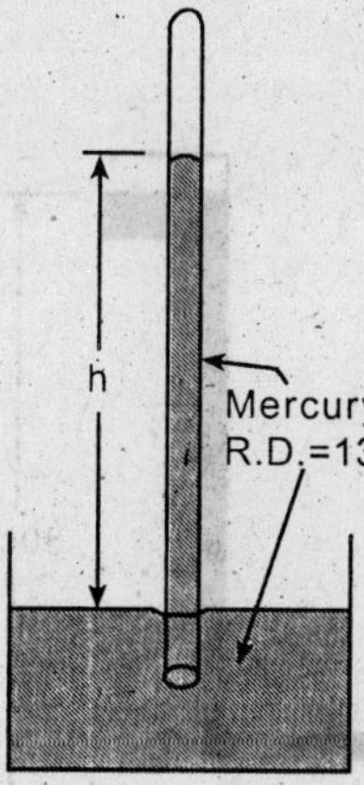

Prob.4.7

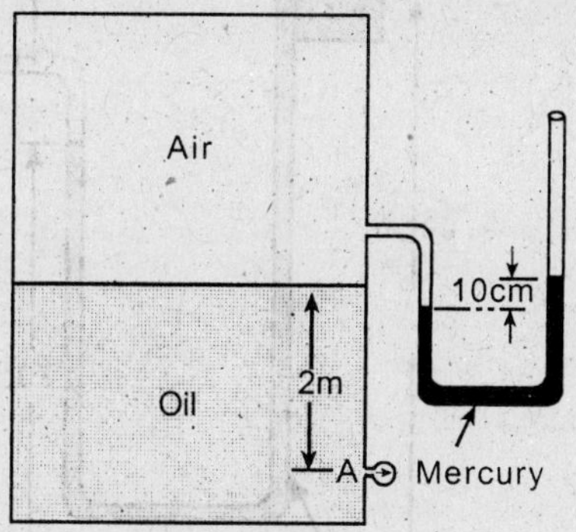

Prob.4.8

4.9 A U tube filled with mercury is connected to piezometers on pipes A and B. Determine the pressure (P_B – P_A).

4.10 Determine h if the pressure difference in the two pipes, ($P_B - P_A$), is equal to 2940 N/m².

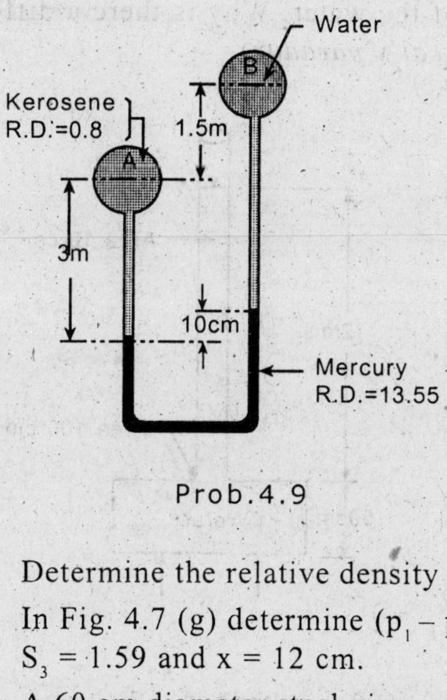

Prob.4.9

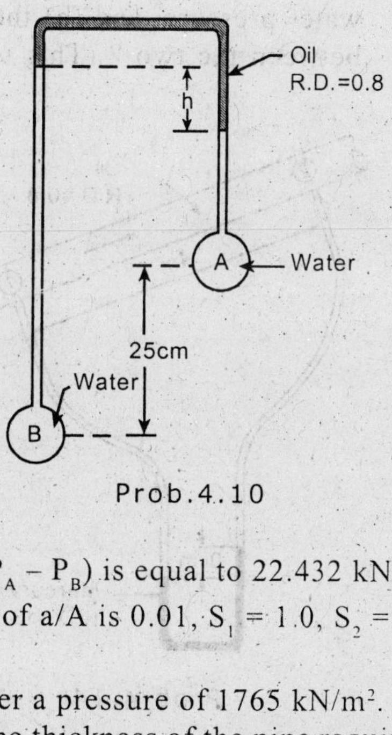

Prob.4.10

4.11 Determine the relative density of liquid x if ($P_A - P_B$) is equal to 22.432 kN/m².

4.12 In Fig. 4.7 (g) determine ($p_1 - p_2$) if the value of a/A is 0.01, S_1 = 1.0, S_2 = 0.80, S_3 = 1.59 and x = 12 cm.

4.13 A 60 cm diameter steel pipe carries water under a pressure of 1765 kN/m². If the allowable stress is 123 560 kN/m² determine the thickness of the pipe required to withstand the pressure.

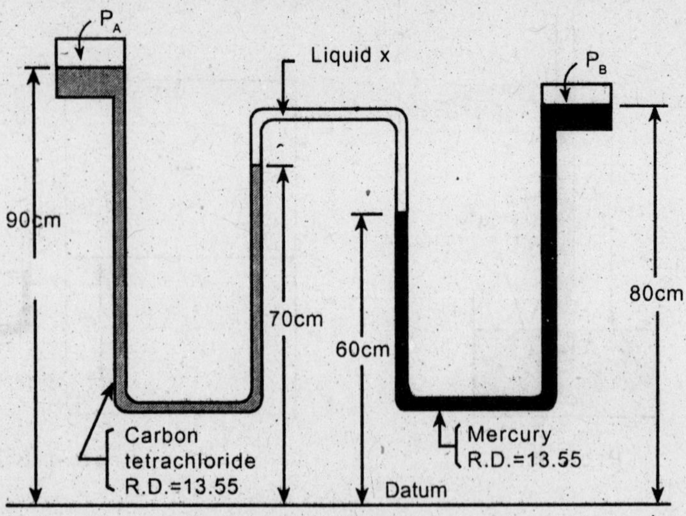

Prob.4.11

4.14 Determine (p_1 - p_2) in the figure shown if difference in elevation between the two points is 1.50 m.

4.15 In the figure shown, compute (a) total force on the bottom of the tank due to the water pressure, and (b) the total weight of the water. Why is there a difference between the two ? (This is known as *Pascal's paradax*).

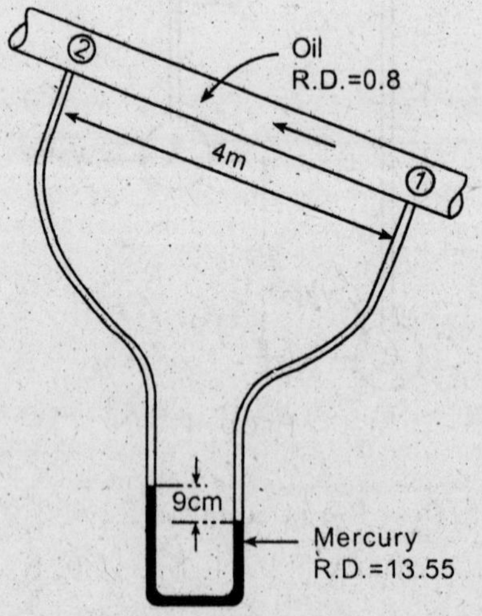

Prob.4.14

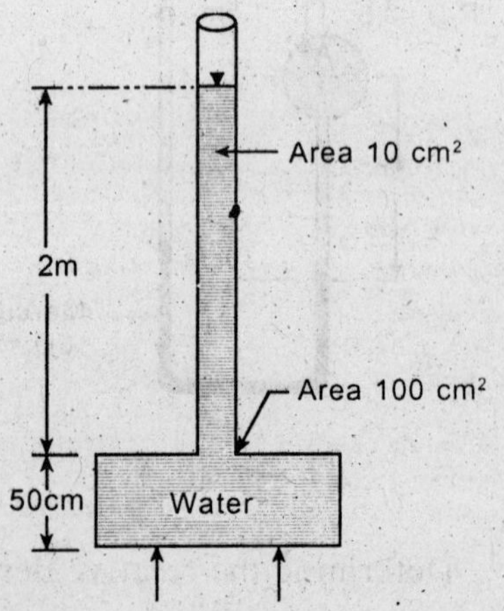

Prob.4.15

4.16 Find the total water pressure and position of centre of pressure for the profile of dam shown in the figure.

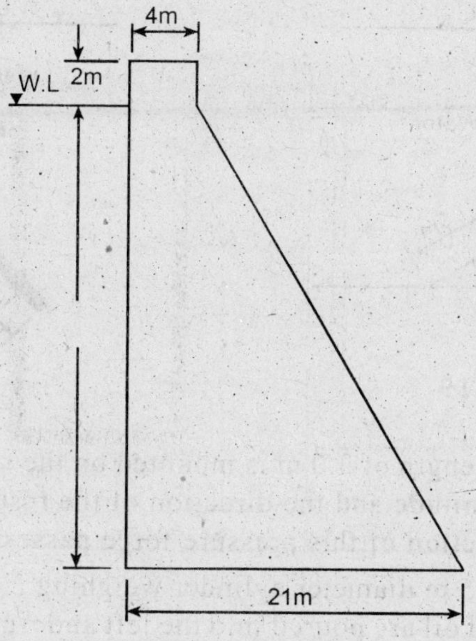

Prob.4.16

4.17 If the top edge of a circular sluice gate of 1.0 m diameter is located at a depth of 4.0 m below the water surface, find the total pressure and position of centre of pressure.

4.18 In the following cases shown in the figure, what will be the total pressure and the position of centre of pressure ?

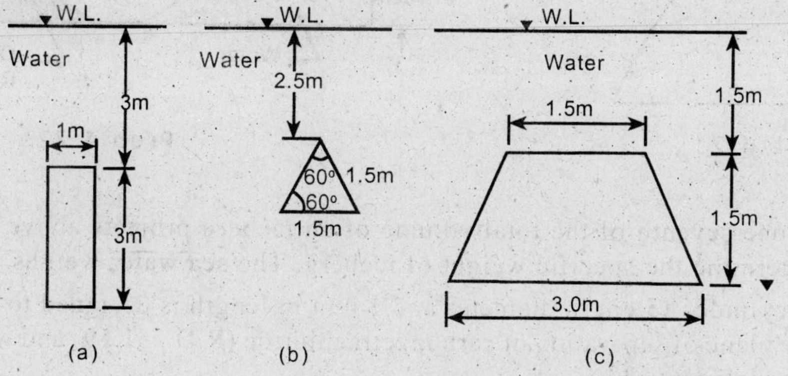

Prob.4.18

4.19 Find the total pressure on the gate located as shown in the figure.

4.20 Find the total pressure and centre of pressure of the plate shown in figure.

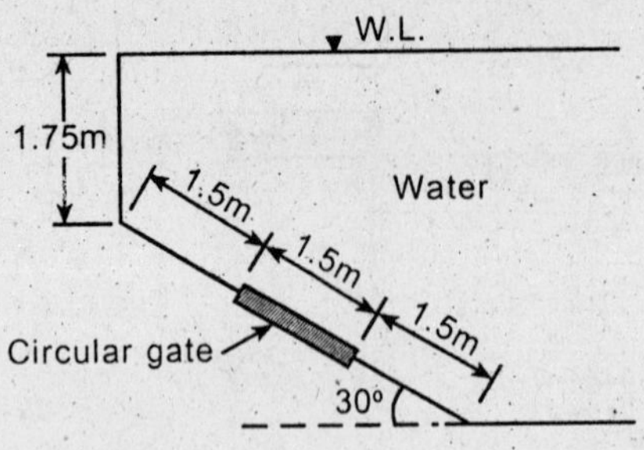

Prob.4.19

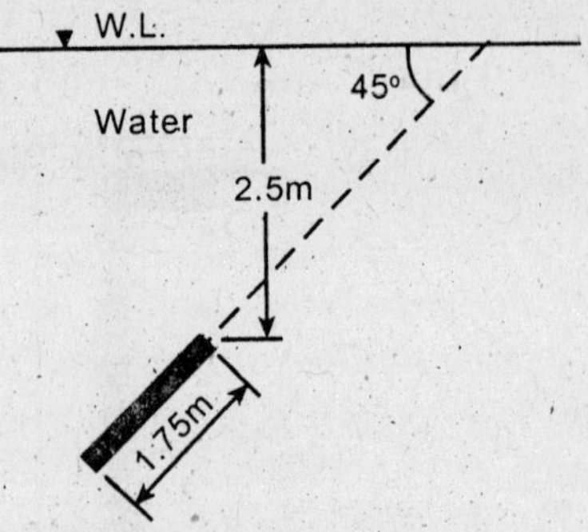

Prob.4.20

4.21 A sector gate with length of 3.0 m is mounted on the spillway of a dam as shown. Determine the magnitude and the direction of the resultant pressure force on the gate. (The line of action of this pressure force passes through the gate axis).

4.22 In the figure, the 2.5 m diameter cylinder weighing 2.432 kN rests on the bottom of a tank. Water and oil are poured into the left and right hand portions of the tank as shown. Find the magnitudes of the horizontal and vertical components of the force which will keep the cylinder just touching the tank bottom.

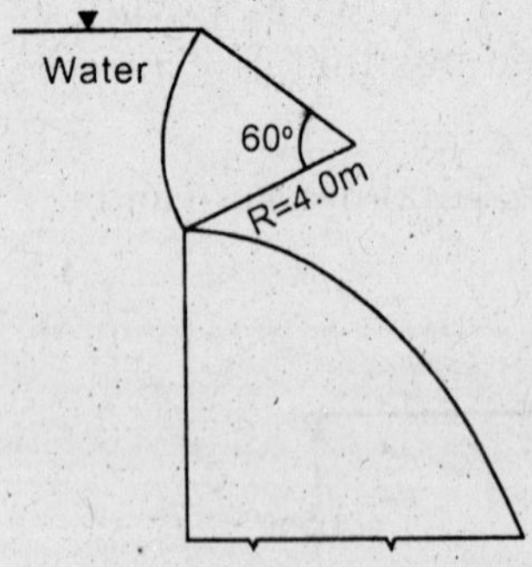

Prob.4.21

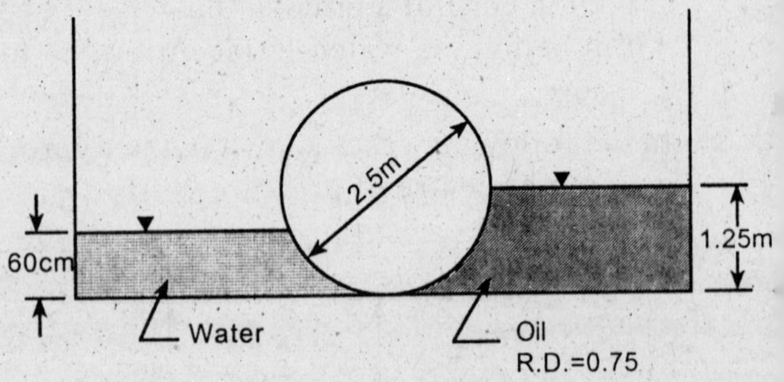

Prob.4.22

4.23 If one seventh of the total volume of an iceberg projects above the sea surface determine the specific weight of iceberg. The sea water weighs 10.20 kN/m^3.

4.24 A cylinder 15 cm in diameter and 1.0 m in length is designed to float half above the plane of separation of carbon tetrachloride (R.D. = 1.59) and water. Determine the metacentric height.

4.25 A rectangular barge 20 m long has a cross-section 5.0 m wide. The water line is 1.5 m above the bottom. If the centre of gravity is 1.8 m from the bottom, determine the metacentric height.

4.26 Calculate the depth H at which the conical valve starts working assuming that the valve projects out by 1.0 m from the base of the tank. Take the weight of valve a 2.256 kN.

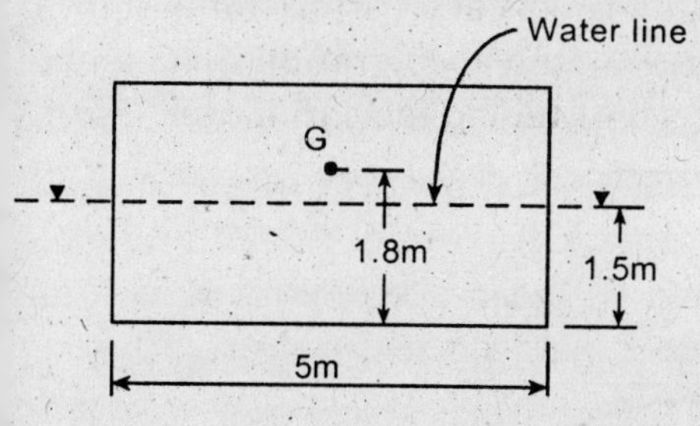

Prob.4.25

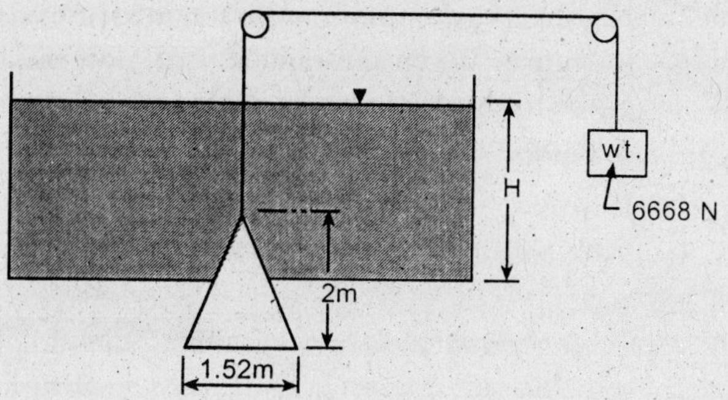

Prob.4.26

4.27 What will be the maximum length of a cylinder of diameter D and relative density S that can float in water in stable equilibrium with its axis vertical ?

4.28 A circular cylinder of 8.0m diameter with bottom closed floats vertically in water with its water line 4.0 m above the base. The centre of gravity of the body is 1.55 m above the base and on the vertical axis. Determine the metacentric height and the limiting height of the centre of gravity for stability.

4.29 A conical buoy having radius of 2.0 m and height of 4.0 m partly floats in water with its axis vertical and vertex downwards. Determine the range of the weight of the buoy if it is to be in stable equilibrium.

4.30 Rectangular tank 12 m long, 2.2 m wide and 2.5 m deep contains water to a depth of 1.5 m. At what uniform acceleration along x direction, will the water surface be 0.5 m below the top on its rear ? Determine the pressure at front and rear corners under such condition.

4.31 A tank as shown in figure is given a uniform acceleration of 5.0 m/s^2 in the x direction. If the tank has a hole at top left corner, determine pressure at top right corner and bottom left corner, if the tank is filled with kerosene of relative density 0.80.

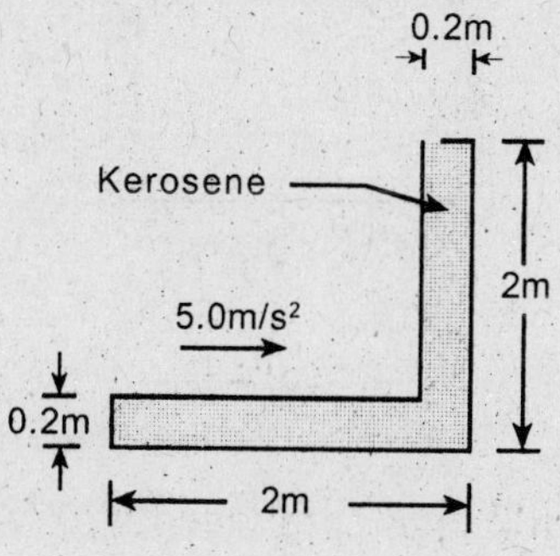

Prob.4.31

4.32 An observation plane with the positions of gasoline tank A and carburator is shown in figure. When the tank is full, determine the maximum acceleration that can be given to the plane without stopping the gravity feed of fuel to the carburator. Tank. A is open to atmosphere.

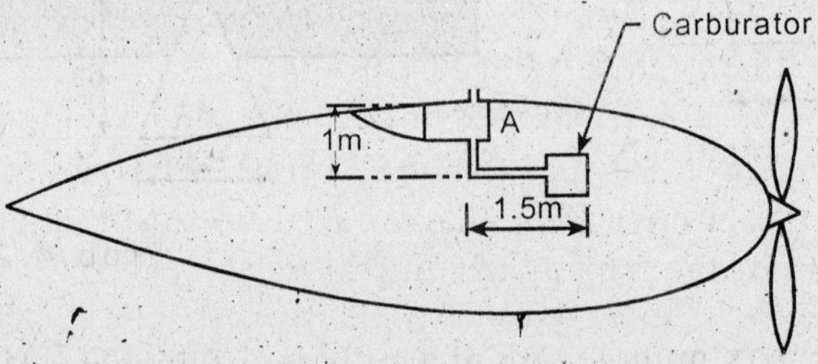

Prob.4.32

4.33 A container filled with glycerine (R.D. = 1.26) to a depth of 2.75 m is given a uniform vertical acceleration of 4.0 m/s^2 in the upward direction. Determine pressure intensity 1.0 m below the free surface.

4.34 A vertical U-tube with the two legs 0.75 m apart is filled with water and rotated about a vertical axis 0.5 m from one leg as shown in the figure. Determine the difference in elevation of the water levels in the two legs, when the speed of rotation is 150 rpm.

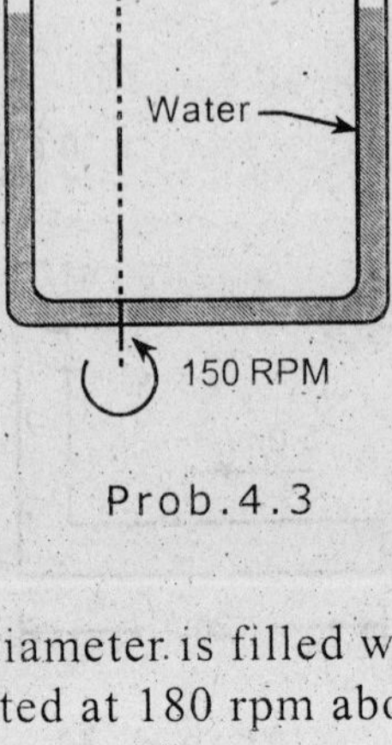

Prob.4.3

4.35 A cylindrical tank 1.0 m in diameter is filled with carbon tetrachloride to a depth of 4.50 m. If the tank is rotated at 180 rpm about a vertical axis passing through centre, determine (i) the pressure at the centre and corner of the tank bottom, and (ii) the height of the tank required so that there is no spilling at 180 rpm.

4.36 An open cylindrical tank 1.2 m in diameter and 2.0 m deep is filled with water and rotated at 60 rpm. Determine the volume of water spilled and the depth of water along the axis.

4.37 Determine the speed of rotation of the tank in Prob. 4.36 at which the centre of bottom of the tank has zero water depth.

4.38 A closed cylindrical tank 2.0 m in diameter and 0.5 m high is completely filled with water and is rotated at 90 rpm about a vertical axis passing through the centre Determine the pressure (i) along the circumference at the top of the tank, and (ii) along the bottom of the tank at a radius of 0.3 m.

Chapter Five

Applications of Bernoulli's Equation

5.1 Introduction

Bernoulli's equation is one of the important tools for solving many problems in fluid mechanics. It is applied either singly or in combination with the equation of continuity depending upon the results desired. While applying this equation, the assumptions and limitations discussed in Chapter 3 should be carefully borne in mind.

Applications of Bernoulli's equation can bc broadly classified in two categories – these are closed conduit flows and flows with free surface. In the problems of closed conduit flows where the flow is rapidly converging, the flow pattern is completely governed by the form of the boundary. In other words, for a given boundary shape there is a unique flownet and hence a unique velocity variation from point to point. Hence application of Bernoulli's equation for irrotational flow between sections 0 and 1 will show shat

$$1-\left(\frac{U_1}{U_0}\right)^2=\frac{\Delta h}{\rho U_0^2/2}$$

in which Δh is change in piezometric head.

In the case of motion of a gas where small changes in elevation do not matter much or when the motion under consideration is in a horizontal plane, with the given boundary, the variation of $\Delta p/(\rho U_0^2/2)$ is also determined. In the case of motion of a liquid in inclined conduits, even though the fluid weight must be taken into account because of changes in elevation, the variation of (U_1/U_0) is fixed and hence is not influenced by gravity. The only way the gravity or fluid weight influences the motion in closed conduits is by changing the pressure variation with changes in elevation according to the relation $(p/\gamma) + z = h$. Problems concerning efflux from orifices fixed in pipes, flow through closed conduits and flow through conduit transitions are included in this category.

Problems of flow over weirs, flow through sluice gates, free liquid jets, and vortex flow problems are included in the second category. These are characterised by the presence of a free surface along which the fluid comes in contact with another fluid of a different specific weight. The characteristic of the free surface is that all along the free surface the pressure intensity is constant (i.e. atmospheric in most of the cases). Therefore, in the second category of the problems the streamline pattern is partly governed by the boundary geometry and partly by the profile of the free surface.

Such a classification of problems does not necessarily change the method of application of Bernoulli's equation, but it helps in a better appreciation of the phenomenon under consideration.

5.2 Pressure Distribution in Irrotational Flow

As a first case of application of Bernoulli's equation consider irrotational flow through a two dimensional conduit. The flownet for this case is shown in Fig. 5.1. Let U_0 and p_0 be the velocity and the pressure at section OO which is sufficiently upstream of the transition and let U_1 and p_1 be the corresponding values at any other point. Then

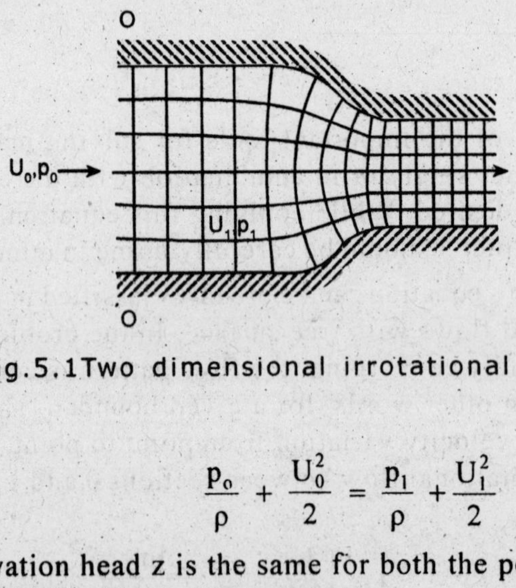

Fig.5.1Two dimensional irrotational flow

$$\frac{p_0}{\rho} + \frac{U_0^2}{2} = \frac{p_1}{\rho} + \frac{U_1^2}{2}$$

assuming that the elevation head z is the same for both the points or the fluid weight is negligible. The above expression can be written as

$$\frac{p_1 - p_0}{\rho} = \frac{U_0^2 - U_1^2}{2} = \frac{1}{2} U_0^2 \left[1 - \frac{U_1^2}{U_0^2}\right]$$

or
$$\frac{\Delta p}{\rho U_0^2/2} = 1 - \left(\frac{U_1}{U_0}\right)^2 \tag{5.1}$$

The variation of (U_1/U_0) along a stream tube can be obtained from the flownet configuration since $(U_1/U_0) = (\Delta n_0/\Delta n_1)$ and therefore, the pressure variation can also be readily found out. It can be noticed that the term $\Delta p/(\rho U_0^2/2)$ is dimensionless and it is often convenient to show the pressure variation in this form.

Once the boundary form for a particular irrotational flow phenomenon is known, the flownet can be drawn and value of $\Delta p/(\rho U_0^2/2)$ can be obtained by subtracting $(U_l/U_0)^2$ from unity at every point. It has been mentioned earlier that for a given geometry of the conduit, the flownet obtained is unique. Hence the variation of $(U_l/U_0)^2$ and of $\Delta p/(\rho U_0^2/2)$ along a stream tube is also unique for a given boundary form.

The parameter $\Delta p/(\rho U_0^2/2)$ can be written in a slightly different form as $U_0/\sqrt{2\Delta p/\rho}$ which is known as *Euler number* after Leonhard Euler-the Swiss mathematician of the eighteenth century. Euler number can be interpreted as the square root of the ratio of the inertial force per unit volume ($\sim \rho U^2/2l$) to the pressure force per unit volume ($\sim \Delta p/l$). From this discussion it follows that if the flow is governed by the pressure force only, each point in the conduit is characterised by a constant value of Euler number.

5.3 Cavitation

As can be seen from Bernoulli's equation, any increase in velocity or elevation at a point results in a corresponding decrease in pressure. In the case of liquids, there is a lower limit for such a decrease in pressure. As has been mentioned earlier, every liquid is characterised by particular value of vapour pressure for a given temperature. If for some reason, the pressure at any point in the flowing liquid reaches the vapour pressure, the liquid will vaporise and form tiny pockets of vapour. If the liquid contains some dissolved air or gases (as is usually the case), these gases will be released at a pressure slightly greater than vapour pressure. The bubbles of vapour thus formed are carried by the flowing liquid into a region of high pressure where they collapse. The formation of bubbles, their transport to the region of high pressure and their subsequent collapse is a continuing process and is known as *cavitation*. This was first observed by Reynolds. Collapsing of the bubbles near the boundary results in excessively high pressure over an infinitesimal time interval. Since the material forming the boundary is subjected to such high pressure variations of large frequency, pitting of the material results. Cavitation is also accompanied by vibration of the structure and objectionable noise. As a result, there is a reduction in the efficiency of the structure.

Bulk cavitation occurs in those cases where the static pressure throughout the flow is lowered to vapour pressure as in the case of contraction followed by expansion and in various types of gates (see Fig. 5.2). Cavitation can also take place when the boundary curves sharply away from the flow as in the case of bends, local boundary curvature, positive or negative step, and surface roughness. Cavitation due to surface roughness takes place in nozzles for fire hoses. Cavitation also takes place in siphons, baffle piers in stilling basins, pumps, turbines and ship propellers. Because of undesirable effects of cavitation, it should be ensured that in any hydraulic structure the pressure does not fall below a certain minimum due to change in cross-section or boundary curvature.

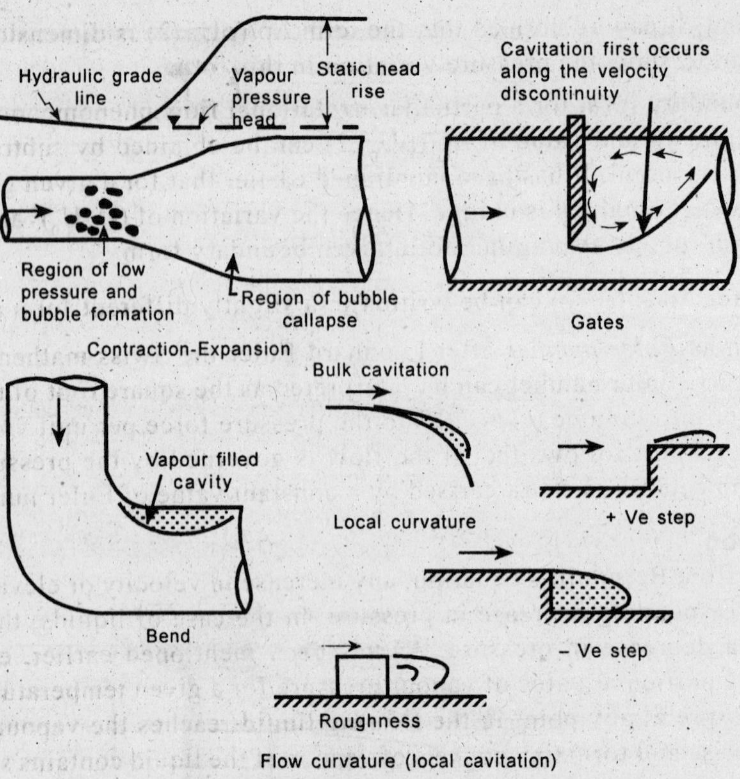

Fig.5.2 Occurrence of cavitation

The parameter $\Delta p/(\rho U_0^2/2)$ can be used as an index for studying the tendency towards cavitation. *Cavitation number* σ can be defined as

$$\sigma = \frac{(p_0 - p_1)}{(\rho U_0^2/2)} = \frac{(h_0 - h_1)}{(U_0^2/2g)}$$

in which p_0 and p_1 are ambient and pressure at a point under consideration, and h_0 and h_i are the corresponding static heads. Theoretically when h_1 is equal to vapour pressure head, cavitation would occur; at that time σ will attain a limiting maximum value. For beginning of cavitation, the value of p_1 will be vapour pressure of water at the given temperature. This varies from about 0.2 m of water at 15°C to about 1.20 m at 50°C. For safe design one can assume that h_1 does not fall below 2.40 m absolute.

5.4 Efflux from Conduit Contractions

If a fluid is discharged from a conduit into the atmosphere through an opening of any form, the pressure intensity along the issuing jet surface is atmospheric. Consider a fluid flowing out of a contracted section of a two dimensional conduit as shown in Fig. 5.3. As the streamlines approach the opening, they tend to converge. They continue to converge beyond the opening upto a certain section at which they are just parallel to each other. The section of the jet at which the streamlines become parallel has the minimum jet area and is known as *vena contracta*. Similar jet contraction takes place for flow through any type of opening fixed in the wall of a container filled with fluid. The ratio of the jet area at the vena contracta to the area of the opening is known as the *coefficient of contraction* and is commonly designated by symbol C_c. Figure 5.3 shows a two dimensional contraction in which the width of the opening is b and therefore, the area of jet at vena contracta is C_c b. It will be evident that the velocity of jet is maximum at vena contracta.

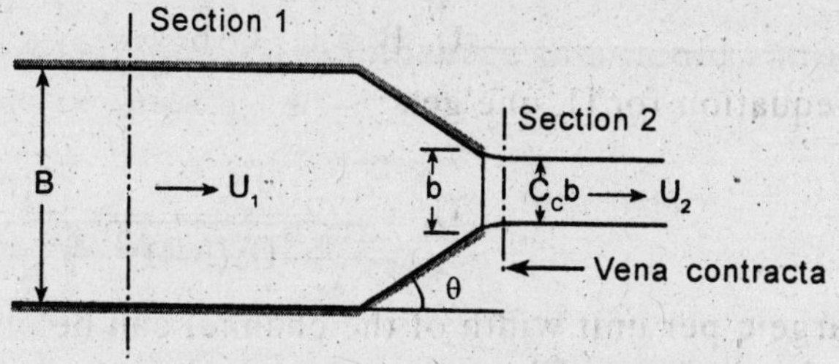

Fig.5.3 A two dimensional contraction

The magnitude of the contraction coefficient depend the geometry of the opening through which efflux is taking place. Therefore, the contraction coefficient C_c can be determined by means of a carefully plotted flownet for the fluid jet issuing from an opening. This process, however, is very tedious and inaccurate due to the inaccuracies involved in the graphical plotting of the flownet.

Kirchhoff has shown that for irrotational flow through a plane orifice in a very large container, the coefficient of contraction C_c has a magnitude of 0.611. The values of C_c for the two dimensional boundary forms shown in Fig. 5.3 are given in Table 5. 1. The values given in Table 5.1 can also be used for three dimensional case if b/B is replaced by the ratio of orifice diameter to pipe diameter d/D. The values listed in Table 5.1 have been obtained theoretically by Von Mises.

The rate of discharge through the contraction can be computed by the application of Bernoulli's equation between sections 1 and 2 in Fig. 5.3.Section 1 corresponds

TABLE 5.1

Values of Coefficient of Contraction

b/B	$\theta = 45°$	$\theta = 90°$	$\theta = 180°$
0.0	0.746	0.611	0.500
0.2	0.747	0.616	0.528
0.4	0.749	0.631	0.564
0.6	0.758	0.662	0.613
0.8	0.789	0.722	0.691
1.0	1.000	1.000	1.000

to the flow in the conduit where the velocity of flow is U_1 and section 2 is at vena contracta at which the area is $C_c b$ and velocity is U_2. Application of Bernoulli's equation yields,

$$p_1 - p_2 = \frac{\rho}{2}\left(U_2^2 - U_1^2\right)$$

in which p_1 and p_2 are the pressure intensities at sections 1 and 2. From the continuity equation it can be seen that,

$$U_1 B = U_2 C_c b$$

Solving these equation for U_2 one gets,

$$U_2 = \frac{1}{\sqrt{1-C_c^2(b/B)^2}}\sqrt{\frac{2(p_1-p_2)}{\rho}} \tag{5.2}$$

and the discharge q per unit width of the channel can be obtained by multiplying the above expression by the area of jet at vena contracta,

$$q = \frac{C_c b}{\sqrt{1-C_c^2(b/B)^2}}\sqrt{\frac{2(p_1-p_2)}{\rho}} \tag{5.3}$$

The term $\dfrac{C_c}{\sqrt{1-C_c^2(b/B)^2}}$ is constant for a particular boundary form and can be replaced by C_d to yield a simplified form of Eq. 5.3 as

$$q = C_d\, b\sqrt{\frac{2(p_1-p_2)}{\rho}} \tag{5.4}$$

The term C_d commonly known as the *coefficient of discharge*, depends only on the boundary form for ideal fluids. Similar expression for efflux through the conduit can also be obtained for a three dimensional flow; this is illustrated in Example 5.1. It is interesting to note that the discharge coefficient and the Euler number are identical. In Eq. 5.4 if the terms are transposed as,

$$C_d \text{ or } \frac{C_c}{\sqrt{1-C_c^2(b/B)^2}} = \frac{q}{b}\sqrt{\frac{\rho}{2(p_1-p_2)}}$$

It can be seen that q/b is the mean velocity of flow U in contracted section and the term on the right can be written as $U/\sqrt{(2\Delta p)/\rho}$ which is the Euler number. As long as the flow is governed by the pressure only, the discharge coefficient assumes a constant value for a given boundary form. In the case of real fluids, where viscosity also influences the flow the discharge coefficient will be dependent on the ratio of inertial force to the viscous force per unit volume. The latter ratio is known as the *Reynolds number* (see sect. 7.9). It follows that for irrotational flow,

$$C_d = f\,(\text{boundary form})$$

and for flow of real fluids in closed conduits

$$C_d = f\,(\text{boundary form and Reynolds number})$$

Example 5.1

Find the expression for the discharge coefficient for flow through a circular contraction placed in a circular conduit discharging into the atmosphere.

If section 1 is located in the undisturbed flow, while section 2 is located at vena contracta, Bernoulli's equation yields (see Fig. 5.4)

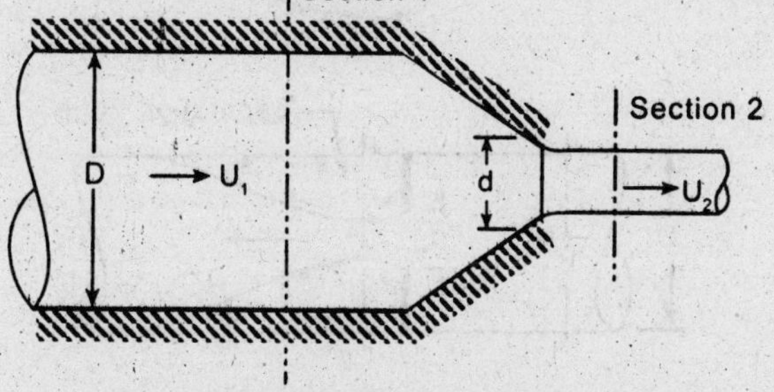

Fig.5.4

$$p_1 - p_2 = \frac{\rho}{2}\left(U_2^2 - U_1^2\right)$$

$$\therefore \qquad \Delta p = \frac{\rho}{2}\left(U_2^2 - U_1^2\right)$$

Continuity equation gives,

$$\frac{\pi}{4} D^2 U_1 = C_c \frac{\pi}{4} d^2 U_2$$

Substituting the value of U_1 in the expression for Δp, one gets,

$$U_2 = \frac{1}{\sqrt{1 - C_c^2 (d/D)^4}} \sqrt{\frac{2\Delta p}{\rho}}$$

The discharge Q will be

$$Q = \frac{C_c}{\sqrt{1 - C_c^2 (d/D)^4}} \frac{\pi}{4} d^2 \sqrt{\frac{2\Delta p}{\rho}}$$

$$= C_d \frac{\pi}{4} d^2 \sqrt{\frac{2\Delta p}{\rho}}$$

where

$$C_d = \frac{C_c}{\sqrt{1 - C_c^2 (d/D)^4}}$$

5.5 Orifice Plate and Venturimeter

Bernoulli's equation can be readily applied to flow through conduits having a constriction in the form of an orifice plate or a venturimeter. An orifice plate is a flow measuring device which takes the form of a circular opening placed in the pipe as shown in Fig. 5.5 Flow rate can be estimated by observing the pressure difference between the two sections, one upstream of the orifice plate where the pressure is unaffected by the introduction of the orifice plate and the other at the vena contracta downstream of the orifice plate.

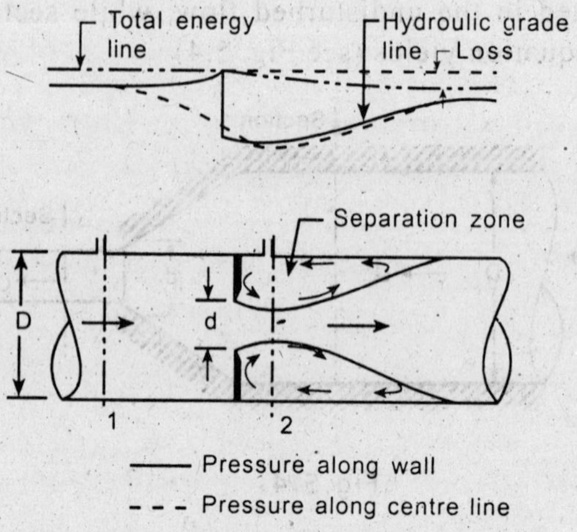

Fig.5.5 Orifice plate

Bernoulli's equation for sections 1 and 2 can be written as,

$$\frac{U_1^2}{2g} + \frac{p_1}{\gamma} + z_1 = \frac{U_2^2}{2g} + \frac{p_2}{\gamma} + z_2$$

in which the U_1, p_1 and U_2 and p_2 are the values of velocity and pressure at sections 1 and 2 respectively. Since the conduit is horizontal, the elevation head can be assumed to be constant and can be omitted. Further the energy loss between the two sections is assumed to be zero because the flow between sections 1 and 2 is rapidly converging. From the continuity equation, one gets,

$$Q = A\,U_1 = C_c\,a\,U_2$$

where C_c is the coefficient of contraction for the orifice. A is the area of the conduit and a is the area of the orifice. Substituting $U_1 = Q/A$ and $U_2 = Q/C_c\,a$, the above equation may be written as,

$$\frac{Q^2}{2g\,A^2} + \frac{p_1}{\gamma} = \frac{Q^2}{2g\,C_c^2 a^2} + \frac{p_2}{\gamma}$$

Solving for Q, one gets,

$$Q = \frac{C_c\,a}{\sqrt{1-(C_c^2(a/A)^2}}\sqrt{2g\frac{(p_1-p_2)}{\gamma}}$$

The above expression can be written as

$$Q = C_d\, a\, \sqrt{2gH} \tag{5.6}$$

where $$C_d = \frac{C_c}{\sqrt{1-(C_c^2(a/A)^2}} \quad \text{and } H = \frac{(p_1 - p_2)}{\gamma}$$

It may be noted that the magnitude of term $(p_1 - p_2)\gamma$ will vary with the location of the piezometer tube connections and thereby change the magnitude of the discharge coefficient. In order to use an orifice plate for measuring the discharge, it has to be calibrated for certain fixed positions of piezometer connections. Usually the upstream piezometer opening is located at a distance of (D – d) to 2 (D – d), while the downstream opening is located at a distance of approximately 0.25 d to 0.33 d. Since the position of vena contracta is a function of d/D and Reynolds number, no exact location of the position of vena contracta can be given. The discharge coefficient C_d for real fluids is a function of the ratio of the diameters of orifice and conduit, and the Reynolds number;

or $$C_d = f\left(\frac{d}{D}, \text{Re}\right) \tag{5.7}$$

Johaansen has studied the variation of C_d with Re for orifices with various values of d/D and his results are presented in Fig. 5.6. For very low values of Reynolds number, C_d rapidly increases but is sáme for all ratios of d/D. Beyond a value of Re = 10, C_d depends on both Re and d/D. For Reynolds numbers greater than approximately 10^4, the discharge coefficient decreases very slowly with increase in Reynolds number and tends to a constant value for a given value of d/D.

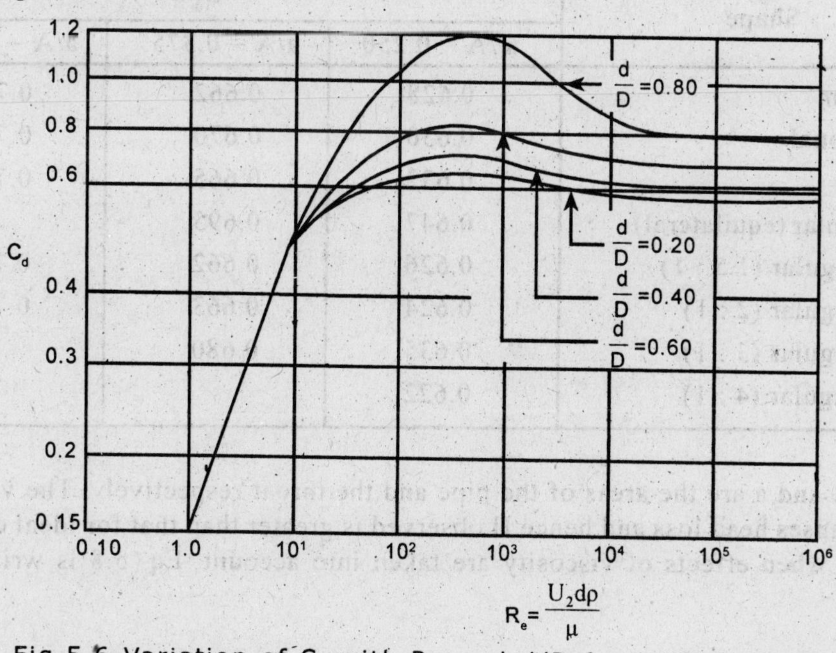

Fig.5.6 Variation of C_d with Re and d/D for orifice plates

Very little information is available concerning the discharge coefficients of non circular orifice plates fixed in circular pipes. Experiments at Roorkee University have yielded the values of C_d for orifices of various shapes fixed in a 10 cm diameter pipe as listed in Table 5.2. The Reynolds number in these cases varied from 2×10^4 to 2×10^5. The discharge coefficients listed below are the limiting values.

A venturimeter (see Fig. 5.9) has a gradual transition from the pipe to the throat and has a much smaller loss of head than that for orifice plate, because the gradual contraction is followed by a more gradual expansion. The point of pressure measurement are defined, one at the throat and the other before the transition starts. A calibrated venturimeter is a very common measuring device for pipe flows. The method of analysis for a venturimeter is similar to that for orifice plate, the only difference between the two being that, because of gradual contraction followed by gradual expansion and because of straight portion in between, the stream lines are parallel at the throat. As a result, section 2 can be taken at the throat with C_c equal to unity. Assuming no head loss as in the case of an orifice plate, the following formula can be derived for the discharge flowing through the Venturimeter,

$$Q = \frac{a}{\sqrt{1-(a/A)^2}} \sqrt{2gH} \qquad (5.8)$$

TABLE 1.2

Discharge Coefficients of Sharp Edged Orifice Plates of Various Shapes

Shape	C_d		
	a /A = 0.250	a/A = 0.375	a/A = 0.500
Circular	0.628	0.662	0.720
Hexagonal	0.630	0.670	0.717
Square	0.632	0.665	0.733
Triangular (equilateral)	0.647	0.695	-
Rectangular (1.5 : 1)	0.626	0.662	0.705
Rectangular (2 : 1)	0.624	0.663	0.733
Rectangular (3 : 1)	0.635	0.680	-
Rectangular (4 : 1)	0.622	-	-

in which A and a are the areas of the pipe and the throat respectively. The viscosity of the fluid causes head loss and hence H observed is greater than that for ideal conditions Therefore, when effects of viscosity are taken into account, Eq. 5.8 is written in the form,

$$Q = \frac{Ca}{\sqrt{1-(a/A)^2}}\sqrt{2gH} \tag{5.9}$$

in which C is a coefficient which depends upon the Reynolds number and the ratio a/A. Usually C varies between 0.91 and 0.99.

Fig. 5.7 shows variation of discharge coefficient C of the venturimeter with Reynolds number at the throat, for venturimeters having d/D ratios between 0.30 to 0.50. The actual dimensions of the venturimeters varied from 30 cm × 10 cm to 10 cm × 5 cm. It can be seen that C increases with increase in Reynolds number $U_2 d\, \rho/\mu$. Further for d/D between 0.30 and 0.50, d/D has no influence on C. The detailed dimensions of venturimeter are given in Fig. 5.9.

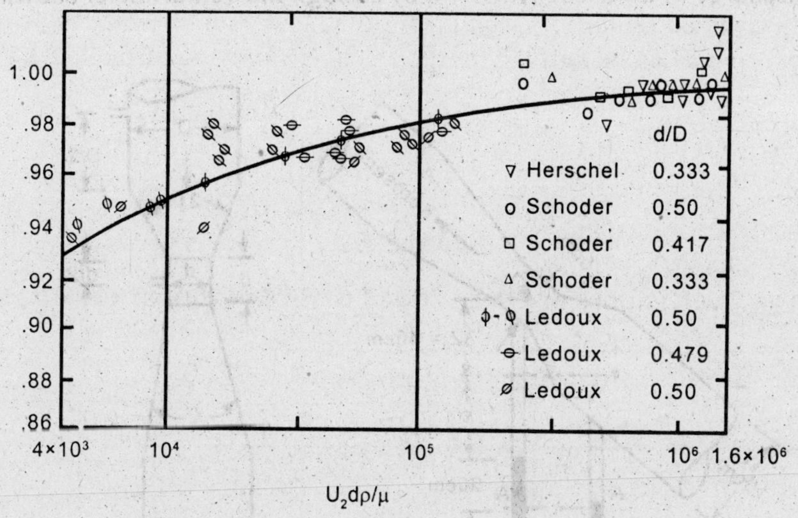

Fig.5.7 Variation of C for venturimeters

A flow nozzle meter or flow nozzle is a device intermediate in character between the venturimeter and orifice plate. As shown in Fig. 5.8, the nozzle meter consists of a short straight section following a well rounded approach centered in the pipe by flanges. In the nozzle, the velocity is increased and pressure is decreased as in the contracting portion of venturimeter; then the jet issues freely into the downstream pipe as in the orifice plate. During contraction the flow is guided by the boundary and hence no vena contracta forms. Therefore C_c is unity. The upstream tap is placed about one pipe diameter upstream of the nozzle and the downstream immediately downstream of the nozzle exit or at D/2 downstream of inlet face. The coefficient C for nozzle is approximately that for a venturimeter and overall pressure loss is approximately that for orifice plate.

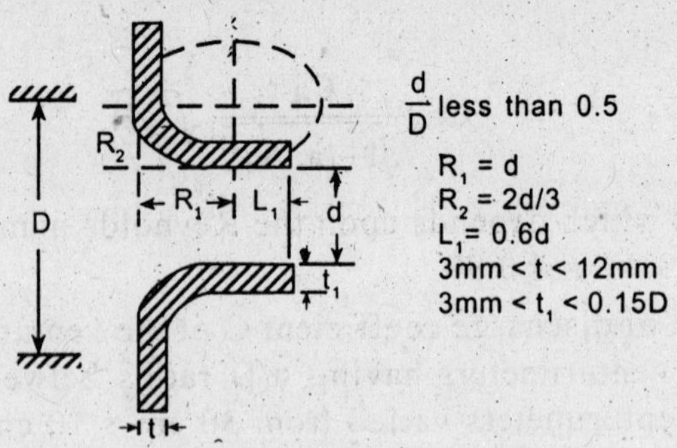

Fig.5.8 Nozzle meter

Example 5.2

Estimate the discharge of kerosene (R.D. = 0.8) through the venturimeter shown in Fig. 5.9.

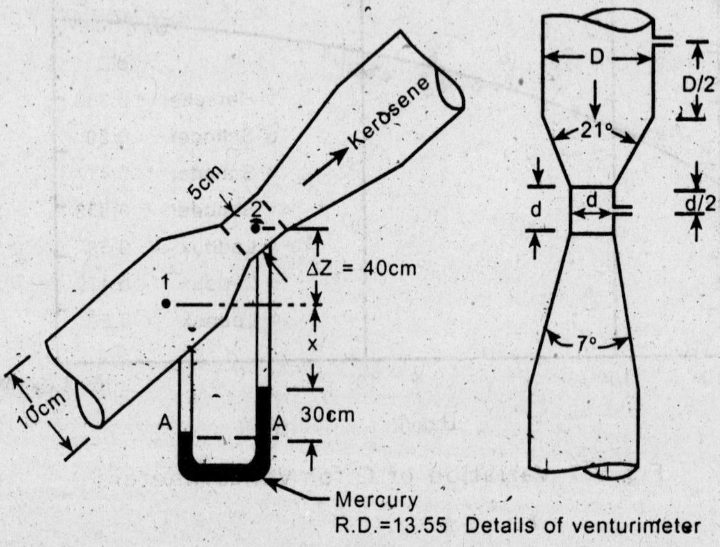

Fig.5.9 Venturimeter

Writing Bernoulli's equation between sections 1 and 2, one gets

$$\frac{p_1}{\gamma} + \frac{U_1^2}{2g} = \frac{p_2}{\gamma} + \frac{U_2^2}{2g} + \Delta z$$

or

$$\frac{p_1}{\gamma} - \left(\frac{p_2}{\gamma} + \Delta z\right) = \frac{U_2^2}{2g} - \frac{U_1^2}{2g}$$

However, from continuity equation $U_2 = 4U_1$.

Hence,
$$\frac{p_1}{\gamma} - \left(\frac{p_2}{\gamma} + \Delta z\right) = \frac{15U_1^2}{2g}$$

The left hand term in the above equation can be found by equating pressures at sections AA in the two limbs of the manometer.

$$\therefore \quad \frac{p_1}{\gamma} + (x + 0.3) = \left(\frac{p_2}{\gamma} + 0.4\right) + x + \left(0.3 \times \frac{13.55}{0.8}\right)$$

$$\frac{p_1}{\gamma} - \left(\frac{p_2}{\gamma} + 0.4\right) = 5.08 - 0.30 = 4.78 \text{ m}$$

$$\therefore \quad \frac{15U_1^2}{2g} = 4.78 \quad \text{or} \quad U_1 = 2.5 \text{ m/s}$$

Hence
$$Q = 0.785 \times 0.01 \times 2.5 = 0.0196 \text{ m}^3/\text{s} = 19.6 \ l/\text{s}$$

5.6 Orifices and Mouthpieces

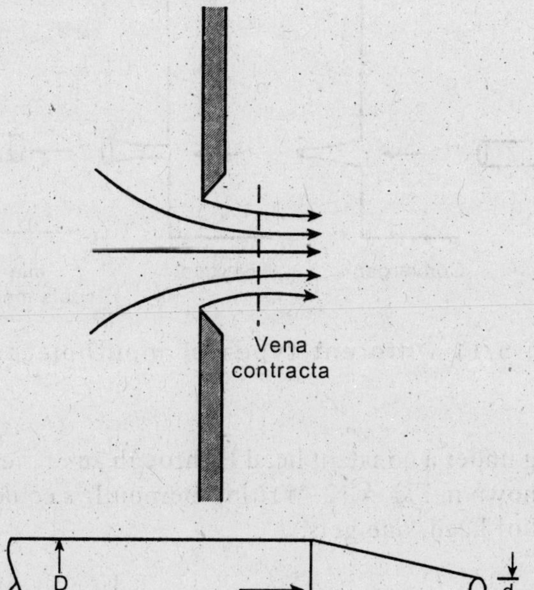

Fig.5.10 An orifice and a nozzle

A stream of fluid may come out from a container through an orifice or a nozzle or a short tube. An orifice is an opening in the walls of a tank containing fluid. It can be circular, square, triangular or of any other shape. The thickness of orifice wall is usually very small relative to the size of the orifice. A standard orifice is one with a sharp edge. Flow through such an orifice is shown in Fig. 5.10. As the fluid flows through the orifice, the stream lines converge and form a jet, the cross-sectional area of jet being smaller than that of the orifice. Since the fluid particles adjacent to the wall cannot change their direction abruptly, the position of vena contracta (i.e. section having minimum area) is slightly away from the wall. If the edge of the orifice is not sharp, the flow is affected by the wall thickness. Since the stream lines between the wall and the vena contracta are curved, the pressure is not constant across the jet upstream of vena contracta. However, at the vena contracta the stream lines are parallel and hence pressure across the jet is atmospheric. Similar conditions occur in the case of an orifice at the end of a conduit.

A nozzle is a converging tube as shown in Fig. 5.10. They are so shaped that C_c is unity. Nozzles are employed when a high velocity jet is desired from a pipe. The pressure at the exit end of the nozzle is atmospheric. By the application of Bernoulli's equation it can be seen that the velocity of the jet, as it leaves the nozzle, is high.

A mouthpiece is a short tube whose length is not more than two or three times its diameter. The mouthpiece may be straight, convergent or divergent and it may be projecting inside the container. The different types of mouthpieces are shown in Fig. 5.11. Orifices and mouthpieces are many times used as flow measuring devices.

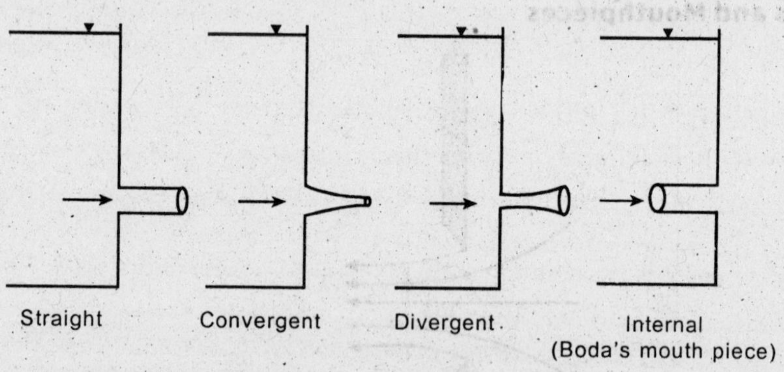

Fig.5.11 Different types of mouthpieces

Coefficient of Velocity

Consider a fluid flowing under a constant head H through an orifice fixed in the side wall of a large container as shown in Fig. 5.12. Writing Bernoulli's equation for sections A and B and assuming no loss of head, one gets,

$$H + O + O = O + \frac{U^2}{2g} + 0$$

Since the cross-sectional area of the container is very large compared to that of the orifice, velocity head at point A is negligible. It may also be mentioned that the assumption of no head loss is reasonable since the flow under consideration is converging. Therefore,

$$H = \frac{U^2}{2g} \quad \text{or} \quad U = \sqrt{2gH} \qquad (5.10)$$

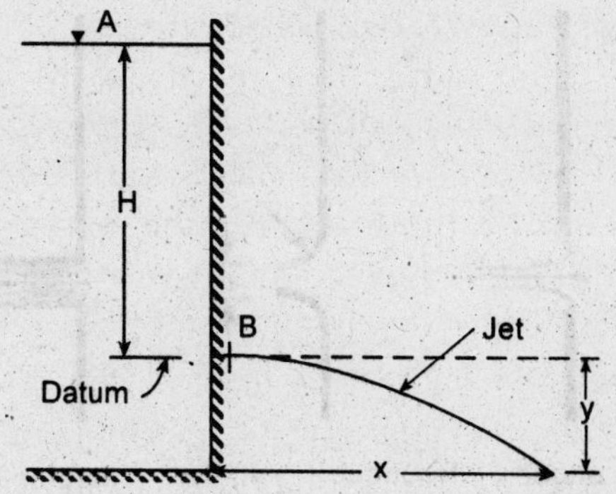

Fig.5.12 Flow through an orifice

Eq 5.10 was first presented by Torricelli and is sometimes known as Torricelli's equation. It has wide applications in fluid flow problems.

The actual velocity at section B, which is at the vena contracta, is slighlty less than $\sqrt{2gH}$ due to friction on the periphery of the orifice. The ratio of the actual velocity to the theoretical velocity $\sqrt{2gH}$ is called the *coefficient of velocity* C_v. Thus the actual velocity is $C_v\sqrt{2gH}$. For liquids having small viscosity e.g. water, the value of the coefficient of velocity is slightly smaller than unity. For an orifice of given dimensions, the coefficient C_v slightly increases with increase in H. For circular orifices C_v varies from 0.95 to 0.98.

The discharge flowing through an orifice is equal to the product of the actual velocity and the actual area at the vena contracta;

or $$Q = C_c\, a \times C_v\, \sqrt{2gH} \tag{5.11}$$

The product of and C_c and C_v is the discharge coefficient C_d discussed earlier. Therefore, discharge from any orifice flowing under a head H is given by

$$Q = C_d\, a\, \sqrt{2gH} \tag{5.12}$$

Values of C_c, C_v and C_d for some of the common types of orifices and mouthpieces are shown in Fig. 5.13.

The above discussion pertains to the flow through orifices running free i.e., when the orifices discharge into the atmosphere. If the downstream side of orifice is submerged in liquid then one has the orifice flowing under submerged condition. Application of Bernoulli's equation will indicate that the discharge equation for this case is,

$$Q = C_d'\, \sqrt{2gH'}$$

in which H′ is equal to the difference in liquid levels between the upstream and the downstream and C_d' is the new discharge coefficient. Experiments have shown that the discharge coefficient of an orifice under submerged condition is slightly smaller than the discharge coefficient under free flow condition.

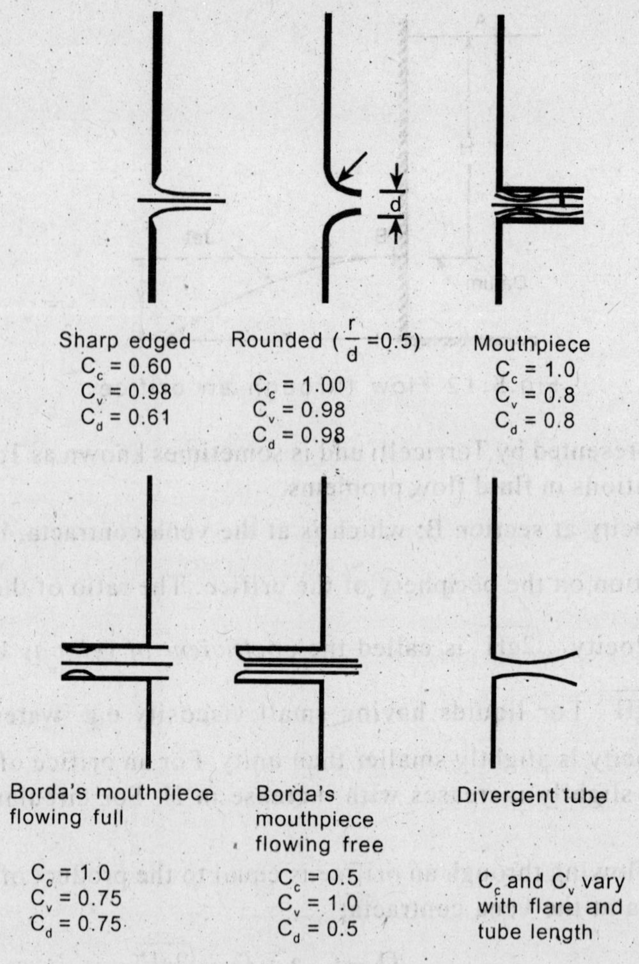

Fig.5.13 Some typical orifices, mouth pieces and tubes

Example 5.3

If a jet issuing from an orifice under a constant head H travels a horizontal distance x from the plane of the vena contracta while it drops through a height y, obtain the expression for coefficient of velocity.

Figure 5.12 shows the x and y distances from the vena contracta. From dynamics, if a particle falls a vertical distance y under the influence of gravity g, then

$$y = vt + \frac{1}{2} gt^2$$

in which v is the initial vertical velocity and t is the time required by the particle to reach a distance y. In case the initial velocity is zero,

$$t = \sqrt{\frac{2y}{g}}$$

The horizontal distance $x = U_{act} \times t$ in which U_{act} is the horizontal velocity at vena contracta.

$$\therefore \quad U_{act} = \frac{x}{t} = \frac{x}{\sqrt{2y/g}}$$

Hence the coefficient of velocity

$$C_v = \frac{x/\sqrt{2y/g}}{\sqrt{2g\,H}}$$

or

$$C_v = \sqrt{\frac{x^2}{4y\,H}}$$

Thus, if the coordinates of any point of a liquid jet issuing from an orifice into the atmosphere are known, the coefficient of velocity can be found out.

Example 5.4

Find the discharge through a 10 cm diameter external mouthpiece flowing under a head of 3.5 m. What will be the pressure at the vena contracta ? Adopt C_c to be 0.62.

In the mouthpiece, the jet contracts upto vena contracta (section 1) and then expands as it comes out. During this process there is loss of energy from section 1 to 2 (see Fig. 5-14) due to expansion of the jet. The velocity at vena contracta can be found from continuity equation as $a_1U_1 = a_2U_2$ or $U_1 = U_2/0.62$. The loss due to expansion of jet is $(U_1 - U_2)^2/2g$, (see Sect. 6.6 (b)). Applying Bernoulli's equation between free liquid surface and section 2 one has

$$3.5 = U_2^2/2g + (U_1 - U_2)^2/2g$$

Substituting the values of U_1 in terms of U_2 and solving the above expression one gets.

$$U_2 = 7.064 \text{ m/s}$$

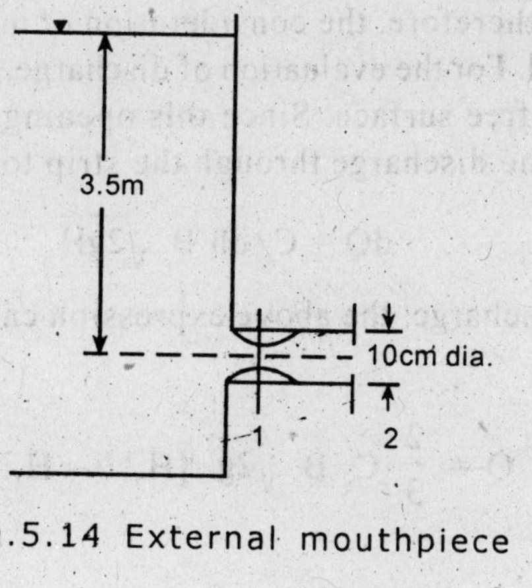

Fig.5.14 External mouthpiece

The discharge is $$Q = \frac{\pi}{4} \times (0.10)^2 \times 7.064$$

$$= 0.0555 \text{ m}^3/\text{s} = 55.5 \; l/\text{s}$$

It may be noted that the loss of energy due to the jet contraction upto vena contracta is extremely small and hence neglected.

The pressure at vena contracta can be found by applying Bernoulli's equation between the free liquid surface and the vena contracta

$$H_a + 3.5 == H_l + U_l^2/2g$$

in which H_a is the atmospheric pressure head on the liquid surface and H_l is the pressure head at vena contracta. Substituting $U_l = U_2/0.62$ and solving the above expression one gets,

$$H_l = H_a + 3.5 - \frac{2.601 \times 7.064^2}{2 \times 9.81}$$

$$H_l = H_a - 3.12 = 10.34 - 3.12 = 7.22 \text{ m}$$

Thus the pressure at the vena contracta of a mouthpiece is less than the atmospheric pressure.

5.7 Large Orifices and Sharp Crested Weirs

In the previous section flow through orifices and mouthpieces has been discussed and an equation for discharge Q has been obtained. The head H causing the velocity is measured as the vertical distance from the centre of the orifice upto the free surface. But a similar procedure cannot be adopted for a very large orifice in which the head over the upper edge of the orifice is smaller than one and half times the height of the orifice opening. In such a case, the average velocity of efflux is not equal to $\sqrt{2gH}$ where H is the head above the centre of orifice.

(a) Flow Through Large Orifices

Consider a large rectangular orifice in the side of a tank as shown in Fig. 5.15. The height of the opening d is large and therefore, the consideration of mean head from the centre of the orifice will not be justified. For the evaluation of discharge, consider a strip of thickness dh at a distance h below the free surface. Since this opening of height dh is very small, Eq. 5.12 can be applied for the discharge through the strip to obtain,

$$dQ = C_c \, dh \, B \sqrt{2gH}$$

In order to obtain the total discharge, the above expression can be integrated between the limits H_1 and H_2 to get,

$$Q = \frac{2}{3} C_c B \sqrt{2g} \, [H_2^{3/2} - H_1^{3/2}] \tag{5.13}$$

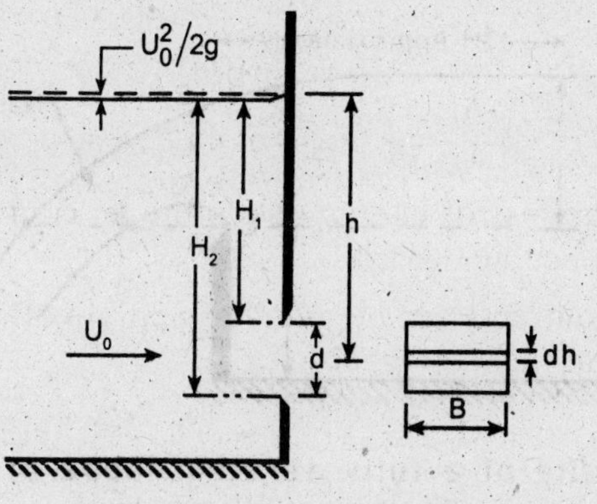

Fig.5.15 Large orifice

When the velocity head is taken into account, Eq. 5.13 takes the form,

$$Q = \frac{2}{3} C_c B \sqrt{2g} \left[\left(H_2 + \frac{U_0^2}{2g} \right)^{3/2} - \left(H_1 + \frac{U_0^2}{2g} \right)^{3/2} \right] \tag{5.14}$$

It may be mentioned here that since the viscous effects have been neglected in this derivation, there is no energy loss; therefore, C_v is unity. As a result, in Eqs. 5.13 And 5.14, C_c is equal to C_d and its value can be obtained from Table 5.1 for symmetrical orifices.

(b) ***Flow Over a Sharp Crested Weir***

The flow over a sharp crested weir can be considered as a limiting case of flow through a large orifice when the free surface falls below the upper edge of thc orifice. A sharp crested weir is an obstruction with a sharp straight edge placed vertically in an open channel, as shown in Fig. 5.16. Relations of different flow dimensions with H are also shown in the figure. As the liquid level falls just below the top edge of the orifice, (see Fig. 5.15) one can replace H_2 by H (which is equal to d) and H_1 by zero in Eq. 5.14. This yields the discharge equation for sharp crested weir in the form

$$Q = \frac{2}{3} C_c B \sqrt{2g} \left[\left(H + \frac{U_0^2}{2g} \right)^{3/2} - \left(\frac{U_0^2}{2g} \right)^{3/2} \right] \tag{5.15}$$

It is customary to write Eq. 5.15 in the form,

$$Q = \frac{2}{3} C_d B \sqrt{2g}\, H^{3/2} \tag{5.16}$$

Comparing Eqs. 5.15 and 5.16, one can see that

$$C_d = C_c \left[\left(\frac{U_0^2}{2gH} + 1 \right)^{3/2} - \left(\frac{U_0^2}{2gH} \right)^{3/2} \right] \tag{5.17}$$

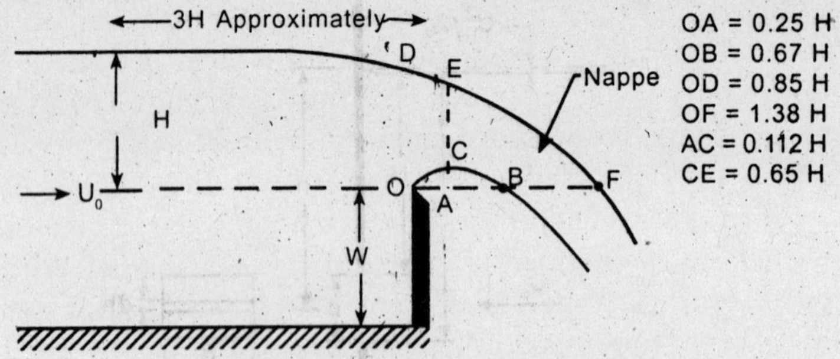

Fig.5.16 Flow profile of a fully aerated nappe of sharp crested weir

Here again C_c can be obtained from Table 5.1 if b/B is replaced by H/(H + W). The terms $(U_0^2/2gH)$ in Eq. 3.17 can be shown to be equal to $[\frac{4}{9} C_d^2 H^2/(H + W)^2]$. Hence C_d becomes a function of H/(H + W) alone since C_c also depends on the same parameter. The variation of C_c and C_d with H/(H + W) is shown in Fig. 5.17. The relationship between C_d and H/W can be expressed in the form

$$C_d = 0.611 + 0.075 \frac{H}{W} \tag{5.17a}$$

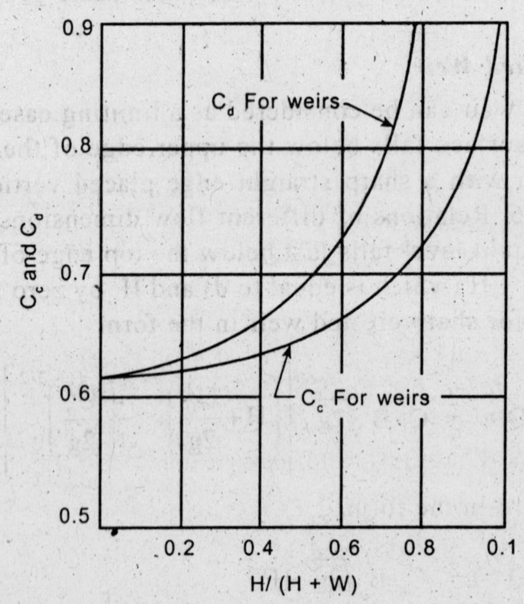

Fig.5.17 Variation of C_c and C_d for sharp created weirs

Since the curves traced by Eq. 5.17 (a) is practically identical with that for C_d in Fig. 5.17 it can be seen that values of C_d obtained from Eq. 5.17 (a), takes into account the effect of velocity head.

It should be noted that the foregoing relationships are based on the assumption that atmospheric pressure prevails on both sides of the nappe. A weir can work as a gauge or a measuring device only if this assumption is fulfilled. On the contrary, if the liquid fills the space below the nappe, the pressure intensity is substantially reduced and consequently the same discharge will be passed under a lower head. In other words, for the same head the discharge will increase. Therefore, if a weir is to be used as a measuring device the same pressure must be maintained over and under the nappe. When the weir extends over the full width of the channel, such a complete ventilation is not possible. In such a case, a certain maximum permissible pressure difference between the two sides of the nappe is prescribed. This is achieved by ventilating the underside of the nappe. The maximum demand of air q_a in m^3/s per metre length of the weir crest required for full aeration is

$$q_a = 0.10 \frac{q}{(H_p/H)^{1.5}}$$

in which q is discharge of water in m^3/s m, H is the head over the weir and H_p is the water depth immediately downstream of the weir. The magnitude of H_p can be calculated using momentum equation in the case of free surface flow, see Fig. 5.18.

While taking observations on a sharp crested weir, it should be remembered that the section where H is measured, should not have any effect of nappe curvature. Usually, the head is measured at a distance of approximately three times the head over the weir.

If the velocity distribution on the upstream side of the weir is not uniform, the term $U_0^2/2g$ in Eq. 5.17 will be replaced by $\alpha\, U_0^2/2g$ where α is the kinetic energy correction factor. Measurements have given α values ranging between 1.02 and 1.08 for H/W upto 4.0. Hence assumption of α to be unity is reasonable. At low heads the effects of surface tension and viscosity affect the discharge over the weir. To account for this, Eq. 5.15 can be written as

$$Q = \frac{2}{3} C_d\, B\, K \sqrt{2g}\; H^{3/2} \tag{5.16a}$$

in which C_d is still given by Eq. (5.17 a) and value of K is determined experimentally. Ranga Raju and Asawa have related K to $Re^{0.2}\, W_1^{0.6}$ in which $Re = g^{1/2} H^{3/2}/\nu$ and $W_1 = gH^2\rho/\sigma$. Variation of K with $Re^{0.2}\, W_1^{0.6}$ for rectangular weirs and triangular notches is given in Table 5.3. The effect of viscosity and surface tension will be important only at small heads over the weir.

TABLE 5.3

Value of K for rectangular weirs and triangular notches

$R_e^{0.2}\, W_1^{0.6}$	30	60	100	400	600	10^3 and above
K	1.27	1.20	1.15	1.04	1.01	1.0

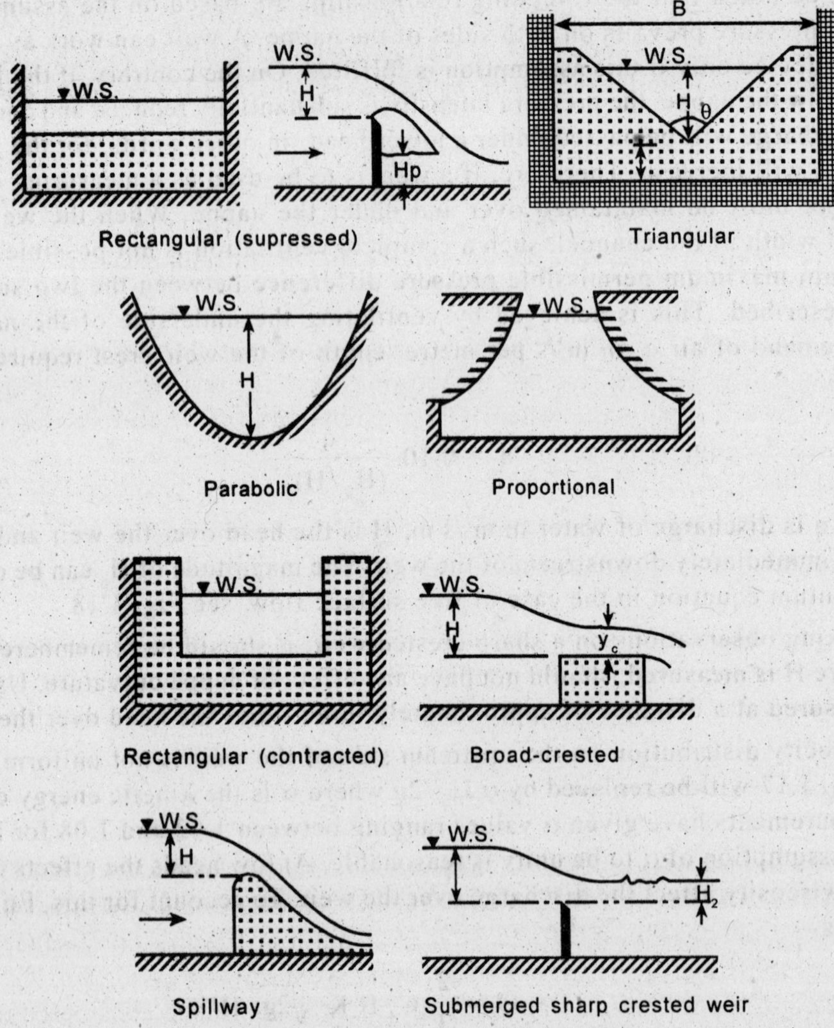

Fig.5.18 Various types of weirs

(c) Other Types of Weirs

Weirs can be classified either according to their shape at right angles to flow or according to their shape in the direction of flow. Thus according to first classification, weirs can be grouped as rectangular, trapezoidal, parabolic, proportional, etc. Furthermore, when the weir extends over the entire width of the channel, it is known as a *suppressed weir;* when the width of the weir is smaller than the width of the channel, the weir is known as *contracted weir*. According to the second classification, in which the weirs are classified according to the shape of the crest, there are sharp crested weirs, broad crested weirs, and round crested weirs which are commonly known as spillways. These are shown in Fig. 5.18. In the case of these weirs, if the downstream liquid level is below the crest of the weir, the downstream conditions do not affect the flow over the weir and such flow is known as nonsubmerged or free flow. If the downstream liquid level is above the crest, the discharge over the weir depends on H_1 as well as H_2 and the flow is known as submerged flow.

When the weir is contracted, it will be appreciated that at the two ends the stream lines will be curved while it is only in the middle section that they will be fairly parallel. As a result the effective width of the weir is reduced. Francis (1815-1892), as a result of extensive experiments, found that the effective width B′ in such case is,

$$B' = (B - 0.1\,nH) \tag{5.18}$$

in which n is the number of contractions. For a weir contracted symmetrically from both sides n is equal to 2. If piers are introduced on the weir crest then the value of n can increase. Equation 5.18 is valid when B is greater than 3H. Therefore, for contracted weir the discharge equation becomes

$$Q = \frac{2}{3} C_d \sqrt{2g}\,(B - 0.1\,nH)\left\{\left(H+\frac{U_0^2}{2g}\right)^{3/2} - \left(\frac{U_0^2}{2g}\right)^{3/2}\right\} \tag{5.19}$$

The discharge coefficient for contracted weirs can be taken as 0.622 as recommended by Francis provided H/W is less than unity. For a triangular notch one can easily show that, if the velocity of approach is neglected, the discharge equation takes the form,

$$Q = \frac{8}{15} C_d \sqrt{2g}\,\tan\left(\frac{\theta}{2}\right) H^{5/2} \tag{5.20}$$

in which θ is the apex angle. Here C_d depends on (H/P), (P/B) and θ. If (H/P) is less than 0.40 and (P/B) is less than 0.20, C_d depends only on θ and varies between 0.959 and. 0 .575 as θ changes from 20° to 100°. For parabolic weirs the discharge can be shown to be proportional to H^2. For a trapezoidal weir, an expression for the discharge can be obtained in the following way. The trapezoidal weir can be considered to be made up of a rectangular weir of width B and a triangular notch of apex angle θ. If C_d and C_d' represent the discharge coefficients of the rectangular weir and the triangular notch respectively, the discharge Q flowing under head H will be

$$Q = \frac{2}{3} C_d \sqrt{2g}\, B\, H^{3/2} + \frac{8}{15} C_d' \sqrt{2g}\,\tan\frac{\theta}{2}\, H^{5/2} \tag{5.21}$$

If the two discharge coefficients are assumed to be same. (as an approximation) Eq. 5.21 becomes

$$Q = \sqrt{2g}\; C_d\, H^{3/2}\left[\frac{2}{3}B + \frac{8}{15}H\tan\frac{\theta}{2}\right] \tag{5.22}$$

Consider a contracted rectangular weir of width B. According to Francis's formula the two end contractions will reduce the effective width by 0.2 H and hence the discharge will be reduced by $\{2/3\ C_d\ \sqrt{2g}\ (0.2\ H)H^{3/2}\}$. Hence if the ends of the weir, instead of being vertical, are inclined at an angle $(\theta/2)$ outwards so that the reduction in discharge due to end contractions is compensated by increase in discharge due to triangular portion, one has

$$\frac{2}{3}\ C_d\ \sqrt{2g}\ \ (0.2H)\ H^{3/2} = \frac{8}{15}\ C_d\ \sqrt{2g}\ \left(\tan\frac{\theta}{2}\right) H^{5/2}$$

or
$$\tan\frac{\theta}{2} = \frac{1}{4}$$

A trapezoidal weir in which the sides slope with 1 horizontal to 4 vertical is known as *Cipolletti weir,* because it was first described by Cipolletti in 1886. For a Cipolletti weir the discharge is given in Eq. 5.16.

The cross sectional shape of a spillway is obtained from the shape of nappe for a sharp crested weir. As shown in Fig. 5.16, the lower surface of the nappe rises by approximately 0.11 H as it leaves the sharp crested weir and then follows the trajectory. The empty portion between the sharp crested weir and the nappe when filled gives the profile of a spillway. Such spillways are used in dam sections of reservoir for disposing off that quantity of water which cannot be stored in the reservoir. Since the position of the nappe is a function of H, the spillway profile is obtained for a design head. At this head the nappe clings the spillway face. The discharge equation for spillways is the same as Eq. 5.16 in which the value of C_d can be taken as 0.75 when H/W is less than 0.75.

The effect of submergence on the discharge coefficient of sharp crested, rectangular (supressed as well as contracted), triangular, parabolic and proportional weirs has been studied by Villemonte. He has shown that

$$\frac{Q}{Q_1} = \left\{\left(1-\frac{H_2}{H_1}\right)^m\right\}^{0.385} \qquad (5.23)$$

in which Q is the discharge over the weir under submergence, Q_1 is the discharge under free flow condition with head H_1, H_2 is the downstream water level above the crest and m is the exponent of H in the discharge equation for free flow condition; e.g. m is 2.5 for triangular weir, and 1.5 for rectangular sharp crested weir.

It may be noted that the discharge coefficients of various weirs discussed above have been shown to be a function of geometry only. In fact the coefficient will also be influenced by viscosity and surface tension. However, these effects are of secondary importance for large heads.

Example 5.5

Find the discharge over a weir 8 m long and 3 m high flowing under a head of 2.4 m. The width of the approach channel is 10 m.

Taking C_d to be 0.622 and assuming the velocity of approach to be negligible, Eq. 5.19 gives ,

$$Q = \frac{2}{3} \times 0.622 \times (8 - 0.1 \times 2 \times 2.4) \sqrt{2\times9.81} (2.4)^{3/2}$$

$$= 51.38 \text{ m}^3/\text{s}$$

Hence the velocity of approach will be

$$U_o = \frac{51.31}{10\times5.4} = 0.952 \text{ m/s}$$

Substituting the value of U_0 in Eq. 5.10 the correct discharge obtained is 52.60 m³/s.

Example 5.6

A sharp crested weir of 1 m width and 30 cm height is installed in a 1 m wide laboratory flume. Two ventilating pipes of 1.5 cm diameter are fixed on either end of the weir. Find the air demand if the difference of pressure between the two sides of the nappe is 0.98 N/m² when water flows under a head of 15 cm. over the weir (Assume -a smooth entrance and no friction in the ventilating pipe and take ρ for air = 1.208 kg/m³)

The discharge coefficient $C_d = 0.611 + 0.075 \times \frac{15}{30} = 0.648$

The discharge $Q = \frac{2}{3} \times 0.648 \times 1 \times \sqrt{2\times9.81}(0.15)^{3/2}$

$Q = 0.11 \text{ m}^3/\text{s}$

Area of the pipes $= 2 \times \pi/4 \times .0150^2 = 0.000\,353 \text{ m}^2$

Velocity of air $U = \sqrt{\frac{2\Delta p}{\rho}} = \sqrt{\frac{2\times0.98}{1.208}} = 1.274 \text{ m/s}$

Air discharge $= 1.274 \times .000\,353 = 0.000\,449 \text{ m}^3/\text{s}.$

r $\frac{\text{air discharge}}{\text{water discharge}} = \frac{0.000\,449}{0.110} = .004$

Therefore the air demand is 0.4% of the discharge.

5.8 Flow Under a Sluice Gate

A sluice gate is a special case of a two dimensional type of orifice as shown in Fig. 5.19. The discharge can be computed by applying Bernoulli's equation and the equation of continuity. As the flow is contracting towards the opening, a flow net can be drawn to determine the pressure distribution. In the same figure, the pressure distribution on the gate is also shown.

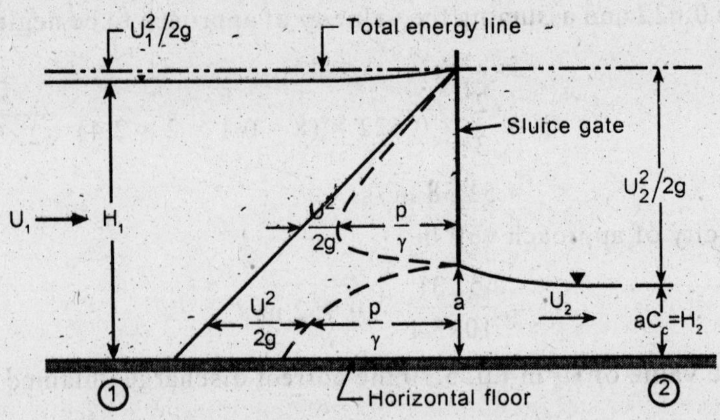

Fig.5.19 Flow under a sluice gate

Assuming no loss and uniform velocity distribution at sections 1 and 2, Bernoulli's equation can be written for sections 1 and 2 as

$$H_1 + \frac{U_1^2}{2g} = H_2 + \frac{U_2^2}{2g}$$

From continuity equation $$U_1 = \frac{H_2}{H_1} U_2$$

Solving for U_2 one gets,

$$H_1 - H_2 = \frac{1}{2g}\left[U_2^2 - \left(\frac{H_2}{H_1}\right)^2 U_2^2\right] = \frac{U_2^2}{2g}\left[1 - \left(\frac{H_2}{H_1}\right)^2\right]$$

$$\therefore \quad U_2 = \frac{1}{\sqrt{1-\left(\frac{H_2}{H_1}\right)^2}} \sqrt{2g(H_1 - H_2)}$$

The discharge per unit width $q = H_2 U_2$ and $H_2 = C_c a$; therefore,

$$q = \frac{C_c a}{\sqrt{1 - C_c^2 (a/H_1)^2}} \sqrt{2g(H_1 - C_c a)}$$

This can be written as

$$q = C_d a \sqrt{2gH_1} \qquad (5.24)$$

where $$C_d = \frac{C_c}{\sqrt{1+C_c\left(\frac{a}{H_1}\right)}}$$

Thus for irrotational flow C_d is a function of (a/H_1) and C_c (which in turn depends on (a/H_1) and geometry). The coefficient of contraction C_c varies between 0.611 and 0.605 as (a/H_1) increases from zero to approximately 0.50. Hence a value of C_c equal to 0.61 may be used for all practical purposes.

In case there is flow through a sluice gate under submerged condition i.e. when the depth of flow on the downstream side t is greater than conjugate depth of $C_c a$ (see Fig. 5.20) the dimensional consideration requires that the discharge coefficient should be a function of t/a, H_1/a and C_c;

or $$C_d = f\left(\frac{t}{a}, \frac{H_1}{a}, C_c\right)$$

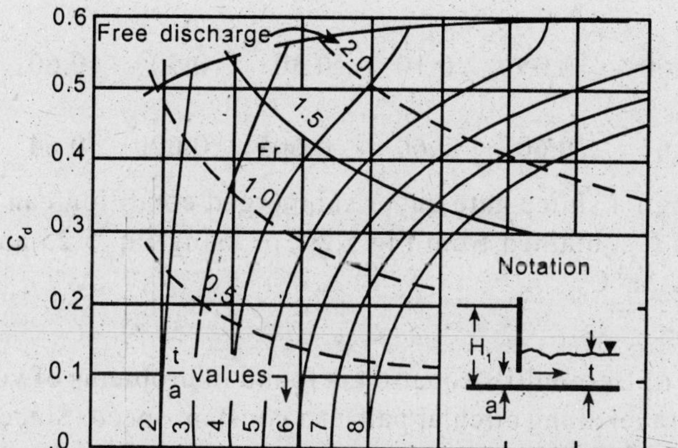

Fig.5.20 Variation of Cd with H_1/a and t/a for sluice gates

Figure 5.20 shows variation of C_d for a sluice gate for submerged and free flow conditions. It may be mentioned that Eq. 5.24 can be written as

$$C_d = \frac{q}{a\sqrt{2gH_1}} = \frac{q}{a\sqrt{ga}}\frac{\sqrt{a}}{\sqrt{2H_1}}$$

It can be recognised that $\frac{q}{a\sqrt{ga}}$ is the Froude number Fr

Therefore $$C_d = f(H_1/a, F_r)$$

For this reason it should be possible to draw lines of constant Froude number on C_d versus H_1/a plot. Such lines are shown in Fig. 5.20.

Alternatively, one can consider that the operating head in submerged flow is $\Delta H = (H_1 - H_2)$ where H_2 is the depth immediately downstream of the gate. Further the flow is confined to a depth $C_c a$. Above this depth there is a roller in which upper layers will have negative velocity whereas lower layers will have positive velocity. By applying Bernoulli's between sections 1 and 2 neglecting energy loss one can write

$$q = C_{ds} a \sqrt{2g\Delta H} \tag{5.25}$$

where C_{ds} is discharge coefficient under submerged conditions and $C_{ds} = C_{dl}$ for free flow condition in

$$q = \frac{C_c a}{\sqrt{1 - C_c^2\left(\frac{a}{H_1}\right)^2}} \sqrt{2g(H_1 - C_c a)} = C_{dl} a \sqrt{2g(H - C_c a)}$$

The values of $C_{dl} = C_{ds}$ obtained by Rajaratnam and Subramanya are

$\frac{a}{H_1}$	0.00	0.05	0.10	0.30	0.50	0.60	0.70
C_{dl}	0.61	0.60	0.60	0.605	0.620	0.64	0.66

Hence discharge through a sluice gate under submerged condition can be determined either using Eq. 5.24 and C_d obtained from Fig.5.20, or using Eq. 5.25 and C_{ds} obtained the above table, taking $C_{ds} = C_{dl}$.

5.9 Vortex Motion

An important application of Bernoulli's equation is found in problems of vortex motion in which the fluid particles travel along circular path at a constant speed. Since the magnitude of velocity of the fluid particle is constant along the circular path, the pressure cannot vary along the tangential direction. Because of the curvature of streamlines, however, there is normal acceleration and hence the pressure must vary along the radial direction in any horizontal plane.

There are two types of vortex motions that are of interest; they are *forced vortex* and *free vortex*. A forced vortex can be obtained by subjecting a fluid mass to a constant torque, e.g. rotating a container filled with liquid at a constant angular velocity. The characteristic of forced vortex is that the tangential velocity is directly proportional to the radial distance. In other words,

$$V = r\,\omega$$

in which ω is angular velocity. This type of motion has been discussed in Section 4.10. The forced vortex occurs in the impeller of the centrifugal pump or a centrifugal compressor. It may be emphasised that the forced vortex flow is of rotational type, and hence unless a constant torque is provided such a motion cannot be sustained.

In the case of a free vortex a liquid rotates not because of any external force but by virtue of some internal action or due to a rotation previously imparted to it. The vortex motion commonly observed in a bath tub or in a wash basin when the liquid is drained through the bottom hole is of free vortex type. Since no external torque is required in a free vortex motion, the rate of change of angular momentum is zero. In other words

$$\frac{\partial}{\partial t}(M\,V\,r) = 0 \qquad \text{or} \qquad (V\,r) = \text{constant } C. \tag{5.26}$$

The motion can be shown to be irrotational motion and hence it is charcterised by constant total energy, (see Fig. 5.21). It can be seen that when r = ∞, V = 0 and hence the total energy is only due to the elevation (on the surface the pressure is atmospheric). With decrease in r, velocity increases and since the pressure is the same on the free surface, there is a corresponding drop in elevation. When r = 0, Eq. 5.26 shows that velocity is infinity. Hence the free surface must drop to minus infinity. In practice this does not happen because for very small values of r the viscous effects, which are neglected, become quite important, hence vortex motion in the vicinity is of rotational type.

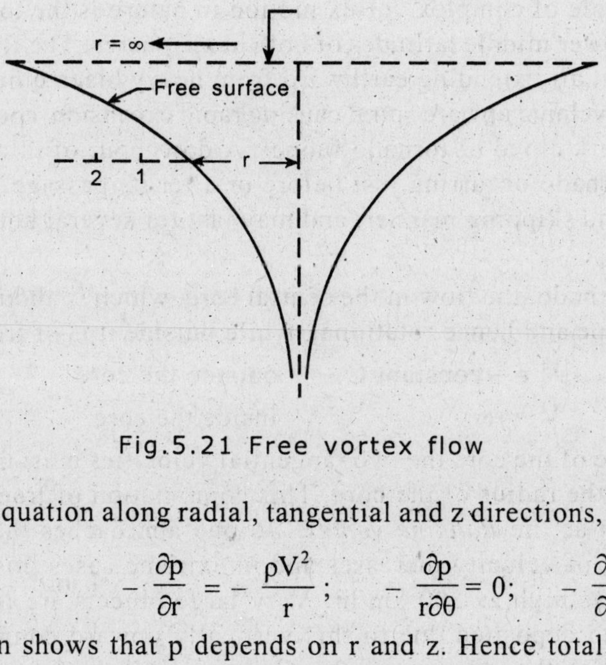

Fig.5.21 Free vortex flow

Writing Euler's equation along radial, tangential and z directions, one gets,

$$-\frac{\partial p}{\partial r} = -\frac{\rho V^2}{r}; \qquad -\frac{\partial p}{r\partial\theta} = 0; \qquad -\frac{\partial p}{\partial z} - \gamma = 0 \tag{5.27}$$

The second equation shows that p depends on r and z. Hence total change in p can be expressed as

$$dp = \frac{\partial p}{\partial z}dz + \frac{\partial p}{\partial r}dr$$

Substituting the values of $\frac{\partial p}{\partial r}$ and $\frac{\partial p}{\partial z}$ from Eq. 5.27 into the above, one gets

$$dp = -\gamma\, dz + \frac{\rho V^2}{r} dr \tag{5.28}$$

Substitution of Eq. 5.26 in Eq. 5.28 and subsequent integration gives

$$\int dp = -\int \gamma\, dz + \int \frac{\rho C^2}{r^3} dr ;$$

or
$$(p_2 - p_1) = \gamma\,(z_1 - z_2) + \frac{\rho C^2}{2}\left(\frac{1}{r_1^2} - \frac{1}{r_2^2}\right)$$

Dividing all terms by γ, the final relationship becomes

$$\frac{p_2 - p_1}{\gamma} = (z_1 - z_2) + \frac{C^2}{2g}\left(\frac{1}{r_1^2} - \frac{1}{r_2^2}\right) \tag{5.29}$$

Thus if points 1 and 2 are at the same r value but at different elevations, the pressure distribution will be hydrostatic.

A graphic example of complex vortex motion in nature is the tornado. Tornadoes are more common in lower middle latitudes of both hemispheres. The flow pattern consists of a whirling funnel of air extending earthward from heavy black clouds. The air motion is characterised by a cyclonic upward spiral causing rapid expansion, cooling and condensation which forms the dark cloud of tornado funnel. A downpour of rain or hail is a common associate of the tornado occurring just before or after its passage. The tornadoes travel mostly in erratic and skipping manner, and may last for several hours as they move with the storms.

In the case of tornado, the flow in the central core, which is about 5-500 m in width, is of forced vortex type and hence rotational, while outside it is of free vortex type, or

$V\, r$ = constant C outside the core

$V = r\omega$ inside the core

Since at the edge of the core the two tangential velocities must match, $r_o\,\omega = C/r_o$ or $C = r_o^2\,\omega$ where r_o is the radius of the core. This combination of free and forced vortex is many times known as the *Rankine vortex.* As one approaches the core, the vertically upward component of velocity increases and in extreme cases this velocity in the core can reach a value as high as 300 km/hr. Very large objects are reported to have been lifted up gently and deposited due to this vertically upward component of velocity in tornadoes. Also since the pressure in the core is considerably reduced as the tornado moves over the buildings, the outside pressure would be much less than that inside. As a result the buildings burst out. The tornadoes have a forward velocity of 40 to 70 km/hr.

A practical application of vortex motion is the cyclone separator used as a gas cleaning device, when the gas contains suspended dust particles. The cyclone separator (see Fig. 5.22) employs, a centrifugal force generated by spinning of gas stream which is caused by tangential gas inlet. The rectangular involute inlet passage has its inner wall tangential to the vertical circular cylindrical container. As the mixture of air and dust particles enters the cylinder, dust particles, due, to their inertia tend to travel in a straight line while gas follows curved path. High rate of spin thus throws dust particles to the outer wall of the cylinder which then slide down the cone in the storage hopper. The cleaned gas gradually reverses its downward spiral and forms a small ascending spiral. A vortex finder tube which extends downward into the cylinder helps in directing inner vortex out of the device. A cyclone separator of this type has a removal efficiency of 80-90 percent for particles coarser than15 microns in size.

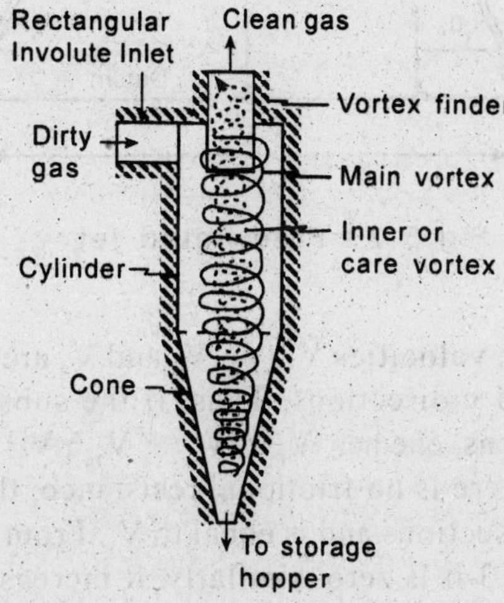

Fig.5.22 Cyclone separator

5.10 Analysis of Liquid Jets

A free liquid jet issuing out of a nozzle into atmosphere can be analysed by the application of Bernoulli's equation. The flow in this case is curvilinear in nature and jet has atmospheric pressure at all sections. Consequently, the pressure head term1 in the energy equation disappears and the flow is under the influence of gravitational effects alone. The sum of velocity head and potential head at all sections on the jet must, therefore, be the same, if energy loss is neglected.

Consider a jet issuing from a nozzle as shown in Fig. 5.23. The initial velocity is V_1 and the jet makes an angle θ with the horizontal.

At sections 1,2,3, and 4 the jet has the velocity V_1, V_2, V_3 and V_4 respectively and the elevations of these sections are z_1, z_2, z_3 and z_4. With the assumption that the jet does not split or disintegrate and that there is no energy loss, one can apply Bernoulli's equation as follows,

$$\frac{V_1^2}{2g} + z_1 = \frac{V_2^2}{2g} + z_2 = \frac{V_3^2}{2g} + z_3 = \frac{V_4^2}{2g} + z_4$$

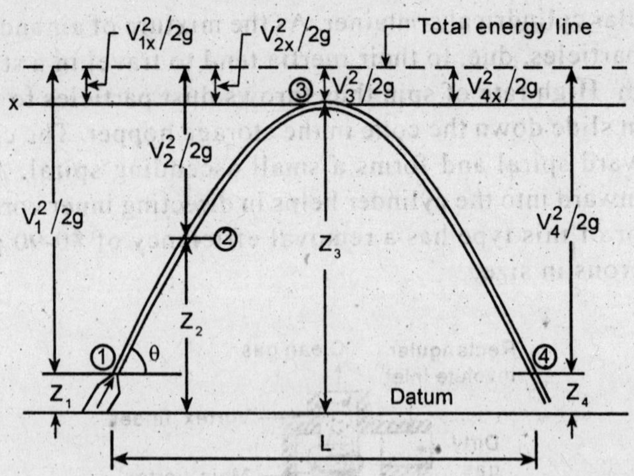

Fig.5.23 Free liquid jet

It should be noted that the velocities V_1, V_2, V_3 and V_4 are the tangential velocities and can be resolved along x and y directions, Thus, if the subscripts x and y designate the components in x and y directions, one has, $V_1^2 = V_{1x}^2 + V_{1y}^2$, $V_2^2 = V_{2x}^2 + V_{2y}^2$, $V_3^2 = V_{3x}^2 + V_{3y}^2$ and $V_4^2 = V_{4x}^2 + V_{4y}^2$. Since there is no frictional resistance, the velocity component in the x direction is the same at all sections and is equal to V_3. From point 1 to 3, the y component of velocity decreases and at 3 it is zero, similarly, it increases from 3 upto 4.

In Fig. 5.23, the total energy line is also shown and it is horizontal since there are no losses. The line XY is drawn through point 3 and is at a distance $V_3^2/2g$ (which is also equal to $V_{1x}^2/2g$, $V_{2x}^2/2g$, and $V_{4x}^2/2g$) below the total energy line. The geometry of the figure will show that the difference in elevation between line XY and any point such as point 1, gives the velocity head due to the vertical component of velocity.

From fig. 5.23, it is obvious that the maximum height to which the jet will rise i.e $(z_3 - z_1)$ is given by

$$(z_3 - z_1) = \frac{V_{1y}^2}{2g} = \frac{V_1^2 \sin^2\theta}{2g}$$

It can also be shown that the horizontal distance L is given by

$$L = \frac{V_1^2 \sin 2\theta}{g}$$

As can be seen from the above equation, L will be maximum for particular velocity when θ is equal to 45°.

Example 5.7

A 7.5 diameter jet leaves the nozzle at angle 30° to the horizontal. Calculate how high the jet will reach and what will be its maximum elevation if the discharge is 50 *l*/s.

The jet velocity $V_1 = \dfrac{50\times10^3}{0.785\times7.5^2} = 1132$ cm/s

or 11.32 m/s

$\therefore$ $V_1 \cos\theta = 11.32 \times 0.866 = 9.80$ m/s

$V_1 \sin\theta = 11.32 \times 0.500 = 5.66$ m/s

The maximum elevation upto which the jet will rise

$$= (Z_3 - Z_1) = \frac{V_1^2 \sin^2\theta}{2g} = \frac{5.66^2}{2\times9.81} = 1.633 \text{ m}$$

The area of the jet at maximum elevation

$$= \frac{50\times10^3}{980} = 51.02 \text{ cm}^2$$

Hence, the diameter of jet at maximum elevation,

$$= \sqrt{\frac{51.02}{0.785}} = 8.06 \text{ cm}$$

PROBLEMS

5.1 In Fig. 2.20 plot the variation of U/U_0 and p/p_0 as a function of distance along the wall. Here U_0 and p_0 are the velocity and pressure in the unaffected flow at C whereas U and p are velocity and pressure at any other section along the wall.

5.2 In a horizontal pipe of 15 cm diameter 4500 *l*/min of carbon tetrachloride flow with a pressure of 215.75 kN/m² at a certain section. If this pipe reduces to 10 cm diameter calculate the pressure at the reduced section. (Take $\gamma = 15.632$ kN/m³).

5.3 A 30 cm pipe pumps 280 *l*/s of water up a hill top which is situated 50 m above the supply reservoir. At the hill top the pipe size decreases to 20 cm. Calculate the pressure at the hill top if the pressure in the pipe line at 22 m above the reservoir is 686.462 kN/m².

5.4 Air of specific weight 11.797 N/m³ flows through a 10cm constriction in a 20cm pipe line. When the flow rate is 2.942 N/s the pressure at the constriction is 10 cm of mercury. Calculate the-pressure in the 20 cm pipe.

5.5 If a 10 cm orifice at the end of 25 cm pipe produces a jet of 8 cm in diameter, what will be the corresponding coefficient of discharge ?

5.6 Determine the pressure difference between a section upstream of an orifice plate and the vena contracta if the ratio of the orifice diameter to the pipe diameter is 2/3.

Oil of relative density 0.8 flows through the pipe at a velocity of 4.0 m/s. Neglect losses.

5.7 Air having a mass density of 1.236 kg/m³ is discharged at the rate of 0.3 m³/s through a 8 cm orifice located at the end of a 15 cm diameter pipe. Determine the diameter of contracted jet and the pressure in the pipe relative to that of the jet.

5.8 A nozzle at the end of a pipe is conical in shape, the apex angle being 90° as shown in the figure. What pressure in pipe would produce a discharge of 150 *l*/s of water?

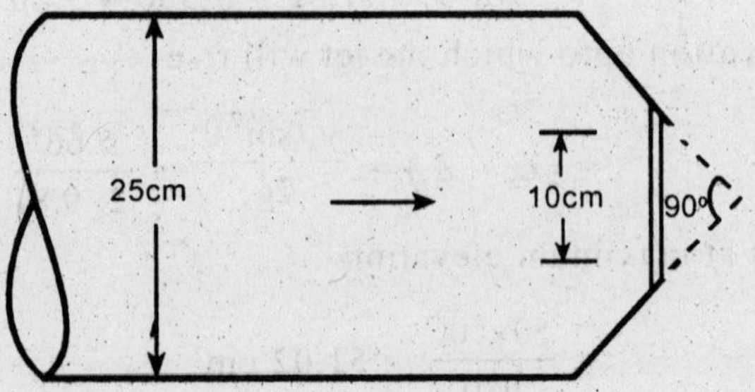

Prob.5.8

5.9 Water flows through a 30 cm × 15 cm venturimeter at the rate of 42.5 *l*/s and the differential gauge is deflected by 115 cm as shown in the figure. If the relative density of the liquid in the differential gauge is 1.25, what is the coefficient of the meter?

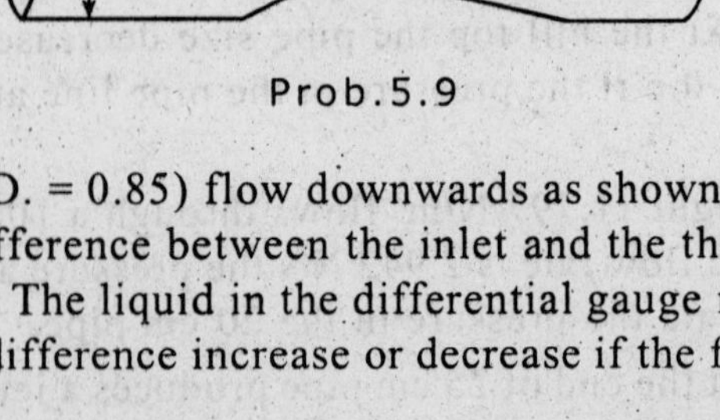

Prob.5.9

5.10 If 70 *l*/s of oil (R.D. = 0.85) flow downwards as shown in venturimeter what will be the pressure difference between the inlet and the throat expressed in terms of differential head ? The liquid in the differential gauge is mercury (R.D. = 13.55). Will the pressure difference increase or decrease if the flow direction is reversed ? Give reasons.

5.11 Calculate the throat diameter required to maintain the same pressure at the inlet and the throat in the vertical venturimeter as shown. The fluid flowing is water.

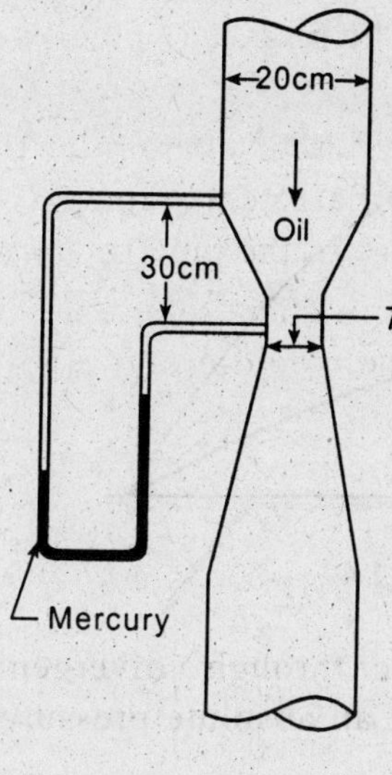

Prob.5.10

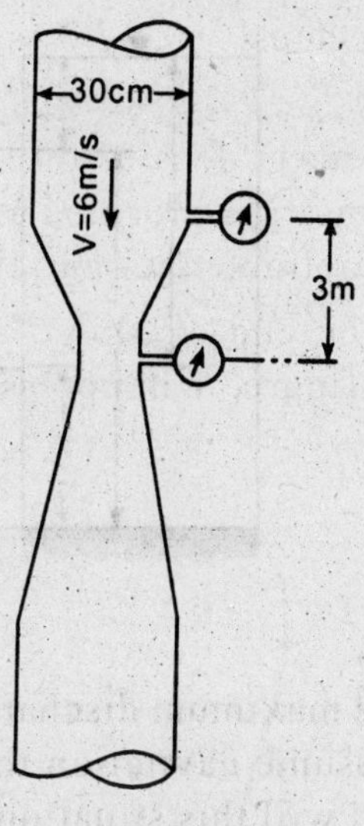

Prob.5.11

5.12 For an air flow of 2.1 m^3/s what is the value of A_2 which will cause water to rise by 2.0 cm in the piezometer shown ? (Air weighs 11.964 N/m^3).

5.13 An open circuit wind tunnel shown in the figure has entrance section 0.8 m^2 and test section 0.09 m^2. An inclined tube connected between A and methyl alcohol (R.D. = 0.80) reservoir shows a rise of 3 cm. Determine the discharge of air and the velocity at the entrance. Take γ for air to be 11.964 N/m^3.

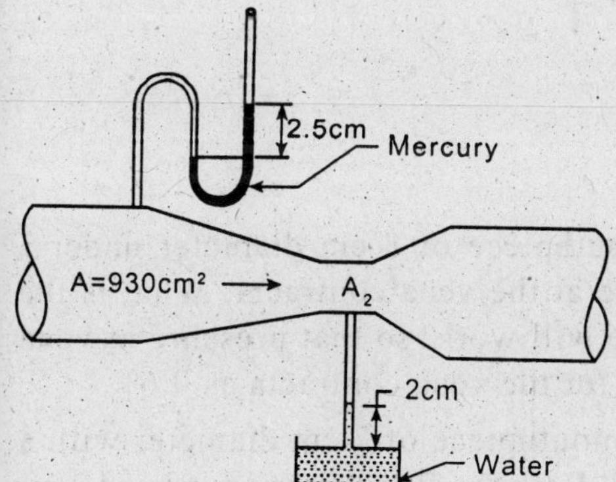

Prob.5.12

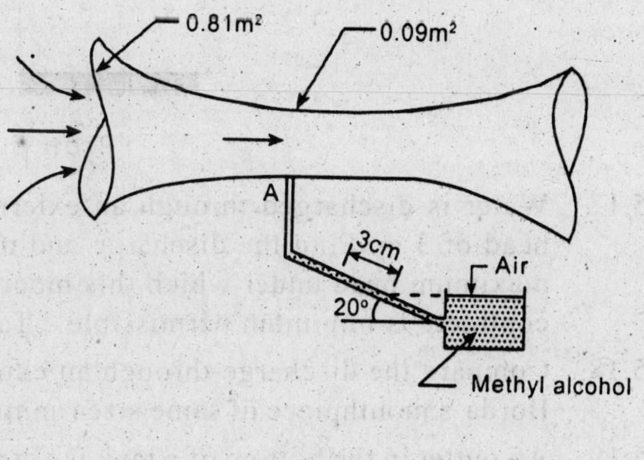

Prob.5.13

5.14 For two orifices placed in the side of tank as shown in the figure, show that $a_1 y_1 = a_2 y_2$ if the two jets intersect a plane through the base of the tank.

5.15 If the depth of water in the tank is 2.0 m at what depth below the free surface should an orifice be located in the side of the tank in order that the jet will attain a maximum horizontal distance from the tank at the base.

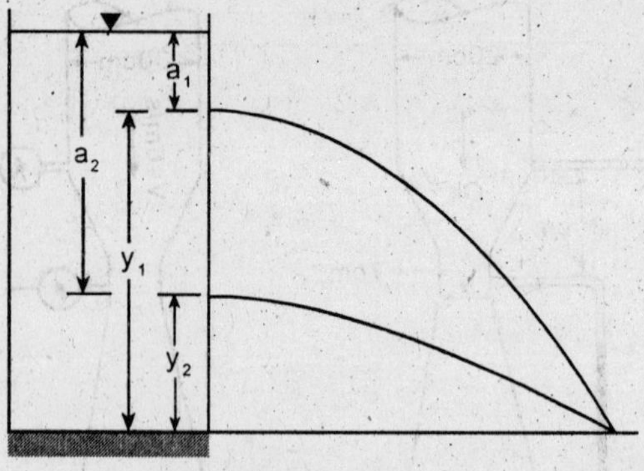

Prob.5.14

5.16 Calculate the maximum discharge of water through a divergent mouthpiece shown in figure. Assume cavitation to occur at an absolute pressure of 6.5 m of water. At what head will this situation occur ?

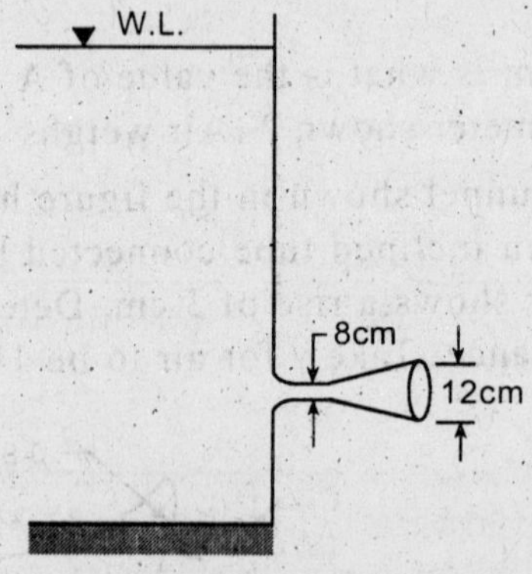

Prob.5.16

5.17 Water is discharged through an external mouthpiece of 8 cm diameter under a head of 3 m. Find the discharge and pressure at the vena contracta. What is the maximum head under which this mouthpiece will work, so that pressure at vena contracta is minimum permissible ? Take C_c for the vena contracta as 0.61.

5.18 Compare the discharge through an external mouthpiece of 7 cm diameter with a Borda's mouthpiece of same size running full. Both are flowing under a head 2 m.

5.19 An outlet in the bottom of a tank is fitted with a vertical tube of length L such that the velocity at the entrance of the tube is 1.5 times the mean velocity in the tube. If the water depth in the tank is 1.0 m, what is the greatest length L of the tube which can be used without producing cavitation ? (Cavitation pressure is 23.536 kN/m^2 absolute). Take atmospheric pressure as 98.066 kN/m^2.

5.20 A rectangular opening 10 cm high is fitted in the end of a long tank as shown in the figure. Determine the discharge per unit width if the coefficient of contraction has a value of 0.63.

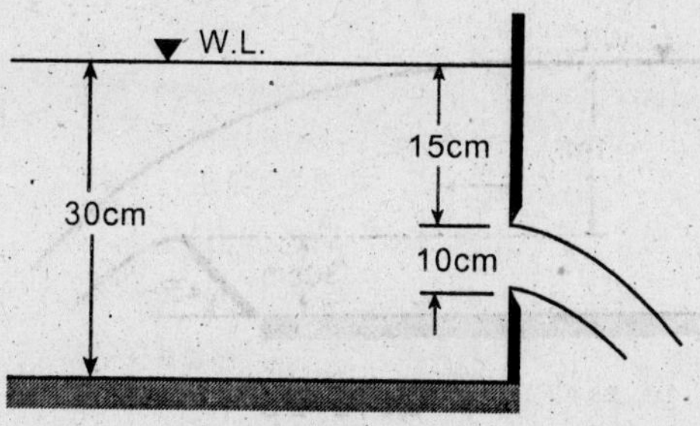

Prob.5.20

5.21 Determine the discharge over a sharp crested weir 4 m long and 1.5 m high if the head over the crest is 1 m.

5.22 A weir is to be installed in the side of a tank for disposing off excess quantity of water. The length of the weir is 15 m and two piers of 60 cm thickness are to be constructed such that the weir length is 13.8 m and the head over the weir is not to exceed 3 m. The approach channel may be assumed as 25 m wide and the weir height to be 3.0 m. Find the discharge over this weir. Take C_d as 0.60.

5.23 A submerged weir of 1.0 m height spans the entire width of 7.0 m wide rectangular channel. Find the discharge when the depth of flow on the upstream side is 1.8 m and on the downstream side it is 1.25 m.

5.24 Develop an expression for the discharge over a V shaped sharp crested weir (commonly known as *triangular notch*) if H is the head over the apex, as shown.

Note –Take a small strip of the thickness dh at a depth of h below surface and express the differential discharge in terms of C_d, h, θ and dh. Integrate the expression between 0 and H to get total flow.

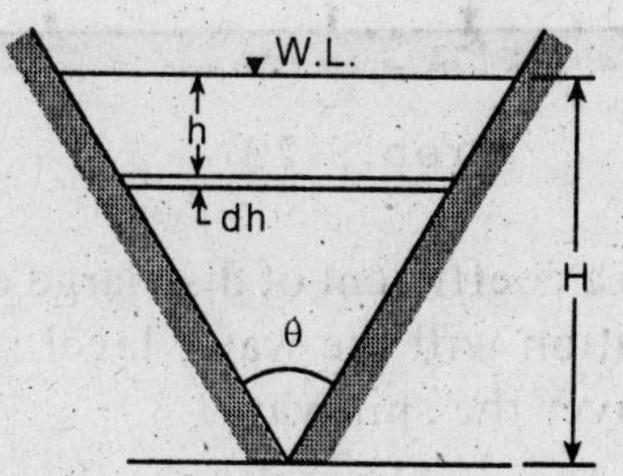

Prob.5.24

5.25 If the discharge over a 90° V-notch is 1.42 m³/s find the head causing the flow. Take C_d to be 0.62.

5.26 Water flows over a weir which has its upstream face inclined at an angle of 45°. If the channel is 3 m wide and has a depth of 1 m above the crest, determine the discharge.

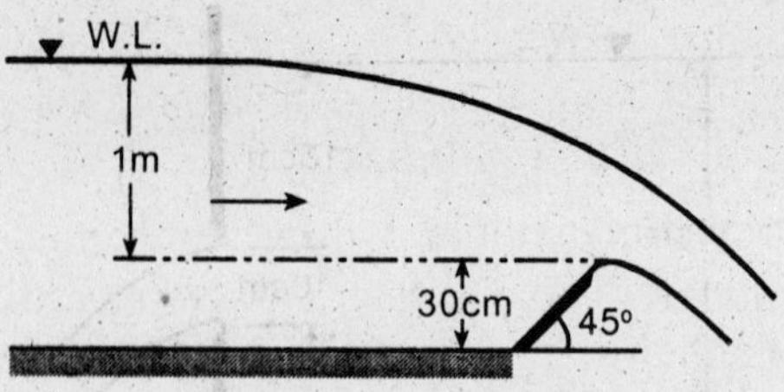

Prob.5.26

5.27 If a weir is designed in such a way that the discharge Q is always proportional to the first power of head H, show that the width B at any head H is given by B = const. $H^{-1/2}$.

5.28 A 1.2 m high contracted weir is to be installed in a 3.5 in wide channel. The maximum flow over the weir is 4.0 m^3/s when the total depth on the upstream of the weir is 2.25 m. What length of the weir should he installed ?

5.29 Find the discharge through the sluice gate 2.0 m wide shown in the figure (i) assuming the submergence of sluice gate opening does not appreciably affect the coefficient of contraction: (ii) using Fig. 5.19.

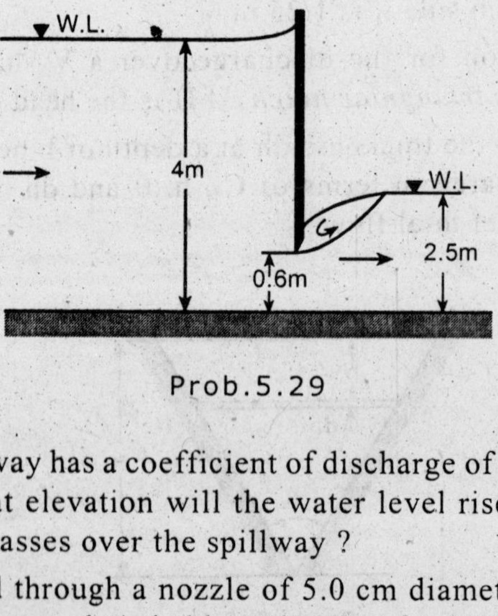

Prob.5.29

5.30 A. 300 m long spillway has a coefficient of discharge of 0.68. If the crest elevation is 100.00, upto what elevation will the water level rise in the reservoir, when a flow of 1500 m^3/s passes over the spillway ?

5.31 Water is discharged through a nozzle of 5.0 cm diameter inclined at an angle of the horizontal. If the nozzle is held at a height of 1.0 m above ground level and if the jet strikes the ground at a horizontal distance of 5.0 m from nozzle, what is the discharge through the nozzle?

5.32 A fireman has to reach a height of 30 m above ground to extinguish a fire in window of a wall with a nozzle of 3.0 cm diameter discharging at the rate of 20l/s. Assuming the fireman has held the nozzle 1.7 m above the ground level, at what maximum distance can he stand and accomplish the job ?

5.33 In a free vortex in air ($\rho = 1.236$ kg/m^3) the velocity at a radius of 1.5 m is 200 m/s and the pressure is 98.07 kN/m^2 absolute. Determine the velocity at radius of 2.5 m. Also determine pressure at that point.

5.34 In a 90° bend in a two-dimensional 3 m wide channel, the sides are concentric circular arcs. The inner radius is 4.0 m and outer radius is 7.0 m. When water flows through this channel there is a pressure difference of 6.864 kN/m^2 between these two sides. Determine the velocities at inner and outer sides of bend assuming free vortex flow.

5.35 In order to aerate the nappe of a vertical sharp crested weir 5.0 m long and 1.5 m high, air is to be supplied at the rate of 0.2 percent of the total discharge when it is specified that the pressure difference on the two sides of the nappe be 4.168 N/m^2. Determine the diameter of the two ventilating pipes that need to be provided, if the head over the weir is 0.50 m. Assume no loss at the entrance.

Chapter Six

Momentum Equation and Applications

6.1 Introduction

In Chapter 3 fluid motion has been studied in relation to the forces that were acting on a fluid. Making use of Newton's second law of motion, an equation of motion for the fluid was developed. However, in order to make use of the equation, energy loss due to internal shear stresses must either be known or must be negligible. Many times such energy loss is not known and therefore details of fluid flow cannot be evaluated. On the other hand, in several engineering problems the details of flow and the knowledge of internal stresses are not required ; however some bulk flow characteristics are sought. In such cases, a different form of equation of motion can be obtained from Newton's second law wherein the information regarding the energy loss due to internal stresses is not required. This is commonly known as the *momentum equation*. In the simplified form of energy equation i.e. Bernoulli's equation, several restrictions were imposed on the character of flow. However, the only assumption in the derivation of the generalized momentum equation is that Newton's second law is applicable. Because of such generality, momentum equation has become as extremely powerful tool in Fluid Mechanics.

6.2 Development of Momentum Equation

Momentum equation to be developed here is analogous to the impulse momentum relationship used in the mechanics of solids. Both are developed from Newton's second law of motion. However, there is an essential difference between the two. The impulse momentum relationship is developed for a discrete body. In the fluid flow, since a continuous flow of the fluid is involved, momentum equation considers a continuous process.

Linear momentum (which will be generally called momentum) in any direction is defined as the mass flowing per unit time multiplied by the velocity in that direction, i.e.

$$M_x = (\rho\ v\ .dA)\ v \cos\theta \tag{6.1}$$

in which $\rho v\ dA$ represents fluid mass per unit time flowing through an elementary area dA, while $v \cos\theta$ is the component of velocity in the direction of *x* axis, see Fig. 6.1. The dimensions of momentum are the same as those of force; hence momentum is a vector quantity. For this reason, momentum equation which relates force and change in momentum is applicable only in a given direction.

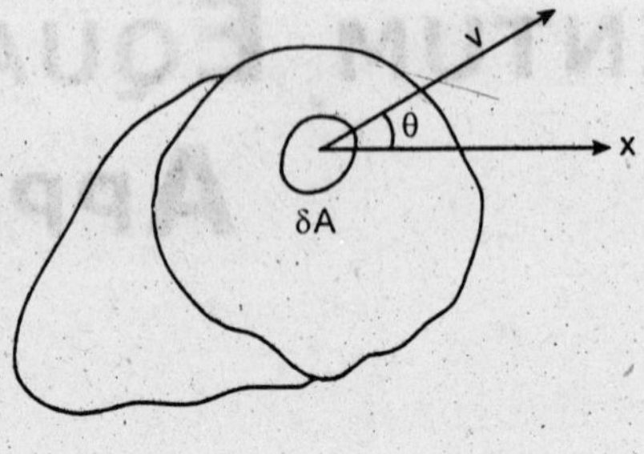

Fig.6.1 Definition sketch

According to Newton's second law of motion the summation of the external forces acting on the body in any direction is proportional to the rate of change of momentum (of the body) in that direction. Considering the forces acting in the direction of *x* axis, one can write,

$$\Sigma F_x = \frac{d}{dt}(m\ v_x) \tag{6.2}$$

in which m is the mass of body and v_x is its velocity in the direction of *x* axis. While applying Newton's second law of motion to a given mass of fluid, it is necessary to consider a control volume, as shown in Fig. 6.2, which is stationary with respect to the co-ordinate frame. At time t_1 it is filled with fluid mass whose momentum, say, in *x* direction, is M_{x1}'. At time $t_2 = t_1 + dt$, some of the fluid mass, which was originally in the control volume, must have gone out and some must have come in. Since the fluid mass is having certain velocity, there will also be a process of some momentum going out and some momentum coming in the control volume. The momentum of the same mass at time t_2 will therefore be (see Fig. 6.2)

$$\left\{\begin{matrix}\text{Momentum of}\\ \text{mass system at}\\ \text{time } t_2\end{matrix}\right\} = \left\{\begin{matrix}\text{Momentum of}\\ \text{mass remaining}\\ \text{in control volume}\end{matrix}\right\} + \left\{\begin{matrix}\text{Momentum of}\\ \text{mass flowed out of}\\ \text{control volume}\end{matrix}\right\}$$

$$- \left\{\begin{matrix}\text{Momentum of}\\ \text{mass flowed into}\\ \text{the control volume}\end{matrix}\right\}$$

$$M_{x2} = M_{x2}' + \delta M_{x0} - \delta M_{xi} \tag{6.3}$$

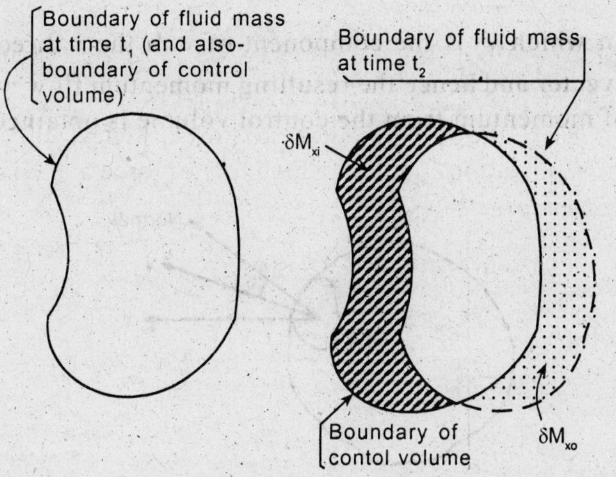

Fig.6.2 Inflow and outflow of momentum in a control volume

Hence the change in momentum in the x direction of the mass system which was originally in the control volume is

$$\delta M_x = (M_{x2} - M'_{x1})$$

or

$$\delta M_x = (M'_{x2} - M'_{x1}) + (\delta M_{xo} - \delta M_{xi}) \tag{6.4}$$

Hence Eq. 6.2 becomes

$$\Sigma F_x = \frac{dM_x}{dt} = \left(\frac{M'_{x2} - M'_{x1}}{dt}\right) + \left(\frac{dM_{x0} - dM_{xi}}{dt}\right) \tag{6.5}$$

Consider the first term on the right hand side. The term $(M'_{x2} - M'_{x1})$ represents the change in momentum inside the control volume. Hence first term indicates the rate of change of momentum inside the control volume. The term $(dM_{x0} - dM_{xi})/dt$ represents the net rate of momentum outflow through the control volume in the direction of x axis. Note that the form of the equation of conservation of linear momentum (Newton's law) as given by Eq. 6.5 applies only in an inertial reference frame. Therefore, the equation and its subsequent simplifications apply only to a nonaccelerating control volume, that is, a nonmoving control volume or one moving with a constant velocity.

Equation 6.5 is the generalized form of momentum equation along x axis. Similar equations can be written along y and z axis. Momentum equation in this form is applicable to steady or unsteady, compressible or incompressible flows with or with out friction. If the flow is steady, the momentum inside the control volume remains same and hence the first term on the right hand side of Eq. 6.5 is zero. In order to write the second term in a simplified and readily calculable form, consider an elementary area dA of the surface of the control volume. Let v be the velocity through area dA and assume that it makes an angle θ with the normal to dA. Then $(\rho dA\ v \cos\theta)$ represents the mass of fluid flowing through area dA per unit time. The momentum flow in the x direction per unit time will be

($\rho dA\ v \cos\theta\ \vec{v}_x$), in which v_x is the component of v in the x direction and the arro indicates that v_x is a vector and hence the resulting momentum flow will have a sign. Th net rate of outflow of momentum from the control volume is obtained by integrating th

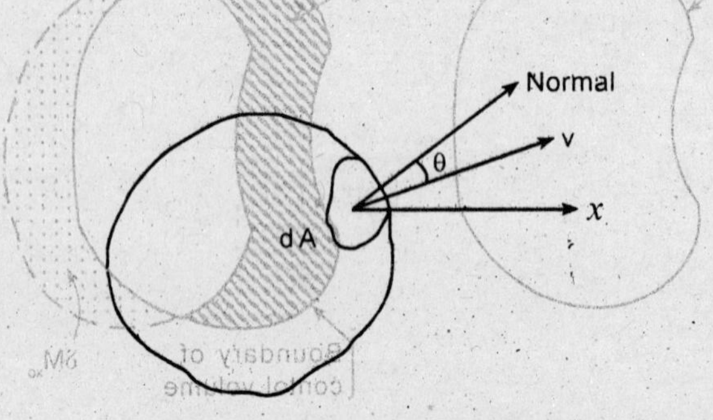

Fig.6.3 Definition sketch

above expression over the surface area A of the control volume.

Hence

$$\frac{dM_{x0} - dM_{xi}}{dt} = \int_A \rho v\, \vec{v}_x \cos\theta\, dA \qquad (6.6$$

For steady state condition, the momentum equation takes the form,

$$\Sigma F_x = \int_A \rho v\, \vec{v}_x \cos\theta\, dA \qquad (6.7$$

and similar equations can be written for forces acting in y and z directions. In man engineering problems a further simplification can be made, viz. in such cases the contr volume can be so chosen that fluid enters through area A_1 and leaves through area A Let V_1, V_2, ρ_1, ρ_2 be the values of mean velocity and mass density of fluid at sections and 2 respectively, see Fig. 6.4. Similarly let θ_1 and θ_2 represent the angles betwee normal to the area and the direction of velocity at sections 1 and 2 respectively. The

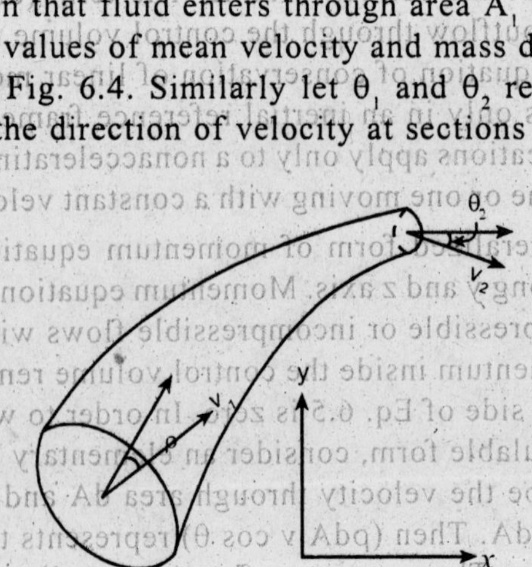

Fig.6.4 Definition sketch

ccording to continuity equation,

$$\rho_1 A_1 V_1 \cos\theta_1 = \rho_2 A_2 V_2 \cos\theta_2$$

e.

$$\rho_1 Q_1 = \rho_2 Q_2 \quad (6.8)$$

n which Q_1 and Q_2 represent volumetric rates of flow of fluid at sections 1 and 2 espectively. Momentum equation now becomes

$$\Sigma F_x = (Q_2 \rho_2 V_{x2} - Q_1 \rho_1 V_{x1})$$

r

$$\left.\begin{aligned} \Sigma F_x &= Q_1 \rho_1 (V_{x2} - V_{x1}) \\ \Sigma F_y &= Q_1 \rho_1 (V_{y2} - V_{y1}) \\ \Sigma F_z &= Q_1 \rho_1 (V_{z2} - V_{z1}) \end{aligned}\right\} \quad (6.9)$$

he forces ΣF_x, ΣF_y and ΣF_z are the external forces acting on the fluid which either ccelerate or decelerate the fluid thereby changing its momentum. The external forces an be forces due to pressure, outside reactions, frictional forces at the boundary of the ontrol volume and the fluid weight. In many problems, however, if the length of the ontrol volume is small, frictional forces at the boundary can be conveniently neglected as in the case of hydraulic jump in open channels, see Chapter 13). The forces ΣF_x, ΣF_y, nd ΣF_z do not include the internal shear stresses which are mutually cancelling. Following e concept of inertial reaction introduced in Chapter 4, one can write Eq. 6.9 as

$$\Sigma F_x - Q_1 \rho_1 (V_{x2} - V_{x1}) = 0 \quad (6.10)$$

nd similar equations for y and z directions. Hence, in such case the external forces are n dynamic equilibrium with the inertial reaction. The inertial force is equal in magnitude nd opposite in direction to the resultant external force in that direction. This is the ' Alembert's principle discussed earlier in section 4.10.

In the application of momentum equation, one must first choose a control volume such at the flow on both sides of the control volume is uniform and thus the region of onuniformity (i.e. region in which the flow is either accelerated or decelerated) is ontained within the control volume. Place on this figure, arrows indicating all the external rces. The direction of unknown force can be assumed. Then apply momentum equation get the unknown force. In all the problems discussed here the fluid weight is neglected e. all the problems are considered in plan in the x y plane. Furthermore, all these problems re of steady state condition.

xample 6.1

etermine the forces exerted by the boundary on the fluid in x and y directions in Fig. .5.

$V_1 = 3.05$ m/s	$V_2 = 12.2$ m/s
$D_1 = 30$ cm	$D_2 = 15$ cm
$p_1 = 206.92$ kN/m² (gauge)	$\theta = 45°$

Mass density of fluid $\rho = 998$ kN/m³

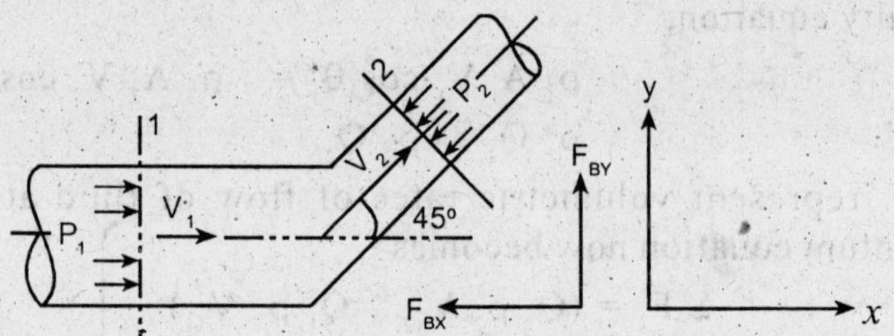

Fig.6.5

Sections 1 and 2 isolate the control volume. On the entire control volume, the atmospheric pressure will also act. However it can be easily seen that atmospheric pressure force acting on the control volume from left to right (in the x direction) is equal to atmospheric pressure force acting from right to left. Similar is the case in the y direction. For this reason only gauge pressures are considered.

Let F_{BX} and F_{BY} be the forces exerted by the boundary on the fluid. They are shown in Fig. 6.5 with the assumed directions.

$$\Sigma F_x = \text{Total force acting in the x direction}$$
$$= (p_1A_1 - p_2A_2 \cos\theta - F_{BX})$$

This must be equal to rate of change of momentum in the x direction i.e. $Q\rho\,(V_2 \cos\theta - V_1)$.

The pressure at section 2 can be found by applying Bernoulli's equation and assuming no loss between sections 1 and 2.

$$\therefore \quad \frac{206.92}{9.787} + \frac{3.05^2}{2\times9.81} = \frac{p_2}{9.787} + \frac{12.2^2}{2\times9.81}$$

$$\therefore \quad \frac{p_2}{9.787} = (21.142 + 0.474 - 7.586)$$

$$\therefore \quad p_2 = 14.03 \times 9.787 = 137.310 \text{ kN/m}^2$$

Therefore

$$(10^3 \times 206.92 \times 0.0706) - \left(10^3 \times 137.31 \times \frac{0.0706}{4} \times 0.707\right) - F_{BX}$$
$$= 0.0706 \times 3.05 \times 998\,(12.20 \times 0.707 - 3.05)$$

$$\therefore \quad F_{BX} = (14\,608.55 - 1713.43 - 1198.15)$$
$$= 11\,696.97 \text{ or } 11.697 \text{ kN}$$

Since this is positive, the assumed direction of F_{BX} is correct. In a similar way, F_{BY} can be found as follows :

$$\Sigma F_Y = F_{BY} - p_2A_2 \sin\theta$$

This must be equal to change in momentum in y direction.

$\therefore \quad Q\rho\,(V_2 \sin\theta - 0) = F_{BY} - p_2 A_2 \sin\theta$

$\therefore \quad F_{BY} = (0.0706 \times 3.05 \times 998)\,(12.2 \times 0.707) + 137.31 \times 10^3 \times (0.0706/4) \times 0.707$

$= 1853.59 + 1713.43 = 3567.02$ N

Resultant force $= \sqrt{11\,696.97^2 + 3567.02^2} = 12\,229$ N or 12.229 kN

Example 6.2

A rocket travels at a velocity of 610 m/s and discharges its exhaust gases at 732 m/s velocity relative to the rocket. The mass rate of exhaust gases is 4.815 kg/s and the exit area is 0.070 m². Assuming the absolute pressure at the exit to be 9.66 N/cm² and outside air pressure to be 8.28 N/cm², find the thrust on the rocket.

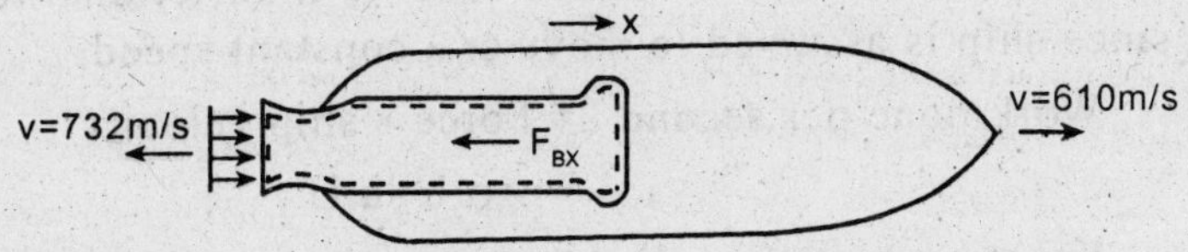

Fig.6.6

The principle of a rocket is quite simple in that the fuel plus oxidizer is burnt in the rocket at a high rate. Either solid or liquid type of fuel is used in the rockets. The combustion gases ejected from the rocket come out at a high velocity. The control volume chosen for the application of momentum equation is shown by dotted line.

The mass of gas which is experiencing a change in momentum is 4.815 kg. Its initial velocity is zero and final velocity V = 732 m/s. To cause this change in momentum, there must be resultant force acting on the gas towards left. The two forces to be considered are the force exerted by the boundary on the gas, which is designated by F_{BX} and a pressure force acting towards right since the outside pressure is higher.

Hence

$$4.815\,(-732.0 - 0) = -F_{BX} + 0.07\,(82\,800 - 96\,600)$$

$$\therefore \quad F_{BX} = 2558.58 \text{ N}$$

This is the force exerted by rocket on the gas. The gas will, in turn, exert a force of 2558.58 N on the rocket towards the right. Since velocity of exhaust gases is given relative to rocket, velocity of rocket need not be known.

Example 6.3

Obtain the relationship for thrust and efficiency for a ship driven by a reaction jet.

Figure 6.7 shows a typical arrangement in a ship propelled by a reaction jet. The water can be sucked in either through side suctions or through front suction and discharged at the rear. Let U be the forward velocity of the ship and u the absolute velocity of the jet. Hence relative velocity of the jet with respect to ship will be $U_r = (U + u)$.

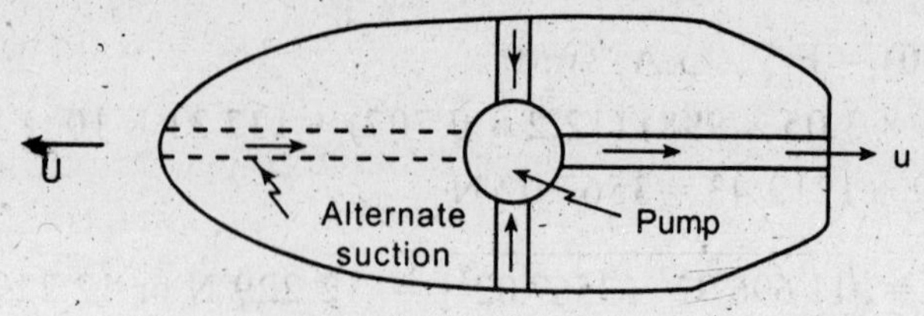

Fig.6.7 Jet propelled ship

The jet discharge $= A\rho U_r$ kg/s

The thrust on the ship $= A\rho U_r (U_r - U)$

$= A\rho U_r u$

where A is the area of the jet. This thrust must be equal to the frictional resistance to the motion of the ship since ship is assumed to move at a constant speed.

Work done per second $=$ Force × ship velocity

$= A\rho U_r u U$

Kinetic energy supplied per second $= (A\rho U_r) U_r^2/2$

The efficiency η of jet propulsion is defined as the ratio of work done per second and kinetic energy of the jet. Therefore

$$\eta = \frac{A\rho U_r u U}{A\rho U_r U_r^2/2} = \frac{2uU}{U_r^2}$$

$$= \frac{2uU}{(U+u)^2}$$

The condition for maximum η will be $d\eta/du = 0$ which yields $u = U$ at which $\eta_{max} = 0.50$. In the case of suction from the front side, the kinetic energy of the water as it enters the suction is $U^2/2$ per unit mass while the kinetic energy as it leaves is $(U + u)^2/2$, i.e. $U_r^2/2$. Hence

$$\eta = \frac{A\rho U_r u U}{A\rho U_r (U_r^2 - U^2)/2}$$

$$= \frac{2uU}{(U_r + U)u} = \left(\frac{2U}{U_r + U}\right)$$

6.3 Momentum Correction Factor

In the above discussion as well as in the examples, it has been assumed that the velocity does not vary across either section 1 or section 2. In other words, the velocity is the same at different points on the cross section of the control volume. However, this may not be so. In fact, in most of the cases the velocity does vary at right angles to the direction of flow due to effect of viscosity and curvature of flow. In such cases, the assumption of constant velocity will give momentum at any section, different from the momentum flux actually flowing. To account for such nonuniformity of velocity at each cross-section, a correction factor β–known as *momentum correction factor*–is introduced. The correction factor is defined in such a way that the momentum flux computed by taking into account the actual velocity distribution is equal to momentum flux computed from average velocity, multiplied by β. In other words,

$$\int_A \rho\, v\, dA\, v_x = \beta Q \rho V_x = \beta A V \rho V_x \qquad (6.11)$$

in which v is the local velocity at area dA (normal to it), V is mean velocity over area A (normal to it) and v_x and V_x are their components in the *x* direction. However, it can be seen that because of conditions of similar triangles,

$$\frac{v}{V} = \frac{v_x}{V_x}$$

Hence Eq. 6.11 can be written as

$$\beta = \frac{1}{A} \int_A \left(\frac{v}{V}\right)\left(\frac{v_x}{V_x}\right) dA$$

or

$$\beta = \frac{1}{A} \int_A \left(\frac{v}{V}\right)^2 dA \qquad (6.12)$$

If the velocity is uniform over the cross-section, β will be equal to unity. If there is considerable variation in the velocity over the cross-section, β will attain a large value. For turbulent flow in open channels as well as in pipes, because of violent mixing between different fluid layers, the velocity is nearly uniform except near the boundary. As a result β is seldom greater than 1.05. Hence for all practical purposes, assumption of β equal to unity is justified. However in laminar flow, the coefficient is large enough to warrant its inclusion in the analysis.

4 Forces on Fixed and Moving Plates

One of the most important applications of momentum equation is in the analysis of forces to which plates and vanes are subjected when fluid jet impinges on them. Such analysis is important in the design of pumps, turbines, propellers, torque converters and such other equipments.

Consider a stationary, smooth plate on which a two dimensional jet of cross-sectional area 'a' impinges obliquely with a velocity V, see Fig. 6.8. Let ρ be the mass density of fluid. Since the jet is exposed to the atmospheric pressure throughout, the pressure is atmospheric every where. Assume the problem to be in horizontal plane. Furthermore, assume no frictional resistance at the plate and no impact loss. Under such conditions, application of Bernoulli's equation yields equal velocity in the two divided jets. Because the pressure is atmospheric and there is no frictional resistance along the plate, there is

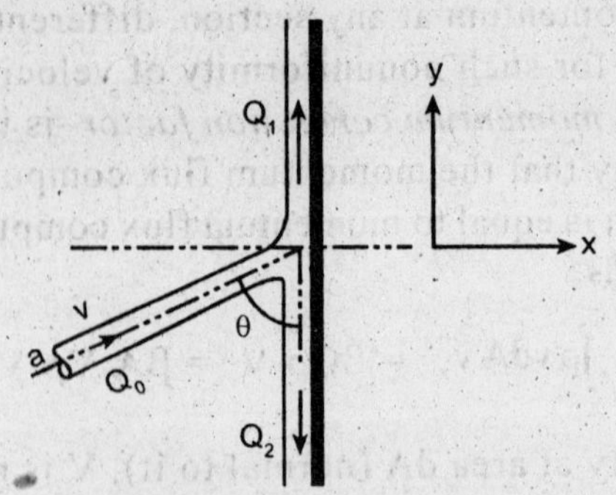

Fig.6.8 Impingement of a jet on plate

no resultant force acting in the direction of plate. For this reason the change in momentum in the direction of plate must be zero. This condition can be made use of in determining the division of discharge. Let Q_1 and Q_2 be the discharges flowing in the two directions ; then

$$(Q_1 \rho V - Q_2 \rho V) - Q_o \rho V \cos\theta = 0 \qquad (6.13)$$

or
$$Q_1 - Q_2 = Q_o \cos\theta \qquad (6.14)$$

Also
$$Q_1 + Q_2 = Q_o \qquad (6.15)$$

Solving Eqs. 6.14 and 6.15, one gets,

$$\left.\begin{aligned} Q_1 &= \frac{Q_o}{2}(1+\cos\theta) \\ Q_2 &= \frac{Q_o}{2}(1-\cos\theta) \end{aligned}\right\} \qquad (6.16)$$

The change in momentum in a direction perpendicular to the plate is

$$Q_o \rho (0 - V \sin\theta) = - Q_o \rho V \sin\theta$$

According to momentum equation

$$\Sigma F_x = - Q_o \rho V \sin\theta \qquad (6.17)$$

Hence the stationary plate will exert a force of magnitude ($Q_o \rho V \sin\theta$) on the fluid in negative x direction. Force exerted by the fluid on the plate will have the same magnitude but will act in positive x direction. Since the plate is fixed, the force that the fluid exerts on the plate cannot do any work.

6.5 Moving Plates and Vanes

In the case of problems concerning design of turbines, pumps etc. one is interested in knowing the forces exerted by the jet on moving plates or vanes, the absolute velocity of the fluid jet when it leaves the plate, and the changes in the kinetic energy that occur during the whole process of deflection of the jet. When a jet of fluid of cross-sectional area "a", velocity V and mass density ρ strikes a plate moving in the same direction with velocity v, the fluid mass that strikes the plate is no longer the fluid mass which would strike against a stationary plate. It is the mass which really overtakes the plate per unit time. Hence in the case of moving plate the mass striking the plate is aρ (V–v). In order to find the changes in the velocity of this fluid mass as it leaves the control volume, either the absolute velocities or the relative velocities at the entrance and exit can be used (since it is the difference that comes in the picture, it makes no difference which one is used).

Example 6.4

A jet of water 5.0 cm in diameter and having a velocity of 18.0 m/s impinges normally on a flat plate. If the plate is moving in the same direction at 3.1 m/s velocity, find the force exerted by jet on the plate, the work done and efficiency of the jet.

Since ρ for water is 998 kg/m³, mass striking the plate per second

$$= 0.785 \times (0.05)^2 \times 998\ (18.0 - 3.1)$$

$$= 29.18 \text{ kg/s}$$

$$F = Q\rho\ (V - v)$$

$$= 29.18 \times 14.90$$

$$= 434.78 \text{ N}$$

$$\text{Work done} = \frac{434.78 \times 3.1}{1000}$$

$$= 1.348 \text{ kW}$$

$$\text{Efficiency of jet} = \text{work done/kinetic energy of jet}$$

$$= 1348/(0.50 \times 29.18 \times 18^{2})$$

$$= 0.286 \text{ or } 28.6 \text{ percent}$$

Example 6.5

A 5.0 cm diameter jet of water having a velocity of 46.0 m/s strikes a vane (see Fig. 6.9) having a deflection angle of 135° and moving at a velocity of 15.0 m/s in the same direction. Assume no friction and compute

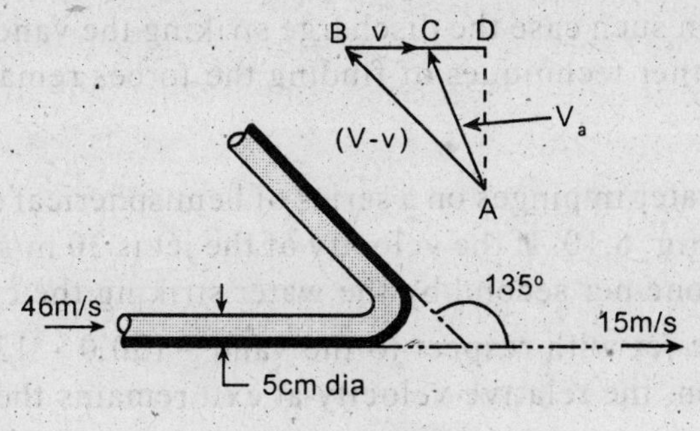

Fig.6.9

i. components of force exerted by the fluid on the vane,

ii. absolute velocity of the jet when it leaves the vane, and

iii. power developed.

The relative velocity of the jet with respect to the vane is (46.0 – 15.0) = 31.0 m/s. Therefore, the discharge striking the vane will be

$$= 0.785 \times (0.05)^2 \times 31.0$$

$$= 0.0608 \text{ m}^3/\text{s}$$

Since there is no friction, the relative velocity as the jet leaves the vane will also be (V–v) = 31.0 m/s. Hence change in momentum in the direction of x axis is

$$\{-(V - v)\cos 45° - (V - v)\} \times 0.0608 \times 998 = \Sigma F_x$$

Since the pressure is atmospheric every where, ΣF_x gives force exerted by the vane on the fluid.

$$\therefore \quad \Sigma F_x = \{(-31.0 \times 0.707 - 31.0)\} \times 0.0608 \times 998$$

$$= -3210.92 \text{ N}$$

$$\Sigma F_y = 0.0608 \times 998(31.0 \times 0.707 - 0) = 1329.89 \text{ N}$$

The force exerted by the fluid on the vane will be

$$F_x = +3210.92 \text{ N and } F_y = -1329.89 \text{ N}$$

The absolute velocity of the jet at exit can be obtained by combining relative velocity with vane velocity vectorially as shown by the velocity triangle.

$$AD = 31.0 \sin 45° = 21.92 \text{ m/s}$$

$$CD = (BD–BC) = (21.92–15.0) = 6.92 \text{ m/s}$$

Hence absolute velocity at exit

$$V_a = AC = \sqrt{21.92^2 + 6.92^2} = 22.99 \text{ m/s}$$

Power developed will be

$$= (3210.92 \times 15)/1\,000 = 48.164 \text{ kW}$$

No work is done by the force F_y since the vane is not moving in that direction.

A single vane used in this way, however, is not quite efficient for development of power. Hence a series of vanes are arranged in such a way that one of the vanes is always deflecting the jet. In such case the discharge striking the vane is $a\rho V$ even though the vane is moving. The other techniques of finding the forces remain the same.

Example 6.6

A 7.5 cm. diameter jet of water impinges on a series of hemispherical cups and is deflected through 180° as shown in Fig. 6.10. If the velocity of the jet is 30 m/s and that of the cups is 12 m/s, find the work done per second by the water striking the cups.

Relative velocity of the jet with respect to the vane = (30.0 – 12.0) m/s = 18.0 m/s. Because there is no friction, the relative velocity at exit remains the same.

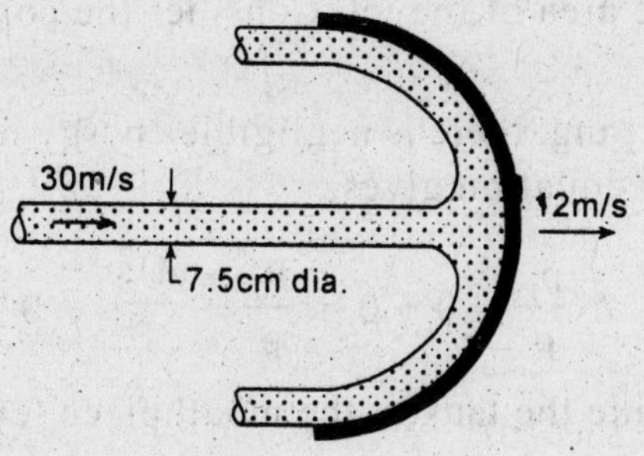

Fig.6.10

Mass of fluid striking the vane per second

$= 0.785 \times (0.075)^2 \times 30 \times 998$

$= 132.20$ kg/s

Hence, the force exerted by the fluid on the vane,

$= - Q\rho\,[-(V - v) - (V - v)]$

$= 132.20 \times 2 \times 18$

$= 4759.2$ N

Work done per second $= \dfrac{4759.2 \times 12}{1000}$

$= 57.11$ kW

6.6 Applicability of Energy and Momentum Equations

While analysing the problems in fluid mechanics, one is primarily interested in knowing one or more of the following quantities : mean velocity, velocity distribution, distribution of pressure, total force and shear stress at the boundary or frictional resistance. Some of these quantities are known and the others need to be found. Depending on the nature of the problem, this information can be obtained by using either momentum equation or energy equation or both.

It must be remembered that the momentum equation and the energy equation have been derived from the same basic principle, viz. Newton's second law of motion. However, they are independent of each other, and hence they are independently useful. The reason for such independence is that the momentum equation does not depend on energy losses due to internal viscous shear and energy equation does not depend on the external boundary shear.

A summary in tabular form, about the abilities of momentum and energy equation in handling the problems, is given in Table 6.1. To illustrate the combined application of energy and momentum equation some more examples will now be discussed.

(a) *Flow Through Borda's Mouthpiece*

A tube projecting inside the tank is commonly known as Borda's mouthpiece or re-entrant tube. The coefficient of contraction of such a mouthpiece can be analytically determined by the application of energy equation and momentum equation. Let A be the cross-sectional area of tube and "a" be the area of the jet. Consider the control volume as shown by the dotted lines in Fig. 6.11.

Since the flow is converging, there is negligible energy loss as the jet comes out of the mouthpiece. Hence energy equation gives,

$$\frac{p_1}{\rho} + 0 + 0 = \frac{P_0}{\rho} + \frac{U^2}{2} + 0$$

in which p_1 is pressure inside the tank at the mouthpiece level,

TABLE 6.1

Capabilities of Momentum and Energy Equations

	Momentum Equation	Energy Equation
Applicable	To any fluid flow, provided an acceleration term is considered when the flow is unsteady.	To steady flows in which the energy changes are zero or are known independently.
Information required	Velocity distribution in the stream at one end of the control volume and either, total forces (pressure and shear) on the boundaries of control volume or velocity distribution at the other end of control volume	Velocity and pressure at one point on the stream line with independent knowledge of energy changes and either, pressure variation along streamline or velocity variation along streamline.
Solution gives	Average final velocity of stream or total force.	Velocity variation along stream line or Pressure variation along stream line.
Solution will not give	Actual velocity distribution within the control volume or at the boundaries, or distribution of pressure and shear forces.	Tangential forces due to friction.
Best application	When energy changes are unknown and only an overall knowledge of the flow is required e.g. total resultant forces and mean velocities	When energy changes are known and detailed information of flow is required e.g. velocity pressure distribution.

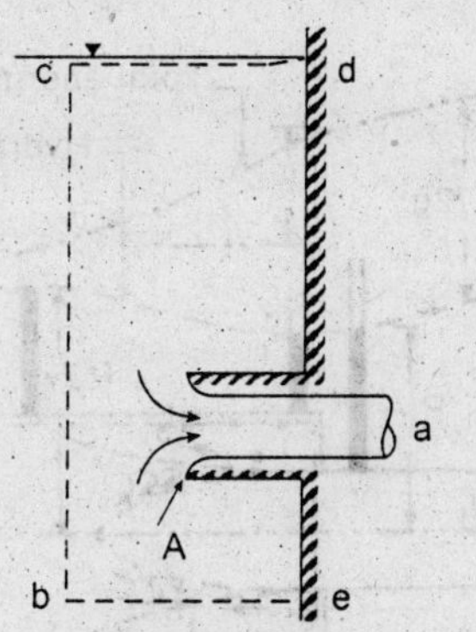

Fig.6.11 Borda's mouthpiece

p_o is atmospheric pressure and U is the jet velocity. Hence

$$\frac{p_l - p_0}{\rho} = \frac{U^2}{2} \quad (6.18)$$

Since the tube is projecting inside the tank, the fluid particles close to the side de have no motion and hence the pressure distribution along the sides de and bc are identical. The only force causing change in the momentum is the pressure force difference aver the area A at bc and de. Hence,

$$(p_l - p_0) A = Q \rho U \quad (6.19)$$

Lastly, continuity equation gives $Q = a U$ (6.20)

Solving Eq. 6.18, 6.19 and 6.20, one gets $\frac{a}{A} = \frac{1}{2}$

Hence, the coefficient of contraction of Borda's mouthpiece is 0.50.

(b) *Sudden Expansion in Pipes*

The energy loss that occurs when a pipe of a given diameter suddenly expands to a larger diameter can be found out by applying energy equation, momentum equation and continuity equation. At the place where the pipe diameter increases abruptly, the flow separates away from the boundary and there are regions of separation as shown in Fig. 6.12. At some distance downstream, the flow follows the pipe wall. As the flow is expanding the velocity continuously decreases in the downstream direction Hence there is a gradual rise in the piezometric head.

Consider the control volume shown by dotted lines. Let p_l and p_2 represent the pressures at sections 1 and 2. Let D_l and D_2 be the diameters and U_l and U_2 the velocities at these sections. It is experimentally found that the pressure against the annular ring joining the two pipes is the same as the pressure in the smaller diameter pipe. Hence pressure force over the upstream face of control volume is $(A_2 - A_l)\, p_l + p_l A_l$ i.e.. $p_l\, A_2$. Momentum equation gives

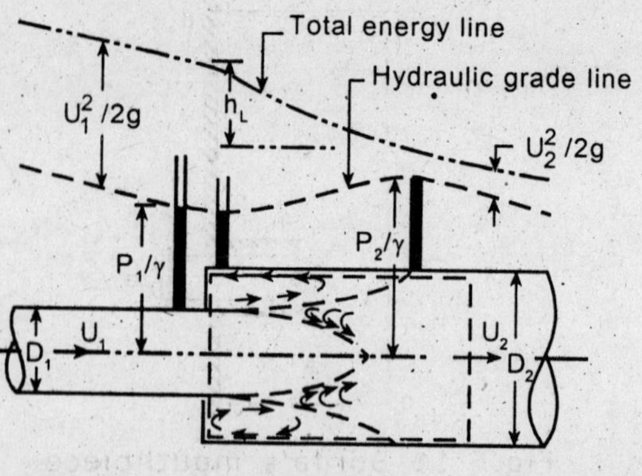

Fig.6.12 Sudden expansion in a pipe

$$(p_1 A_2 - p_2 A_2) = Q \rho (U_2 - U_1) \tag{6.21}$$

Here A_1 and A_2 are the areas at sections 1 and 2 respectively. In writing Eq. 6.21, boundry friction and component of gravity force in flow direction are assumed to be negligible. According to continuity equation,

$$A_1 U_1 = A_2 U_2 \tag{6.22}$$

Combining Eqs. 6.21 and 6.22

$$A_2 (p_2 - p_1) = A_2 U_2 \rho (U_1 - U_2)$$

or

$$\frac{(p_2 - p_1)}{\rho} = U_1 U_2 - U_2^2 \tag{6.23}$$

Applying energy equation between sections 1 and 2, one gets,

$$\frac{p_1}{\rho} + \frac{U_1^2}{2} = \frac{p_2}{\rho} + \frac{U_2^2}{2} + g h_L \tag{6.24}$$

in which h_L is the head loss between two sections due to expansion. Here it is assumed that the pipe expansion is horizontal. Substituting the value of $(p_2 - p_1)/\rho$ from Eq. 6.23 in Eq. 6.24, one gets

$$U_1 U_2 - U_2^2 = \frac{U_1^2}{2} - \frac{U_2^2}{2} - g h_L$$

or

$$h_L = \frac{1}{2g} (U_1^2 - 2 U_1 U_2 + U_2^2)$$

or

$$h_L = \frac{(U_1 - U_2)^2}{2g} \tag{6.25}$$

Similarly head loss in a hydraulic jump in an open channel can be found by the combined use of energy equation and momentum equation. This has been discussed in Chapter 13.

6.7 Angular Momentum

Up till now attention was focused on rectilinear motion only. Next consider a fluid mass rotating about a given axis. Consider a fluid mass δm which is rotating about the z axis. Let x and y be its co-ordinates (see Fig. 6 13) and V_x and V_y be its velocity components in x and y directions respectively. If $a_x = (dV_x/dt)$ and $a_y = (dV_y/dt)$ represent the acceleration components of the fluid mass, then according to Newton's second law of motion, one gets

$$dF_x = \delta m \frac{dV_x}{dt}$$

and

$$dF_y = \delta m \frac{dV_y}{dt}$$

where dF_x and dF_y are components of external forces causing the acceleration. The torque produced (counter clockwise being considered positive) $d\tau_z$ about z axis is

$$d\tau_z = dF_y . x - dF_x . y$$

$$= \delta m \, x \frac{dV_y}{dt} - \delta m \, y \frac{dV_x}{dt}$$

∴

$$d\tau_s = \delta m \left(x\frac{dV_y}{dt} - y\frac{dV_x}{dt} \right) \qquad (6.26)$$

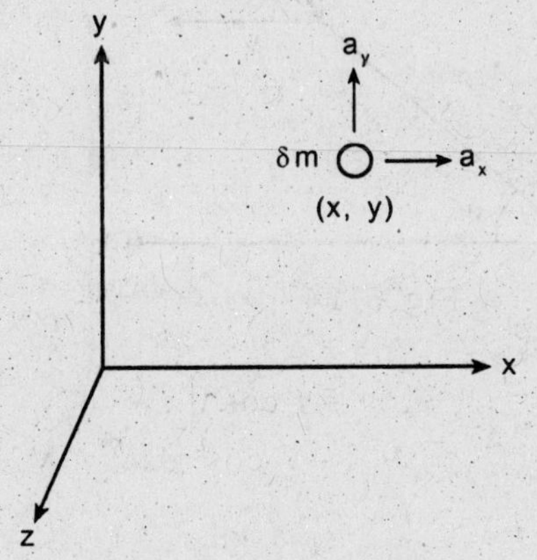

Fig.6.13 Definition sketch

Add and subtract $\delta m \, V_x V_y$ to right hand side of Eq. 6.26. However $V_x V_y$ can be written either as $V_x \frac{dy}{dt}$ or $V_y \frac{dx}{dt}$. Hence add $\delta m \, V_y \frac{dx}{dt}$ and subtract $\delta m \, V_x \frac{dy}{dt}$ from the right hand side of Eq. 6.26.

$$d\tau_z = \delta m \left\{ x\frac{dV_y}{dt} + V_y\frac{dx}{dt} - y\frac{dV_y}{dt} - V_x\frac{dy}{dt} \right\}$$

$$= \delta m \frac{d}{dt}\{xV_y - yV_x\}$$

$$d\tau_z = \frac{d}{dt}\{\delta m\, x\, V_y - \delta m\, y\, V_x\} \qquad (6.27)$$

since δm does not depend on t. The quantities $x\delta m\, V_y$ and $y\, \delta m\, V_x$ represent the moments of momentum about z axis. This moment of momentum is known as *angular momentum*.

Therefore, $\frac{d}{dt}(x\, \delta m\, V_y - y\, \delta m\, V_x)$ represents the rate of change of angular momentum about z axis and this is equal to the external torque applied. Hence, the resultant external torque about any axis is equal to the rate of change of angular momentum about that axis.

With respect to Fig. 6.14 the term $(x\, V_y - y\, V_x)$ can be expressed as follows.

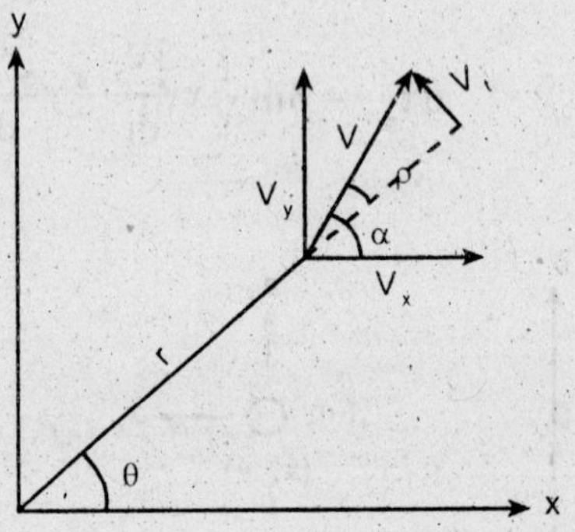

Fig.6.14

$$x = r\cos\theta\,; \qquad y = r\sin\theta$$
$$V_x = V\cos\alpha\,; \qquad V_y = V\sin\alpha$$

Hence

$$(xV_y - yV_x) = r\cos\theta\, V\sin\alpha - r\sin\theta\, V\cos\alpha$$
$$= r\, V\sin(\alpha - \theta) = r\, V_t$$

in which V_t is the tangential velocity. Following a procedure similar to derivation of momentum equation, one can write

$$\tau_z = Q\,\rho\,(r_2\, V_{t2} - r_1\, V_{t1}) \qquad (6.28)$$

for steady flow. Here r_2 and V_{t2} are the radius and tangential velocity at section 2 and r_1 and V_{t1} the same quantities at section 1.

The concepts of torque and angular momentum are useful in the design and study of the performance of turbines, pumps and fans. Flows through such machines as turbines undergo change in angular momentum because the blades derive torque from the flow; in the case of compressors, the torque is imposed on the blades and the fluid increases its angular momentum.

Example 6.7

For a frictionless shaft in the rotating sprinkler shown in Fig. 6.15 and equal flow through each nozzle (relative velocity V_r = 10 m/s), find its speed of rotation.

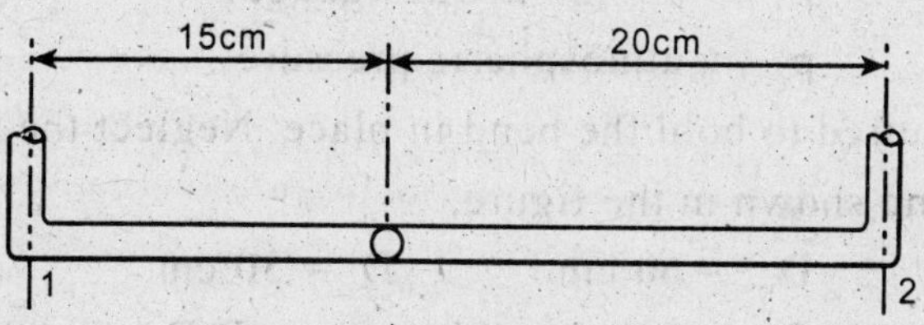

Fig.6.15

The sprinkler will rotate in the clockwise direction. Since the fluid entering the sprinkler has no angular momentum and since no external torque is applied to the system, the moment of momentum of the fluid leaving the sprinkler must be zero.

$$\therefore \quad r_1 Q \rho V_{t1} - r_2 Q \rho V_{t2} = 0$$

where V_{t1} and V_{t2} are absolute velocities of jet at nozzles 1 and 2 respectively.

$$V_{t1} = V_r + r_1 \omega \text{ and } V_{t2} = V_r - r_2 \omega$$

where ω is the angular velocity of sprinkler. Hence

$$Q \rho (10 - 0.20 \omega) \times 0.20 = Q \rho (10 + 0.15 \omega) \times 0.15$$

$$\therefore \quad 2.0 - 0.04 \omega = 1.5 + 0.0225 \omega$$

$$\therefore \quad \omega = \frac{0.50}{0.0625} = 8.0 \text{ rad/s}$$

$$N = \frac{60 \times 8}{2 \times 3.142} \; 76.38 \text{ rpm}$$

PROBLEMS

6.1 A 30 cm diameter pipe is reduced to 5 cm diameter by means of a nozzle. If the pipe carries 65 *l*/s of water which is then discharged into the atmosphere, determine the force exerted by water on the pipe assembly. Neglect frictional loss.

6.2 A 2.5 cm diameter nozzle is connected to a 7.5 cm diameter pipe. If the pressure at the upstream end of the nozzle is 514.85 kN/m² (gauge), what will be the force exerted by the nozzle on the water if the water is discharged in atmosphere?

6.3 For a 90° pipe bend shown in the figure, if pipe diameter 30 cm, Q = 330 *l*/s

p_1 = 138.27 kN/m² (gauge)

p_2 = atmospheric pressure

find the force required to bold the bend in place. Neglect the bend losses.

6.4 For a 90° pipe bend shown in the figure,

D_1 = 60 cm D_2 = 30 cm

Q = 900 *l*/s of kerosene (R.D. = 0.80)

p_1 = 299.1 kN/m² (gauge)

If the bead loss between section 1 and 2 is 0.90 m of kerosene, determine F_{BX} and F_{BY} the forces exerted by the bend on the fluid.

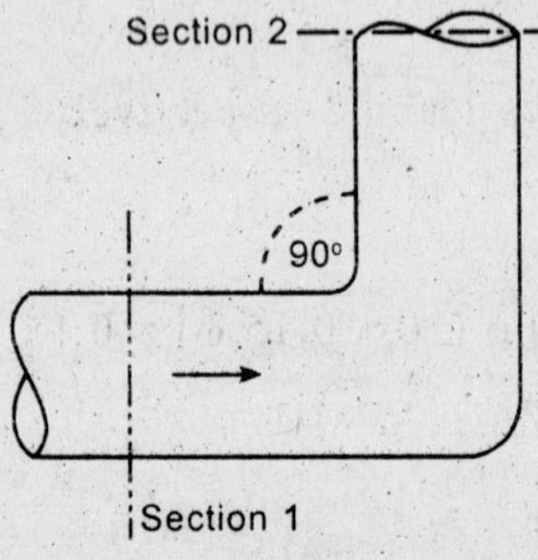

Prob.6.3

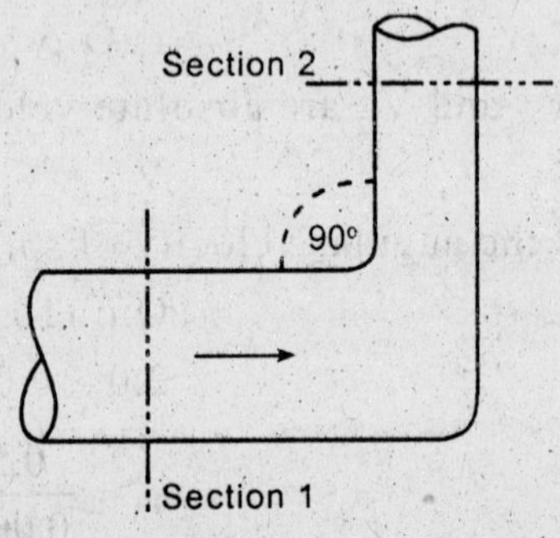

Prob.6.4

6.5 For a 60° pipe bend shown, the following data are given :

D_1 = 15 cm D_2 = 10 cm

V_1 = 6 m/s p_1 = 205.94 kN/m² (gauge)

If water is flowing through the bend and if there is no energy loss in the bend, determine the resultant force required to hold the bend in place.

6.6 Calculate the components of the force exerted by the jet on the tank shown in figure, if the tank is moving at 3 m/s towards right.

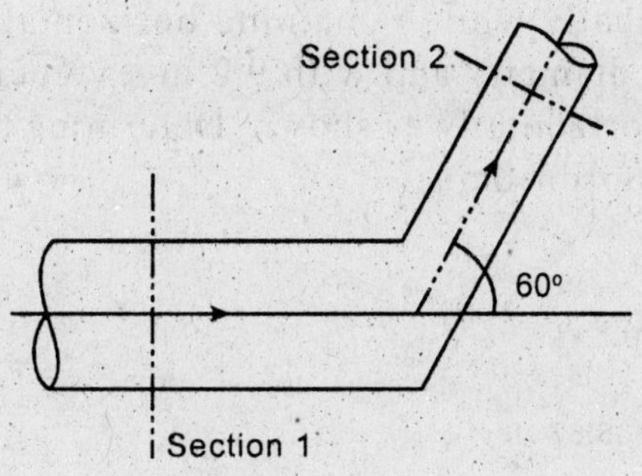

Prob.6.5

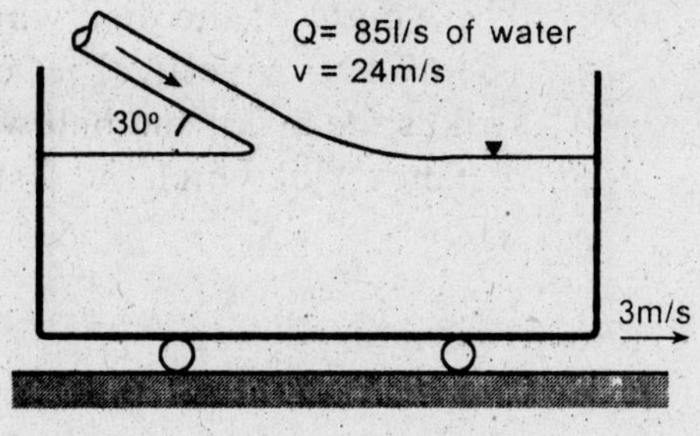

Prob.6.6

6.7 Find the momentum correction factor in the cases shown in the figure.

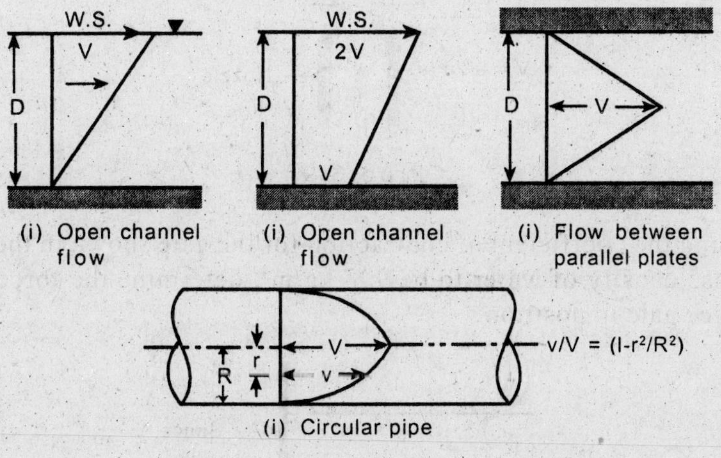

Prob.6.7

6.8 For a two dimensional water jet deflected as shown, determine F_{BX} and F_{BY}. Take volume of water on the block as 0.2 m^3 per unit width.

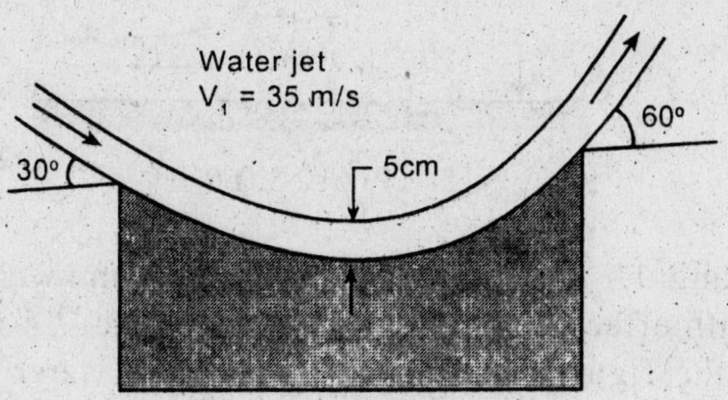

Prob.6.8

6.9 The weight of the disk which can move vertically while remaining horizontal is 168.67 kN. A vertical jet of water 7.5 cm in diameter and with 9.2 m/s velocity strikes the disk from below and is deflected horizontally as shown. Determine the distance Y at which the disk will be held in equilibrium.

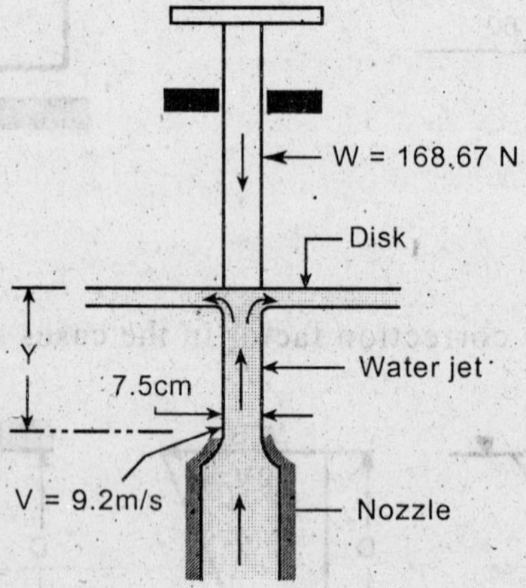

Prob.6.9

6.10 Assuming the coefficient of contraction for the gate shown in the figure to be 0.60 and mass density of water to be 998 kg/m³, determine the force required to hold the sluice gate in position.

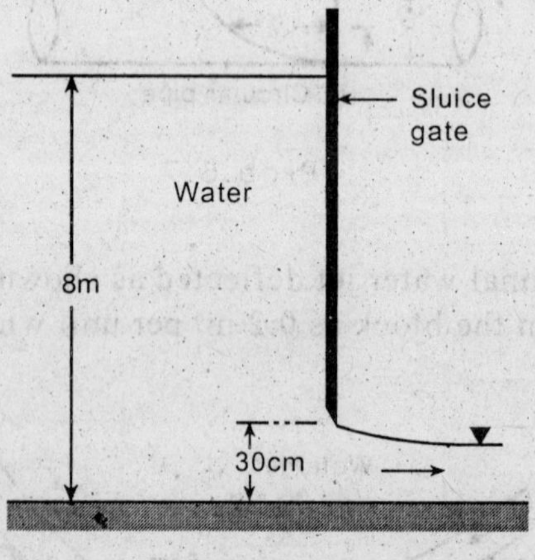

Prob.6.10

6.11 A closed rectangular tank 1m × 1m × 4 m height and weighing 1177.0 N has a hole in the side with effective area 6.5 cm² and situated 15 cm above the tank bottom as shown in the figure. The tank is filled with water to a depth of 3 m. If the coefficient of friction between the ground and the wheels is 0.01, determine the air pressure in the tank that is required to move the tank.

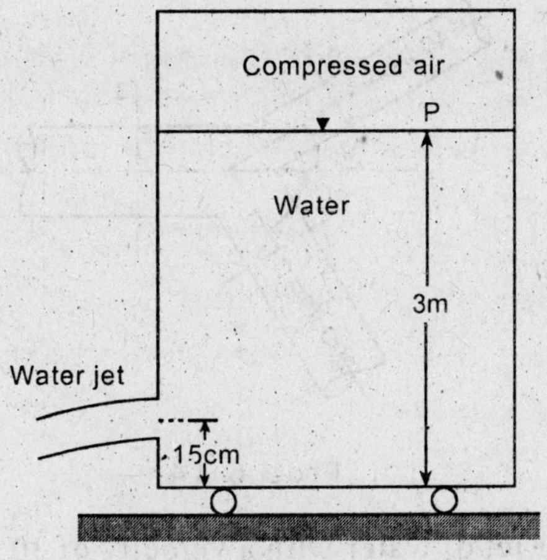

Prob.6.11

6.12 A rocket which exhausts the gases at a rate of 39.23 N/s develops a thrust of 4903.3 N. The exit diameter of the nozzle is 3.5 cm and the gases are exhausted at a pressure of 117.68 kN/m³. Assuming the atmospheric pressure surrounding the rocket to be 88.26 kN/m², determine the speed of exhaust gases.

6.13 The profile drag of an airfoil can be computed by the application of momentum equation. Experiments conducted in a free air stream gave the velocity distributions as shown in the figure. Assuming the pressures at sections 1 and 2 to be same, determine the drag force per unit length. Take ρ to be 1.226 kg/m³.

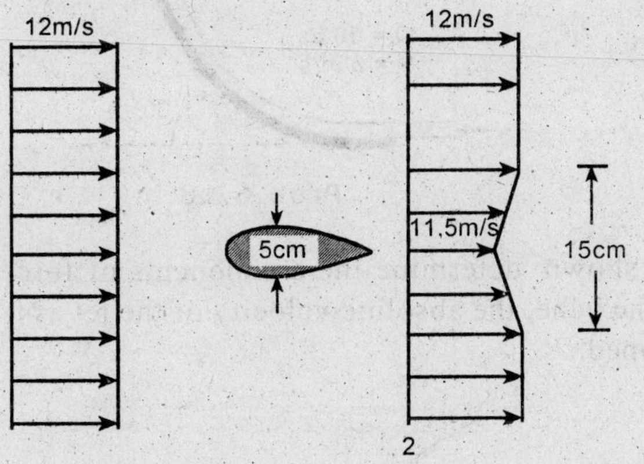

Prob.6.13

6.14 Find the resultant force acting on the pipe junction shown in the figure if

D_1 = 20 cm	D_2 = 15 cm	D_3 = 30 cm
p_3 = 245.165 kN/m²		Q_1 = 200 l/s
Q_2 = 140 l/s	θ_1 = 60°	θ_2 = 30°

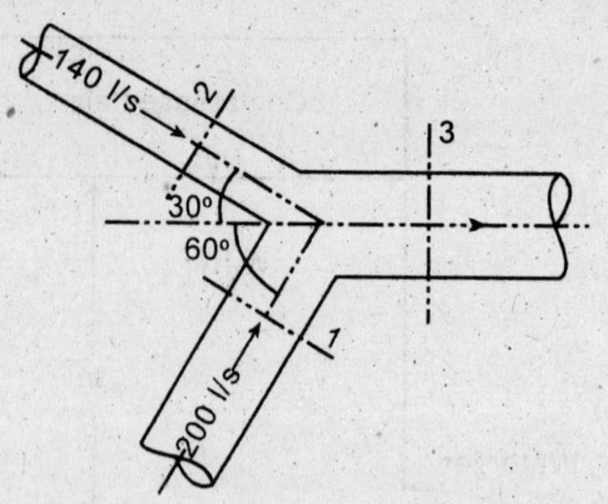

Prob.6.14

6.15 A 6.0 cm diameter jet of water with a velocity of 30 m/s strikes a stationary plate held at right angles to the flow. Determine the force exerted by the fluid on the plate.

6.16 A 2.5 cm diameter jet of water strikes against a plate held perpendicular to the flow, and exerts a force of 784.53 N. Determine the discharge.

6.17 If the plate in Problem 6.15 is moving in the same direction as the flow with a velocity of 5 m/s, determine the force on the plate and the power developed.

6.18 Determine the force exerted by the circular water jet on the curved stationary vane, shown in the figure.

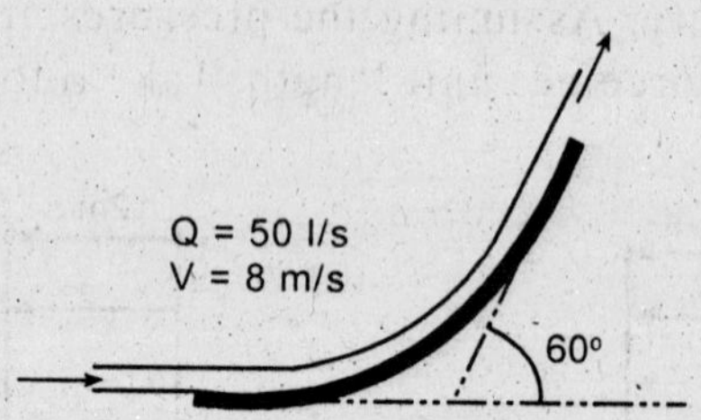

Prob.6.18

6.19 In the figure shown, determine the components of force exerted by the circular water jet on the vane, the absolute velocity of the jet as it leaves the vane, and the power developed.

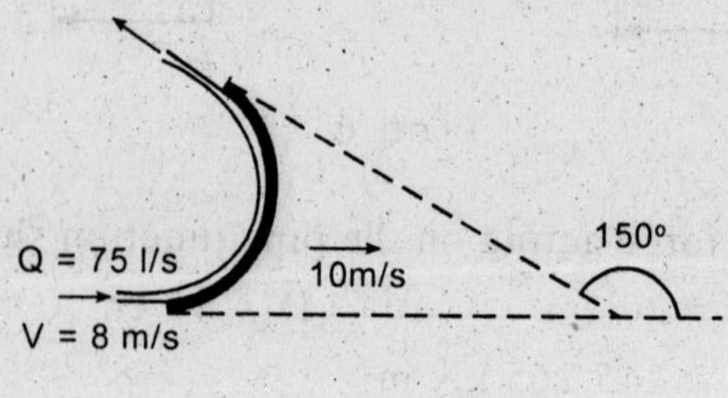

Prob.6.19

6.20 A 5.0 cm diameter jet of water issuing at 20 m/s impinges on a series of vanes moving at a velocity or 5.0 m/s in the same direction. Determine the force on the plate, work done, and the efficiency.

6.21 A stationary curved vane having an inlet angle of zero degrees and an outlet angle of 25° leaves water at a velocity of 50m/s. Determine the components or force acting on the vane. Also calculate the work done if the vane is moving in the same direction at a velocity of 20 m/s. Perform the calculations for unit rate of mass flow.

6.22 A boat driven by jet propulsion, discharges water at a speed of 20 m/s relative to the ship in a jet of 0.02 m² cross-sectional area. If the boat velocity is 20 km/hr, find the resistance to motion, power of the jet and efficiency. Take the inlet opening to face the flow.

6.23 A lawn sprinkler which has 1cm diameter nozzle at the end of a rotating arm, discharges water at 8.0 m/s velocity as shown. Determine the torque required to hold the rotating arm stationary. Neglect the friction and determine the constant speed of rotation of the arm.

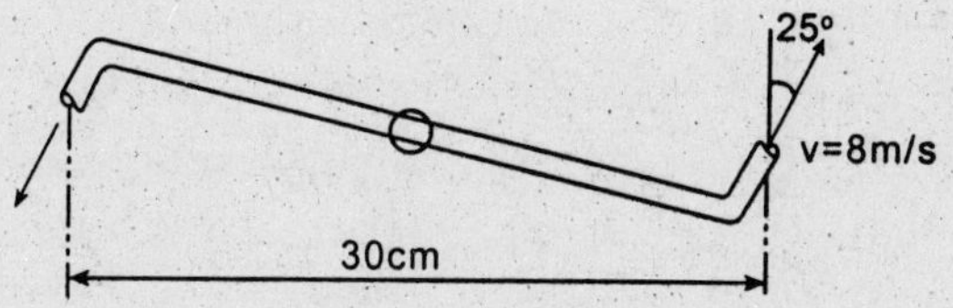

Prob.6.23

CHAPTER SEVEN

DIMENSIONAL ANALYSIS AND SIMILITUDE

7.1 Introduction

Any phenomenon in physical sciences and engineering such as fluid mechanics, soil mechanics, physics, chemical engineering, electrical engineering can be described by making use of quantities such as mass, acceleration, force, temperature, viscosity, stress, etc. With the rapid development of each of these branches, the engineers and scientists every day come across new problems which need to be analysed. Some of these problems can be solved analytically; however, there are many others which are so complicated and involved that they cannot be completely solved by analytical methods. The solutions of such problems are considerably simplified by using the method of *dimensional analysis*.

Dimensional analysis is a method by which one obtains certain information about a phenomenon on the assumption that the phenomenon can be described by a dimensionally homogeneous equation among certain variables. Dimensional analysis, when properly used, is a powerful tool and yields valuable information. It is used for research purposes, for developing design criteria, checking the theoretical development and for conducting model tests. In order to study the principles of dimensional analysis, a preliminary discussion about dimensions and dimensionally homogenous equations is necessary.

7.2 Dimensions

As mentioned earlier, the engineers and scientists use various physical quantities to describe a given phenomenon. These quantities can be described by a set of fundamental or *primary units*. These primary units are mass, length, time and temperature designated by M,L,T and θ respectively. Using Newton's second law of motion, viz

$$\text{Force} = \text{Mass} \times \text{Acceleration},$$

one can alternatively consider force as a primary unit instead of mass. Once a particular set of primary units is chosen, the units of all other physical quantities can be expressed from their definition in terms of the primary units. The expression for a derived unit of measurement in terms of the primary unit is called the *dimension of the physical quantity*. Thus the dimensions of velocity which is defined as distance travelled per unit time, can be expressed as

$$[\text{Velocity}] = \frac{[\text{Distance}]}{[\text{Time}]} = \left[\frac{L}{T}\right]$$

The rectangular bracket signifies that the dimensions of the quantity are being considered. In the same way the dimensions of acceleration and force are

$$[\text{Acceleration}] = \frac{[\text{Change in Velocity}]}{[\text{Time}]} = \left[\frac{L}{T^2}\right]$$

$$[\text{Force}] = [\text{Mass}] \times [\text{Acceleration}] = \left[\frac{ML}{T^2}\right]$$

One may choose any particular system of units for defining the primary variables, viz. MKS or FPS system. In this way, the dimensions of various physical quantities can be found. It may be mentioned that while studying the electromagnetic theory one uses a unit charge [Q] as another primary unit. Table 7.1 gives the dimensions of various physical quantities.

7.3 Physical Quantities in Fluid Flow

Limiting the discussion to the problems concerning fluid flow, one can classify the various physical quantities in the following categories:

(a) Variables Describing Fluid Properties

Mass density (ρ), specific weight (γ), dynamic viscosity (μ), kinematic viscosity (ν), volume modulus of elasticity (E), and coefficient of surface tension (σ).

Table 7.1

Dimensions of Physical Quantities

Quantity	Dimensions	Quantity	Dimensions
Velocity	LT^{-1}	Angular velocity	T^{-1}
Acceleration	LT^{-2}	Angular acceleration	T^{-2}
Mass density	ML^{-3}	Force	MLT^{-2}
Specific weight	$ML^{-2}T^{-2}$	Work or energy	$ML^{2}T^{-2}$
Power	$ML^{2}T^{-3}$	Frequency	T^{-1}
Momentum	MLT^{-1}	Angular momentum	$ML^{2}T^{-1}$
Pressure	$ML^{-1}T^{-2}$	Strain	$M^{o}L^{o}T^{o}$
Torque	$ML^{2}T^{-2}$	Surface tension	MT^{-2}
Dynamic viscosity	$ML^{-1}T^{-1}$	Kinematic viscosity	$L^{2}T^{-1}$
Heat	$ML^{2}T^{-2}$	Specific heat	$L^{2}T^{-2}\theta^{-1}$

(b) Variable Describing Flow Characteristics

Velocity (U), angular velocity (ω), acceleration (a), pressure (p), force (F), discharge (Q), work, energy, etc.

(c) Variables Describing Geometry

Length l, area, volume, angle, etc.

Any phenomenon under consideration may not involve all these variables but only a few. Suppose one considers the case of period of oscillation of a simple pendulum. It is known that the period of oscillation t depends only on its length l and the gravitational acceleration g. Here t is the dependent quantity or variable, while l and g are independent variables. Dependent variable is the one about which information is required. Independent variables are the ones which govern the variation of dependent variable and whose values can be changed.

One may pose the question in the following way. What is the length of the pendulum which gives a certain period of oscillation for given value of g? It will be realized that under such condition l becomes the dependent variable and t and g the independent variables. Thus it may be noted that the terms independent and dependent variables are interchangeable, depending on how the problem is posed.

While using the method of dimensional analysis, it is necessary to ensure that only one dependent variable is included at each time. The independent variables on which this variable depends must be guessed logically, and this requires some insight into the mechanism of the problem. However, in the present discussion it will be assumed that the independent variables are known.

7.4 Dimensionally Homogenous Equations

If the dimensions of the term on the left and the right hand sides of a given equation are the same, the equation is said to be dimensionally homogenous. Consider the equation for the period of oscillation of a simple pendulum

$$t = 2\pi\sqrt{\frac{l}{g}} \tag{7.1}$$

It is known that 2π has no dimensions since it is a pure number. The dimensions of $\sqrt{(l/g)}$ are $[L/(L/T^2)]^{1/2} = [T]$. Thus the dimensions of terms on both sides of Eq. 7.1 are the same and hence it is dimensionally homogenous.

Other dimensionally homogenous equations are:

Flow over weir $$q = \frac{2}{3} C_d \sqrt{2g}\, H^{3/2} \tag{7.2}$$

Laminar flow in pipes $$\Delta p = \frac{32\pi U l}{D^2} \tag{7.3}$$

Turbulent flow in pipes $\Delta p = f \dfrac{l}{D} \dfrac{\rho U^2}{2}$ (7.4)

In the above equations, Δp is the loss of pressure in a length l of pipe of diameter D, U is the average velocity in pipe and other quantities have their usual meaning. By actual substitution of the dimensions of various quantities, it can be verified that Eqs. 7.2, 7.3 and 7.4 are homogenous and that f and C_d are dimensions quantities. In general, any physical law obtained by rational analysis gives dimensionally homogenous equation. It may be further stated that if an equation is dimensionally homogenous, the value of constants in such equations remains unchanged even if the system of units is changed, i.e. such an equation can be used without modification in either MKS or FPS system of units.

There are several equations which are dimensionally nonhomogeneous, e.g.

$$U = 0.84\, y_o^{0.64}$$

is Kennedy's equation relating average velocity to depth of flow y_0 in alluvial channels. Since it is a dimensionally nonhomogeneous equations, in the form it is given, it can be used only in FPS units with U in ft/s and y_0 in ft. If MKS system of unit is used, the constant 0.84 will change. For this reason, one must exercise great care in using dimensionally nonhomogeneous equations. Example 7.1 illustrates how such equation can be changed so that it can be used in other system of units.

Example 7.1

The equation $U = 90\sqrt{RS}$ gives the relation between velocity U, hydraulic radius R and channel slope S for steady uniform flow in an open channel with cement plastered surface. This equation is valid for MKS units. Modify it so that it can be used in FPS system.

The equation can be written as

$$U = K\sqrt{RS}$$

In which K will have the dimensions

$$[K] = \frac{L/T}{L^{1/2}} = \frac{L^{1/2}}{T} \text{ or } \frac{m^{1/2}}{s}$$

Thus in the above equation K is 90 $m^{1/2}/s$.

Since 1m = 3.28ft it follows that

$$K = 90\,\frac{m^{1/2}}{s} = 90\,[3.28]^{1/2} = 163\,\frac{ft^{1/2}}{s}$$

Consequently, when the above formula is adopted for FPS system of units, it becomes

$$U = 163\sqrt{RS}$$

7.5 Characteristics of Homogeneous Equations

Equation 7.1, 7.2, 7.3 and 7.4 which are dimensionally homogeneous, can be written as

$$\frac{t}{\sqrt{l/g}} = 2\pi \tag{7.1a}$$

$$\frac{q}{\sqrt{gH^{3/2}}} = \frac{2}{3} C_d \sqrt{2} \tag{7.2a}$$

$$\frac{\Delta pD}{\pi U} = 32\left(\frac{l}{D}\right) \tag{7.3a}$$

$$\frac{\Delta p}{\rho U^2/2} = f\left(\frac{l}{D}\right) \tag{7.4a}$$

The following table lists the number of variables, the number of primary units which describe these variables, and the number of dimensionless groups in which the equation is arranged. A dimensionless group or parameter is one which has no dimensions.

Eq. No.	n Number of variables	m Number of primary units	Number of dimension-less groups
7.1 a	3, (l, g, t)	2, (L, T)	1
7.2 a	4, (q, g, H, C_d)	2, (L, T)	2
7.3 a	5, (Δp, μ, U, l, D)	3, (M, L, T)	2
7.4 a	6, (Δp, ρ, U, l, D, f)	3, (M, L, T)	3

From this analysis the following observations can be made:

i. All dimensionally homogeneous equations can be expressed in the form of equations involving only dimensionless groups.

ii. The number of dimensionless groups that can be formed is equal to the number of variables minus the number of primary units.

7.6 Buckingham's π Theorem

Suppose that certain information is sought about a given phenomenon. Let x_1 be the dependent variable and let x_2, x_3, x_4, x_5, x_6 be the independent variables on which x_1 depends. Then,

$$x_1 = f(x_2, x_3, x_4, x_5, x_6) \tag{7.5}$$

in which f stands for the expression "is a function of". Eq.7.5 can also be written as

$$f_1(x_1, x_2, x_3, x_4, x_5, x_6) = 0 \tag{7.6}$$

According to the definition of dimensional analysis one can assume that the phenomenon under consideration is expressible in the form of a dimensionally homogeneous equation among the above listed variables. In other words, Eq. 7.6 must be dimensionally homogenous.

The discussion in the preceding paragraph has shown that, if Eq.7.6 is dimensionally homogeneous, it can be written in terms of a number of dimensionless groups which will be equal to (number of variables minus the number of primary units) i.e., (n–m). Hence Eq. 7.6 can be written as

$$f_2(\pi_1, \pi_2, \pi_3) = 0 \tag{7.7}$$

assuming m = 3. Here π_1, π_2, π_3 are the dimensionless groups. The principle embodied in the above discussion is commonly known as *Buckingham's π theorem*. It can be stated as follow:

If there are n variables which govern a certain phenomenon and if these variables involve m primary units, then the phenomenon can be described by (n – m) independent dimensionless parameters.

These (n – m) dimensionless parameters namely π_1, π_2, π_3... π_{n-m} are independent of one another. In other words one cannot get π_1, as a combination of two or more of remaining parameters. Same statement holds good for π_2, π_3. π_{n-m}. It is for this reason that π_1, π_2, π_3. π_{n-m} are said to form a *complete set* of dimensionless parameters formed from the variables x_1, x_2, x_3 .... x_n.

It may be mentioned that there are certain exceptions to this theorem; Example 7.7 illustrates such a case.

7.7 Calculation of Dimensionless Parameters

The method of calculation of dimensionless parameters will be explained by means of an actual example. Assume that a certain phenomenon is governed by the following variables:

Volume modulus of elasticity E, force F, length l, velocity U, dynamic viscosity μ, gravity g, mass density of fluid ρ, and surface tension σ.

These eight variables E, F, l, U, μ, g, ρ and σ involve three primary units M, L, and T and hence the number of independent dimensionless parameters is (8–3) = 5. These parameter are :

$$\frac{U}{\sqrt{E/\rho}} = \text{Mach Number M}$$

$$\frac{F/l^2}{\rho U^2/2} = \text{Drag coefficient or pressure coefficient } C_D$$

$$\frac{UL\rho}{\mu} = \text{Reynolds number Re}$$

$$\frac{U}{\sqrt{gl}} = \text{Froude number Fr}$$

$$\frac{\rho U^2 l}{\sigma} = \text{Weber number W}$$

Several observations can be made concerning these parameters. These are as follows:

(a) The variables E, F, μ, g and σ occur only once. Thus E occurs only in Mach umber and not in others; similarly μ occurs only in Reynolds number. For this reason it is ot possible to form, say, Mach number by combining two or more of the remaining imensionless parameters. In other words M, C_D, Re, Fr, and W form a complete set of imensionlest parameters, made from E, F, *l*, U, ρ, μ, g, and σ.

(b) The variables U, *l* and ρ occur in all the five dimensionless parameters, as the eed arises, to make E, F, μ, g and σ dimensionless. Hence U, *l*, ρ are aptly called *epeating variables*, while E, F, μ, g and σ are known as *nonrepeating variables*. If ne can isolate repeating variables from nonrepeating variables, the problem of forming imensionless parameters becomes easy, because, all the repeating variables will then ombine with each one of the nonrepeating variables, to form dimensionless groups. heoretically any three repeating variables could have been chosen. The maximum number f dimensionless group $\overline{N}$ that can be formed from n variables in m primary units, is iven by

$$\overline{N} = \frac{n!}{(m+1)!\,(n-m-1)!}$$

hus with n = 8 and m = 3, $\overline{N}$ = 70. However all these can be expressed as combination five dimensionless parameters given above. From the point of view of physical gnificance, these five dimensionless parameters are the most significant. The choice of peating variables is governed by the following considerations:

(i) The number of repeating variables should be equal to the number of primary units hich describe the given variables. (ii) As far possible, the dependent variable should not included in the repeating variables. This limitation arises from the fact that, if the pendent variable occurs in more than one dimensionless parameter, the resulting mogenous equation is not explicit. (iii) The repeating variables should be such that gether they contain all the primary units and they do not combine among themselves to rm a dimensionless parameter. (iv) For problems in Fluid Mechanics, a geometrical aracteristic, one fluid property and one flow characteristic are a good choice of repeating riables. It must be emphasized that the dimensionless groups obtained depend entirely the choice of repeating variables.

(c) If in certain problem the variables include, say, two lengths or two velocities or o mass densities they will yield dimensionless parameters comprising ratios of lengths, locities or mass densities.

(d) Once the repeating variables are chosen, it is known that they will combine with each one of the nonrepeating variables to form the various dimensionless numbers. Suppose U, l, ρ are these repeating variables and F is one of the nonrepeating variables. A certain combination of F, U, l, and ρ must, then yields a dimensionless parameter π_1. One can write.

$$\pi_1 = F^a U^b l^c \rho^d = M^0 L^0 T^0$$

since π_1 is dimensionless. Writing dimensions of all quantities the above equation can be written as

$$M^0 L^0 T^0 = \left[\frac{ML}{T^2}\right]^a \left[\frac{L}{T}\right]^b [L]^e \left[\frac{M}{L^3}\right]^d$$

By equating the exponents of M, L, and T, the following equations are obtained:

$$a + d = 0$$

$$a + b + c - 3d = 0$$

$$-2a - b = 0$$

The three simultaneous equations have four unknowns. These can be solved in terms of any one unknown say "a"

Hence $\quad d = -a,\ b = -2a$

and $\quad c = -3a + 2a - a$

i.e., $\quad c = -2a$

Therefore,

$$\pi_1 = \frac{F^a}{U^{2a}\, l^{2a}\, \rho^a} = \left(\frac{F}{\rho l^2 U^2}\right)^a$$

It is immaterial what value is assigned to a. If $a = 1$, $\pi_1 = (F/\rho\, l^2 U^2)$. Any other value will give some power of $(F/\rho\, l^2 U^2)$. In this way other dimensionless parameters can be computed.

This method of dimensional analysis will now be applied to several problems.

Example 7.2

If the critical depth y_c in a right angled triangular channel depends on the discharge Q and gravitational acceleration g, obtain an expression for y_c.

Assuming the relationship between these variables is dimensionally homogeneous, method of dimensional analysis can be applied. There are three variables involving two primary units. Hence the number of dimensionless parameters is one.

Let $\quad y_c = \text{const. } Q^a g^b$

Writing the dimensions of each variable and equating the exponents of L and T, one gets

gets

$$L^1 = \left[\frac{L^3}{T}\right]^a \left[\frac{L}{T^2}\right]^b \quad \text{or} \quad \left.\begin{aligned} 3a + b &= 1 \\ -a - 2b &= 0 \end{aligned}\right\}$$

which give, $a = \frac{2}{5}$ and $b = -\frac{1}{5}$

Hence $$y_c = \text{const.}\ \frac{Q^{2/5}}{g^{1/5}} = \text{const.}\ \sqrt[5]{\frac{Q^2}{g}} \tag{7.8}$$

or $$\frac{y_c}{\sqrt[5]{\frac{Q^2}{g}}} = \text{constant}$$

Example 7.3

The viscous force F_D exerted by the fluid on a sphere of diameter D depends on viscosity μ, mass density of fluid ρ and velocity of the sphere U. Perform the dimensional analysis.

The dependence of F_D can be expressed as

$$F_D = f(D, \mu, \rho, U)$$

According to Buckingham's π theorem it can be assumed that the above equation is dimensionally homogeneous. Since there are five variables involving three primary units, the number of dimensionless parameters is two. Choosing U, D and ρ as the repeating variables, these two parameters will be

$$\pi_1 = F_D\ U^a\ D^b\ \rho^c$$

$$\pi_2 = \mu\ U^{a_1}\ D^{b_1}\ \rho^{c_1}$$

It may be noticed that the exponents of F_D and μ are arbitrarily chosen as unity. Writing the dimensions of each quantity, one gets

$$[\pi_1] = M^0\ L^0\ T^0 = \left[\frac{ML}{T^2}\right] \left[\frac{L}{T}\right]^a [L]^b \left[\frac{M}{L^3}\right]^c$$

and $$[\pi_2] = M^0\ L^0\ T^0 = \left[\frac{M}{LT}\right] \left[\frac{L}{T}\right]^{a_1} [L]^{b_1} \left[\frac{M}{L^3}\right]^{c_1}$$

Solution of the simultaneous equations obtained by equating the exponents of M, L, and T in these two expressions gives

$$a = -2 \qquad a_1 = -1$$
$$b = -2 \quad \text{and} \quad b_1 = -1$$
$$c = -1 \qquad c_1 = -1$$

Hence $\pi_1 = \dfrac{F_D}{\rho D^2 U^2}$ and $\pi_2 = \dfrac{UD\rho}{\mu}$

Therefore, $$\frac{F_D}{\rho D^2 U^2} = f\left(\frac{UD\rho}{\mu}\right) \tag{7.9}$$

Thus for spheres, the drag coefficient $C_D = (F_D/\rho\ U^2\ D^2)$ is a function of Reynolds number Re. Figure 12.4 shows the experimentally determined relationship between $F_D/\ (\pi D^2/4)\ (\rho U^2/2)$ and $UD\rho/\mu$ for the sphere.

It might be mentioned that by choosing another set of repeating variables, one can get different dimensionless parameters. If μ, D and ρ are the repeating variables, the two parameters obtained are $(F_D\rho/\mu^2)$ (i.e., $F_D/\rho\nu^2$) and $(UD\rho/\mu)$. Which of these two set of parameters is significant depends on the type of information required (See Sec.12.5)

Example 7.4

The pressure drop Δp in a pipe of diameter D and length l depends on mass density of the fluid ρ and viscosity μ of the fluid flowing, average velocity of flow U, and on the average height of protuberances of pipe surface k. Obtain a dimensionless expression for Δp.

It can be seen that,

$$\Delta p = f\,(U,\ l,\ D,\ k,\ \rho,\ \mu)$$

Since there are seven variables and three primary units, the number of dimensionless groups will be four. In order to form significant dimensionless groups, the repeating variables chosen are U, D and ρ. A question may arise as to why l or k was not chosen as the repeating variable in place of D. The length l comes in picture only as related to Δp, and as such one might as well take $(\Delta p/l)$ as a single variable. Similarly k cannot be varied easily in experimental work. For these reasons D is chosen as the most significant length parameter. The four dimensionless parameters are,

$$\pi_1 = \Delta p\ U^a\ \rho^b\ D^c$$

$$\pi_2 = l\ U^{a_1}\ \rho^{b_1}\ D^{c_1}$$

$$\pi_3 = k\,U^{a_2}\ \rho^{b_2}\ D^{c_2}$$

$$\pi_4 = \mu\,U^{a_3}\ \rho^{b_3}\ D^{c_3}$$

By following a procedure similar to one used in Example 7.3. it can be seen that the four dimensionless parameters are

$$\pi_1 = \frac{\Delta p}{\rho U^2},\ \pi_2 = \frac{l}{D},\ \pi_3 = \frac{k}{D} \text{ and } \pi_4 = \frac{UD\rho}{\pi}$$

Hence $$\frac{\Delta p}{\rho U^2} = f\left(\frac{l}{D}, \frac{k}{D}, \frac{UD\rho}{\pi}\right)$$

Since Δp will increase linearly as l increases, the above equation can be written as

$$\frac{\Delta p}{\rho U^2} = \frac{l}{D} f\left(\frac{k}{D}, \frac{UD\rho}{\pi}\right) \tag{7.10}$$

It may be mentioned that in the above problem, more than one length parameter was involved; hence two dimensionless ratio obtained were ratios of lengths viz. (l/D) and (k/D).

Example 7.5

The discharge Q through a rotating machine such as a pump, a turbine or a compressor depends on the shaft work (gH), power supplied P, speed of rotation N, characteristic length D, fluid density ρ and viscosity μ. Obtain a set of significant dimensionless parameters.

There are seven variables involving three primary units; hence according to Buckingham's π theorem, there will be (7–3) = 4 dimensionless group. Choosing N, ρ and D as the repeating variables, the following parameters are obtained,

$$\pi_1 = Q\, N^a\, \rho^b\, D^c$$

Therefore, $$M^0 L^0 T^0 = \left[\frac{L^3}{T}\right]\left[\frac{1}{T}\right]^a\left[\frac{M}{L^3}\right]^b [L]^c$$

which gives, $$a = -1,\ c = -3 \text{ and } b = 0$$

Hence $$\pi_1 = \frac{Q}{ND^3}$$

Similarly $$\pi_2 = PN^{a_1}\, p^{b_1}\, D^{c_1} \text{ and it yields}$$

$$\pi_2 = \frac{P}{\rho N^3 D^5}$$

Similarly $$\pi_3 = \frac{(gH)}{N^2D^2} \text{ and } \pi_4 = \frac{\rho ND^2}{\mu}$$

Thus $$\frac{Q}{ND^3} = f\left(\frac{P}{\rho N^3 D^5}, \frac{gH}{N^2D^2}, \frac{\rho ND^2}{\mu}\right) \tag{7.11}$$

If the compressibility of the fluid E were also included, an additional dimensionless group ($E/\rho N^2 D^2$) would have obtained.

Example 7.6

The loss of pressure Δp for laminar flow in a pipe is a function of pipe length l, its diameter D, average velocity U, and the dynamic viscosity μ. Obtain an expression for the pressure loss.

Since there are five variables involving three primary units, the number of dimensionless group will be two. Assume the expression for Δp to be of the form

$$\Delta p = \text{Const. } U^a\, \mu^b\, l^c\, D^d$$

or writing the dimensions of each variable one gets,

$$\left[\frac{M}{LT^2}\right] = \left[\frac{L}{T}\right]^a \left[\frac{M}{LT}\right]^b [L]^c [L]^d$$

Equating the exponents of M, L, T, the following three equations are obtained

$$b = 1$$

$$a - b + c + d = -1$$

$$-a - b = -2$$

Since there are three equations and four unknowns, all can be expressed in terms of on unknown, say c. Hence

$$b = 1,\ a = 1 \text{ and } d = -(1 + c)$$

Therefore expression for Δp becomes

$$\Delta p = \text{const}, \mu U \frac{l^c}{D^{1+c}} = \text{const.} \frac{\pi U}{D}\left(\frac{l}{D}\right)^c \quad (7.12$$

Experimentally c is found to be equal to unity, and constant equal to 32. This method c obtaining dimensionless parameters is known as Rayleigh's method. Equation (7.12) ca be written as

$$\frac{\Delta p \cdot D}{\mu U} = \text{const.} \left(\frac{l}{D}\right)^c$$

Example 7.7

If the capillary rise h in a tube of radius R depends on the specific weight γ and surfac tension σ of the fluid, perform the dimensional analysis.

The functional relationship can be written as

$$h = f(R, \gamma, \sigma)$$

The dimensions of h, R, γ and σ are L, L, M/L^2T^2 and M/T^2 respectively. One may sa that there are four variables and three primary units, therefore according to Buckingham' π theorem, there will be one dimensionless parameter. However, a close look at th dimensions of h, R, γ and σ indicates a peculiarity that the primary units M and T alway occurs as M/T^2. Hence the effective primary units are only two viz. L and M/T^2 instea of M, L and T. Thus only two repeating variables need to be chosen and two dimensionles parameters will be obtained.

It may be further emphasised that the problem under consideration is of statics an therefore mass and time units should not enter into the results. Instead force and lengt should have been used as primary units. In that case the dimensions of h, R, γ and σ wi be L, L, F/L^3 and F/L respectively. Therefore choosing R and γ as repeating variables can be easily seen that the two dimensionless parameters are

$$\pi_1 = \frac{h}{R} = \text{ and } \pi_2 = \frac{\sigma}{\gamma R^2}$$

Hence $$\frac{h}{R} = f\left(\frac{\sigma}{\gamma R^2}\right)$$

Thus it can be seen that even though this case seems like an exception to Buckingham's π theorem, it is not so when one applies the theorem in its wider perspective.

7.8 Similitude

Before undertaking expensive engineering projects, the engineer always tries to find out how the structure would behave when it is constructed. In order to do this, models (or small scale replica) of the structures are constructed and tests are performed on them to obtain the desired information. Such model studies provide useful information which can be used for modifying the original design if necessary. Designs of spillways, stilling basins, gates and such other appurtenances of dams, plans for river improvement involving channel straightening, construction of levees etc., performance of hydraulic machines such as centrifugal pumps, compressors etc., and design and performance of air planes, ships, missiles, torpedoes are now a days tested with the help of models.

There are two types of models that are usually constructed for testing. These are known as *geometrically similar models* and *distorted models.* Geometrically similar models are easy to design and construct and interpretation of results is also rather easy. Hence, as far as possible geometrically similar models are used. However models of rivers, estuaries and harbours are invariably distorted models.

Types of Similarities

When one deals with shapes of the model and the prototype (i.e. actual structure) and compares flow characteristics around them, one has to deal with three types of similarities.

Geometrical similarity implies the similarity in shape. In other words, for geometrical similarity to exist, the ratios of corresponding length dimensions between the model and the prototype must be same. Figure 7.1 shows two geometrically similar figures. Here

$$\frac{AB}{ab} = \frac{BC}{bc} = \frac{CD}{cd} = \frac{DE}{de}$$

and all the corresponding included angles are equal. From this it will be clear that if the model and prototype are geometrically similar, by mere change in scale they can be superimposed. In the *distorted models* i.e. geometrically dissimilar models this condition is not satisfied. In the present text distorted models are not dealt with.

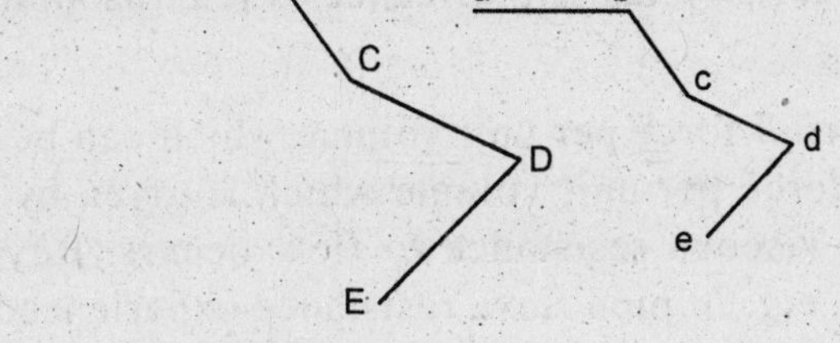

Fig.7.1 Geometrically similar figures

In addition to geometrical similarity, the condition for *kinematic similarity* must also be satisfied. As the name implies, kinematic similarity signifies similarity of the motion. It means that at all corresponding points in the model and in the prototype, the ratios of velocity as well as acceleration must be same. The velocity and acceleration vectors at the corresponding points must also point in the same direction. Such similarity can be attained if flow nets for the model and the prototype are geometrically similar, which in turn means that by mere change in scale the two flownets-one for the model and the other for prototype can be superimposed. This fact comes from the property of flownet viz. velocity and acceleration are related to the spacing and its variation for stream lines. Since velocity and acceleration have magnitude and direction, kinematic similarity implies that velocities and accelerations at corresponding points are parallel and have a constant ratio of magnitudes at all the corresponding of points.

There is also a third type of similarity known as *dynamic similarity* which implies similarity of forces. For flows to be dynamically similar, identical types of forces (such as viscous, pressure, elastic, etc.) must be parallel and must bear the same ratio at all the corresponding sets of points in the model and in the prototype. This idea can be made clear by considering two corresponding points where pressure force f_p, viscous force f_v, and gravity force f_g are acting. The force polygons for the two points are shown in Fig. 7.2 (a). Here f_i and f_i' which are the inertial forces, are equal in magnitude and opposite in direction to resultant force in each case. By dividing all forces in each polygon by f_i and f_i' respectively, the two force polygons take the form as shown in Fig. 7.2 (b). For flows to be dynamically similar, the corresponding sides of the two force polygons in Fig. 7.2 (b) must be parallel and equal i.e.

$$\frac{f_p}{f_i} = \frac{f_p'}{f_i'}, \quad \frac{f_v}{f_i} = \frac{f_v'}{f_i'} \text{ and } \frac{f_g}{f_i} = \frac{f_g'}{f_i'}$$

It may be mentioned that when two flows are geometrically, kinematically and dynamically similar, then they are said to be *completely similar.* Furthermore it can be shown that if two flows are kinematically similar, and if the ratio of fluid density at corresponding points has the same value for all corresponding sets of points, then the flows are also dynamically similar.

7.9 Physical Significance of Dimensionless Parameters

In Section 7.7 five dimensionless parameters were formed, namely, Reynolds number, Froude number, pressure or drag coefficient, Weber number, and Mach number. These parameters have a great physical significance as regards similarily.

Reynolds Number

It is a ratio of inertial force per unit volume which can be represented by $\rho u (\partial u/\partial x)$ ie $\rho U^2/l$, to viscous force per unit volume which is given by $(\partial \tau/\partial y)$ i.e. $(\mu U/l^2)$. In all the problems where viscous resistance to flow occurs, Reynolds number becomes an important parameter, e.g. in pipe flow, resistance experienced by submarines, airplanes, immersed bodies, etc.

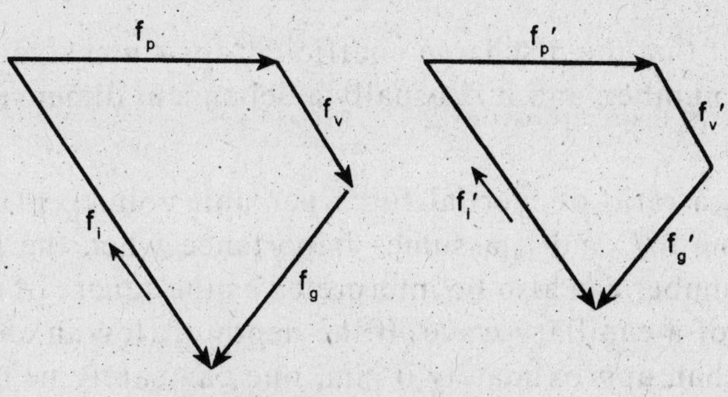

(a) Force polygons for two corresponding points

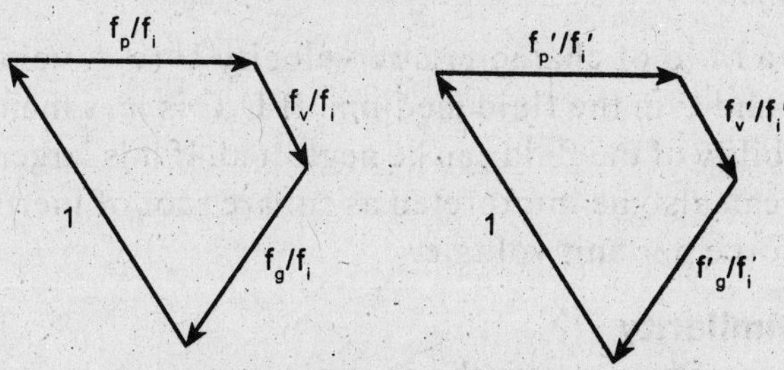

(a) Force polygons for two corresponding points (Unit inertial forces)

Fig.7.2 Force polygons

Froude Number

Froude number can be interpreted as a ratio of inertial force per unit volume i.e. $\rho U^2/l$ to gravitational force per unit volume (which is ρg). As is discussed in greater detail elsewhere, Froude number can also be interpreted as a ratio of average velocity to the celerity of a small gravity wave. Froude number is important in the following cases:

1. free surface phenomena in which gravity is a motivating force e.g. flow over spillways, flow under a sluice gate, etc.
2. problems in which waves are likely to be formed on the surface.
3. problems in which fluids of different mass densities flow, one over another e.g. density currents in storage reservoirs.

Pressure or Drag Coefficient (or Euler Number)

Euler number is given by the square root of the ratio of inertial force to pressure force per unit volume.

$$\text{Euler Number} = \sqrt{\frac{\rho U^2}{l} \cdot \frac{l}{\Delta p}} = \frac{U}{\sqrt{\Delta p/\rho}}$$

Similarly, drag coefficient C_D is a ratio of force per unit volume to inertial force per unit volume. Euler number comes in picture whenever the flow is governed by the pressure.

It may be pointed out that the discharge coefficient for sluices, mouthpieces, etc. can be interpreted as Euler number, and it is usually a dependent dimensionless parameter.

Weber Number

Weber number is a ratio of inertial force per unit volume $\rho U^2/l$, to surface tension force per unit volume σ/l^2 and it assumes importance when the length dimensions are very small. Weber number can also be interpreted as the square of ratio of the velocity of flow to the celerity of a capillary wave. If the depth of flow in an open channel or over spillway is greater than approximately 6 mm, one can safely neglect effects of surface tension.

Mach Number

Mach number is a ratio of characteristic velocity U (e.g. velocity of an airplane, etc.) to the velocity of sound C in the fluid medium. If U/C is less than approximately 0.40, the effects of compressibility of the fluid can be neglected. If it is larger, then the compressibility is of importance. It can also be interpreted as square root of inertial force per unit volume to compressibility force per unit volume.

7.10 Complete Similarity

If the model and the prototype satisfy the conditions of geometrical, kinematic and dynamic similarity, they are said to be completely similar. It can be seen that for model and prototype to be completely similar, the various dimensionless ratios obtained during the dimensional analysis must be equal. Thus for circular pipes (see Example 7.4) if l/D, k/D and Re are same for the model and the prototype, the values of $\Delta p/\rho U^2$ will also be the same.

In many instances more than one force ratio is involved. Thus in the case of motion of a ship in the sea, both Re and Fr come into picture. In such cases, it is quite difficult to satisfy condition that both Re and Fr numbers be the same for the model and the prototype. Hence, models are designed on the basis of equality of predominant force ratio. As such there are models based on Reynolds law, models based on Froude's law, etc.

Models based on Reynolds law include those concerning pipe flow, lift and drag on airfoils, boundary layer studies etc. Froude's modelling is used for spillways, resistance to ship motion, waves studies, models of rivers. harbours, outlets, etc. In the same way, one can have models based on either Weber number or Mach number equality, depending on whether the surface tension or compressibility is important.

7.11 Model Studies and Model Scales

As mentioned earlier, many complex problems in fluid mechanics and hydraulic engineering defy any analytical solution and hence design information can be obtained for these problems through model studies alone.

(a) Closed conduit flows and fully submerged flows

When the flow is completely bounded as in the case of pipes or ducts flowing full or when one considers the flow around submerged bodies, e.g. submarines, cars, aeroplanes, buildings etc. the free surface effects are absent and hence equality of Froude number is not required. Further, if characteristic velocities are low, compressibility effects defined by Mach number can also be ignored. In such a case equality of Reynolds number ensures dynamic similarity between model and prototype. Drag on immersed bodies, flights of subsonic aircrafts, flow of gases through conduits at moderate velocities and flow of liquids in pipes fall under this category.

It may however be mentioned that, in the case of most of the flows which depend on Reynolds number, the Reynolds number effects become asymptotic as Reynolds number becomes large. This can be seen from variation of discharge coefficients of flow measuring devices with Re, variation of average and local drag coefficients in boundary layer flows (Chapt. 9) and drag coefficients of bodies (Chapt. 12) with Re. Hence if Reynolds number is large, absolute equality of Re may not be essential as long as Reynolds number in model is sufficiently large. If Mach number is less than about 0.40, compressibility effects can be neglected. If M is greater than 0.40, it is difficult to satisfy equality of both the Reynolds number and Mach number. In such cases equality of Mach number becomes the criterion for model studies. However, if the viscous motion of a fluid close to the boundary in supersonic flow is the phenomenon to be modelled, Reynolds number equality will be the governing criterion.

(b) Free Surface Flows

In free surface flows the effect of gravity becomes important and therefore Froude number equality becomes the governing criterion. In such cases Reynolds number in model is kept reasonably large. Models of spillways, energy dissipators, and other open channel structures are built and tested according to equality of Froude number.

(c) Rotodynamic Machines

Example 7.5 in this chapter has indicated that the relevant dimensionless parameters for rotodynamic machines are Q/ND^3, gH/N^2D^2, $P/\rho N^3D^5$, $\rho ND^2/\mu$ and other geometric ratios. For geometrically similar machines running at high values of Reynolds numbers $\rho ND^2/\mu$, condition of equality of $\rho ND^2/\mu$ can be neglected. Hence one can write

$$\frac{P}{\rho N^3 D^5} = f\,(Q/ND^3,\ gH/N^2D^2)$$

Each of these parameters will have same value in the model and prototype. Models of such machines are normally run with the same fluid as in the prototype, however it is possible to run the model with air or pressurised gas, since Re number effect can be neglected.

The technique of determining the model scales is simple. This is illustrated for models following Reynolds law.

Let U_m, ρ_m, l_m and μ_m represent the velocity, mass density, length and viscocity in the model; U_p, ρ_p, l_p and μ_p represent the corresponding quantities in the prototype. Since Reynolds number is same for model and prototype, one can write,

$$\frac{U_m l_m \rho_m}{\mu_m} = \frac{U_p l_p \rho_p}{\mu_p}$$

Let $\frac{l_m}{l_p}$ = length scale l_r, $\frac{U_m}{U_p}$ = velocity scale U_r

and $\frac{\rho_m}{\rho_p}$ = mass density scale ρ_r, $\frac{\mu_m}{\mu_p}$ = dynamic viscosity scale μ_r.

Then one gets from the condition of equality of Reynolds number,

$$\frac{U_r l_r \rho_r}{\mu_r} = 1$$

Hence for known values of l_r, ρ_r and μ_r, $U_r = \frac{\mu_r}{l_r \rho_r}$. Since length divided by velocity has the dimensions of time, the time scale becomes,

$$t_r = \frac{l_r}{U_r} = \frac{l_r^2 \rho_r}{\mu_r}$$

Similarly the acceleration scale $a_r = \frac{U_r}{t_r} = \frac{\mu_r^2}{l_r^3 \rho_r^2}$

Force scale f_r is given by $f_r = m_r \times a_r$

or $f_r = \rho_r\, l_r^3 \frac{\mu_r^2}{l_r^3 \rho_r^2} = \frac{\mu_r^2}{\rho_r}$

In the same way, scale ratios for Froude's law can be found out. Scale ratios for models governed by Reynolds law and Froude's law are tabulated in Table 7.2.

TABLE 7.2

Scale Ratios for Models Governed by Reynolds Law and Froude's Law

Quantity	Reynolds law	Froude's law
Velocity	$\mu_r / l_r \rho_r$	$l_r^{1/2} g_r^{1/2}$
Acceleration	$\mu_r^2/\rho_r^2\, l_r^3$	g_r
Time	$l_r^2\, \rho_r/\mu_r$	$l_r^{1/2}/g_r^{1/2}$
Discharge	$l_r\, \mu_r/\rho_r$	$l_r^{5/2}\, g_r^{1/2}$
Force	μ_r^2/ρ_r	$l_r^3\, g_r\, \rho_r$
Pressure intensity	$\mu_r^2/l_r^2\, \rho_r$	$l_r\, g_r\, \rho_r$

Example 7.8

A model of reservoir is completely drained in 10 minutes by means of a sluice gate. If the model is built to a scale 1:100, what will be the time required to drain the prototype?

This model is governed by Froude's law for which

$$t_r = l_r^{1/2}/g_r^{1/2}$$

Since $g_r = 1,\ t_r = l_r^{1/2} = 1/10$

∴ the time for draining the prototype = 10 × 10

= 100 minutes.

Example 7.9

A turbine develops 600 kW under a head of 30 m at 450 rpm speed. Estimate the speed and power at 24 m head.

From Example 7.5 it can be seen that

$$\frac{P_1}{\rho N_1^3 D^5} = \frac{P_2}{\rho N_2^3 D^5} \quad \text{and} \quad \frac{gH_1}{N_1^2 D^2} = \frac{gH_2}{N_2^2 D^2}$$

Hence

$$P_2 = P_1 \left(\frac{N_2}{N_1}\right)^3 \quad \text{and} \quad \left(\frac{N_2}{N_1}\right)^2 = \frac{H_2}{H_1} = 0.80$$

∴ $$\frac{N_2}{N_2} = 0.895 \quad \text{and} \quad N_2 = 402 \text{ rpm}$$

$$P_2 = P_1\ (0.895)^3 = 430.15 \text{ kW}$$

PROBLEMS

7.1 The average shear stress τ (N/m²) that the flowing liquid exerts on the wall of a concrete flume is given by the empirical formula

$$\tau = 0.00141\ \rho\ U^2\ R^{-1/3}$$

in which ρ is the mass density of liquid in kg/m³, U is the average velocity of liquid in m/s and R is the hydraulic radius in metres. Modify the formula so that it yields equivalent results in FPS system where ρ is measured in slugs per ft³.

7.2 Form the dimensionless parameters from the following variables.

(i)	U, g, *l*	(vi)	Δp, ρ, U
(ii)	U, ρ, σ, *l*	(vii)	*l*, t, ν
(iii)	E, ρ, U	(viii)	Δp, *l*, μ, U
(iv)	U, t, ν	(ix)	Shear stress τ, μ, du /dy
(v)	Q, *l*, μ, ρ	(x)	Δp, γ, *l*

7.3 Check whether the following equations are dimensionally homogeneous,

(i) $Q = AU$ (ii) $U = C\sqrt{hS}$

(iii) $\tau_0 = \gamma hS$ (iv) $\tau_0 = \text{const.}\sqrt{\dfrac{U^3\rho\mu}{x}}$

(v) $F_L = L\rho U\Gamma$

in which Q is discharge per unit time, U is the velocity, h is the flow depth, A is the area, S is the slope, τ_0 is the shear stress, C is a constant, F_L is the lift force, Γ is the circulation with dimensions L^2/T and x is the distance.

7.4 By checking the dimensions, indicate which of the following two equations is dimensionally homogeneous.

$$u = \frac{\partial p/\partial x}{4\mu}\left[b^2 - r^2 - \left(b^2 - a^2\right)\frac{\log b/r}{\log b/a}\right]$$

$$u = \frac{4\mu}{\partial p/\partial x}\left[b^2 - r^2 - \left(b^2 - a^2\right)\frac{\log(b/r)}{\log(b/a)}\right]$$

Here u is the velocity at a distance r from the centre-line for steady laminar flow between concentric cylindrical walls of radii a and b, and μ is the dynamic viscosity of the fluid.

7.5 The critical depth y_0 in a rectangular channel depends on the discharge per unit width q and the gravitational acceleration g. Obtain the general form of equation for y_c by dimensional analysis,

7.6 The power P delivered by the pump is a function of the discharge Q, head H and specific weight of the fluid γ. Obtain the general form of the equation for P by dimensional analysis.

7.7 The discharge Q of an ideal fluid flowing through an orifice in a pipe of diameter D depends on the mass density of the fluid ρ difference of pressure Δp across the orifice, and the diameter of orifice d. Find the equation for Q by dimensional analysis.

7.8 The thickness of the boundary layer δ at any distance x from the leading edge of the plate depends on the stream velocity U, mass density ρ, and viscosity of the fluid μ. Find the dimensionless parameters involving these variables.

7.9 The thickness of laminar sublayer δ′ depends on shear stress τ_o, mass density of fluid ρ and the viscosity μ. Find the form of equation for δ′.

7.10 The velocity u in the laminar sub-layer at any distance y above the boundary depends on shear velocity u_* and kinematic vicosity ν. Perform the dimensional analysis.

7.11 The power P required to drive the pump depends on the impeller diameter D, the angular velocity ω, the discharge Q and the mass density of fluid ρ. Derive expression for P by dimensional analysis.

7.12 The stability of laminar flow depends on ρ, μ, y and du/dy. Determine the dimensionless number which gives criterion for stability of laminar flow.

7.13 In a fluid rotated as a solid about a vertical axis with angular velocity ω, the pressure rise p in radial direction depends on ω, radius r and the fluid density ρ. Obtain form of equation for p.

7.14 Obtain the scaling ratio for torque T on a disk of radius R that rotates at an angular velocity ω over a fixed plate, the clearance between the two being y. The fluid between the fixed plate and disk is of dynamic viscosity μ.

7.15 The shear stress τ_o on the bed of an open channel, at which the sediment particle of size d forming the bed just move, depends on the difference in specific weights of sediment and water $\Delta\gamma_s$, viscosity μ and mass density of water ρ. Perform dimensional analysis in order to obtain explicit expression for τ_o.

7.16 The discharge q per unit width over a rectangular suppressed sharp crested weir depends on the head over the weir crest H, weir height W. fluid density ρ and gravitational acceleration g along with dynamic viscosity μ and surface tension σ of the liquid. Perform the dimensional analysis.

7.17 From dimensional considerations show that the period of oscillation t of a pendulum of length *l* depends on the gravitational acceleration g, but it does not depend on its mass.

7.18 The efficiency η of a fan depends on ρ, ω (angular velocity), D, Q, and μ. Obtain a functional relationship for η in terms of dimensionless parameters.

7.19 The performance of a lubricating oil ring depends on the inside diameter of the ring d, shaft speed N, oil discharge Q, and the fluid properties μ, ρ, and σ. Find the functional relationship.

7.20 The drag force exerted by the water on geometrically similar ships is function of U, *l* ρ, g and μ. Determine expression for drag coefficient.

7.21 The pressure loss Δp due to a valve or an orifice fixed in a pipe depends on the pipe diameter D, average velocity in the pipe U, mass density ρ, viscosity μ, and characteristic length of orifice or valve d. Determine general form of a dimensionally homogeneous equation.

7.22 The drag, F exerted on geometrically similar airplanes is a function of U, *l*, ρ, μ and E. Determine the general form of dimensionally homogeneous equation.

7.23 At very small velocities, when the inertia effects are negligible, the drag F experienced by a sphere of diameter D depends on the velocity of the sphere U and the dynamic viscosity of the fluid μ. Obtain the corresponding homogeneous equation for F and change it to the form, C_D = Const./Re.

7.24 The weight W of a drop of liquid that falls slowly from the tube depends on the tube diameter D, specific weight γ, and coefficient of surface tension σ of the liquid. Obtain an expression for W.

7.25 The stagnation pressure p_s in a compressible fluid depends on the ambient velocity U_o, pressure p_o, mass density ρ_o, and volume modulus of elasticity E of the fluid. Obtain an expression for p_s.

7.26 In the case of a free overfall (see Fig. 13.18) in an open channel, the depth of flow y at a distance *x* from the fall depends on discharge per unit width q, and gravitational acceleration g. Obtain from dimensional analysis an expression for y.

7.27 The height h of the wave, caused by the steady wind of velocity U blowing over a lake, depends on the average depth D of the lake, its length L, and mass density ρ and specific weight γ of the liquid. Carry out the dimensional analysis.

7.28 The frequency n of eddies shed by a circular cylinder of diameter D depends on the flow velocity U, and mass density ρ and dynamic viscosity μ of the fluid. Obtain an expression for n.

7.29 The river models are usually distorted i.e. the horizontal length scale L_r and the vertical scale h_r are different. Find the discharge scale Q_r.

7.30 If a model is governed by (i) pressure and elastic forces, (ii) gravity and surface tension forces, and (iii) viscous and gravity forces, determine the length scale in each case assuming g_r to be unity.

7.31 Air at 20°C, flows through a 80 cm diameter pipe at 2.5 m/s velocity. For obtaining dynamic similarity using water at 20°C, what velocity in the pipe is required if the diameter is 5.0 cm?

7.32 A 1:25 scale model of a 250 m long ship is to be tested to determine the wave resistance. If the prototype is to travel at 32 km/hr, at what velocity should the model be towed in water?

7.33 A prototype water meter fixed in a 60 cm diameter pipe gives a pressure loss of 4786 N/m² at a water discharge of 340 *l*/s at 20°C. What will be the corresponding loss of pressure and the discharge for a geometrically similar model with a scale 1:5.

7.34 A 7.2 m high and 15 m long spillway discharges 94 m³/s under a head of 2.0 m. If a 1 : 9 scale model of this spillway is to be constructed, find the model dimensions, head over the model and the model discharge.

7.35 Oil of kinematic viscosity 50×10^{-2} stokes is to be used in a prototype in which both viscous and gravity forces are predominant. With a model scale of 1:6 determine the viscosity of model liquid that is necessary to make both the Froude number and Reynolds number the same in model and prototype.

7.36 What force would be exerted against a break water if 1:20 scale model with length of 1m experiences a wave force of 15 N?

7.37 Show that if using the same liquid in model and prototype, the condition of equality of Reynolds number and Froude number is to be satisfied simultaneously, the model must be as large as the prototype.

7.38 A tank containing water drains through a 1.5 cm hole in 4 minutes and 40 seconds. How long would it take for benzene to drain from a geometrically similar tank with 7.5 cm hole? Neglect viscous effect and consider only the effect of gravity.

.39 A model of an aeroplane is built to a scale of 1:18. If the model is to be tested in a wind tunnel at a speed equal to flying speed of the prototype, what must be the pressure in tunnel? Assume same temperature and viscosity in model and prototype.

.40 Obtain the velocity scale and acceleration scale for model governed by equality of Mach number.

.41 For making the model test of the following situations, state whether Reynolds number, Froude number, the Mach number, or a combination of these is significant

(a) Tidal estuary (b) drag on a parachute (c) total resistance of ship (d) supersonic jet (e) flow over a spillway of a dam (f) high velocity gas flow in a pipe (g) model of a smoke stack, (h) vortex formation at tunnel intake.

.42 Following measurements were taken of capillary rise in three glass tubes using water, glycerine and kerosene all at 20°C. Using value of γ and σ from Table 1.2 obtain the relation between h/R and $\sigma/\gamma R^2$ deduced in Example 7.7 by plotting h/R versus σ/rR^2.

Radius R of capillary tube in mm	Capillary rise b in mm		
	Water	Glycerine	Kerosene
0.50	32	20	12
1.0	14	9	7
2.0	8.5	5	3

CHAPTER EIGHT

LAMINAR FLOW

8.1 Introduction

In Chapter 1, fluid viscosity has been discussed as an important fluid property which gives rise to internal stress opposing deformation during the fluid flow. It has been shown in Chapter 2 that in several problems, the assumption of ideal fluid leads to very satisfactory solutions. However, there are many other problems of fluid flow such as the flow in conduits at low velocities (in which the viscous forces are sufficiently large as compared to the inertial forces), the flow through porous media and problems of lubrication where the effects of viscosity cannot be neglected. Unlike in the case of ideal fluids the real fluid sticks to the wall and velocity of fluid at the wall is zero if wall is stationary. In studying the flow of real fluids the ratio of the inertial force per unit volume to the viscous force per unit volume, known as the Reynolds number, serves to characterise the flow. At Reynolds number less than 2100, the flow in pipes is *laminar*, which is characterised by the fact that the fluid moves in layers, one layer sliding over the adjacent layer. In this type of flow, shear forces are exclusively due to viscosity. Further because of large viscous forces compared to inertial force, any disturbance in velocity is damped and flow remains laminar. On the other hand the *turbulent* flow, which occurs in pipes at Reynolds numbers greater than 3000, is characterised by rapid and continuous fluctuations in the velocity components; these cause transfer of momentum in all the three directions and consequently give rise to additional shear and normal stresses of large magnitude.

8.2 Dependence of Shear on Pressure

Viscosity of fluid induces viscous shear which acts on the moving fluid in addition to the gravitational force and the normal stress due to pressure intensity. In laminar flow the fluid layers slide over each other whereby opposing shear stresses are created. This viscous shear is maximum at the boundary where the velocity gradient is maximum and its magnitude keeps on decreasing with increase in the distance from the boundary. The real fluids adhere to the boundary unlike the ideal fluids in which the velocity at the wall is not zero. In other words, the real fluids have a zero velocity at the wall and therefore, they cannot slip at the boundary; this is known as the *no slip* condition. If the boundary is moving at a certain velocity, the velocity of the fluid at the boundary is equal to the velocity of the boundary itself. An expression has been developed earlier for pressure force per unit volume when a pressure gradient exists in a given direction. In the same way an expression for shear force per unit volume can be developed for a steady two dimensional laminar flow.

Consider an elementary parallelopiped of sides δx, δy and δz. As can be seen from Fig.8.1, the layer ab is moving at a higher velocity than the layer below it and hence ab exerts a shear in the positive direction on the lower layer. On the other hand the lower layer exerts an equal and opposite shear on the layer ab. A similar analysis shows that a positive shear is exerted on layer cd. Since the velocity is varying in y direction, the magnitudes of shear on faces ab and cd are different and vary with respect to y, hence these are designated as τ and $\tau + (\partial\tau/\partial y)\,\partial y$. The net shear force on the parallelopiped is

$$= \left(\tau + \frac{\partial \tau}{\partial y}\delta y\right)\delta x\,\delta z - \tau\,\delta x\,\delta z$$

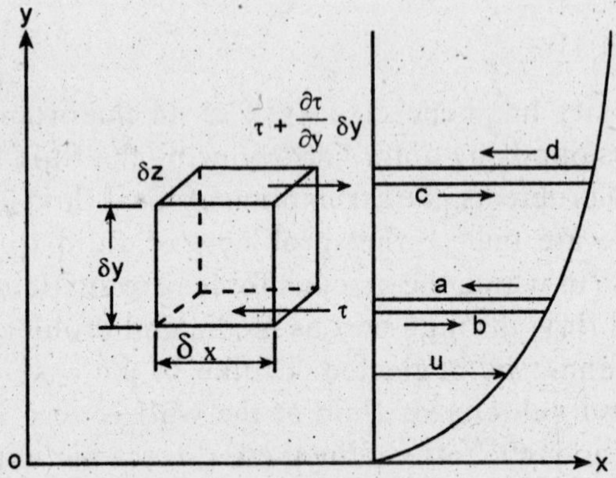

Fig. 8.1 Definition sketch

or

$$= \frac{\partial \tau}{\partial y}\,\delta x\,\delta y\,\delta z$$

Therefore, shear force per unit volume = $(\partial\tau/\partial y)$, since the volume of the parallelopiped is $(\delta x\,\delta y\,\delta z)$. If a certain fluid element is acted on by a pressure force, a viscous force and an external force (such as gravity) then the equation of motion can be obtained by equating the summation of forces in the direction of flow with mass times acceleration or

$$\rho\, a_x = X_1 - \frac{\partial p}{\partial x} + \frac{\partial \tau}{\partial y} \qquad (8.1)$$

Here X_1 is the component of gravity force per unit volume. As discussed earlier, the gravity is not important in the case of enclosed flows. Furthermore, if the flow is steady and uniform, there is no acceleration. Hence Eq. 8.1 gives

$$\frac{\partial p}{\partial x} = \frac{\partial \tau}{\partial y} \tag{8.2}$$

Thus in a two dimensional steady uniform enclosed flow, the pressure gradient in the direction of motion is equal to the shear gradient in the normal direction. Since for laminar flow $\tau = \mu \frac{du}{dy}$ Eq. 8.2 becomes,

$$\frac{\partial p}{\partial x} = \mu \frac{d^2u}{dy^2} \tag{8.3}$$

The velocity distribution in steady uniform laminar flows can be obtained by integration of Eq. 8.3 with respect to y. It can be shown that $\partial p/\partial x$ is independent of y and hence $\partial p/px$ is constant; the integration of Eq. 8.3 is therefore straight forward. If the conduit is inclined, p is replaced by γh and $\partial p/\partial x$ by $\gamma\ \partial h/\partial x$ where h is the piezonetric head.

It may be mentioned that Eq. 8.1 is a simplified form of general equations of motion for laminar flow of incompressible fluids. These are known as Navier-Stokes' equations and are given below for cartesian coordinate system:

$$\left.\begin{aligned}
\frac{\partial u}{\partial t} + u\frac{\partial u}{\partial x} + v\frac{\partial u}{\partial y} + w\frac{\partial u}{\partial z} &= X - \frac{1}{\rho}\frac{\partial p}{\partial x} + \nu\left(\frac{\partial^2 u}{\partial x^2} + \frac{\partial^2 u}{\partial y^2} + \frac{\partial^2 u}{\partial z^2}\right)\\
\frac{\partial v}{\partial t} + u\frac{\partial v}{\partial x} + v\frac{\partial v}{\partial y} + w\frac{\partial v}{\partial z} &= Y - \frac{1}{\rho}\frac{\partial p}{\partial y} + \nu\left(\frac{\partial^2 v}{\partial x^2} + \frac{\partial^2 v}{\partial y^2} + \frac{\partial^2 v}{\partial z^2}\right)\\
\frac{\partial w}{\partial t} + u\frac{\partial w}{\partial x} + v\frac{\partial w}{\partial y} + w\frac{\partial w}{\partial z} &= Z - \frac{1}{\rho}\frac{\partial p}{\partial z} + \nu\left(\frac{\partial^2 w}{\partial x^2} + \frac{\partial^2 w}{\partial y^2} + \frac{\partial^2 w}{\partial z^2}\right)
\end{aligned}\right\} \tag{8.4}$$

In the above equations u, v and w are the velocity components in the x, y and z directions; X, Y, Z represent the components of gravity forces per unit mass, p is the pressure and ν and ρ represent the kinematic viscosity and mass density of the fluid respectively. Navier-Stokes equations are nonlinear partial differential equations and hence their general solution is not available.

8.3 Laminar Flow through Circular Pipes

Steady, uniform flow through a circular pipe of constant cross section can be analysed to determine the velocity distribution, discharge and the pressure drop. In a horizontal pipe, shown in Fig. 8.2, consider a cylindrical free body of fluid having radius r and length dx. Since the flow is steady and uniform, the particles of fluid are not accelerated. The forces acting on the fluid element are the pressure force acting on both faces of the cylinder and the shear resistance on the periphery of the cylinder acting in the direction opposite to that of flow.

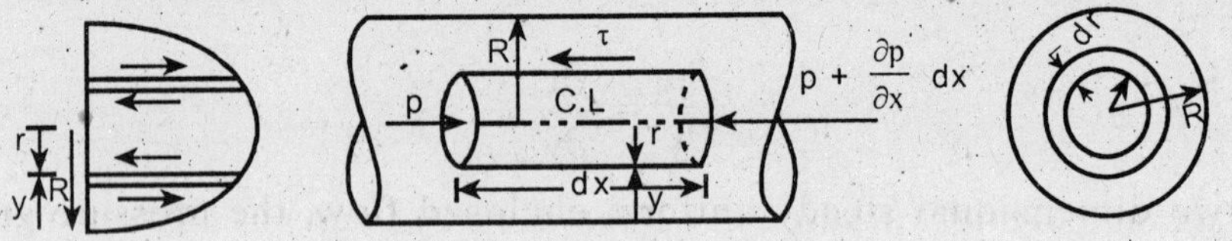

Fig. 8.2 Equilibrium of a cylindrical fluid element

Let p be the pressure intensity on the left face and $\left(p+\frac{\partial p}{\partial x}\delta x\right)$ on the right face. As there is no acceleration, the summation of forces in the flow direction must be zero;

$$\therefore \quad p\,\pi\,r^2 - \left(p+\frac{\partial p}{\partial x}\delta x\right)\pi\,r^2 - 2\pi\,r\,\delta x\,\tau = 0$$

in which $2\pi\,r\,\delta x\,\tau$ is the total shear resistance acting on the periphery of the cylindrical element. Dividing the terms in the above equation by the volume of the cylinder $\pi\,r^2\,\delta x$ and simplifying the resulting expression one gets,

$$\tau = -\frac{\partial p}{\partial x}\frac{r}{2} \tag{8.5}$$

This equation shows that the shear stress τ has a linear variation along the radius of pipe. At the centre of the pipe where r = 0, the shear τ is zero and at the pipe wall where r = R, it is

$$\tau_0 = \frac{\partial p}{\partial x}\frac{R}{2} \tag{8.6}$$

Introducing $\tau = \mu\frac{du}{dy}$ in Eq. 8.5 with dy = – dr, (since y is the distance from the pipe wall) one gets

$$\frac{du}{dr} = \frac{\partial p}{\partial x}\frac{r}{2\mu} \tag{8.7}$$

For steady uniform flow ∂p/∂x must have a constant value. Integrating Eq. 8.7 with respect to r, one gets,

$$u = \frac{\partial p}{\partial x}\frac{r^2}{4\mu} + C \tag{8.8}$$

The value of the constant of integration C can be found from the boundary condition that at r = R, the velocity u = 0.

$$C = -\frac{\partial p}{\partial x}\frac{R^2}{4\mu}$$

Equation 8.8 then becomes,

$$u = \frac{1}{4\mu}\left(-\frac{\partial p}{\partial x}\right)(R^2 - r^2) \tag{8.9}$$

which shows that the velocity variation in laminar flow through circular pipes is parabolic. The surface of the velocity distribution is a paraboloid of revolution. From the geometry of the paraboloid of revolution it can be seen that the average velocity U and the maximum velocity u_{max} are related by

$$U = \frac{u_{max}}{2} = -\frac{\partial p}{\partial x}\frac{R^2}{8\mu} \tag{8.10}$$

This can also be shown by integrating Eq. 8.9 over the cross-sectional area to get the discharge Q and then obtaining the mean velocity. The variation of velocity u and shear stress τ are shown in Fig. 8.3.

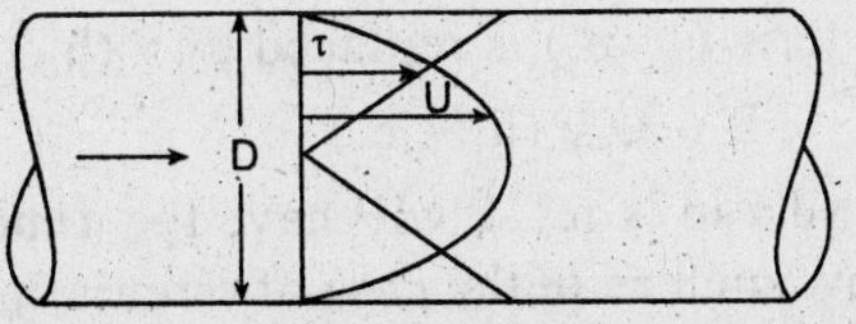

Fig. 8.3 Shear and velocity distribution in laminar flow

Introducing 2R = D, Eq. 8.10 can be presented as

$$-\frac{\partial p}{\partial x} = \frac{32\pi\, U}{D^2} \tag{8.11}$$

The term $(-\partial p/\partial x)$ can be replaced by $(p_1 - p_2)/l$ where p_1 and p_2 represent the pressure at two sections distance l apart. Thus,

$$(p_1 - p_2) = \frac{32\mu\, U\, l}{D^2} \tag{8.12}$$

Equation 8.12 is known as the Hagen – Poiseuille's equation for laminar flow in circular pipes. It can also be written in terms of the discharge Q as

$$(p_1 - p_2) = \frac{128\mu\, l\, Q}{\pi D^4} \tag{8.13}$$

Equations 8.12 and 8.13 are for steady uniform flow in which the viscosity μ influences the fluid motion. Since the diameter D is constant the pressure gradient is directly proportional to the average velocity of flow and the dynamic viscosity of the fluid.

If the pipe through which the viscous fluid is flowing is inclined, Hagen – Poiseuille's law would still hold provided the fluid is not accelerating. In such a case, $[(p_1 + \gamma z_1) - (p_2 + \gamma z_2)]$ replaces the pressure loss term. Equation 8.12 can then be written as,

$$h_1 - h_2 = \frac{32\mu U l}{\gamma D^4} \tag{8.14}$$

in which h_1 and h_2 are the piezometric head values at the two sections, and γ is the unit weight of fluid.

Problems of flow through pipes involve the estimation of power required to maintain a certain flow through the pipe. Since power is the rate of doing work, it is equivalent to the product of force and velocity. The force is $(-\partial p/\partial x)$ per unit volume and the total force is $(-\partial p/\partial x)\,Al$ where A and l are the area and length of the pipe respectively. With the average velocity of flow U, the power P is

$$P = -\frac{\partial p}{\partial x} A\, l\, U = -\frac{\partial p}{\partial x} l\, Q$$

Or $$P = (p_1 - p_2)\, Q$$

If the pipe is inclined, the term $(p_1 - p_2)$ is replaced by $\gamma\,(h_1 - h_2)$ to yield

$$P = Q\,\gamma\,(h_1 - h_2)$$

If Q is in m³/s, h in m and γ in N/m³, P will have the dimensions of N m/s or W. For steady uniform laminar flow such as in the case of circular pipe the kinetic energy of the fluid per unit volume remains the same. If the pipe is horizontal the potential energy per unit volume of the fluid also remains unaltered. Therefore, the work done (per unit volume of fluid and per unit time) by the pressure force must result in a continuous generation of heat. In this way the mechanical energy is converted into heat. It can be shown that the rate at which work is done per unit volume of fluid is given by $\mu\,(du/dy)^2$. Therefore for laminar flow it will be maximum at the wall and zero at the centre where (du/dy) is equal to zero.

Example 8.1

What power is required per kilometer of a 8.0 cm pipe line to maintain a flow of 5.0 l/s of castor oil having a dynamic viscosity of 0.98 kg/ms? The pipe may be assumed to be horizontal.

Velocity through pipe $$U = \frac{Q}{A} = \frac{0.005}{(\pi/4)\,(0.08)^2}\ 0.995 \text{ m/s}$$

$$(p_1 - p_2) = \frac{32\mu U l}{D^2} = \frac{32 \times 0.98 \times 0.995 \times 1000}{0.08 \times 0.08}$$

$$= 4875\ 500.0 \text{ N/m}^2$$

Power $$P = Q\,(p_1 - p_2) = 0.005 \times 4875.5 = 24.3785\ \frac{\text{kN m}}{\text{s}}$$

$$= 24.379 \text{ kW}$$

8.4 Laminar Flow Through Noncircular Pipes

The Hagen – Poiseuille's equation for laminar flow through circular pipes has been derived in the previous section. Similar equations can be obtained for the laminar flow through conduits of any shape: a general form of such equation is,

$$(p_1 - p_2) = k\,\frac{\mu U l}{D^2} \tag{8.16}$$

in which $(p_1 - p_2)$ is the pressure drop in a length l, U is the average velocity of flow and D is the characteristic length parameter. The factor k is a constant which depends upon the shape of the conduit, the value of k being 32 in the case of a circular pipe of diameter D.

For flow between two parallel plates, the value of k is 12 and the formula takes the form,

$$(p_1 - p_2) = \frac{12\,\mu U l}{D^2} \tag{8.17}$$

where D is the spacing between the two plates and the other terms are as explained earlier. It is a case of two dimensional flow and the velocity distribution is parabolic, the average velocity being two third of the maximum velocity. The derivation of this relation has been given in Example 8.2.

For steady uniform viscous flow in an infinitely wide open channel, the shape factor k in the Eq. 8.16 is 3 and the formula becomes

$$(p_1 - p_2) = \frac{3\,\mu U l}{D^2} \tag{8.18}$$

in which D is the depth of flow. It is a special case of lower half flow between parallel plates held inclined as shown in Fig. 8.4. The open channel flow is characterised by a free surface and therefore there is no pressure gradient to maintain the flow. In such a case the flow is maintained by the drop in the potential energy (i.e. due to gravity). Therefore, the term $(p_1 - p_2)$ in Eq. 8.18 should be replaced by $\gamma(h_1 - h_2) = \gamma h_f$ (see Fig. 8.4). The term h_f/l is the slope of the total energy line which is also equal to the bed slope of the channel S_o and water surface slope in case of steady uniform flow. Hence,

$$S_o = \frac{3\,\mu U}{\gamma D^2}$$

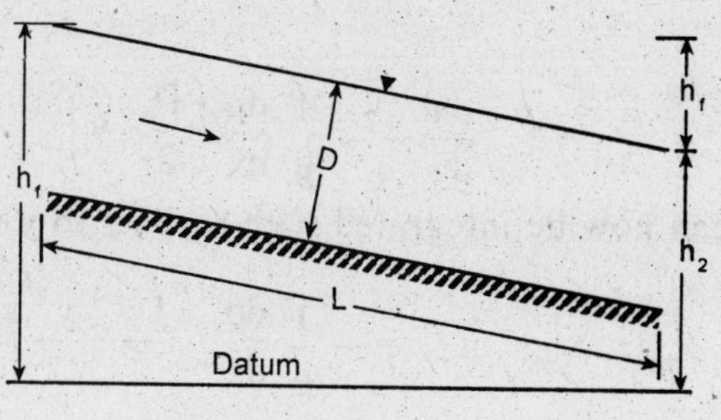

Fig. 8.4 Uniform flow in an open channel

Example 8.2

Derive an expression for pressure drop for a steady two dimensional laminar flow between parallel plates.

Since there is no acceleration, Eq. 8.1 can be readily applied. If τ is the shear stress and p is the pressure intensity, Eq. 8.1 gives

$$\frac{dp}{dx} = \frac{\partial \tau}{\partial y}$$

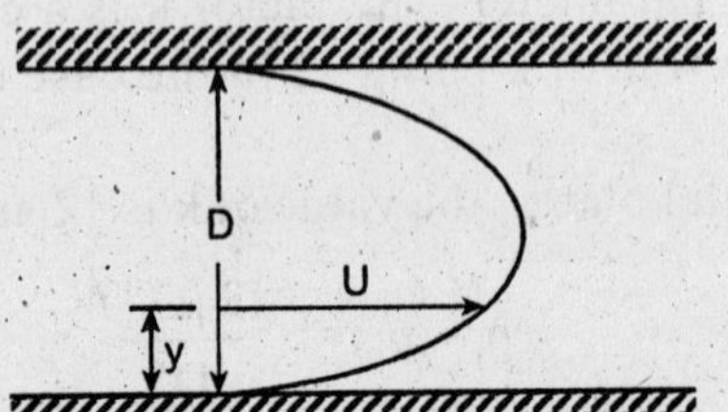

Fig. 8.5 Flow between parallel plates

Integrating the above equation with respect to y one gets,

$$\tau = \frac{dp}{dx} y + C_1$$

At $y = D/2$, $\tau = 0$ and at $y = 0$, $\tau = \tau_0$. Thus with the first condition, C_1 can be evaluated as

$$C_1 = -\frac{dp}{dx}\frac{D}{2}$$

Therefore, $$\tau = -\frac{dp}{dx}\left(\frac{D}{2} - y\right)$$

The shear stress τ_o at the boundary is then

$$\tau_o = -\frac{dp}{dx}\frac{D}{2}$$

However the relationship $\tau = \mu\,(du/dy)$ can be introduced in place of τ in the above equation and hence,

$$\frac{du}{dy} = -\frac{1}{\mu}\frac{dp}{dx}\left(\frac{D}{2} - y\right)$$

The above equation can now be integrated with respect to y to yield

$$u = -\frac{1}{\mu}\frac{dp}{dx}\left(\frac{Dy}{2} - \frac{y^2}{2}\right) + C_2$$

The constant of integration C_2 can be found to be zero from the no-slip condition that velocity u = 0 at y = 0. Therefore, the general velocity distribution law is given by

$$u = -\frac{1}{2\mu}\frac{dp}{dx}(Dy - y^2)$$

which is an equation of a parabola, see Fig. 8.5. The average velocity of flow U can be obtained as follows:

$$U = \frac{q}{D} = \frac{1}{D}\left(-\frac{1}{2\mu}\frac{dp}{dx}\right)\int_O^D (Dy - y^2)\,dy$$

$$= \left(-\frac{1}{2\mu D}\frac{dp}{dx}\right)\left(\frac{Dy^2}{2} - \frac{y^3}{3}\right)_O^D$$

$$U = -\frac{dp}{dx}\frac{D^2}{12\mu}$$

Since $(-dp/dx)$ is equal to $(p_1 - p_2)/l$, the above expression yields,

$$(p_1 - p_2) = \frac{12\,\mu\,Ul}{D^2}$$

8.5 Flow Through Porous Media

Equation 8.16 can be applied for flow through porous media in which case the characteristic length is the grain diameter D_s of the porous material. The interstices of the porous material form countless little conduits through which the flow takes place. It is not possible to consider the flow through such individual conduits but the porous material as a whole is considered as the fluid passage bounded by impervious boundaries which limit the movement. Consider a porous material in a tube of area A and let the flow take place under piezometric head difference $h_f = (h_1 - h_2)$, see Fig. 8.6. The apparent mean velocity of the flow U is given by Q/A where Q is the discharge through the tube and A is the cross-sectional area. The actual mean velocity of the fluid through the interstices will be greater than U because part of the cross-sectional area is blocked by the material. If the term *porosity* e is defined as the ratio of volume of pores to the total volume and if this definition is extended to the cross-sectional area, the actual area through which the fluid is flowing is given by Ae. The actual mean velocity through the pores is then Q /Ae i.e. (U/e) It can further be assumed that the average size of the pores is proportion to the grain diameter D_s. Replacing U by U/e and D by D_s in Eq. 8.16, one obtains,

$$(p_1 - p_2) = k\frac{\mu\,Ul}{eD_s^2}$$

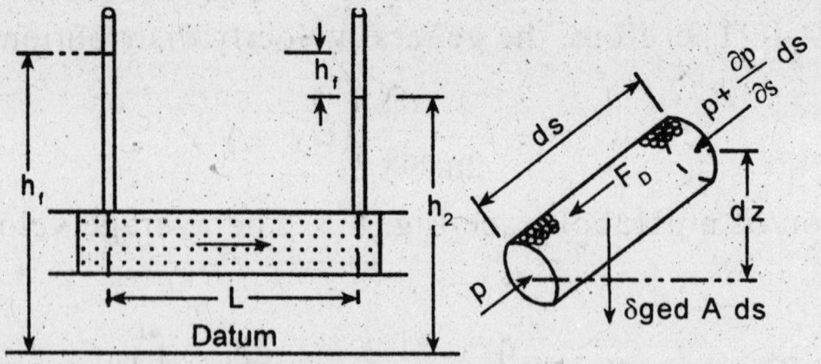

Fig. 8.6 Flow through porous media

or $$h_f = \frac{k \mu U l}{\gamma e D_S^2} \tag{8.19}$$

This equation can be written as

$$U = \frac{\gamma e i D_S^2}{k \mu} \tag{8.20}$$

or $$U = K i \tag{8.21}$$

in which i is the hydraulic gradient (h_f/l) and K is known as *coefficient of permeability* having the dimensions of velocity. Equation 8.21 is commonly known as *Darcy's Law,* named after Henry Darcy, a French engineer who first presented it in 1856. Darcy's law has many applications in the field of ground water flow, for example in the design of earthen embankment, and design of tube wells. It should be noted that Darcy's law is applicable upto a Reynolds number, ($U D_s/\nu$) of unity. As can be seen from Eq. 8.20, coefficient of permeability is proportional to square of sediment size and inversely proportional to viscosity of fluid. Within $U D_s/\nu < 1.0$, K values are of the order of a few metres per day.

The above derivation of Darcy's law is based on the capillary tube model in which the porous medium is supposed to consist of straight parallel capillaries of uniform diameter. This model suffers from certain defects. Firstly, here the capillaries are assumed to be straight whereas actually the flow lines are curved. Secondly, it is also difficult to estimate the Reynolds number value since velocity and pore size are difficult to measure. These defects are overcome in a drag model for flow through porous material in which the total resistance to flow is considered to be the sum of drag forces on individual particles forming the porous medium. It can be shown that for porous medium composed of uniform, sized spheres

$$\frac{\partial h}{\partial s} = -\frac{F_D}{\rho g e\, dA\, ds}$$

in which $(\partial h)/\partial s)$ is the hydraulic gradient and $h = (p/\gamma) + z$, F_D is the resistance offered by all the particles in a volume (dA ds) and e is the porosity. Since $F_D = N f_D$ where N is the number of particles and f_D is the drag on a single particle which is given by Stokes' law (see below)

$$f_D = 3\pi D_s \mu u$$

these values can be substituted in the expression for (∂h/∂s). However,

$$N = \frac{(1-e)dA\,ds}{(\pi D_s^3)/6}$$

Therefore, $$\frac{\partial h}{\partial s} = -\frac{18(1-e)\mu u}{D_s^2 \rho g e}$$

where u is the total average velocity of flow around the particle which can be expressed as U/e where U is the superficial velocity. Hence one gets,

$$U = -\frac{D_s^2 \gamma e^2}{18(1-e)\mu} \cdot \frac{\partial h}{\partial s}$$

or $$U = -Ki$$

in which $$K = \frac{D_s^2 \gamma e^2}{18(1-e)\mu} \quad \text{and} \quad i = -\frac{\partial h}{\partial s}$$

The advantage of this model is that the Reynolds number, as prescribed by this model, gives excellent correspondence with the observed values since departure from Darcy's law is found to take place beyond Reynolds number values about 1.0.

8.6 Stokes' Law

So far the problems of laminar flow in conduits have been discussed. The fluid viscosity plays an important role in the analysis of such problems. Yet there is another class of problems in which solid body moves through a fluid of infinite extent. As the body travels through the fluid, it experiences a resistance which acts in the direction opposite to the motion of the body. This resistance depends upon the size of the body, the velocity with which it moves, the viscosity of the fluid and its mass density. In the case of a sphere of diameter D moving with a constant velocity U in the fluid of viscosity μ, Stokes found that the resistance F_D is given by formula,

$$F_D = 3\pi \mu DU \tag{8.22}$$

at very low values of Reynolds number. Stokes' law is derived from N. S. equations with the following assumptions : (i) no slip at the boundary, (ii) fluid is infinite in extent and calm, (iii) particle is spherical, and (iv) inertial force is very small compared to viscous force, i.e. Re is less than 0.20. If the sphere is moving down through the fluid because of its own weight, the accelerating force will be equal to the submerged weight of the sphere which is equal to $\frac{\pi}{6} D^3 (\gamma_s - \gamma)$ in which γ_s and γ are the specific weights of the solid and fluid respectively. If the sphere is falling in the fluid at a constant velocity (i.e. there is no acceleration), known as *terminal fall velocity*, these two forces will be balanced.

or $$\frac{\pi D^3}{6}(\gamma_s - \gamma) = 3\pi\, D\mu U$$

Hence, $$U = \frac{(\gamma_s - \gamma)}{18\mu} D^2 \qquad (8.23)$$

If the velocity is known, the viscosity of the fluid μ can be computed. Drag force is expressed by a formula

$$F_D = C_D\, A\, \frac{\rho U^2}{2} \qquad (8.24)$$

in which C_D is known as *coefficient of drag* (which is a dimensionless term), A is the projected area of the body at right angle to flow and ρ is the mass density of the fluid. Eliminating F_D from Eqs. 8.22 and 8.24 one gets,

$$C_D = \frac{24\,\mu}{U\,D\rho} = \frac{24}{Re} \qquad (8.25)$$

This is an important relation between the drag coefficient C_D and the Reynolds number Re which is valid only in the range of Reynolds number less than 0.2. Equations 8.22, 8.23 and 8.25 will be followed in the case of mist droplets falling in air, and small silt and clay particles settling in water.

The fall velocity of particles is affected significantly by the presence of other particles such as in dilute suspensions. If U_c is the reduced fall velocity, U is the fall velocity of single particle and C is the absolute volume concentration, U_c is given by the equation

$$\frac{U_d}{U_c} = (1 - C)^{-n}$$

where n is a function at UD/ν according to Maude and Whitmore as shown below

UD/γ	<0.40	1.0	10	100	1000
n	4.65	4.4	3.7	2.8	2.35

This equation can be used beyond Stokes' range also.

Applications

One of the principal applications of Stokes' law in environmental engineering is in *sedimentation,* a process of removal of suspended solids from water and waste waters. The raw water contains fine silts and clays in suspension whereas waste waters may contain organic matter in addition. By adding coagulants, flocks of larger diameter and smaller density are formed. When water or waste waters are allowed to flow horizontally through a tank of large dimension, a very low velocity is attained at which, these silt and clay particles as well as flocks settle to the bottom while water passes through the sedimentation tank and relatively clear water flows out. These tanks are either circular or rectangular in shape. The material settled at the bottom is usually pumped out from the bottom.

The hydraulic design of the sedimentation tank is based on the principle that during the time water flows horizontally at a reduced velocity U from inlet to exit through the length of tank L, the sediment particle must settle through depth of tank h, at its fall velocity ω. Since the fall velocity is affected by the turbulence and presence of other particles in the basin, a lower value of ω is usually adopted.

Even after the water passes through the sedimentation tank, it contains some fine sediments in suspension which need to be removed before water has acceptable turbidity as regards human consumption. This is achieved through a *filtration* process in which water passes through a granular medium of varying porosity and density supported by a gravel layer, see Fig. 8.7. The medium may be graded sand or mixture of sand, anthracite, garnet or resins. As the muddy water passes through the filter due to gravitational action, the fine sediments and a large percent of viruses are held back due to various removal mechanisms which include straining, gravity settling, adsorption and biological activity.

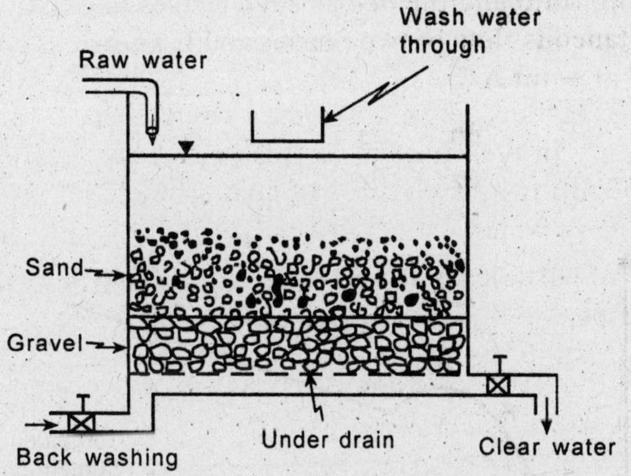

Fig. 8.7 Water filter

Flow through filters is necessarily laminar flow and hence follows Darcy's law. However, as time progresses, the porosity of the top few centimeters of filter decreases due to clogging and the head loss increases. As filter clogging proceeds, at a certain stage the deposited particles begin to shear off and effluent solid concentration begins to rise. This is the time when filter needs to be backwashed. In the process of backwashing clean water enters from the bottom under pressure and fluidizes the bed. Head loss incurred during fluidization is equal to the buoyant weight of the bed. The deposited particles are removed during backwashing and the medium is thus cleaned. At the end of backwashing the coarsest material settles at the bottom while the finest at top. The filter needs to be backwashed at regular intervals.

8.7 Fluidization

Consider a fluid flowing upwards through a column of porous material of spherical shape. For a given porous material the porosity e is constant. Hence as the superficial velocity U is increased the loss of pressure over a unit depth also increases. At low velocities the particles remain stationary; however, at higher velocities and hence at larger pressure gradients, the particles no longer remain stationary but 'fluidize' at which stage $\partial p/\partial z$ equals the submerged weight of particles in unit volume. This condition is indicated by point A on Fig. 8.8. If the velocity is further increased, the bed expands slightly and porosity somewhat increases as a result of which the rate of increase of pressure gradient decreases as indicated by curve AB. Then the pressure gradient sometimes diminishes to C. The region ABC is known as transition region. As the velocity is further increased the particles separate and true fluidization begins; the particles move vigorously and contents of column resemble a boiling liquid. This is known as batch fluidization indicated by the range CE. If velocity is further increased, a stage is reached where all particles are entrained in the flowing fluid and the *bed* as such ceases to exist. The phenomenon then becomes that of simultaneous flow of two phases and is known as continuous fluidization. As mentioned earlier, at point A

$$\gamma \frac{\partial h}{\partial z} = \frac{\partial p}{\partial z} = (1 - e)\,(\gamma_S - \gamma)$$

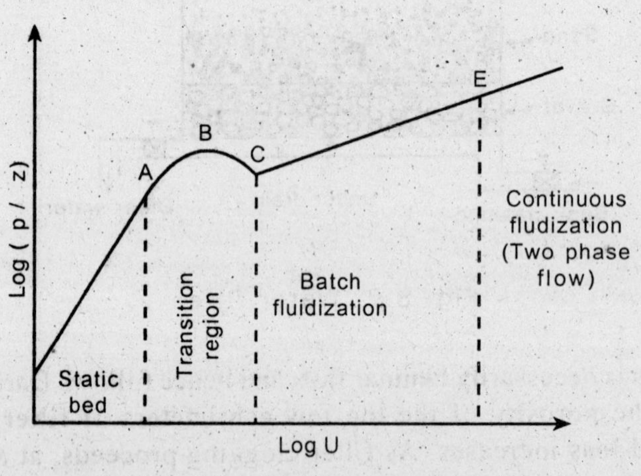

Fig. 8.8 Stages of fluidization

Combining this equation with

$$\frac{\partial h}{\partial z} = \frac{18\,(1-e)\,\mu U}{D_S^2 \gamma\, e^2}$$

One gets the following equation for incipient fluidization velocity U_f for laminar flow

$$U_f = \frac{(\gamma_S - \gamma)\, D_S^2\, e^2}{18\,\mu}$$

f particles are larger, the flow around the particles will not be laminar and hence one ust use another relationship for pressure gradient.

Fluidization is extensively used in chemical engineering; its chief advantage is that it nsures contact of fluid with all parts of particles. It is, therefore, used in catalytic processes herein contact is essential and also in the drying of crystals. Hydraulic sorting of onuniform sized particles can be accomplished using fluidization. Hydraulic filters in ater treatment plants are cleaned of accumulated deposits by this process.

.8 Elements of Lubrication Mechanics

ubrication mechanics is very closely related to the theory of laminar flow discussed in etail in the earlier sections of this chapter. Simple aspects of the lubrication mechanics e presented here.

When fluid is wedged between two surfaces which are slightly inclined, large forces e developed as one of the surfaces moves in the longitudinal direction. The pressure stribution under such a motion can be determined from the basic laminar flow equations. onsider a plane surface of finite length, kept slightly inclined over a horizontal surface shown in Fig. 8.9.

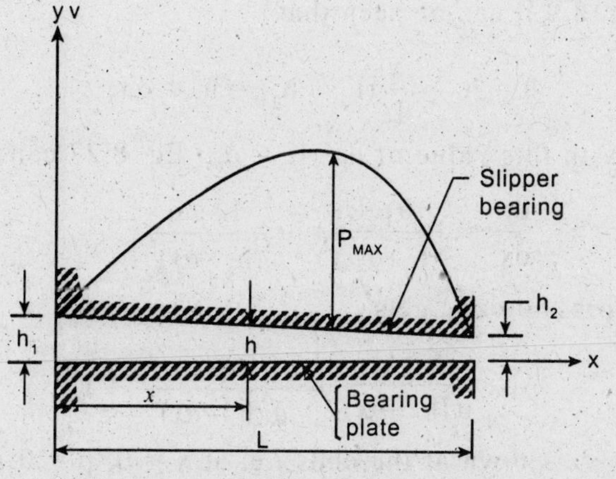

Fig.8.9 Slipper bearing

It is assumed that there is no flow from ends normal to the plane of the figure, so that e problem is two dimensional. The fluid film is very thin and viscous so that viscous rce is much larger than the inertial force and therefore the latter can be neglected. The sic equation, Eq. 8.1 can be used to solve this problem.

$$\frac{dp}{dx} = \mu \frac{d^2u}{dy^2}$$

tegrating the above equation twice, one gets an expression for velocity as

$$u = \frac{y^2}{2\mu} \frac{dp}{dx} + C_1 y + C_2$$

The constants of integration. C_1 and C_2 can be determined from the known boundary conditions. The lower surface is assumed to move in the *x* direction with a velocity U while the upper inclined surface is at rest i.e. at y = 0, u = U, and at y = h, u = 0. Substituting these values of y and u, the constants C_1 and C_2 can be found as

$$C_1 = -\frac{1}{h}\left(\frac{dp}{dx}\frac{h^2}{2\mu} + U\right) \text{ and } C_2 = U$$

Hence the general expression for velocity is

$$u = \frac{y}{2\mu}\frac{dp}{dx}(y - h) + U\left(1 - \frac{y}{h}\right) \tag{8.26}$$

With the expression for velocity distribution known, the unit discharge q can be calculated by integrating the term udy over a particular section after assuming dp/dx as constant.

$$q = \int_0^h u dy = \frac{Uh}{2} - \frac{h^3}{12\mu}\frac{dp}{dx} \tag{8.27}$$

In order to obtain pressure distribution along the length x, it is necessary to express h in terms of *x*. From the Fig. 8.9 it can be seen that

$$h = h_1 - \frac{x}{L}(h_1 - h_2) = h_1 - \alpha x$$

where $\alpha = (h_1 - h_2)/L$. With this value of $h = h_1 - \alpha x$, Eq. 8.27 can be rearranged as

$$\frac{dp}{dx} = \frac{6\mu U}{(h_1 - \alpha x)^2} - \frac{12\mu q}{(h_1 - \alpha x)^3}$$

Integrating the above expression one gets,

$$p = \frac{6\mu U}{\alpha(h_1 - \alpha x)} - \frac{6\mu q}{\alpha(h_1 - \alpha x)^2} + C_3$$

The pressure intensities are known at the ends i.e. at x = 0, p = 0 and at x = L, p = 0 because atmospheric conditions can be assumed to prevail at the ends. The constant C_3 and q can be obtained as,

$$C_3 = \frac{-6\mu U}{\alpha(h_1 + h_2)} \text{ and } q = \frac{U h_1 h_2}{h_1 + h_2}$$

With these values of C_3 and q, the pressure at any point is

$$p = \frac{6\mu U x(L - x)(h_1 - h_2)}{L h^2(h_1 + h_2)} \tag{8.28}$$

The maximum pressure can be shown to be

$$p_{max} = \frac{3\mu U(h_1 - h_2)L}{2h_1h_2(h_1 + h_2)}$$

and it will occur at $x/L = \dfrac{h_2}{h_1 + h_2}$

The total force on the bearing surface per unit width can be obtained by integrating the pressure intensity over the length L,

$$F = \int p dx = \frac{6 \mu U L^2}{(h_1 - h_2)^2} \left(\log_e \frac{h_1}{h_2} - 2 \frac{h_1 - h_2}{h_1 + h_2} \right) \quad (8.29)$$

It is evident from this expression that F will be zero when the two surfaces are parallel i.e. $h_1 = h_2$. For given values of μ, U and L, F is maximum when $(h_1/h_2) = 2.2$ and the maximum value of F is

$$F_{max} = 0.16 \frac{\mu U L^2}{h_2^2} \quad (8.30)$$

The drag force required to move the lower surface at a velocity U can be obtained by integrating the shear stress on the surface over the distance L. The force F_D when $h_1/h_2 = 2.2$ is given by the relation

$$F_D = 0.75 \frac{\mu U L}{h_2} \quad (8.31)$$

The Reynolds number characterising the flow in a slipper bearing is formed by combining (UL/ν) and (h_m/L) viz. $Re^* = (UL/\nu)(h_m/L)^2$ where h_m is mean spacing between two surfaces. The above analysis is valid when Re* is much smaller than unity. Furthermore, in the above analysis it has been assumed that the viscosity is constant. However in reality, because of the heat generated through friction, the temperature rises and the viscosity decreases. As a result F_D also decreases. This effect is taken into consideration in a more complete analysis of the problem.

The above discussion is for a typical slipper bearing. The other type of bearing, such as a Journal bearing, shown in Fig. 8.10 develops its force by a similar principle, except that the surfaces in the journal bearing are curved.

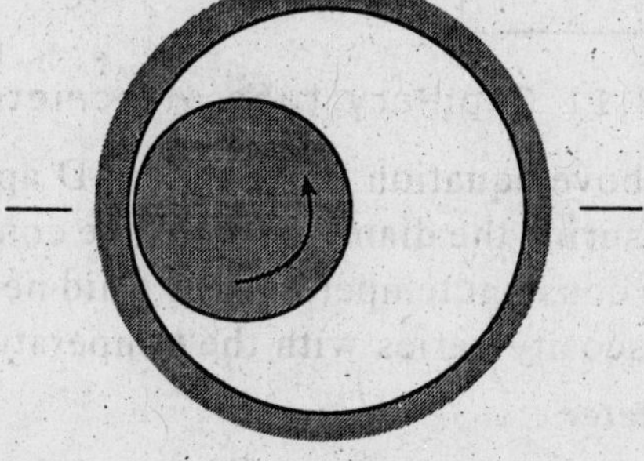

Fig.8.10 Journal bearing

In practice, the total load supported by the bearing, the viscosity of the lubricant and the velocity of the slipper may be known and it is usually required to determine the best proportions for the interspace in which the flow of the lubricant takes place.

8.9 Measurement of Viscosity

Complete solutions to the problems of laminar flow can be obtained only when the viscosity of the fluid is known. Viscosity can be measured in a number of ways; by the use of Hagen-Poiseuille's equation, by the use of Newton's law, by use of instruments which are calibrated with fluids of known viscosity, etc. The subject of measurement of viscosity is known as *viscometry* and the instruments employed for this purpose are known as *viscometers.*

Capillary Tube Viscometer

The capillary tube viscometer is based on the Hagen-Poiseuille's law. Figure 8.11 shows the capillary tube viscometer. As the fluid passes from the tank into the tube, fluid near the tube wall is retarded due to formation of boundary layer (see Chapter 9) while fluid at the central core is accelerated. As a result some distance is required to establish a truely steady uniform laminar flow with parabolic velocity distribution. This is achieved downstream of the section where the b.L. reaches center line. The pressure head is measured at a point downstream of the point of establishment of flow. The discharge Q can be measured and with the known value of the diameter D, the length l and the specific weight of fluid γ the viscosity of the fluid μ can be computed by rearranging Hagen Poiseuille's equation as

$$\mu = \frac{\pi \gamma h D^4}{128 Q l}$$

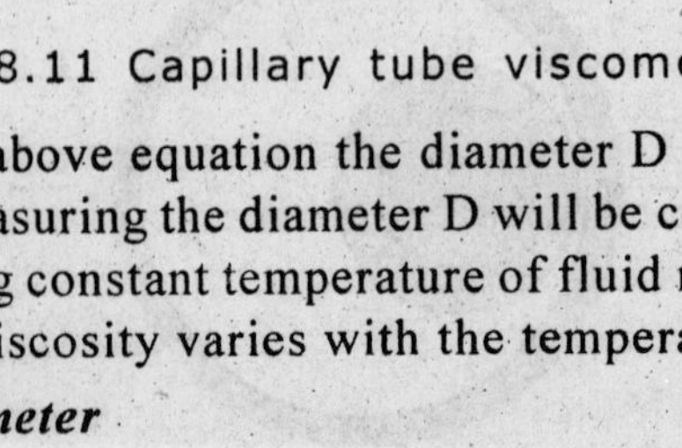

Fig.8.11 Capillary tube viscometer

It can be noticed that in the above equation the diameter D appears to the fourth power and therefore any error in measuring the diameter D will be considerably magnified. Also the importance of maintaining constant temperature of fluid need not be over emphasised in view of the fact that the viscosity varies with the temperature.

Concentric Cylinder Viscometer

This type of viscometer works on the principle of Newton's law of viscosity $\tau = \mu$ (du/dy). By measuring the velocity gradient du/dy and the shear stress τ, the viscosity of the fluid μ is determined. As shown in Fig. 8.12 a thin film of the liquid, the viscosity of which is to be determined, is enclosed between two co-axial cylinders. The outer cylinder rotates at a known speed while the inner cylinder is stationary and is suspended by a torsion wire. The torque-deflection curve for this wire is previously obtained. The torque on the inner cylinder, when the outer one rotates at a constant speed, can be measured and thus the shear stress τ can be computed.

In Fig. 8.12 let R_1 and R_2 be the radii of the inner and outer cylinders such that difference $(R_2 - R_1)$ is very small, and let space between the two cylinders be filled with liquid under consideration. If the outer cylinder rotate at a speed of N rpm, the liquid velocity at the surface of the outer cylinder will be $2\pi R_2 N/60$, while the inner one is stationary. Hence, a velocity gradient that is developed is,

$$\frac{du}{dy} = \frac{2\pi R_2 N}{60(R_2 - R_1)}$$

The torque T on the inner cylinder can be measured by the deflection of the torsion wire attached to the inner cylinder. If h is the depth of the liquid in the cylinder, the torque T and shear stress τ can be related as,

$$T = 2\pi R_1^2 h\tau$$

or

$$\tau = \frac{T}{2\pi R_1^2 h}$$

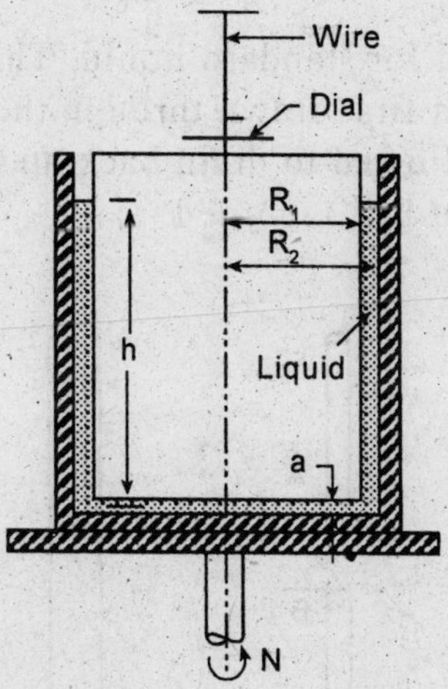

Fig.8.12 Concentric cylinder viscometer

Substituting these values of τ and du/dy, in Newton's law of viscosity; the viscosity μ can be obtained as

$$\mu = \frac{15\,T(R_2 - R_1)}{\pi^2 R_1^2 R_2 h N} \tag{8.32}$$

In order to determine torque T from the deflection θ of the wire, the calibration curve of the wire is needed. The torque contribution from the bottom of the cylinder can be appreciable if the clearance between the two cylinders at their bottom is very small. If it is large, then the torque contribution from the bottom can be neglected. For very small clearance the torque T can be computed from equation

$$T = \frac{\mu \pi^2 N R_1^2}{15}\left(\frac{R_1^2}{4a} + \frac{R_2 h}{R_2 - R_1}\right) \tag{8.33}$$

in which a is the clearance between bottoms of the cylinders.

Two common viscometers of the torque type are the Stormer and Mac Michael instruments.

Ostwald Viscometer

This is another type of capillary tube viscometer in which the pressure causing the flow is due to the weight of the liquid itself. In this instrument a constant quantity of liquid is allowed to flow through a certain distance and the time for this flow is recorded. This is done for some standard liquid of known viscosity μ_o and density ρ_o. Any other liquid of viscosity μ_1 and density ρ_1 is allowed to flow the same distance and the time t_1 is recorded. From proportionality, the viscosity μ_1 is obtained as

$$\mu_1 = \mu_o \frac{\rho_1 t_1}{\rho_o t_o} \tag{8.34}$$

in which t_o is the time required for standard liquid. The Ostwald viscometer is shown in Fig. 8.13 in which the liquid is first drawn through the capillary tube into the bulb well above the mark A. It is then allowed to drain back and the time required for the flow of the liquid from point A to point B is recorded.

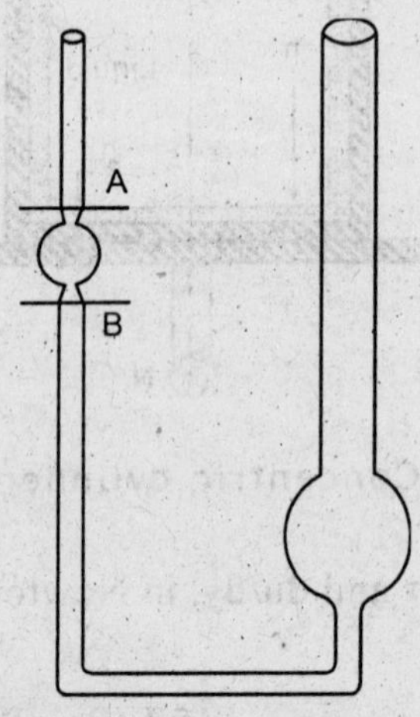

Fig.8.13 Ostwald viscometer

A number of viscometers have been developed which work on the same principle as that of Ostwald viscometer. In all these types, the viscosity, the density and the time for a standard liquid have to be known to determine the viscosity of another liquid of known density.

Saybolt Viscometer

Another commonly used viscometer is the Saybolt viscometer which has been developed for measurement of the viscosity of oils. There are two Saybolt instruments, the Saybolt Universal which is used for lubricating oils and the Saybolt Furol, which is employed for determining the viscosity of heavy fuel oils and liquid asphaltic materials. Both of them have the same general design but the dimensions of their components are a little different.

The Saybolt viscometer consists of an oil tube, a constant temperature bath, a receiver, a thermometer, a timer and a withdrawal tube. Time required for the flow of 60 cc of the liquid through the tube is measured under a falling head. That time in seconds is the Saybolt reading. The device measures the kinematic viscosity which can be obtained by rearranging the Hagen Poiseuille's equation as

$$\frac{\mu}{\rho} = \frac{gh\,\pi\,D^4}{128\,Ql}$$

in which Q is the volume of liquid flowing per unit time. Thus

$$\nu = \frac{gh\,\pi\,D^4 t}{128\,(\text{vol.})\,l} - C_2/t \qquad (8.35)$$

There is a subtractive correction C_2/t which has to be applied to this value of kinematic viscosity. The diameter of the capillary tube for this Saybolt Universal is 0.75 cm to 0.178 cm and the length is 1.215 cm to 1.235 cm. The corresponding values for Saybolt Furol are D = 0.313 cm and 1.235 m. The equations of viscosity for these instruments are:-

Saybolt Universal $\quad \dfrac{\mu}{\rho} = 0.0022\,t - \dfrac{1.80}{t}$

Saybolt Furol $\quad \dfrac{\mu}{\rho} = 0.0022\,t - \dfrac{2.03}{t}$

The form of equation for Saybolt viscometer can be obtained from dimensional considerations discussed in Chapter7. The time t should depend on μ and ρ for the liquid, the diameter d and length l of capillary tube, and g. Hence one can write

$$t = f(\mu, \rho, g, l, d)$$

Taking ρ, l and g as the repeating variables, one gets

$$\frac{t}{\sqrt{l/g}} = f_1\left(\frac{\mu}{\rho\sqrt{gl^3}}, \frac{d}{l}\right)$$

For constant d/l one can write

$$\frac{t}{\sqrt{l/g}} = f_2\left(\mu/\rho\sqrt{gl^3}\right) \text{ or } f_2\left(\nu/\sqrt{gl^3}\right)$$

The dimensionless form of this equation which will give rise to equation for ν quote above will be

$$\frac{\nu}{\sqrt{gl^3}} = C_1 \frac{t}{\sqrt{l/g}} + C_2 \frac{\sqrt{l/g}}{t}$$

which simplifies to

$$\nu = C_1 gl\, t + \frac{c_2 l^2}{t}$$

This indicates the dependence of coefficients of t and $\frac{1}{t}$ on g and l.

Figure 8.14 shows the Saybolt viscometer. The oil tube is immersed in a consta temperature bath which permits the determination of viscosity at different temperature The liquid to be tested is poured in the large reservoir and is allowed to flow through tl outlet tube by removing the cork beneath it. The liquid fills the glass container having mark indicating a value of 60 cc and the time in seconds to fill up the volume of 60 cc noted. From the above mentioned formulae, the viscosity in poise can be computed. Saybc Universal viscometer can be satisfactorily used upto a temperature of 100°C.

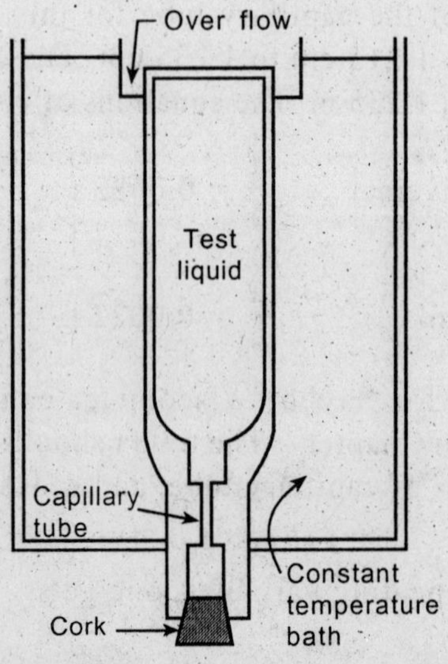

Fig.8.14 Saybolt viscometer

Example 8.3

Determine the velocity of rise of an air bubble of 1.00 mm diameter through an oil of kinematic viscosity 40 cst (centistokes)

Assume Stokes' law to be valid. Therefore, the resisting force will be

$$F_D = 3\pi\, D\, \mu\, U$$

which will act in the downward direction. This will be balanced by the buoyancy force, equal to weight of fluid displaced.

$$F_B = \rho g \times \frac{\pi D^3}{6}$$

Equating the two, one gets, $U = \dfrac{gD^2}{18\nu}$

$$\therefore \quad U = \frac{9.81\times(1\times10^{-3})^2}{18\times(40\times10^{-6})} = 0.0136 \text{ m/s}$$

The Reynolds number will be $Re = \dfrac{0.0136\times1\times10^{-3}}{40\times10^{6}} = 0.34.$

Hence the assumption made at the begining is reasonable.

Example 8.4

Fine quartz particle of 0.14 mm diameter is found to have 15.0 mm/s fall velocity in water at 13°C. Calculate the fall velocity of quartz particles when their concentration is 0.189 by volume. Take $\mu = 0.0012$ N s/m^2

Here $C = 0.189$

For using Maude and Whitmore's method, ud/ν is

$$Re = 0.015 \times 0.00014 \times 998/0.0012 = 1.75$$

The value of n obtained by interpolation is

$$n = 4.4 - \frac{0.70}{9.0} \times 0.75 = 4.34$$

$$\therefore \quad \frac{15}{U_c} = (1 - 0.189)^{-4.34}$$

$$= 2.482$$

$$\therefore \quad U_c = 15 \mid 2.482 = 6.044 \text{ mm/s}$$

Example 8.5

A 80 mm diameter cylinder is mounted concentrically in a drum of 81.5 mm internal diameter. The space between the two is filled with oil to a depth of 20 cm. If a torque of 5.0 N m is required to rotate the cylinder at 500 rpm, determine the dynamic viscosity of the oil.

$$\tau = \mu \frac{du}{dy}$$

$$T = 2\pi\ R_1^2\ h\tau$$

$$\mu = \frac{T}{2\pi R_1^2 h\left(\frac{du}{dy}\right)}$$

But $\frac{du}{dy} = \frac{2\pi R_2 N}{60\,(R_2 - R_1)} = \frac{2\times 3.142\times 0.0815\times 500}{60\times 0.0015}$

$$= 2845.25\ s^{-1}$$

$$\therefore \quad \mu = \frac{5.00}{2\times 3.142\times (.04)^2 \times 0.20\times 2845.25}$$

$$= 0.874\ N\ s/m^2$$

8.10 Transition from Laminar to Turbulent Flow

In the begining of this chapter a brief mention was made about the laminar and turbulent flows and the significance of the Reynolds number. Osborne Reynolds was the first to study the flow characteristics extensively and to investigate the criterion for the change of the laminar flow into the turbulent flow. He studied this with an apparatus shown in Fig. 8.15 which consists of a glass tube with a bell mouthed entrance inserted in a supply reservoir. At the other end of the glass tube a valve is fitted which controls the flow rate. A small container of dye is so arranged that it discharges a fine streak of dye into the bell mouthed end of the glass tube through a fine nozzle. If the valve at the end of the glass tube is opened gradually, initially the filament of dye remains well defined as a streak of colour. This state of flow continues as the valve is opened further, until a velocity is reached at which the filament of dye begins to waver. With further increase in velocity the fluctuations in the colour thread become more intense and at last the dye diffuses over the cross-section of the tube. Thus the behaviour of this dye indicates the nature of flow, see Fig. 8.15.

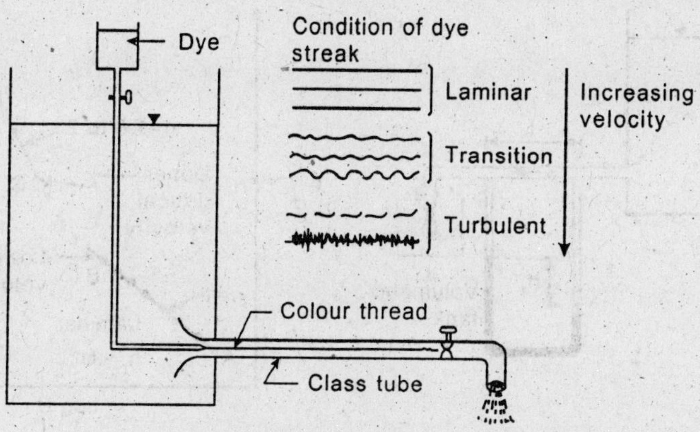

Fig.8.15 Reybolds experiment and results

The flow in which coloured filament travels straight and does not mix with fluid layers above or below it is known as the laminar flow. In the case of laminar flow the fluid molecules from one layer move into a layer above or below it by molecular diffusion only. However, with increase in velocity a stage is reached (which is indicated by the blurring of the coloured thread) when there must be a continuous exchange of fluid masses at right angles to the direction of flow. Such flow is known as the turbulent flow. It is because of this continuous exchange of fluid masses that the coloured molecules mix with several layers. In between these two stages is the transition stage. The velocity at which the flow changes from laminar to transition for the case of a given fluid at a given temperature and in a given pipe is known as the *lower critical* velocity. Such a change from laminar to turbulent flow in a pipe occurs at a Reynolds number ($UD\,\rho/\mu$) of approximately 2100. The velocity at which flow ceases to be turbulent is known as upper critical velocity; the corresponding Reynolds numbers are known as the lower and upper critical reynolds numbers.

Another distinguishing feature between the laminar and the turbulent flow is the relationship between energy gradient and velocity, which can be obtained by performing a simple experiment. The apparatus required consists of a pipe of known diameter to which a manometer is connected for measuring the head loss h_f occurring in a length l of the pipe (see Fig. 8.16a). For any particular discharge, the head loss can be obtained from the manometer reading and the average velocity can be determined from measured discharge. Several values of the head loss can thus be obtained for the corresponding values of the velocity. The data can be plotted with the energy gradient h_f/l as ordinate and velocity U as abscissa. A plot on a logarithmic scale is more convenient as shown in Fig. 8.16 (b). The curve consists of two straight lines which are connected by a smooth transition. The first portion AB has a slope of unity while second line CD has an inclination of about 1.8. The line AB corresponds to the laminar flow, while the line CD indicates turbulent flow. Between the points B and C, the flow is in a transitional stage. The velocity indicated by point B is the lower critical velocity, while the velocity at which flow ceases to be turbulent i.e., U_c is the *upper critical* velocity.

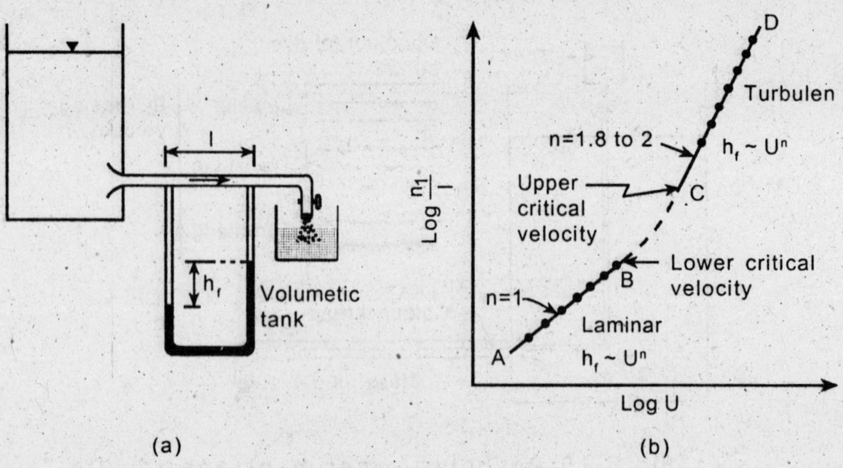

Fig.8.16 Experiment for flow classification

Since the slope of the line AB is unity, the head loss for the laminar flow is proportional to the first power of velocity which is evident from Hagen-Poiseuille's law. For the turbulent flow, indicated by the line CD, the loss is proportional to a power of velocity greater than one, the power varying from 1.75 to 2.

8.11 Instability of Laminar Flow

Considerable research is being conducted about the mechanism of transition from laminar flow to turbulent flow, According to the present day knowledge, this is explained on the basis of the concept of instability of laminar flow. In any flow there are always present disturbances of various magnitudes as are caused by the inlet to the pipe, pump vibration, etc. These are essentially longitudinal and transverse velocity components superimposed on the main flow. These components vary with time also. In the laminar flow there are two forces which ultimately decide whether these disturbances will be damped or amplified. The inertial forces associated with the fluid mass try to amplify these disturbances; on the other hand the viscous forces try to damp the disturbance.

This inertial tendency of a fluid to cause the amplification of the disturbance is shown schematically in Fig. 8.17 for two layers of a viscous fluid flowing at different velocities. If a disturbance is caused at the surface of discontinuity, it will alter the spacing between adjacent streamlines in the two layers. A reduction in spacing means increase in velocity and corresponding decrease in pressure. On the other hand increase in spacing means reduction in velocity and increase in pressure. The resulting pressure difference across the surface of discontinuity increases the displacement of stream lines at all points in the direction of initial deviation. However, since the velocity of the upper layer is greater than that of the lower layer, the crests of the disturbance will travel faster than the trough while they increase in magnitude, and a series of vortices will be formed at the surface of discontinuity.

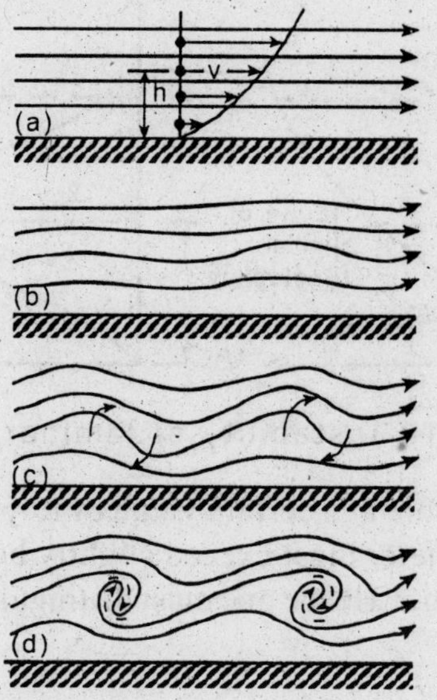

Fig.8.17 Instability at the surface of discontinuity

Depending on the flow and the fluid characteristics such as mass density, viscosity, velocity gradient, proximity of the boundary, etc., such disturbances are either damped or amplified. If the disturbance is damped, the flow remains laminar. On the other hand if the disturbance is amplified the flow is unstable and ultimately becomes turbulent. In the laminar (or stable) flow the energy associated with the disturbance is absorbed by the main flow and hence the disturbance is damped. In unstable flow, the disturbances extract energy from the main flow and hence they are amplified.

Rouse has developed a criterion for the stability of laminar flow at any point and has presented a parameter χ (chi) in the following form:

$$\chi = \frac{y^2 \rho \dfrac{du}{dy}}{\mu} \qquad (8.36)$$

where y is the distance from boundary, du/dy is the velocity gradient at y, ρ is the mass density and μ is the fluid viscosity. With this parameter Rouse found that if the magnitude of χ exceeded 500, the laminar flow would become unstable. Therefore, if parameter χ does not approach 500 at any point in a given flow, such flow is inherently stable.

It can be observed from the structure of the parameter χ that if the viscosity is large, the χ parameter will be small and the flow will tend to be stable. On the other hand if ρ, y and du/dy are large, the χ value will be large and the flow will tend to be unstable. The χ parameter will be zero at the wall, (where y = 0) and also at the centre of the pipe (where du/dy is zero). At some intermediate distance, χ will attain a maximum value as shown in Figure. 8.18. Hence if χ exceeds the limiting value, instability will be created at this point first.

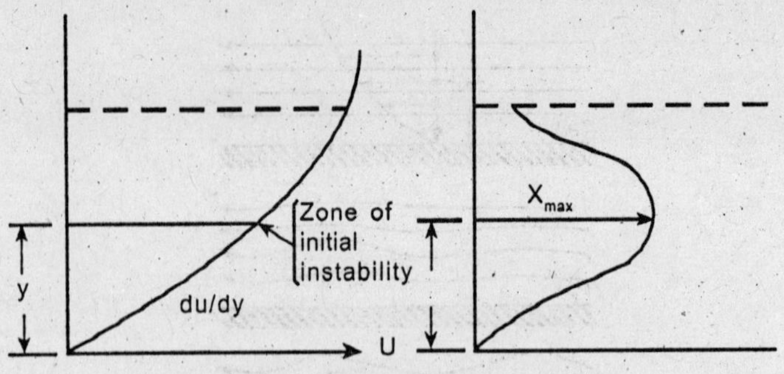

Fig.8.18 Instability of laminar flow

After the flow becomes unstable at a certain value of Reynolds number or χ parameter, the Reynolds number or χ parameter must exceed slightly before the instability leads to a transition and then to turbulent flow. Hence one must distinguish between point of instability and the point of transition.

Example 8.6

Obtain an expression for χ_{max} in terms of velocity U, diameter D and kinematic viscosity ν for laminar flow in pipe.

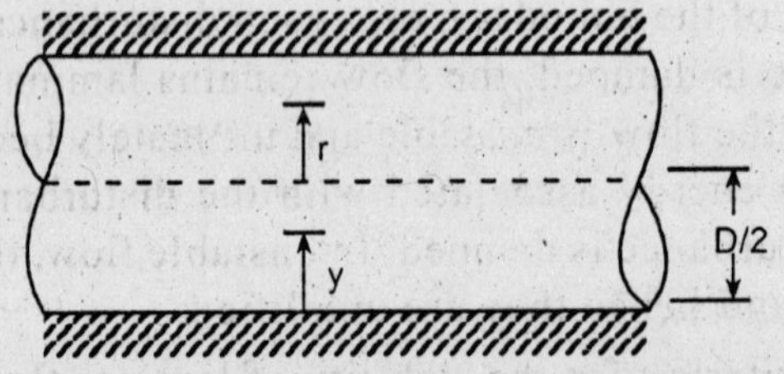

Fig.8.19

In pipe
$$\frac{du}{dy} = -\frac{du}{dr}$$

$$\left(\text{Since } y = \frac{D}{2} - r \qquad \therefore dy = -dr\right)$$

$$\tau = -\frac{dp}{dx}\frac{r}{2} = \mu\frac{du}{dy}$$

$$\therefore \quad \frac{du}{dy} = -\frac{du}{dr} = -\frac{dp}{dx}\frac{r}{2\mu}$$

From Hagen -Poiseuille equation

$$\frac{dp}{dx} = -\frac{32\mu U}{D^2}$$

So $$\frac{du}{dy} = 16\,\frac{Ur}{D^2} \text{ and } y = \frac{D}{2} - r$$

$$\therefore \quad \chi = \left(\frac{D}{2} - r\right)^2 \left(\frac{16\,Ur}{D^2}\right) \frac{\rho}{\mu}$$

Differentiating the above equation with respect to r and equating it to zero, one gets $r = \frac{D}{6}$ for χ to be maximum.

Therefore,

$$\chi_{max} = \left(\frac{D}{2} - \frac{D}{6}\right)^2 \left(\frac{16\,UD}{6\,D^2}\right) \frac{\rho}{\mu} = \frac{8}{27}\,\frac{UD}{\nu}$$

8.12 Blood Circulation in Human Body

It is interesting to discuss briefly the circulation of blood in human body in order to understand the fluid mechanics aspects of the problem. The mean pressure of the blood leaving the left ventricle of the heart in a man is about 1.33×10^4 N/m² while it falls to about 0.13×10^4 N/m² by the time the blood returns to the heart. The velocity of flow ranges from 0.10 m/s in arteries (1 to10 mm in diameter) to 10^{-3} m/s or less in capillaries (about 8 mm in diameter). The dynamic viscosity of blood can be taken as 0.0035 Ns/m² and a mass density of about 1.06×10^3 kg/m³. The critical Reynolds number at which flow changes from laminar to turbulent condition is found to be about 800, which is considerably lower than the value 2100 mentioned earlier. Curvature in arteries, sharp bends and branching are partly responsible for such low value of critical Reynolds number. Hence turbulent flow is expected to occur in arteries of 3.0 mm and larger, while laminar flow occurs in smaller diameter arteries. Estimation of resistance to blood flow becomes complicated because as the arteries branch, turbulence is generated and flow in the arteries is seldom fully established. Another feature of arterial flow is its pulsatory nature. The pressure wave created by pulsatory flow travels at a speed of 10 to 20 times that of blood flow. However, due to elastic nature of walls the arteries expand during high pressure (systolic) and collapse during low pressure (diastolic). The combined effect of these two actions is to offset the fluctuations in blood flow. Hence the pulsatory flow is nearly damped by the time blood reaches smaller arteries and capillaries.

Each ventricle discharges about 8.3×10^{-5} m³/s of blood. Knowing the pressure differences it has been estimated that the mechanical power outputs of left and right heart are 1.1 W and 0.2 W respectively. During heavy exercise the maximum output is of the order of 7 to 8 W.

Ejection from the heart into the arota is remarkably rapid, occurring with an acceleration of 10–50 m/s² and with a peak velocity as high as 1 m/s. In spite of this, kinetic energy of flow is but a small fraction of the energy of the heart beat. The major fraction of the pulse energy appear as elastic inflation of the arota.

PROBLEMS

8.1 Oil having a relative density of 0.75 and dynamic viscosity of 0.08 poise flows through a horizontal pipe of 2.25 cm diameter and 15 in length. Compute the pressure drop in order to maintain the flow of 0.15 *l*/s.

8.2 A power of 61.75 kW is required to maintain a flow of 5.5 *l*/s of oil through a 7.5 cm diameter and 1.6 km long pipe. Determine the dynamic viscosity of the oil if the flow is laminar.

8.3 An oil of R.D. 0.9 and viscosity 1.196×10^{-1} kg/m s flows through a 2.5 cm pipe with a pressure drop of 34.3 kN/ m² in a length of 30 m. Determine the discharge, shear stress intensity at the pipe wall and the power required to maintain the flow.

8.4 What size of pipe should be installed to carry a discharge of 7.0 *l*/s of fuel oil if a head loss of 6.0 m is permissible in a length of 300 m. Take ν to be 2.04 St and R.D. of the oil as 0.90.

8.5 It is required to transport 20.0 *l*/s of castor oil at 20°C to a distance of 500.0 m. Determine the size of the pipe that should be installed if permissible energy gradient is 0.02. What power will be required for such a transport?

8.6 The velocity distribution for flow between parallel plates is given by $u=(dp/dx)(y^2 - Dy)/2\mu$ where D is the distance between the plates and u is the velocity at a vertical distance y from the bottom plate. Show that the average velocity is 2/3 the maximum velocity.

8.7 Assuming that Stokes' law is applicable upto Reynolds number equal to four, determine the diameter of hard wood sphere of R.D. 0.75 which can rise in kerosene at 20°C at a uniform velocity of 1.0 cm/s ?

8.8 For laminar flow through a 7.5 cm dia. pipe with glycerine (ρ = 1260 kg/m³ and μ = 0.718kg/m s) the shear stress at the wall was found to be 284.4 N/m². Determine (i) pressure gradient (ii) average velocity, and (iii) Reynolds number.

8.9 If a lead sphere of 1.0 mm diameter having a R.D. of 11.2 has a terminal fall velocity of 0.7 cm/s in a fluid of R.D. 1.26, determine the dynamic viscosity of the fluid and ascertain that the Reynolds number is within the Stokes' range.

8.10 Determine the viscosity of an oil filled in the space between two concentric cylinders of radii 12 cm and 12.5 cm and length 30 cm if a torque of 0.98 N m is required to maintain a speed of 60 rpm.

8.11 What is the viscosity of a fluid which requires 40 s for flow of 16 cc through a capillary tube viscometer having a tube diameter 2.0 mm and length of 30 cm ? The pressure difference is equivalent to 20 cm of water.

8.12 Following data are obtained from a capillary tube viscometer:

Temperature of water 20 C

Volume of water 69.5 cc

Time of collection 400 s

Diameter of capillary tube 2.0 mm

Loss of head in 1.0 m = 4.5 cm

Determine viscosity of water in poise.

8.13 A container is filled upto a depth of 15 cm with a liquid of R.D. 0.9. A 1.5 mm diameter vertical tube 30 cm long is attached to the bottom of the container. Estimate the discharge in l/s through the tube if dynamic viscosity of the liquid is 3.5×10^{-3} kg/m s.

8.14 The slipper bearing shown in Fig. 8.7 moves towards left with a velocity of 1.5 m/s. The other data are:

$L = 30$ cm, $h_1 = 0.075$ cm, $h_2 = 0.025$ cm and $\mu = 0.075$ kg/ms. Find the maximum load which can be sustained by the bearing. Also find the maximum pressure intensity.

8.15 For laminar flow between parallel plates determine the value of y at which the χ parameter will have the maximum value. Express this in terms of Reynolds number.

8.16 Oil of dynamic viscosity 0.835 kg/m s flows through two parallel plates kept 2 cm apart. If the velocity midway between the plates is 6 m/s, what is the pressure gradient in the direction of flow? Also determine average velocity.

8.17 From Hagen-Poiseuille law obtain an expression for head loss h_f in a pipe of diameter D and length L in term of Reynolds number Re and velocity head $U^2/2g$.

8.18 Show that the power absorbed due to viscous resistance in a bush bearing shown below is

$$P = \frac{\pi^3 D^3 \mu L N^2}{3600\, b}$$

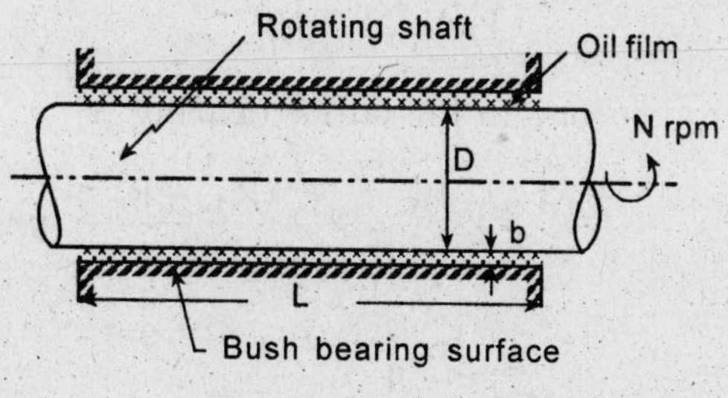

Prob.8.18

8.19 A 7.5 cm diameter shaft runs at 1200 rpm in a sleeve with a radial clearance of 0.1 mm. If the sleeve is 10 cm long and space is filled with oil having a dynamic viscosity of 0.096 kg/m s, determine the torque resistance.

8.20 A 10 cm diameter pipe carries oil of R.D. 0.97 at the rate of 21 l/s. Two sections A and B are located on the pipe in such a way that A is 2 m above B and the distance between AB is 200 m. If the oil flows from A to B find the pressure difference between the sections. (Take $\mu = 0.96$ kg/m s).

8.21 A solid cylinder of 10.0 cm diameter and 24.0 cm length which weighs 9.8 N slides vertically downwards inside a vertical cylindrical tube of 10.20 cm inside diameter. The space between the two is filled with crude oil of dynamic viscosity of 4.41×10^{-1} kg/m s. Determine the velocity at which the solid cylinder will slide vertically.

8.22 Compute α and β for laminar flow in a circular pipe.

8.23 Determine the velocity of fall through air ($\mu = 1.85 \times 10^{-5}$ kg/m s) of mist droplets having a diameter of 2.92×10^{-2} mm.

8.24 Show that for the cone bearing shown in the figure, the torque T required to rotate the shaft at a constant angular velocity of ω radius per second is

$$T = \frac{\pi\mu\omega}{2d} H^4 \tan^3\theta \sec\theta$$

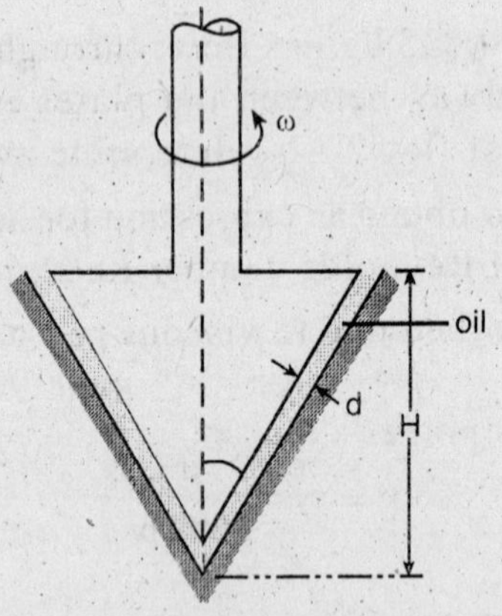

Prob.8.24

8.25 Show that the power absorbed in the collar bearing is

$$P = \frac{\pi^3 \mu N^2 (R_2^4 - R_1^4)}{1800\,b} \text{ W}$$

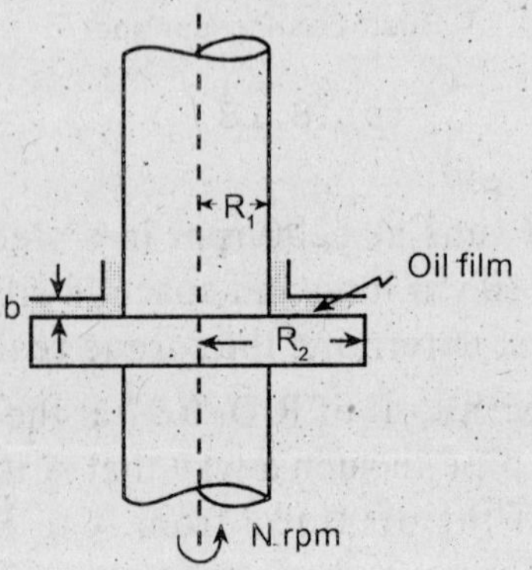

Prob.8.25

CHAPTER NINE

BOUNDARY LAYER THEORY

9.1 Introduction

It has been emphasised in the previous Chapter that the flow of real fluids differs from flow of an ideal fluid in certain respects. It was pointed out that in the case of real fluids, however small their viscosity may be, the fluid particles adhere to the boundary and hence the condition of *no slip* prevails. If the wall or boundary is stationary, the fluid velocity at the wall is zero. However, if the wall is moving, the fluid adhering to the wall will have the same velocity as the wall itself. Farther away from the wall, the velocity will be necessarily higher and as such there is a velocity gradient $\partial u/\partial y$. As a result the fluid exerts a shear or tangential stress

$$\tau_o = \mu \left(\frac{\partial u}{\partial y}\right)_{y=0}$$

on the wall in the direction of motion. The force caused by this stress in the direction of motion is known as surface drag or drag. The wall in turn exerts a force on the fluid which is equal in magnitude but opposite in direction to the drag mentioned above. This is known as shear resistance to flow, see Fig. 9.1.

Because of no slip condition, the fluid is always retarded at and near the boundary. Farther away from the boundary, this retardation due to presence of viscosity is negligible. Hence at greater distance from the wall, the velocity remains constant if the flow is parallel as in Fig. 9.1, or the velocity variation at such great distances can be predicted by ideal fluid theory since variation is due to change in boundary shape. For high velocity flows and provided the fluid does not separate away from the boundary (e.g. in converging flows) this retardation of the fluid due to viscosity is limited to a thin layer near the boundary which is commonly known as *boundary layer*. Formation of boundary layer gives rise to frictional resistance to flow. It may be pointed out that in the vicinity of the boundary, the velocity gradient is very large and hence even if the fluid has small viscosity, the corresponding shear stress is of appreciable magnitude.

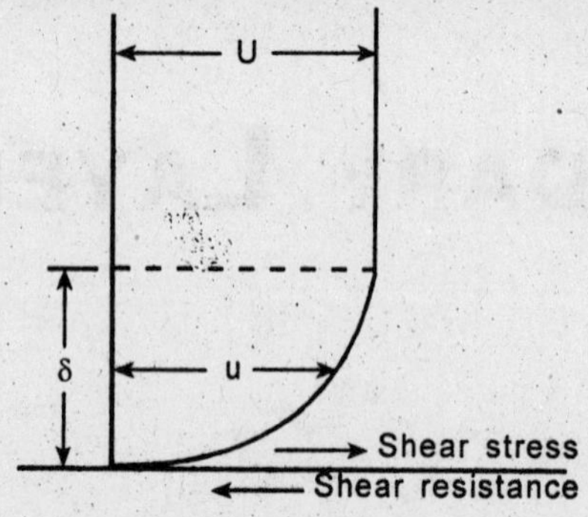

Fig.9.1 Definition sketch

The concept of boundary layer was first introduced by Ludwig Prandtl in 1904. Later, under his guidance, several of his students analysed the mathematical details of boundary layer formed under a variety of conditions. Since several branches of engineering concern with fluid flow – such as open channel flow, flow through pipes, lubrication, aeronautics, chemical engineering – one is always confronted with problems of relative motion between solid wall or an immersed body and the real fluid, concept and analysis of boundary layers assume prime importance. It is not an exaggeration if it is said that there is rarely problem of real fluid flow in which boundary layer concept and hence skin friction do not creep in.

9.2 Boundary Layer Thickness and its Characteristics

Consider a thin flat plate held parallel to the flow in a uniform stream of velocity U and consider the velocity distribution at any vertical (see Fig. 9.1). Theoretically, the transition of the velocity from zero to U (many times known as *ambient velocity, free stream velocity or potential velocity*) takes place asymptotically. Hence, there is difficulty in defining the thickness of the boundary layer. This difficulty is overcome by arbitrarily defining the boundary layer thickness as that distance from the plate where the velocity differs by one percent from the ambient velocity U. In other words at $y = \delta$, $u = 0.99\,U$ in which δ is the boundary layer thickness. This is many times known as *nominal thickness* of boundary layer. Two other definitions of boundary layer thickness are used in the development of boundary layer theory. The *displacement thickness* δ^* is defined as the distance the actual boundary would have to be displaced in order that the actual discharge under potential flow condition through δ^* would be the same as decreases in flow rate caused by friction. In other words,

$$U\,\delta^* = \int_0^\infty (U-u)\,dy$$

or

$$\delta^* = \int_0^\infty \left(1-\frac{u}{U}\right)dy \approx \int_0^\delta \left(1-\frac{u}{U}\right)dy$$

since beyond y values greater than δ the local velocity is almost equal to U. The *momentum thickness* θ is defined as the distance from the actual boundary such that the momentum flux through this distance θ at ambient velocity is the same as the deficit of momentum flux due to boundary layer formation. In other words,

$$\rho U^2 \theta = \int_0^{\infty} \rho u (U-u)\, dy$$

or

$$\theta = \int_0^{\infty} \frac{u}{U}\left(1-\frac{u}{U}\right) dy \approx \int_0^{\delta} \frac{u}{U}\left(1-\frac{u}{U}\right) dy$$

It can be seen that displacement thickness is smaller than nominal boundary layer thickness while momentum thickness is smaller than the displacement thickness; or $\theta < \delta^* < \delta$.

Figure 9.2 shows a thin flat plate held parallel to the flow (sometimes called as held at zero incidence), in a stream of uniform velocity U. As the fluid reaches section 1, the velocity of fluid at the boundary becomes zero and hence a velocity gradient is set up which develops shear resistance. Near the leading edge of the plate, it is only in a vary thin layer that the fluid is retarded. As this retarded layer moves downstream, continued action of shear resistance causes retardation in increasing quantities of the fluid. As a result, thickness of the boundary layer δ goes on increasing in the downstream direction as shown in Fig. 9.2. This figure also shows the velocity distributions at successive sections along the flat plate. Since the boundary layer thickness is increasing in the downstream direction and since δ represents the vertical distance in which velocity changes from 0 to 0.99 U, it is evident that the velocity gradient $(\partial u/\partial y)_{y=0}$ decreases in the downstream direction of the flow. Consequently the shear stress at the wall $\tau_o = \mu(\partial u/\partial y)_{y=0}$ decreases in the direction of the flow, from section 1 to 4.

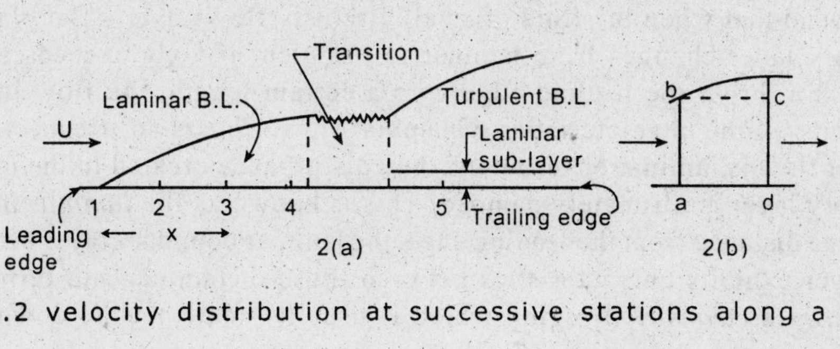

Fig.9.2 velocity distribution at successive stations along a plate

Considering the fluid passing into and out of a layer abcd (Fig. 9.2b), it can be seen that, since there is a continuous retardation of fluid along ad, fluid flowing in through ab is greater than the fluid flowing out through cd. Naturally the excess fluid must flow at right angles to bc. In other words, in the boundary layer there is a small velocity component at right angles to the direction of flow. Since the plate is nonporous, this vertical velocity component is zero along ad.

Following are the important factors which influence the boundary layer thickness δ on a flat smooth plate:

a. As discussed earlier greater the distance from the leading edge of the plate, greater is the thickness of the boundary layer.

b. Greater the ambient or free stream velocity, smaller is the boundary layer thickness at any section.

c. Greater the kinematic viscosity, greater is the boundary layer thickness.

d. Boundary layer thickness is significantly affected by the pressure gradient $\partial p/\partial x$ in the direction of flow. In the case of a flat plate in a stream of uniform velocity U, $\partial p/\partial x = 0$ i.e. the free stream velocity U does not depend on x. If the pressure decreases in the direction of flow (i.e., if the $\partial p/\partial x$ is negative) as in the case of converging flows, the resulting pressure force acts in the direction of flow and it accelerates the decelerated fluid in the boundary layer. As a result, the boundary layer growth is retarded in the presence of negative pressure gradient. The case of positive pressure gradient is more important. In the flows with positive pressure gradient (i.e., diverging flows) the fluid in the boundary layer is further decelerated, and can give rise to separation and reverse flow near the boundary.

9.3 Laminar and Turbulent Boundary Layers and Laminar Sublayer

The phenomenon of boundary layer formation along a flat plate discussed above is essentially governed by the inertial force and the viscous force which retards the motion of the fluid. Thus it is governed by the free stream velocity U, characteristic length x measured along the plate from the leading edge, mass density of fluid ρ and its dynamic viscosity μ. In other words the Reynolds number $R_{ex} = (Ux\rho/\mu)$, becomes an important parameter in the study of boundary layers.

It. has been pointed out that in the case of flow in pipes, as the Reynolds number UD/ν exceeds 2100, the character of the flow changes from laminar to turbulent. Similarly, it has been found that when the fluid of small viscosity flows over a flat plate, the flow in the boundary layer changes from laminar to turbulent if Ux/ν exceeds a certain limit; see. Fig. 9.2 a. From the leading edge upto a certain length, the flow in the boundary layer exhibits all the characteristics of laminar flow. This is so irrespective of whether the ambient flow is laminar or turbulent. Any disturbance created in the laminar flow, in the boundary layer is ultimately damped. This is known as the *laminar boundary layer.* Beyond some distance from the leading edge, the laminar boundary layer becomes unstable and the layer exhibits characteristics between those of laminar and turbulent motions. This is known as *transition region* which is usually small. At the downstream of this transition region, the flow in the boundary layer becomes turbulent. If the flow does not separate from the boundary, the boundary layer thickness continually increases. This portion of the boundary laver is known as the *turbulent boundary layer.* It will be evident that, for given flow and fluid characteristics, whether the boundary layer will be laminar alone or laminar and turbulent necessarily depends on length of the plate.

If the plate is smooth, then even though the boundary layer is turbulent, there is a very thin layer near the boundary in which the flow is still laminar. This layer is commonly known as the *laminar sublayer.*

The change of boundary layer from laminar to turbulent is primarily governed by the Reynolds number Ux/ν and by other factors such as roughness of the plate, plate curvature, pressure gradient and the intensity and scale of turbulence. In general, this critical Reynolds number varies between 3×10^5 to 6×10^5. In exceptional cases, where the ambient flow is free from any disturbances, value of critical Reynolds number can reach 10^6 or even higher. However, for practical purposes the value of critical Reynolds number Re_x can be taken as 5×10^5.

9.4 Laminar Boundary Layer

Outside the boundary layer, the effect of viscous forces on the flow pattern is negligible. On the other hand, inside the boundary layer the viscous force is a predominant force. Hence it is reasonable to assume that the inertial force and viscous force are of the same order of magnitude at the edge of the laminar boundary layer. Inertial force per unit volume is given by $\rho u(\partial u/\partial x)$ which is proportion to $\rho U^2/x$ for the case of flat plate.

Viscous force per unit volume is $(\partial\tau/\partial y)$ which for laminar flow becomes $\frac{\partial}{\partial y}(\mu\partial u/\partial y)$

i.e. $\mu(\partial^2 u/\partial y^2)$. In the boundary layer $(\partial u/\partial y) \sim (U/\delta)$; hence $(\partial\tau/\partial y) \sim \mu\, U/\delta^2$. If these two forces are proportional, one gets

$$\frac{\rho U^2}{x} = k^2 \frac{\mu U}{\delta^2}$$

or

$$\frac{\delta}{x} = \frac{k}{\sqrt{\frac{Ux}{\nu}}} \tag{9.1}$$

in which k is a constant. By analytical solution Blasius has obtained a value of 5.0 for k. Hence,

$$\frac{\delta}{x} = \frac{5.0}{\sqrt{\frac{Ux}{\nu}}} = \frac{5.0}{\sqrt{Re_x}} \tag{9.2}$$

or

$$\delta = 5\sqrt{\frac{x\nu}{U}} \tag{9.3}$$

Expression for the shear can be obtained in a similar way.

Since in the boundary layer $\left(\frac{\partial u}{\partial y}\right)_{y=0} \sim \frac{U}{\delta}$

$$\tau_o = \mu \left(\frac{\partial u}{\partial y}\right)_{y=0} \sim \mu \frac{U}{\delta} \quad (9.4)$$

Substituting the value of δ from Eq. 9.1 in Eq. 9.4 one gets,

$$\tau_o = \text{const.} \sqrt{\frac{U^3 \rho \mu}{x}}$$

$$\tau_o/(\rho U^2/2) = c_f = \frac{0.664}{\sqrt{Re_x}} \quad (9.5)$$

after introducing the experimental value of the proportionality constant obtained by Blasius. The coefficient c_f is known as the *local drag coefficient*. The total horizontal force on one side of the plate on which laminar boundary layer exists can be obtained as follows:

Total horizontal force $F_D = \int_O^L \tau_o B\, dx$

in which B is the width of the plate and L is the length on which laminar boundary layer exists. Substituting the value of τ_o from Eq. 9.5, the average drag coefficient C_f can be obtained as

$$C_f = \frac{F_D/BL}{\rho U^2/2} = \frac{1.328}{\sqrt{Re_L}} \quad (9.6)$$

in which $Re_L = (UL/\nu)$. Since the flow in the laminar boundary layer is laminar, one would expect that the velocity distribution in the vertical follows a parabolic law. This velocity distribution for flow over a flat plate, must satisfy three basic conditions., namely,

i. Since the fluid adheres to the boundary,

$$u = 0, \text{ at } y = 0$$

ii. Beyond the boundary layer thickness the velocity is constant at various y values, Hence

$$u = U \text{ at } y \text{ equal to and greater than } \delta.$$

iii. At the edge of boundary layer there is no velocity gradient, or

$$\frac{\partial u}{\partial y} = 0 \text{ and } \frac{\partial^2 u}{\partial y^2} = 0 \text{ at } y = \delta$$

A typical velocity distribution which satisfies the above conditions is given by

$$\frac{u}{U} = 2\left(\frac{y}{\delta}\right) - 2\left(\frac{y}{\delta}\right)^3 + \left(\frac{y}{\delta}\right)^4 \quad (9.7)$$

Example 9.1

Obtain values of δ^* and θ for the laminar boundary layer on a flat plate for which the velocity distribution is given by Eq.9.7.

The velocity distribution law is

$$\frac{u}{U} = 2\left(\frac{y}{\delta}\right) - 2\left(\frac{y}{\delta}\right)^3 + \left(\frac{y}{\delta}\right)^4$$

$$\delta^* = \int_0^\delta \left(1 - \frac{u}{U}\right) dy$$

$$= \int_0^\delta \left(1 - 2\left(\frac{y}{\delta}\right) + 2\left(\frac{y}{\delta}\right)^3 - \left(\frac{y}{\delta}\right)^4\right) dy$$

$$= \left[y - \frac{y^2}{\delta} + \frac{y^4}{2\delta^3} - \frac{y^5}{5\delta^4}\right]_0^\delta$$

$$= \delta\left[1 - 1 + \frac{1}{2} - \frac{1}{5}\right]$$

$$= \frac{3}{10}\delta$$

Similarly

$$\theta = \int_0^\delta \frac{u}{U}\left(1 - \frac{u}{U}\right) dy$$

$$\theta = \int_0^\delta \left[2\left(\frac{y}{\delta}\right) - 2\left(\frac{y}{\delta}\right)^3 + \left(\frac{y}{\delta}\right)^4\right] \times \left[1 - 2\left(\frac{y}{\delta}\right) + 2\left(\frac{y}{\delta}\right)^3 - \left(\frac{y}{\delta}\right)^4\right] dy$$

$$= \int_0^\delta 2\left(\frac{y}{\delta}\right) - 4\left(\frac{y}{\delta}\right)^2 + 4\left(\frac{y}{\delta}\right)^4 - 2\left(\frac{y}{\delta}\right)^5$$

$$- 2\left(\frac{y}{\delta}\right)^3 + 4\left(\frac{y}{\delta}\right)^4 - 4\left(\frac{y}{\delta}\right)^6 + 2\left(\frac{y}{\delta}\right)^7$$

$$+ \left(\frac{y}{\delta}\right)^4 - 2\left(\frac{y}{\delta}\right)^5 + 2\left(\frac{y}{\delta}\right)^7 - \left(\frac{y}{\delta}\right)^8 \Bigg] dy$$

$$= \int_0^\delta \left[2\left(\frac{y}{\delta}\right) - 4\left(\frac{y}{\delta}\right)^2 - 2\left(\frac{y}{\delta}\right)^3 + 9\left(\frac{y}{\delta}\right)^4 \right.$$

$$\left. - 4\left(\frac{y}{\delta}\right)^5 - 4\left(\frac{y}{\delta}\right)^6 + 4\left(\frac{y}{\delta}\right)^7 - \left(\frac{y}{\delta}\right)^8 \right] dy$$

$$= \delta\left[1 - \frac{4}{3} - \frac{2}{4} + \frac{9}{5} - \frac{4}{6} - \frac{4}{7} + \frac{4}{8} - \frac{1}{9}\right] = \frac{37}{315}\delta$$

It can be seen that the displacement thickness is greater than the momentum thickness.

Example 9.2

Air (ν = 1.44 × 10^{-1} stokes) flows over a 0.60 m long and 1.0m wide flat plate at a velocity of 8.0 m/s. Determine (i) the boundary layer thickness at the end of plate, (ii) shear stress at 0.30 m from the leading edge and (iii) total drag force on both sides of the plate. Take ρ = 1.208 kg / m³

$$R_{eL} = \frac{UL}{\nu} = \frac{8.0 \times 0.60}{1.44 \times 10^{-5}} = 3.33 \times 10^5$$

Hence the boundary layer remains laminar over the entire length of the plate.

(i) $$\delta_{x = 60cm} = 5\sqrt{\frac{0.144 \times 60}{800}} = 5\sqrt{0.0108}$$

$$= 0.52 \text{ cm}$$

(ii) shear stress at 30 cm from the leading edge

$$c_f = \frac{0.664}{\sqrt{Re_x}} = \frac{0.664}{\sqrt{\frac{800 \times 30}{0.144}}} = \frac{0.664}{\sqrt{1.667 \times 10^5}} = 0.00163$$

$$(\tau_o)_{x = 30cm} = \frac{.00163 \times 1.208 \times 8^2}{2} = 0.063 \text{ N/m}^2$$

(iii) Total drag force on both sides of the plate

$$C_f = \frac{1.328}{Re_L^{1/2}} = \frac{1.328}{\sqrt{3.33 \times 10^5}} = 0.00231$$

$$F_D = 2 \times BL \times C_f \frac{\rho U^2}{2} = 2 \times 0.6 \times 1.0 \times 0.00231 \times 1.208 \times 8^2$$

$$= 0.214 \text{ N}$$

9.5 Turbulent Boundary Layer

Once the boundary layer changes from laminar to turbulent, there is considerable mixing between different layers of the fluid in the boundary layer. In turbulent flow there is a continuous exchange of fluid mass from a layer of lower velocity to a layer of higher velocity and vice versa. This brings about an equalising effect on the velocity distribution. As a result the velocity distribution in the turbulent boundary layer is much more uniform than that in the laminar boundary layer. The velocity distribution in the major portion of the turbulent boundary layer follows a logarithmic law i.e. $u \sim \log y$. It can also be represented by power law i.e. $(u/U) = (y/\delta)^m$. The value of the exponent m was originally found to be 1/7; however it is now known that m varies with the Reynolds number. With the increase in Reynolds number m changes from about 1/6 to 1/10. In the case of laminar sub-layer the velocity distribution is parabolic. However, since the laminar sublayer thickness δ' is very small, the velocity distribution can be approximated by a straight line relationship.

The expressions for δ, c_f and C_f for the turbulent boundary layer are as follows:

$$\frac{\delta}{x} = 0.377 / Re_x^{1/5} \qquad (9.8)$$

$$c_f = 0.059/Re_x^{1/5} \qquad (9.9)$$

$$C_f = 0.074/Re_L^{1/5} \qquad (9.10)$$

It can be seen from Eqs. 9.2 and 9.8 that the boundary layer thickness increases as $x^{1/2}$ for laminar case while it increases as $x^{4/5}$ for turbulent case. Hence the turbulent boundary layer thickness increases much faster than the laminar boundary layer thickness. Another characteristic of the turbulent boundary layer is that, near the boundary large velocity change occurs in a relatively small vertical distance. As a result $(\partial u/\partial y)_{y=0}$ is much larger for turbulent boundary layer than for the laminar boundary layer. Hence the shear stresses are large in turbulent boundary layer. In fact there is a steep rise in τ_o as boundary layer changes from laminar to turbulent and then it decreases, with increase in x values.

Equation 9.6 for the average drag coefficient is applicable provided Reynolds number is less than 5×10^5. Equation 9.10 is applicable within the range 5×10^5 to 2×10^7 of the Reynolds number provided the boundary layer is turbulent from the leading edge. This means that some special measures must be taken to make the boundary layer turbulent right from the leading edge, or the length of plate over which laminar boundary layer exists is small as compared to the total length of the plate. However, for Reynolds numbers slightly exceeding 5×10^5, an appreciable fraction of the upstream flat plate is covered with laminar boundary layer and this decreases the drag. This reduction in drag is taken into account by introducing a subtractive term in Eq. 9.10. In such cases, where the plate is covered with laminar and turbulent boundary layers, Eq. 9.11 as proposed by Prandtl can be used.

$$C_f = \frac{0.074}{Re_L^{1/5}} - \frac{1700}{Re_L} \qquad (9.11)$$

It may be mentioned that the constant 1700 depends on the Reynolds number at which the laminar boundary layer becomes turbulent. Below are given the values of this constant for various critical Reynolds numbers.

TABLE 9.1

Variation of Constant in Eq. 9.11 with Critical Reynolds Number

Critical Re_x	3×10^5	5×10^5	10^6	3×10^6
Constant	1050	1700	3300	8700

Equation 9.11 is applicable for Reynolds number values between 5×10^5 and 10^7. In practical problems concerning steamers and large air plane wings, however, Re_L, exceeds even 10^7. In such cases, Eq. 9.12, which is applicable at Reynolds number values 5×10^5 to 10^9, for turbulent boundary can be used.

$$C_f = \frac{0.455}{(\log_{10} Re_L)^{2.58}} - \frac{A}{Re_L} \qquad (9.12)$$

in which the value of A depends on critical Reynolds number and is the same as given in Table 9.1. Equations 9.6, 9.10, 9.11 and 9.12 are plotted in Fig. 9.3 with some experimental data. It may be emphasised that when second term A/Re_L is omitted from either Eq. 9.11 or Eq. 9.12 one gets relation for C_f for a flat plate where turbulent boundary layer is assumed to start from the leading edge.

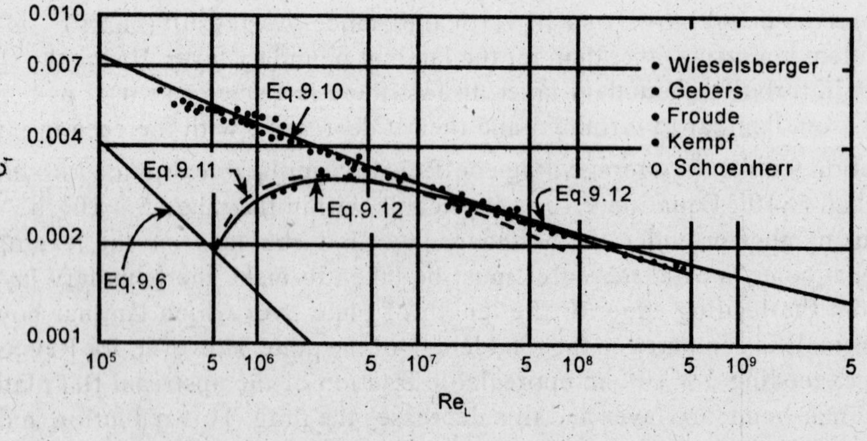

Fig.9.3 Variation of C_f with Re_L

Example 9.3

A 4.5 m wide and 36 m long smooth flat plate is towed through water ($\mu = 0.01$ poise) at a speed of 6.0 m/s. Determine the total drag on one side of the plate and the drag on the first 3 m of the plate.

$$Re_L = \frac{6 \times 36 \times 998}{0.01 \times 10^{-1}} = 2.16 \times 10^8$$

The place where boundary layer becomes turbulent is given by

$$\frac{Ux\rho}{\mu} = 5 \times 10^5$$

or

$$x = \frac{5 \times 10^5 \times 0.01 \times 10^{-1}}{6 \times 998} = 0.0830 \text{ m}$$

Since x is very small compared to the total length., it can be neglected as can be seen below. Using Eq. 9.12

$$C_f = \frac{0.455}{(8.334)^{2.58}} - \frac{1700}{2.16 \times 10^8}$$

or

$$C_f = 0.001\,92 - 7.88 \times 10^{-6}$$

$$= 0.001\,92 \text{ (since the second term is negligible).}$$

$$\therefore \quad F_D = 4.5 \times 36 \times 0.00192 \times \frac{998 \times 6^2}{2} = 5587.5 \text{ N}$$

In the second case the Reynolds number will be

$$Re_L = \frac{6 \times 3 \times 998}{0.01 \times 10^{-1}} = 1.8 \times 10^7$$

$$\therefore \quad C_f = \frac{0.074}{(1.8 \times 10^7)^{1/5}} - \frac{1700}{1.8 \times 10^7} = 0.002\,62 - 0.000\,095$$

$$= 0.002\,53$$

$$F_D = \frac{4.5 \times 3 \times 0.00253 \times 998 \times 6^2}{2}$$

$$= 613.56 \text{N}$$

9.6 Laminar Sublayer

Even in the case of turbulent boundary layer, the flow in the immediate vicinity of the smooth boundary possesses the characteristics of laminar flow. Thickness of turbulent boundary layer in which the flow is laminar is known as the *laminar sublayer* δ'.

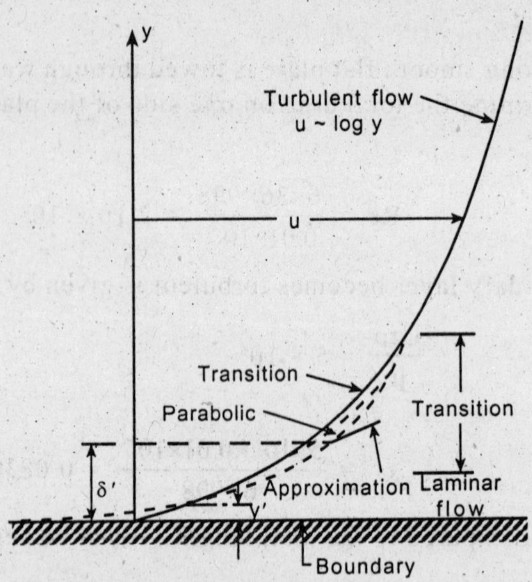

Fig.9.4 Velocity distribution in a turbulent boundary layer on a smooh flat plate

The logarithmic velocity distribution law in the turbulent boundary layer has a peculiarity that at $y = 0$ it gives minus infinite velocity and at a certain distance above the boundary, $y = y'$, it gives zero velocity. This can be explained if the existence of laminar sublayer is accepted. Since the flow in the laminar sublayer is laminar, it will follow a parabolic velocity distribution law (which can be approximated by a straight line if the thickness δ' is small); hence logarithmic law cannot be applied within this thickness. Indeed there is a gradual change from parabolic to logarithmic law as shown in Fig. 9.4. Arbitrarily the intersection of parabolic and logarithmic curves can be taken as the limit of laminar sublayer. Experimental results have shown that

$$\delta' = \frac{11.6\nu}{\sqrt{\frac{\tau_o}{\rho}}} = \frac{11.6\nu}{u_*} \tag{9.13}$$

in which $u_* = \sqrt{\tau_o/\rho}$ is known as *shear velocity* and τ_o is the average shear stress on the boundary at *x*. The concept of laminar sublayer is quite useful in classification of boundaries. It may be added that detailed flow structure within the laminar sublayer is much more complex and is a subject of investigation in recent times. Detailed observations of flow within the laminar sublayer have conclusively shown that the sublayer exhibits a remarkably regular and almost periodic variation in velocity across the flow. It has also been noticed that the sublayer consists of lengthwise vortices. However, for an elementary analysis, the simplified model of laminar sublayer given above is adequate.

9.7 Application of Momentum Equation

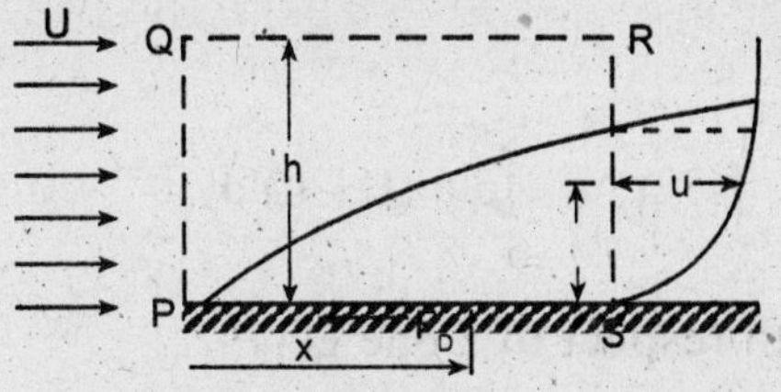

Fig.9.5 Definition sketch

Consider boundary layer development on a flat plate with zero pressure gradient, i.e. where pressure is constant along the plate and free stream velocity the same. Further assume fluid to be incompressible and flow steady. With reference to Fig. 9.5 choose P Q R S as the control volume, h being such that the upper boundary of the control volume is in undisturbed flow. Since velocity at section RS is reduced due to the formation of boundary layer, the discharge passing through section RS is less than that passing through PQ. The difference must flow out through QR. Considering unit width in the normal direction, one can write the momentum equation in the following manner.

$$\left\{\begin{array}{c}\text{Force exerted by}\\ \text{the boundary on the}\\ \text{fluid, } -F_D\end{array}\right\} = \left\{\begin{array}{c}\text{Rate of momentum}\\ \text{flux going out}\\ \text{through RS}\end{array}\right\} + \left\{\begin{array}{c}\text{Rate of momentum}\\ \text{flux going out}\\ \text{through QR}\end{array}\right\} - \left\{\begin{array}{c}\text{Rate of momentum}\\ \text{flux coming in}\\ \text{through PQ}\end{array}\right\}$$

As $\int_0^h (U-u)dy$ is the discharge flowing out through QR, and its velocity when it entered the control volume was U, the second term on right hand side becomes $\rho U \int_0^h (U-u)\, dy$.

Hence above equation becomes,

$$-F_D = \int_0^h \rho u^2\, dy + \rho U \int_0^h (U-u)dy - \int_0^h \rho U^2\, dy$$

or

$$-F_D = \int_0^h \rho u\,(u-U)\, dy$$

The force ($-F_D$) is equal to $\int_0^h \tau_0 \, dx$; therefore

$$\int_0^h \tau_0 \, dx = \int_0^h \rho \, u \, (U - u) \, dy$$

Differentiating both sides with respect to x one gets

$$\tau_o = \rho \frac{d}{dx} \int_0^h u \, (U - u) \, dy$$

It can be seen that $\int_0^h u \, (U - u) \, dy = U^2\theta$ where θ is the momentum thickness of the boundary layer. Hence one gets

$$\frac{\tau_0}{\rho} = U^2 \frac{d\theta}{dx} \tag{9.14}$$

The above equation is valid for laminar boundary layer and approximately true for turbulent boundary layer. In order to use this equation for determining δ, c_f and C_f one must assume a velocity distribution law for the boundary layer flow.

Let $\frac{u}{U} = f(\eta)$ where $\eta = \frac{y}{\delta}$ represent the velocity distribution in the boundary layer. It must satisfy at least two boundary conditions, viz. $f = 0$ at $\eta = 0$, and $f = 1$ at $\eta = 1$. Eq. 9.7 is one such distribution. Further assume that the velocity distribution has the same form for all *x* values, which is true for laminar boundary layer. Hence,

$$\theta = \int_0^\delta \frac{u}{U}\left(1 - \frac{u}{U}\right) dy = \delta \int_0^\delta f\,(1 - f)\,d\eta$$

$$= \alpha_1 \, \delta$$

where $\alpha_1 = \int_0^1 f\,(1 - f)\,d\eta$ will be constant for a given velocity distribution. Similarly since $\tau_o = \mu \, (\partial u/\partial y)_{y=0}$ one can write

$$\tau_o = \frac{\mu U}{\delta}\left(\frac{\partial f}{\partial \eta}\right)_{\eta=0} = \frac{\mu U \beta_1}{\delta}$$

where $\beta_1 = (\partial f/\partial \eta)_{\eta=0}$ will also be a constant. Substituting these values of θ and τ_o in Eq. 9.14, one obtains

$$\frac{\mu U \beta_1}{\rho \delta} = U^2 \alpha_1 \frac{d\delta}{dx}$$

integration of which gives

$$\frac{\delta^2}{2} = \frac{\mu \beta_1 x}{U \rho \alpha_1} + \text{constant}$$

The constant of integration is zero since at $x = 0$, $\delta = 0$. Therefore the above equation can be written as

$$\frac{\delta}{x} = \sqrt{\frac{2\beta_1}{\alpha_1}} \frac{1}{Re_x^{1/2}} \tag{9.15}$$

Value of δ from Eq. 9.15 can be substituted in the expression for τ_o viz. $\tau_o = \mu U \beta_1/\delta$. Subsequent rearrangement yields

$$c_f = \frac{\tau_O}{\rho U^2/2} = \sqrt{2\alpha_1\beta_1} \frac{1}{Re_x^{1/2}} \tag{9.16}$$

Equations 9.15 and 9.16 can be compared with Eqs. 9.2 and 9.5. Once the velocity distribution law is assumed, the constants in Eqs. 9.15 and 9.16 and can be evaluated. In the same way it can be shown that

$$C_f = 2\sqrt{2\alpha_1\beta_1} / Re_L^{1/2} \tag{9.16a}$$

Example 9.4

f the velocity distribution in a laminar boundary layer is given by $\frac{u}{U} = \frac{3}{2}\left(\frac{y}{\delta}\right) - \frac{1}{2}\left(\frac{y}{\delta}\right)^3$ obtain expressions for τ_o and δ.

$$\alpha_1 = \int_0^1 f(1-f)\, d\eta \text{ where } \eta = \frac{y}{\delta}$$

$$= \int_0^1 \left(\frac{3}{2}\eta - \frac{1}{2}\eta^3\right)\left(1 - \frac{3}{2}\eta + \frac{1}{2}\eta^3\right) d\eta$$

$$= \int_0^1 \left(\frac{3}{2}\eta - \frac{9}{4}\eta^3 + \frac{3}{4}\eta^4 - \frac{1}{2}\eta^3 + \frac{3}{4}\eta^4 - \frac{1}{4}\eta^6\right) d\eta$$

$$= \frac{39}{280}$$

Similarly $\quad \beta_1 = \left(\frac{\partial f}{\partial \eta}\right)_{\eta=0} = \left(\frac{3}{2} - \frac{3}{2}\eta^2\right)_{\eta=0} = \frac{3}{2}$

$$\therefore \quad \frac{\delta}{x} = \sqrt{\frac{2\beta_1}{\alpha_1}}\,\frac{1}{Re_x^{1/2}} = \sqrt{2 \times \frac{3}{2} \times \frac{280}{39}}\left(\frac{1}{Re_x^{1/2}}\right) = \frac{4.64}{Re_x^{1/2}}$$

$$c_f = \left(\sqrt{2\alpha_1\beta_1}\right)\frac{1}{Re_x^{1/2}} = \sqrt{\frac{39}{280} \times 2 \times \frac{3}{2}}\left(\frac{1}{Re_x^{1/2}}\right)$$

$$= \frac{0.646}{Re_x^{1/2}}$$

Similarly $C_f = 2\sqrt{2\alpha_1\beta_1}/Re_L^{1/2}$ which gives $C_f = 1.292/Re_L^{1/2}$

These expressions can be compared with Eqs. 9.3, 9.5 and 9.6.

9.8 Hydrodynamically Smooth and Rough Boundaries

If any surface over which the fluid flows is closely examined through a microscope, i will be found to consist of innumerable irregularities of various sizes. Assume that th average height of these irregularities is k. Then, in conventional sense, a boundary wit large values of k will be called a rough boundary and the one with smaller k value will b called smooth. However, in fluid mechanics the boundaries are classified as smooth o rough by taking into consideration the flow and the fluid characteristics in addition to th boundary characteristics.

Consider the case of a boundary of roughness height k, where the thickness of lamina sublayer δ' is much greater than k, see Fig. 9.6 (a). Since the flow outside the lamina sublayer is turbulent, eddies of various sizes are present in it. These eddies try to penetrat through the laminar sublayer and reach the roughness elements. However, because c the larger thickness of laminar sublayer and the inherent stability of laminar flow, th eddies cannot reach the roughness elements or surface irregularities and as such, thes elements are not exposed to the turbulent flow. Hence the boundary acts as a smoot boundary and is known as *hydrodynamically smooth boundary.* The resistance in suc a case is dependent only on Reynolds number.

With increase in Reynolds number the thickness of the laminar sublayer decreases an it can be much smaller than k, as shown in Fig. 9.6 (b). Being much smaller than k, th laminar sublayer is completely destroyed since most of roughness elements protrud through it. Wakes are formed behind each roughness element and there is considerab energy loss. Once the laminar sublayer is destroyed, the resistance no longer depends o Reynolds number, but depends on the relative roughness defined as roughness heig divided by characteristic length. In the case of pipes the relative roughness parameter k/D where D is the diameter of the pipe; for flat plates the corresponding parameter is k/ where L is the length of the plate. Experiments have shown that when k/δ' is less tha 0.25 the boundary acts as a hydrodynamically smooth boundary. If k/δ' is greater tha 6.0 the boundary is *hydrodynamically rough.* For $0.25 < k/\delta' < 6.0$, the boundary classified as *boundary in transition* in which the resistance depends both on Reynol number and on relative roughness.

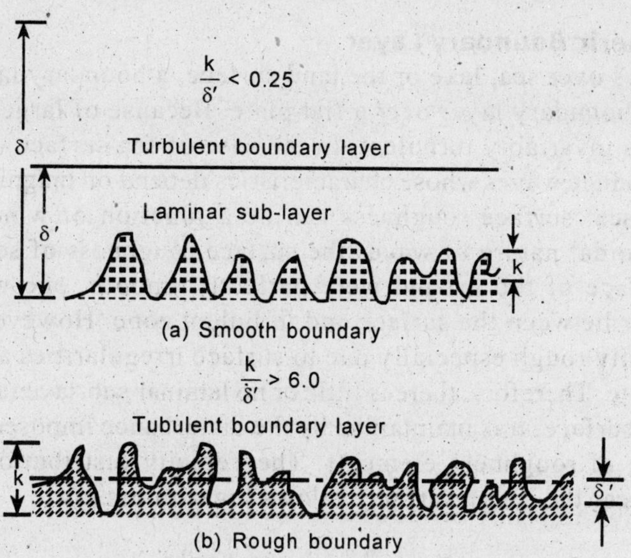

Fig.9.6 Definitions of smooth and rough boundaries flow

9.9 Boundary Layer on Rough Surface

In most practical applications connected with boundary layer development on a flat plate e.g. ships, airplane wings etc., the surface cannot be considered hydrodynamically smooth.

In the case of rough pipes, k/D is taken as the relative roughness. This is now replaced by k/δ where δ is the thickness of boundary layer. However, whereas k/D for pipe remains constant, k/δ for a flat plate will decrease in the downstream direction because of increase in δ. As a result the front portion of the plate will behave differently from its rear portion as far as the influence of roughness on drag is concerned. If one assumes that the boundary layer is turbulent from the leading edge, the front portion of the plate will act as rough followed by the transition region and the downstream portion of the plate will be hydrodynamically smooth if the plate is sufficiently long. The limits between these three regions are determined by the value of $\frac{u_* k}{\nu}$. If $\frac{u_* k}{\nu}$ is less than 5.0 the boundary is smooth, if it is greater than 70, it acts as rough and for the intermediate values it is in transition.

In the completely rough region the local drag coefficient c_f and average drag coefficient C_f are given by the equations:

$$c_f = \left(2.87 + 1.58 \log_{10} \frac{x}{k}\right)^{-2.5} \tag{9.17}$$

$$C_f = \left(1.87 + 1.52 \log_{10} \frac{L}{k}\right)^{-2.5} \tag{9.18}$$

These formulae are valid for $10^2 < L/k < 10^6$.

9.10 Atmospheric Boundary Layer

As the wind blows over sea, lake or the land surface, a boundary layer forms over it just as in the case of boundary layer over a flat plate. Because of large length involved, this boundary layer is invariably turbulent. In the case of sea surface, it can deform at high velocities and produce waves whose characteristics depend on magnitude of wind velocity. Hence over the sea, surface roughness can be a function of wind velocity. However, because of sinusoidal nature of waves the surface roughness of sea is small and varies little. If the surface of thc ground were perfectly smooth, one would expect to have laminar sub-layer between the surface and turbulent zone. However, the earth's surface is characteristically rough especially due to surface irregularities and presence of crops, trees, buildings, etc. Therefore, there is little or no laminar sub-layer and turbulence extends very close to the surface; it is maintained by the disturbance imposed on the air movement through the drag of roughness elements. The velocity distribution in the atmospheric boundary layer near the rough surface follows logarithmic low

$$\frac{u}{u_*} = \frac{2.3}{K} \log_{10}\left(\frac{y-d}{k}\right) \qquad (9.19)$$

in which d is known as the zero plane displacement length which needs to be subtracted from y to obtain logarithmic relationship; k is such a length as to make the wind velocity zero at k = (y – d). see Fig. 9.7. The length k is a measure of size, shape and concentration of roughness elements. K is Karman constant which is usually taken as 0.40. The length d for dense crop is almost equal to the crop height h; however it will be smaller than h as denseness reduces. As a rough approximation one can take d = 0.63h where h is the crop height; however for other types of roughness it must be determined experimentally. Analysis of data over different crops has given a value of k equal to 0.15 h. It has also been found that for the same crop as the wind velocity increases, k slightly decreases. This is partly due to bending of the crop and partly due to viscous effects.

The velocity distribution in atmospheric boundary layers can also be expressed according to the power law,

$$\frac{u}{U} = \left(\frac{y}{\delta}\right)^n$$

where U is the velocity above the boundary laver thickness δ. The average values of k, n and δ for different surfaces have been given by Davenport, and are listed below:

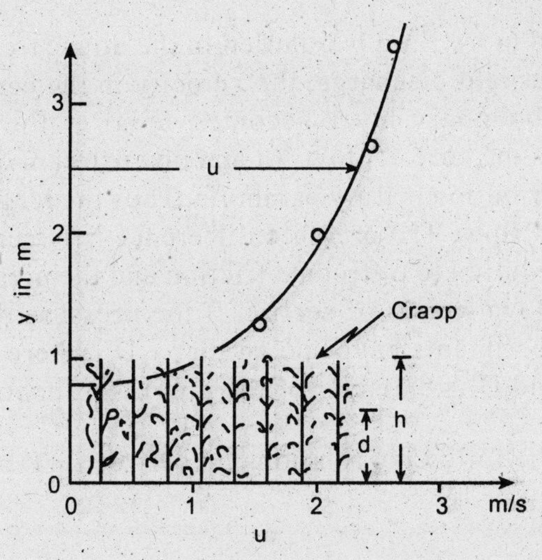

Fig.9.7 Atmospheric boundary layer

TABLE 9.2

Average Values of k, δ and n for Atmospheric Boundary Layers

Description	Open Sea	Flat open country	Woodland forest	Urban area
k cm	0.025 – 0.35	3.5	35	400
δ m	–	300	425	560
n	0.10–0.13	0.16	0.28	0.40

In the absence of detailed information these values can be used to estimate velocity distribution for known value of U.

It needs to be mentioned that the above relationships are valid if the temperature gradient in the air is so small that variation in the density of air does not lead to complex buoyancy effects.

9.11 Establishment of Flow in Pipes

The boundary layer concept is introduced in this chapter by considering the boundary layer formed on a flat plate. However, the phenomenon of boundary layer formation is important in all the problems where real fluids flow past boundaries either straight or curved. This is illustrated by considering boundary layer formation at the entrance to a pipe, Figure. 9.8 (a) shows a pipe with bell mouth entrance, connected to a large reservoir. Consider steady laminar flow in the pipe. If the entrance to the pipe is well designed and head causing the flow is sufficiently large, the velocity in the major portion of the pipe at the entrance will be uniform. It is only close to the boundary that fluid will be retarded due to the formation of laminar boundary layer. With the increase in the thickness of boundary layer, more and more fluid is retarded in the downstream direction. Therefore, in order to maintain a constant discharge, the velocity in the central core must increase. When the thickness of boundary layer becomes equal to the radius of the pipe, the retardation effect reaches the core of flow. At and downstream of this section the flow is uniform and velocity distribution is truly parabolic. Thus the length AB is required for the establishment of uniform flow. The pressure difference between A and B is made up of the pressure difference required to overcome friction and the pressure difference required to accelerate the flow. Downstream of section B the pressure difference is only due to frictional resistance. Experiments have shown that x/D (where x is the length required for flow establishment and D is diameter of the pipe) is a function of Reynolds number $\frac{UD\rho}{\mu}$. Rouse has given the following relationship between x/D and Re for establishment of laminar flow.

$$x/D = 0.07 \text{ Re} \tag{9.20}$$

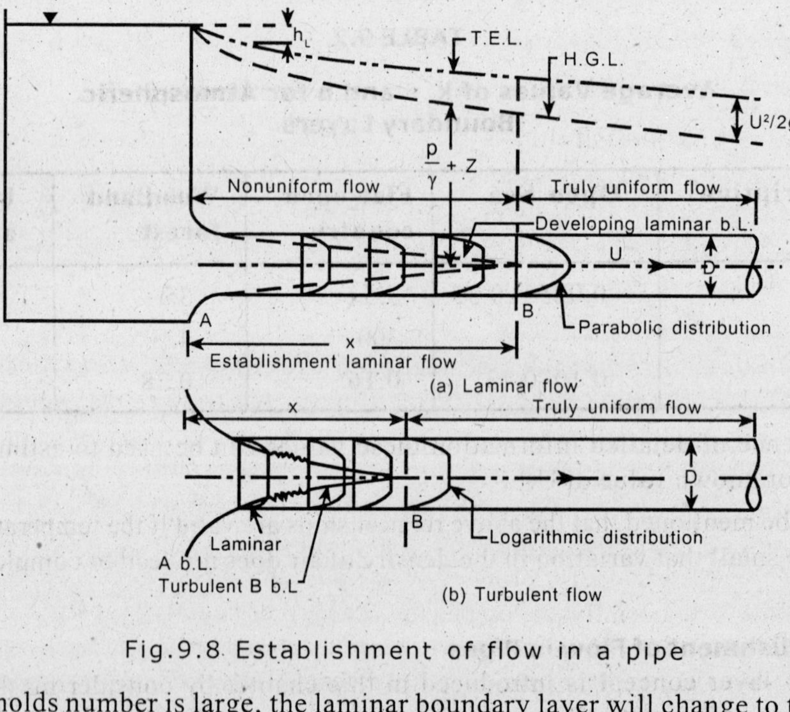

Fig.9.8 Establishment of flow in a pipe

If the Reynolds number is large, the laminar boundary layer will change to the turbulent boundary layer before the boundary layer reaches the centre line. As soon as the boundary layer become turbulent, it will grow much faster and in a short length it will reach the pipe centre. Therefore, uniformity of flow will be attained much earlier, see Fig. 9.8 (b). Kristen found that for turbulent flow

$$x/D = 50 \text{ to } 100$$

while Nirkuradse obtained a value between 25 to 40. The limit $x/D = 50$, may be used to find the distance required for establishment of turbulent flow in a pipe.

Example 9.5

Determine tile pipe length required for establishing uniform flow in a 7.5 cm diameter pipe carrying glycerine ($\nu = 3.72 \times 10^{-4}\,m^2/s$) if the mean velocity is 1.25 m/s. What will be the length if the fluid is water at 20° C?

For $U = 1.25$ m/s, $\quad Re = \dfrac{UD}{\nu} = \dfrac{1.25 \times 0.075}{3.72 \times 10^{-4}} = 252$

Hence, $\quad \dfrac{x}{D} = 0.07 \times 252 = 17.64$

$\therefore \quad x = 17.64 \times 7.5$ cm

$= 132$ cm or 1.32 m

In the second case, $\quad \nu = 1 \times 10^{-6}\,m^2/s$

$$Re = \frac{1.25 \times 0.075}{1 \times 10^{-6}} = 93\,750$$

Since the flow is turbulent, $x/D = 50$

$\therefore \quad x = 50 \times 7.5 = 375$ cm or 3.75 m

9.12 Effect of Compressibility

Investigations have shown that in the case of compressible flow, the local drag coefficient c_f as well as average drag coefficient C_f are function of both Reynolds number and Mach number. In general, as the Mach number increases c_f and C_f both decrease for laminar as well as turbulent boundary layers.

9.13 Separation

While discussing the factors affecting boundary layer thickness it was mentioned that an adverse or positive pressure gradient further retards the fluid in the boundary layer and causes separation and back flow. Consider flow through a two dimensional expanding channel downstream of section A, as shown in Fig.9.9. As the fluid flows from left to right, the velocity of flow must decrease since the cross sectional area is increasing. This decrease in velocity is accompanied by a rise in pressure and thus a positive pressure gradient is set up. The velocity profiles at various sections in the downstream direction are shown in Fig.9.9. Initially, as long as $\partial p/\partial x$ is either negative (upstream of A) or zero, the free stream velocity either increases or remains constant. The pressure gradient which is negative, tends to minimize the viscous effects. However, in the region of positive pressure gradient because of the decelerating effect, the boundary layer thickness is increased further and does not remain small. Because of thickening of the boundary layer, the velocity gradient near the wall decreases in the direction of flow. In the flow with positive pressure gradient the velocity gradient at the wall can become zero as shown in the figure. A further retardation of flow can even start a reverse or back flow. Equation 8.3 $\left(\text{i.e. } \mu \dfrac{\partial^2 u}{\partial y^2} = \dfrac{\partial p}{\partial x}\right)$ shows that a change in the sign of $\partial p/\partial x$ gives rise to a similar change in the sign of second derivative of velocity near the boundary i.e. reversal in the curvature of velocity profile. The flow separates from the boundary from some distance downstream of the point where $\frac{\partial p}{\partial x} = 0$. If all the points below which a reverse flow occurs are joined by a smooth curve such as AB, it represents the region of separation. However, such a region of separation is very difficult to locate, because the point where separation starts depends on roughness, form of the boundary and Reynolds number. Further such a line indicating region of separation oscillates and never remains stationary. Since the separation is ultimately affected, by retarding of the fluid in the boundary layer, it can be seen that the laminar boundary layer is more susceptible to earlier separation than the turbulent boundary layer. If the boundary layer becomes turbulent, velocity distribution near the boundary is much more uniform than in laminar boundary layer because of intense lateral mixing. As a result, relatively higher velocities prevail within the boundary layer when it is turbulent than when it is laminar. This reduces the tendency of separation. Therefore, if the boundary layer is made turbulent earlier by roughening the surface, there is an appreciable decrease in the tendency for separation.

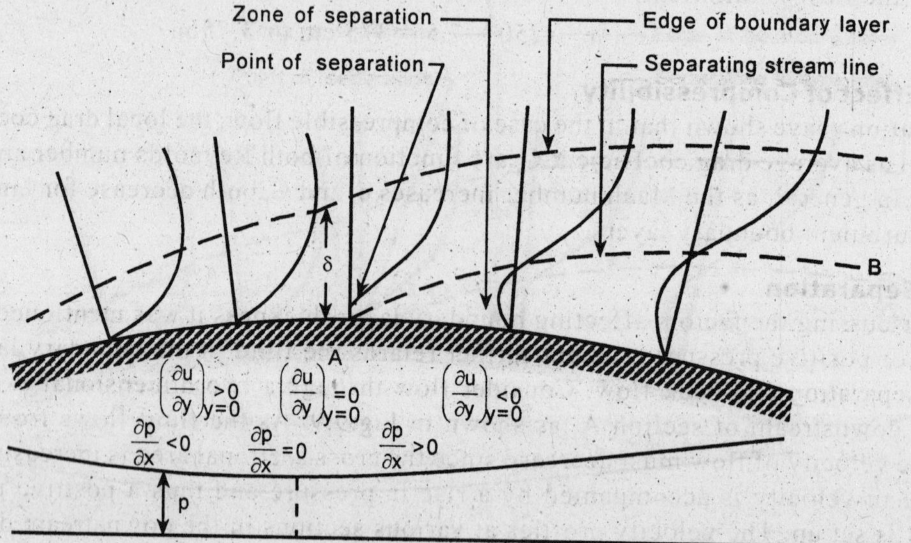

Fig.9.9 Separation of boundary layer in an expanding flow

As a result of separation, a certain portion adjacent to the boundaries has a reverse flow and eddies are continuously formed in the region. This formation of a separation zone or zone of back flow, actually constricts the effective area of flow. Formation of eddies is accompanied by continuous loss of energy since the eddies are formed at the expense of mean flow-energy and this energy is ultimately lost as heat. Because of intermittent shedding of eddies the body is also subjected to lateral vibrations which are dangerous and hence undesirable. As a result of eddy formation, the level of turbulence is higher in the region of separated flow as compared to other region. Further, since the-separation occurs near the point of minimum pressure and since the pressure in the separation zone is essentially constant, such a pressure difference gives rise to longitudinal and sometimes lateral boundary forces.

The net force in the direction of motion caused by pressure difference is known as *pressure-drag* or *form drag*, the magnitude of which depends on the flow pattern obtained due to separation. For efficient design of several boundaries, the primary aim must be to reduce the tendency for separation and thereby reduce the resistance appreciably. Such problems are encountered in the design of channel and conduit transitions, design of airplanes, steamers, etc. This is achieved by streamlining the boundary shape. An alternative method is to use guide vanes to guide the flow and prevent separation in bends and transitions.

9.14 Methods of Avoiding Separation

Since for several reasons discussed above, it is undesirable to have separation, efforts are made either to avoid or delay the occurrence of separation. One way of avoiding separation is by making the angle of divergence of channel (and hence the pressure gradient) sufficiently small. In such a case the flow outside the boundary layer has sufficient energy to pull the fluid particles within the boundary layer with it thereby avoiding separation. This is done by designing diffusers, and expanding transitions in open channels with small angle of divergence. The same principle applies to flow past streamlined bodies such as airplane wings. By thinning them gradually, the pressure gradient is kept within tolerable limits. In design of hydraulic structures the separation is reduced by rounding of the corners and using smoothly curved boundaries.

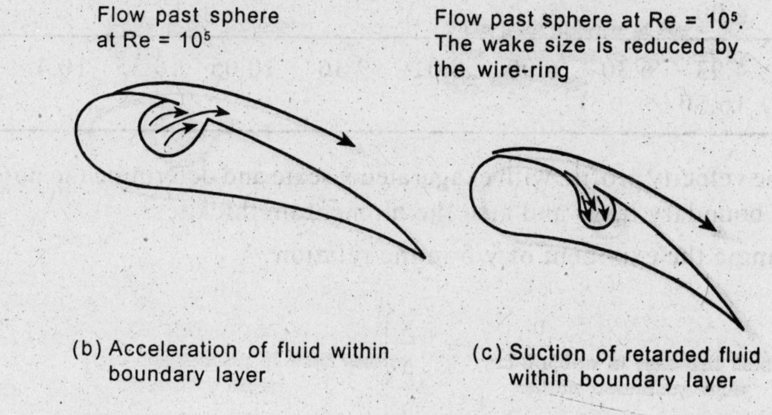

Fig.9.10 Methods of boundary layer control

It has been already mentioned that separation and backflow take place when pressure force acts in the opposite direction on fluid particles already slowed down within the boundary layer. Therefore separation can be delayed (i.e. made to occur farther downstream) if the fluid particles in the boundary layer are accelerated. This can be done by changing the laminar boundary layer into turbulent boundary layer by providing artificial roughness. This was very well illustrated by Wieselsberger who reduced the size of the dead area or wake behind the sphere by providing a thin wire ring as shown in Fig. 9.10 (a). This reduced the pressure drag of sphere appreciably.

The same object can be achieved by injecting high velocity fluid in the boundary layer thereby accelerating the retarded fluid particles, see Fig. 9.10 (b). The same object is achieved by giving motion to the body in the direction of motion. This method was first suggested by Prandtl who applied it for the case of cylinder. However this method offers great practical difficulties.

The separation can also be controlled by continuously sucking the slow moving fluid in the boundary layer. See Fig. 9.10 (c). The sucking can be done at one section or along the boundary length. The power required for the process of sucking the fluid is relatively small since very small volume of fluid is sucked.

Lastly use of vanes in diverging flows for controlling separation may be mentioned. A typical example is that of a 90° bend. The head loss through such a bend is large because of separation and stagnation. This is reduced by providing vanes as shown in Fig. 11.9. The vanes direct the flow in the zones of separation and stagnation and accelerate the flow there. Such vanes are also sometimes used in open channel expanding transitions.

PROBLEMS

9.1 Below are tabulated the actual velocity measurements at various points in the vertical at particular station in the wind tunnel:

y cm	0.21	0.50	0.70	0.90	1.35	1.75	2.25	3.00	3.25	3.50	4.00
u m/s	4.93	6.30	6.90	8.01	9.36	10.05	10.35	10.48	10.48	10.50	10.50

Plot the velocity profile with exagerated y scale and determine the nominal thickness of the boundary layer and also the momentum thickness.

9.2 Determine the exponent of y/δ in the relation

$$\frac{u}{U} = \left(\frac{y}{\delta}\right)^n$$

by making use of data in Problem 9. 1.

9.3 Determine the type of boundary layer that will form on a flat plate held parallel to the stream in each of the following cases.

(i) U =3.0 m/s, L = 30 m, Fluid : Water at 20°C

(ii) U = 1.25 m/s, L = 3.0 m, Fluid : Glycerine at 20°C

(iii) U = 100 m/s, L = 20 m, Fluid : Air at 15°C ($\nu = 1.47 \times 10^{-5}$ m²/s)

9.4 Compare the thickness of boundary layer formed on a flat plate at 0.60 m from the leading edge if the free stream velocity is 1.25 m/s and the fluid is (i) air at 20°C, and (ii) water at 20°C. Is the boundary layer laminar or turbulent in each of the two cases?

9.5 A 1.0 m × 3.0m flat plate is kept in water ($\nu = 1.0 \times 10^{-6}$ m²/s) flowing at 3.30 m/s parallel to the flat plate. Find,

(i) Ratio of boundary layer thickness at the trailing edge of the plate and

(ii) Ratio of the total drag forces on the plate,

if once plate is kept with 3 m side parallel to flow and then the 1.0 m side parallel to flow. Assume boundary layer to be turbulent over the whole plate in both the cases.

9.6 A thin rectangular plate 2.25 m long and 12.5 m wide is towed through water ($\nu = 1.48 \times 10^{-6}$ m²/s) at 1.0 m/s velocity. Determine the total drag force on both sides of the plate and also shear stress at trailing edge of the plate.

9.7 When 2.5 m × 0.90 m plate is held perpendicular to the flow of water at 1.50 m/s velocity it is found to give a pressure drag of 3040 N. Determine the fraction of this drag that will be encountered by the plate when the plate is held parallel to flow with 2.5 m side in the flow direction. Assume water temperature to be 20°C.

9.8 Find the power required to tow a plate of dimensions 1.25 m × 3.0 m in water with 3.0 m side in the flow direction ($\nu = 0.93 \times 10^{-6}$ m²/s) at 1.00 m/s velocity. Make allowance for the fact that the boundary layer changes from laminar to turbulent on the plate.

9.9 Thickness of the turbulent boundary layer at the end of 3.0 m long plate is 2.40 cm. If the fluid is water at 15°C, determine (i) Reynolds number at the trailing edge of the plate (ii) free stream velocity (iii) average shear stress on the plate, and (iv) shear stress at the end of the plate.

9.10 Find the ratio of friction drag on the front 2/3 and the rear 1/3 of a flat plate kept in a stream at zero incidence. Assume boundary layer to be turbulent over the whole plate. What will be this ratio for the front and rear halves under similar conditions?

9.11 A 50 m long ship and with a wetted area of 410 m² requires 169 kW power to overcome the resistance to motion at 7.0 m/s velocity. The total resistance to the motion consists of frictional resistance and the residual resistance which is partly due to wave formation and partly due to shape effect. Determine the frictional resistance and the residual resistance.

Take $\rho = 1030$ kg/m³, $\nu = 0.93 \times 10^{-6}$ m²/s

9.12 In following cases determine whether the pipe surfaces will act as smooth, rough or in transition

(i) $\tau_o = 7.845\ N/m^2$ $\rho = 1000\ kg/m^3$

$\nu = 0.93 \times 10^{-6}\ m^2/s$

$k = 0.01\ mm$

(ii) $u_* = 0.06\ m/s$ $\nu = 1.57 \times 10^{-5}\ m^2/s$

$k = 1.80\ mm$

9.13 Water flows in a 15 cm diameter smooth pipe with a 118 N/m^2 pressure loss in a 5 m length. Assuming $\nu = 1 \times 10^{-6}\ m^2/s$ and $\rho = 1000\ kg/m^3$ determine the minimum height of roughness such that pipe acts as a rough pipe.

9.14 Determine the length of the pipe required for establishment of flow, if 23 l/s of glycerine is carried through a 15 cm diameter pipe at 20°C. What will be this length if the same discharge is carried through 30 cm diameter pipe.

9.15 For the following velocity distributions within the laminar boundary layer, compute δ^*/δ and θ/δ

(i) $\frac{u}{U} = \frac{y}{\delta}$ (ii) $\frac{u}{U} = \frac{3}{2}\frac{y}{\delta} - \frac{1}{2}\left(\frac{y}{\delta}\right)^3$

9.16 Apply momentum equation to the boundary layer on a flat plate and obtain expression for average drag coefficient C_f in terms of α_1, and β_1, and Re_L.

9.17 If velocity distribution in the laminar boundary layer is given by $u/U = 2\ (y/\delta) - 2\ (y/\delta)^3 + (y/\delta)^4$, obtain expressions for δ/x, c_f and C_f.

9.18 For turbulent boundary on a flat plate, the velocity distribution follows the law $u/U = (y/\delta)^{1/7}$. Obtain expressions for δ/x and c_f and compare them with Eqs. 9.8 and 9.9. Take.

$$\frac{\tau_0}{\rho U^2} = 0.0225\left(\frac{\nu}{U\delta}\right)^{\frac{1}{4}}$$

Chapter Ten

Turbulent Flow

10.1 Nature of Turbulent Flow

It has been mentioned in Chapter 8 that Reynolds number gives the criterion for determining the flow condition in a pipe. Below a Reynolds number of 2100, the flow is laminar and when it exceeds a value of 3000, the flow becomes turbulent*. As mentioned earlier, turbulent flow results from the instability of laminar flow. Eddies formed in the flow spread over the whole flow section and thereby produce a complex pattern of fluid motion. In such a turbulent flow, even though the average motion is in x direction, superimposed on this motion are the velocity components in x, y and z directions which vary with time and space, Because of these fluctuations in velocity, intermixing between different fluid layers takes place on a scale, much larger than the molecular diffusion in laminar flow. Such a large scale diffusion or macroscopic intermixing is an important characteristic of turbulence.

Turbulence is an irregular condition of flow in which the various quantities related to flow, show random variation with time and space coordinates, so that statistical average quantities can be obtained. Thus while discussing the turbulent flow one distinguishes between *instantaneous velocity, fluctuation velocity and time averaged velocity.* This is made clear in Fig. 10.1 where the variation of velocity in x direction with time is shown.

---

*It may be mentioned that by improving the inlet conditions of the pipe, it is possible to maintain laminar flow for still larger Reynolds numbers. Ekmann (1910) succeeded in obtaining laminar flow in a pipe at 24000 Reynolds number. However, for Reynolds number less than 2100, the flow remains laminar whatever may be the inlet condition or level of disturbances.

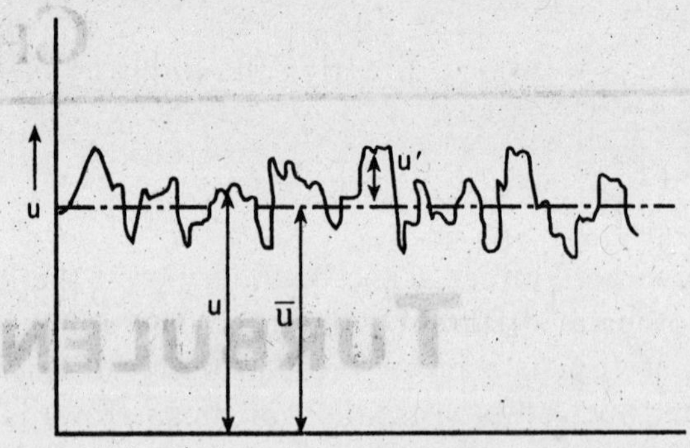

Fig.10.1 Variation in velocity u with time

At any instant, the instantaneous velocity u is equal to the time averaged velocity $\bar{u}$ plus the turbulent fluctation velocity u′. The component u′ can be positive, negative or zero. The velocity $\bar{u}$ is known as the time averaged velocity since it is found averaging velocity at point over a certain time interval. Thus the instantaneous velocities in the three coordinate directions, u, v and w and the instantaneous pressure p at any point in turbulent flow are given by

$$u = \bar{u} + u'$$
$$v = \bar{v} + v'$$
$$w = \bar{w} + w'$$
$$p = \bar{p} + p'$$

where $\bar{u}, \bar{v}, \bar{w}$ and $\bar{p}$ are the time averaged quantities and u′, v′, w′ and p′ are their fluctuating components.

The time average can be found by integrating the instantaneous values over a time interval T ; thus

$$\bar{u} = \frac{1}{T}\int_t^{t+T} u\,dt$$

It should be noted that the average values are considered over a sufficiently long interval of time T. It can be easily seen that the averages of all the quantities describing fluctuations are equal to zero. i.e.

$$\overline{u'} = 0, \quad \overline{v'} = 0, \quad \overline{w'} = 0 \quad \text{and} \quad \overline{p'} = 0$$

Since time averages of u′, v′, and w′ are zero, the level of turbulence is estimated in terms of root mean square values of the turbulent fluctuations, viz. $\sqrt{\overline{u'^2}}$, $\sqrt{\overline{v'^2}}$ and

$\sqrt{\overline{w'^2}}$. Indeed for the mean flow in x direction the *intensity of turbulence* at a point is

defined as $\sqrt{\frac{1}{3}\left(\overline{u'^2}+\overline{v'^2}+\overline{w'^2}\right)}\Big/\bar{u}$.

The turbulence is generated either at the boundary or at the interface of two streams flowing one over the other at different velocities. The common feature of these two types of flow is that there exists a mean shear in both the flows. In fact, existence of mean shear (as exhibited by velocity gradient of mean flow) is absolutely essential if turbulence is not to die out. The turbulent flow consists of eddies of various sizes. The smallest size is of microscopic nature whereas the larger eddies are of the size of the flow i.e. the largest eddy in pipe flow will be as large as diameter of the pipe. Larger eddies continuously extract energy from the mean flow. These eddies continuously break into smaller eddies and thereby transfer energy to the smaller eddies. As eddies become smaller and smaller, the Reynolds number of eddy decreases i.e. viscous force becomes important. Ultimately the energy of small eddies is converted into heat energy because of viscous shear. For this reason a continuous supply of energy to the turbulent motion is required if it is to sustain itself. Presence of mean shear provides a mechanism of continuously extracting energy from mean flow and supply to turbulent eddies. The average size of the eddies will be minimum near the boundary and will increase with the increase in distance from the boundary. The measure of the size of eddies is provided by what is known as the *scale of turbulence*.

For laminar flow in pipes expressions for velocity distribution and pressure drop were conveniently obtained from the basic differential equation $\tau = \mu\frac{du}{dy}$. A similar analysis for turbulent flow in pipes is rather difficult since the fluctuating nature of velocity components gives additional terms in the equation for shear stress and normal stress, thereby making it more difficult to integrate. Nevertheless, study of turbulent flow is of greater significance than that of the laminar flow because the former occurs more frequently in nature.

It was seen in the discussion of laminar flow that the energy loss for laminar flow varies as the average velocity U while for turbulent flow the energy loss varies as U^n where n ranges from 1.75 to 2. The lower value corresponds to the flow in pipes with hydrodynamically smooth boundaries. Thus for the same average velocity of flow, there will be greater energy loss in turbulent flow as compared to the energy loss in laminar flow. The reason for this is that additional shear stresses introduced in the flow, once the flow becomes turbulent, cause increased energy loss.

10.2 Shear Stress Due to Turbulence

The mechanism governing the turbulent flow is extremely complex. The rapid fluctuations in velocity components in all the three directions cause a turbulent mixing which results in a transfer of momentum. Multitudes of lumps of fluid particles from one fluid layer move into the layers above and below and get merged in them. Since each fluid layer has a different velocity, such movement brings about a transfer of momentum causing additional shear and normal stresses of high magnitude. Thus, in turbulent flow, there is turbulent shear in addition to viscous shear as well as normal stress. The movement of the lumps of fluid particles from one layer to other is possible because of turbulent fluctuations which in themselves are a manifestation of the presence of eddies. Turbulent mixing is responsible not only for the exchange of momentum but it also causes transfer of heat and mass in the main flow.

Similar to the expression for the laminar shear, the turbulent shear has been expressed by Boussinesq as

$$\bar{\tau} = \eta \frac{d\bar{u}}{dy} \tag{10.1}$$

In this equation $\bar{u}$ and $\bar{\tau}$ represent the time averaged velocity and shear at any point. The constant of proportionality η (eta) is known as *eddy viscosity* and is analogous to the dynamic viscosity μ. The difference between eddy viscosity η and dynamic viscosity μ is significant. While viscosity μ is the fluid property and is a function of temperature of fluid alone, eddy viscosity η is found to be a function of fluid properties as well as the characteristics of flow. As such, η varies from one place to another while μ is constant (if the temperature remains constant). Dividing eddy viscosity η by the mass density of the fluid ρ one obtains *eddy kinematic viscosity* ε as

$$\frac{\eta}{\rho} = \varepsilon \tag{10.2}$$

which is comparable to the kinematic viscosity ν.

Consider two fluid layers A and B a certain distance apart as shown in Fig. 10.2. The time averaged velocity of A is $\bar{u}_1$ and that of layer B is $\bar{u}_2$. Assuming $\bar{u}_1 > \bar{u}_2$, the relative velocity of layer A with respect to layer B is $(\bar{u}_1 - \bar{u}_2) = u_A$. Since it is the relative velocity that matters, one can assume layer B to be stationary and layer A to be moving at a uniform velocity u_A. Let a small mass of fluid from the layer B move to the layer A at a velocity v_A. This mass merges with layer A and keeps moving with layer A at a velocity u_A. If the cross motion is assumed to be uniform over a small area a, the mass $(a\rho v_A)$ has moved upwards and started moving with a velocity u_A and therefore, a transfer of momentum equal to $(\rho\, a\, u_A \cdot v_A)$ has taken place. Consequently a shear stress acts on the surface of layer A towards left and it is equal to

$$\tau = \frac{-\rho\, a\, u_A v_A}{a} = -\rho\, u_A\, v_A$$

The negative sign indicates that the stress acts towards left. Fluid masses moving

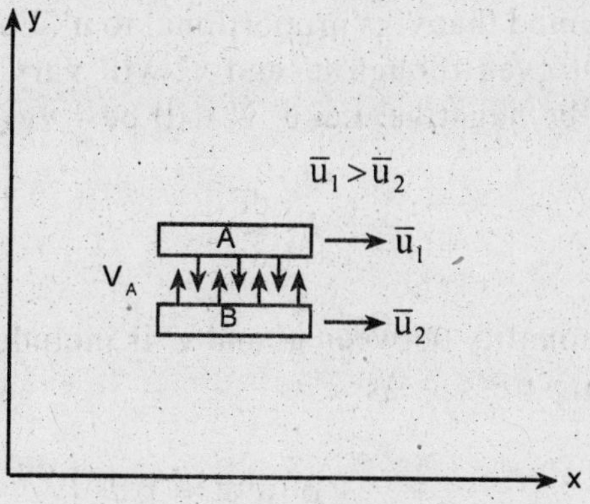

Fig. 10.2 Turbulent mixing

rom layer A to layer B will exert a force on the layer B which is equal in magnitude but pposite in direction to τ. Thus a slow moving layer exerts a retarding force on a fast noving layer and a fast moving layer exerts an accelerating force on the slow moving ayer.

In a similar manner one can explain that the additional shear stress in turbulent flow is ue to the rate of change of momentum transport of fluid mass due to their motion across n imaginary plane parallel to the main flow. The turbulent fluctuations u' and v' will be esponsible for such a shear. Because of fluctuating nature of the turbulent velocity omponents, the time averaged turbulent shear exerted by the surrounding fluid is given y

$$\bar{\tau} = -\rho\, \overline{u'v'}$$

ence in order to compute the turbulent shear stress one must have knowledge about the agnitude of $\overline{u'v'}$. Since it is difficult to measure $\overline{u'v'}$, Prandtl presented a *mixing length ypothesis* which can be used to express $\overline{u'v'}$ in terms of easily measurable quantities.

According to Prandtl, the *mixing length l* can be considered as a transverse distance etween two layers such that the lumps of fluid particles from one layer could reach the ther layer and be embedded in it, thus retaining their momentum in the x direction during eir travel through distance l. Prandtl further hypothesised that the fluctuating velocity has the same magnitude as the difference in the time average velocities in the x direction etween the two layers distance l apart. In other words

$$u' = l\frac{d\bar{u}}{dy}$$

he mixing length is somewhat analogous to the mean free path in the kinetic theory of ses, the difference being that the mean free path in kinetic theory of gases is based on otion of individual molecules, whereas the mixing length is based on motion of lumps of fluid molecules. Prandtl assumed that v′ is proportional to u′. Further, it can be seen from continuity consideration that even though u′ and v′ will vary haphazardly, when u′ is positive, v′ is most likely to be negative, i.e. u′ v′ will be – ve. Hence one gets

$$\overline{u'v'} = -l^2\left(\frac{d\bar{u}}{dy}\right)^2$$

in which constant of proportionality between u′ and v′ is included in l^2. From this Prandtl evaluated the turbulent shear stress $\bar{\tau}$ as

$$\bar{\tau} = -\rho\,\overline{u'v'} = \rho\, l^2\left(\frac{d\bar{u}}{dy}\right)^2$$

In turbulent flow, the total shear stress at any section is the sum of the viscous shear and the turbulent shear and can be written as

$$\bar{\tau} = \mu\frac{d\bar{u}}{dy} + \rho l^2\left(\frac{d\bar{u}}{dy}\right)^2 \tag{10.3}$$

Actually the viscous shear part in Eq. 10.5 is negligibly small except near the boundary and therefore the shear is assumed to be due to the turbulence alone. Fig. 10.3 gives typical results of variation of $\sqrt{\overline{u'^2}}$, $\sqrt{\overline{v'^2}}$ and $\overline{u'v'}$ in the case of a rectangular conduit.

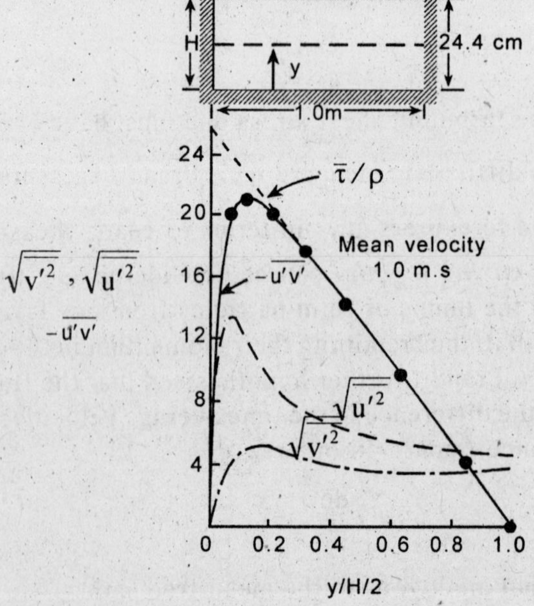

Fig. 10.3 Typical distribution of $\sqrt{\overline{u'^2}}$ and $\sqrt{\overline{v'^2}}$ and $\overline{u'v'}$ in cm/s for turbulent flow in conduits

Similar results are obtained in the case of turbulent flow in circular pipes. It can be observed that turbulent fluctuations $\sqrt{u'^2}$ and $\sqrt{v'^2}$ are zero at the wall, they reach maximum at some distance away front the wall and then reduce towards the centre.

Comparing Eq. 10. 1 with Eq. 10.4 one gets

$$\eta = \rho\, l^2 \frac{d\bar{u}}{dy}$$

Since $l \dfrac{d\bar{u}}{dy} \approx u'$ or v' or $\sqrt{u'^2}$, one can write

$$\frac{\eta}{\rho} = \varepsilon \approx l \sqrt{v'^2}$$

As mentioned earlier, size of the eddies increases with increase in distance from the wall.

Also $\sqrt{v'^2}$ follows variation as shown in Fig. 10.3. Hence ε will be zero at wall, will reach maximum and then decrease towards the centre of pipe. Fig. 10.4 shows variation

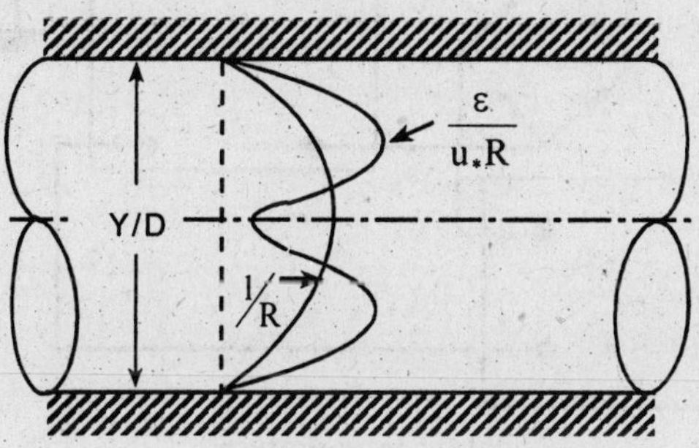

Fig. 10.4 Variation of (l/R) and (ε/u*R) for turbulent flow in pipes

of $\dfrac{l}{R}$ and $\dfrac{\varepsilon}{u_* R}$ with $\dfrac{y}{D}$ where R and D are the pipe radius and diameter D respectively.

Several techniques have been developed to measure turbulent velocity fluctuations in liquids and gases. The most versatile among them for measurement in gases is the hot wire anemometer. This instrument has a probe in the form of a very short and thin platinum or tungsten wire heated by an electric current. When this wire is exposed to the flowing air it is cooled as a consequence of which its temperature and resistance are reduced. If the air velocity is fluctuating so will the resistance or temperature. The hot wire forms one arm of the Wheatstone bridge. For carrying out the measurement of turbulent fluctuations, two methods are used. In the constant temperature (or resistance) method, the temperature of the wire is kept constant by varying the electric current which then is a measure of fluctuating velocity. In the constant current method, the heating current is maintained the same; hence fluctuations in velocity yield fluctuations in the electrical resistance of the wire. The length and diameter of the wire are governed by the considerations of correct response by the wire to very rapid velocity fluctuations. Usually wire from 2.5 to 5 microns in diameter and about 1.0 mm in length is used. Actual equipment consists of a complicated electronic circuitry, block diagram for which is shown in Fig.10.5. Hot wire anemometer is not suited for measurement of turbulence in liquids because of evaporation and electrolysis that may take place. For measuring turbulence in water, hot film anemometer is used.

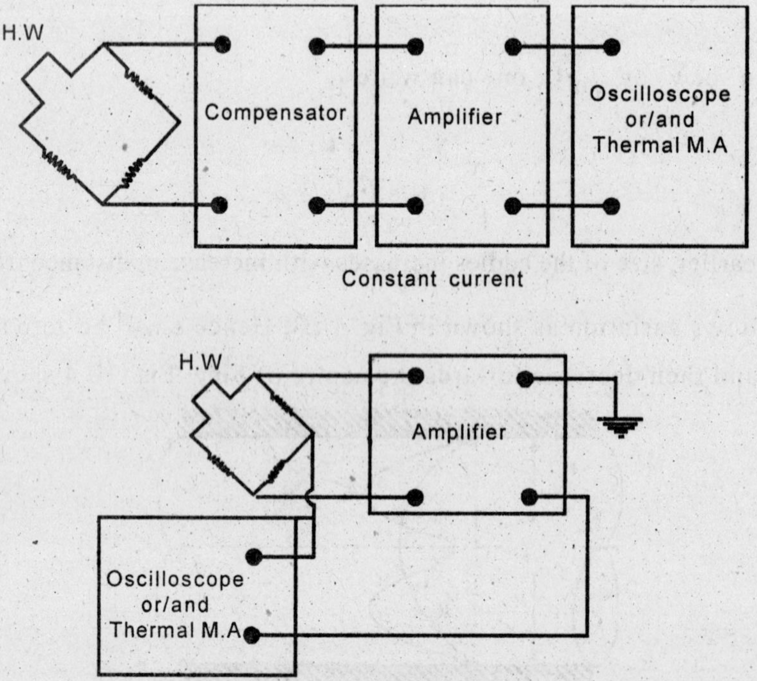

Fig. 10.5 Circuitry for hot wire anemometer

10.3 Equations of Motion for Turbulent Flows

To change equations of motion from laminar to turbulent flow, one uses what are commonly known as *Reynolds rules of averaging*. If $f = \bar{f} + f'$ and $g = \bar{g} + g'$ are to turbulent variables, where f and g are their instantaneous values, $\bar{f}$ and $\bar{g}$ are time averaged values and f' and g' are the fluctuating components, Reynolds rules state that·

(i) $\overline{f + g} = \bar{f} + \bar{g}$

(ii) $\overline{cf} = c\bar{f}$ where c is a constant

(iii) $\overline{fg} = \bar{f}\,\bar{g}$

(iv) $\overline{\dfrac{\partial f}{\partial x}} = \dfrac{\partial \bar{f}}{\partial x}$

As a consequence $\overline{fg} = \bar{f}\,\bar{g} + \overline{f'g'}$

It is assumed that instantaneous values of u, v, w, and p satisfy continuity and N.S. equations. It one introduces $u = \bar{u} + u'$, $v = \bar{v} + v'$ and $w = \bar{w} + w'$ in continuity equation

$$\frac{\partial u}{\partial x} + \frac{\partial v}{\partial y} + \frac{\partial w}{\partial z} = 0,$$

one gets $\frac{\partial}{\partial x} + (\bar{u} + u') + \frac{\partial}{\partial y}(\bar{v} + v') + \frac{\partial}{\partial z}\left(\bar{w} + w'\right) = 0$

when Reynolds rules are used and time average is taken, we get

$$\frac{\partial \bar{u}}{\partial x} + \frac{\partial \bar{v}}{\partial y} + \frac{\partial \bar{w}}{\partial z} = 0 \qquad (10.4)$$

By subtracting Eq.(10.4) from continuity equation for instantaneous velocity components, it can be seen that

$$\frac{\partial u'}{\partial x} + \frac{\partial v'}{\partial y} + \frac{\partial w'}{\partial z} = 0$$

that is the fluctuating components also satisfy continuity equation. Similarly one can start from Navier-stokes equations (8.4) and substitute intantaneous values of u, v, w and p and use Reynolds rules of averages to get the following *Reynolds equations of motion* for turbulent flow in incompressible fluids

$$\left.\begin{aligned}
&\rho\left\{\frac{\partial \bar{u}}{\partial t} + \bar{u}\frac{\partial \bar{u}}{\partial x} + \bar{v}\frac{\partial \bar{u}}{\partial y} + \bar{w}\frac{\partial \bar{u}}{\partial z}\right\} = \\
&x - \frac{dP}{\partial x} + \mu\left(\frac{\partial^2 \bar{u}}{\partial x^2} + \frac{\partial^2 \bar{u}}{\partial y^2} + \frac{\partial^2 \bar{u}}{\partial z^2}\right) - \left(\frac{\partial \rho u'^2}{\partial x} + \frac{\partial \rho u'v'}{\partial y} + \frac{\partial \overline{\rho u'w'}}{\partial z}\right) \\
&\rho\left(\frac{\partial \bar{v}}{\partial t} + \bar{u}\frac{\partial \bar{v}}{\partial x}\bar{v} + \frac{\partial \bar{v}}{\partial y} + w\frac{\partial \bar{v}}{\partial z}\right) = \\
&Y - \frac{\partial \bar{P}}{\partial y} + \mu\left(\frac{\partial^2 \bar{v}}{\partial x^2} + \frac{\partial^2 \bar{v}}{\partial y^2} + \frac{\partial^2 \bar{v}}{\partial z^2}\right) - \left(\frac{\partial \overline{\rho u'v'}}{\partial x} + \frac{\partial \overline{\rho v'^2}}{\partial y} + \frac{\partial \overline{\rho v'w'}}{\partial z}\right) \\
&\rho\left(\frac{\partial \bar{w}}{\partial t} + \bar{u}\frac{\partial \bar{w}}{\partial x} + \bar{v}\frac{\partial \bar{w}}{\partial y} + \bar{w}\frac{\partial \bar{w}}{\partial z}\right) = \\
&z - \frac{\partial \bar{P}}{\partial z} + \mu\left(\frac{\partial^2 \bar{w}}{\partial x^2} + \frac{\partial^2 \bar{w}}{\partial y^2} + \frac{\partial^2 \bar{w}}{\partial z^2}\right) - \left(\frac{\partial \rho u'w'}{\partial x} + \frac{\partial \rho v'w'}{\partial y} + \frac{\partial \overline{\rho w'^2}}{\partial z}\right)
\end{aligned}\right\} \qquad (10.5)$$

It can be seen that the first nine terms in each equation are similar to those in Eq.(8.4) in N.S equations, except that there are time averaged terms in these equations. However, the last three terms in each of the three equations are additional normal and shear stresses caused by turbulent fluctuations. These are three normal stresses are six shear stresses in the Renolds stress tensor

$$\begin{vmatrix} -\rho\overline{u'^2} & -\rho\overline{u'v'} & -\rho\overline{u'w'} \\ -\rho\overline{u'v'} & -\rho\overline{v'^2} & -\rho\overline{v'w'} \\ -\rho\overline{u'w'} & -\rho\overline{v'w'} & -\rho\overline{w'^2} \end{vmatrix}$$

Here $-\rho\overline{u'^2}$, $-\rho\overline{v'^2}$, and $-\rho\overline{w'^2}$ are the normal stresses and the remaining shear stresses. Evidently $-\rho\overline{u'v'} = -\rho\overline{v'w'}$ etc. Thus solution of three -dimensional turbulent flow problem involves ten unknowns $\bar{u}, \bar{v}, \bar{w}, \bar{p}, \overline{u'^2}, \overline{v'^2}, \overline{w'^2}, \overline{u'v'}, \overline{v'w'}$ and $\overline{u'w'}$ and there are only four equations, namely Eq.(10.4) and Eq.(10.5). Hence unless some drastic assumptions are made to simplify the problem and some assumptions are made to express turbulent stresses in terms mean velocity gradients, it is not possible to get solution of Reynolds equations of motion.

10.4 Velocity Distribution in Turbulent Flow

In the previous section it is mentioned that total shear stress in turbulent flow is the sum of viscous shear and turbulent shear and that the viscous shear part is negligibly small. Thus it can be assumed that in turbulent flow the shear stress is given by Eq. 10.4.

The velocity distribution in two dimensional turbulent flow can be obtained from this expression for the turbulent shear, if a relation between the mixing length l and y can be assumed. The analysis of Nikuradse's experimental data on velocity distribution in turbulent flow in pipes has shown that, near the boundary, the mixing length is related to y by the relationship $l = Ky$. The term K, known as *Karman constant* has a value of 0.4. Thus the turbulent shear near the boundary can be written as

$$\tau_o \approx \tau = \rho K^2 y^2 \left(\frac{d\bar{u}}{dy}\right)^2 \tag{10.6}$$

It may be seen that the bars over time averaged quantities have been omitted for convenience in what follows. Rearranging the terms, one gets

$$\frac{du}{dy} = \frac{1}{Ky}\sqrt{\frac{\tau_o}{\rho}} \tag{10.7}$$

in which $\sqrt{\tau_o/\rho}$ has dimensions of velocity and is commonly known as the shear velocity u_*. Using the value of K equal to 0.4, one can integrate Eq. 10.7 to yield

$$u = 2.5\, u_* \log_e y + C_1 \tag{10.8}$$

The expression states that the velocity distribution in turbulent flow is logarithmic in nature. This is shown in Fig. 9.4. The constant of integration can be evaluated from the condition that at a certain distance y from the boundary, the velocity will be zero. Thus, with the condition that at $y = y'$, the velocity $u = 0$, the constant C_1 can be obtained as

$$C_1 = -2.5\, u_* \log_e y'$$

When this constant of integration is introduced in Eq. 10.8 and the terms are divided by the shear velocity, one gets,

$$\frac{u}{u_*} = 2.5 \log_e \frac{y}{y'} = 5.75 \log_{10} (y/y') \qquad (10.9)$$

In obtaining this equation no assumption is made as to whether the boundary is hydrodynamically smooth or rough. Hence Eq. 10.9 gives velocity distribution in turbulent flow near smooth and rough boundaries. At this stage the significance of y' should be noted. In the case of a hydrodynamically smooth boundary, laminar sublayer having a parabolic velocity distribution exists near the boundary. Hence in the vicinity of the boundary, where laminar sublayer exists, logarithmic law cannot hold. Therefore, it can be assumed that y' is proportional to δ'. Nikuradse's experimental data indicate that

$$y' = \frac{\delta'}{107}$$

and δ' has a value of $\frac{11.6\nu}{u_*}$. With this value of δ' substituted in the above relation, the distance y' becomes equal to $0.108\, \nu/u_*$. Introducing this value of y' in Eq. 10.9, one gets

$$\frac{u}{u_*} = 5.75 \log_{10} \frac{u_* y}{\nu} + 5.5 \qquad (10.10)$$

This equation is known as Karman-Prandtl equation for velocity distribution in turbulent flow near hydrodynamically smooth boundaries.

As mentioned earlier, Eq. 10.10 is not valid near the boundary where viscous shear exists. In the laminar sublayer one can write

$$\tau_o = \mu \frac{du}{dy}$$

or

$$u_*^2 = \nu \frac{du}{dy}$$

Hence integration gives

$$\frac{u}{u_*} = \frac{u_* y}{\nu} \qquad (10.10a)$$

Experimental data indicate that Eq. 10.10(a) is valid for $(u_* y/\nu)$ less than five, whereas Eq. 10.10 is valid for $(u_* y/\nu)$ greater than thrity. Von Karman has suggested that for $5 < (u_* y/\nu) < 30$, Eq. 10-10 (b) is applicable

$$\frac{u}{u_*} = 11.5 \log_{10} \frac{u_* y}{\nu} - 3.05 \tag{10.10b}$$

In the case of hydrodynamically rough boundaries, laminar sublayer is destroyed and hence one would expect y′ to be proportional to the average height of protrusions k. Nikuradse's data for pipes coated from inside with uniform sand of size k, gave $y' = k/30$ for the hydrodynamically rough boundaries. Introducing this value of y′ in Eq. 10.9 one gets

$$\frac{u}{u_*} = 5.75 \log_{10} \frac{y}{k} + 8.5 \tag{10.11}$$

This is Karman-Prandtl equation for velocity distribution in turbulent flow near rough boundaries. Even though Eqs. 10.10 and 10.11 are supposed to be valid only near the boundary, it has been found experimentally that these equations are applicable farther away from the boundary also. Equations 10.10 and 10.11 indicate the general velocity distribution at any point y for flow over smooth and rough boundaries. Therefore, they are applicable to the turbulent flow in pipes.

The average velocity U through the pipe can be obtained by first finding out the total discharge and then dividing the discharge by the area of the pipe section. Using Eq. 10.10, discharge through a smooth pipe can be obtained as

$$Q = \int_0^R 2\pi r u \, dr$$

$$= \int_0^R 2\pi r u_* \left[5.75 \log_{10} \frac{u_*(R-r)}{\nu} + 5.50 \right] dr$$

The distance y from the wall has been replaced by $(R - r)$ in which R is the radius of the pipe and r is the distance from the centre, see Fig. 10.6. The above expression is for the discharge through a smooth pipe. Integration of the above expression and subsequent simplification yields the following relation for average velocity U

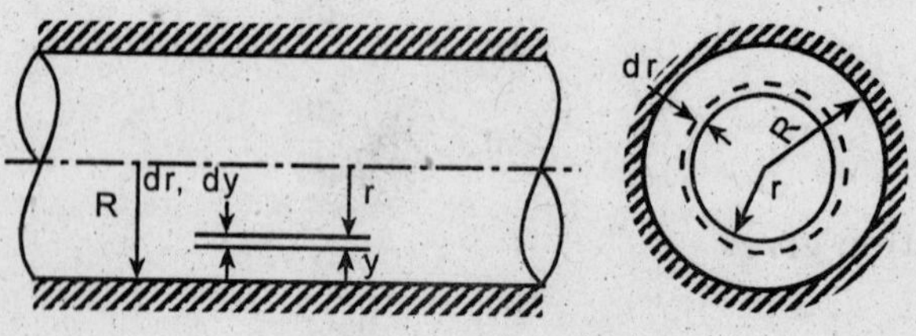

Fig. 10.6 Definition sketch

$$\frac{U}{u_*} = 5.75 \log_{10} \frac{u_* R}{\nu} + 1.75 \tag{10.12}$$

A similar expression for average velocity through rough pipes can be obtained as

$$\frac{U}{u_*} = 5.75 \log_{10} \frac{R}{k} + 4.75 \qquad (10.13)$$

It will be of interest to note that the difference of the velocity at any point and the average velocity, (u – U) will be the same in both the cases of smooth and rough boundaries. Subtracting Eq. 10.12 from Eq. 10.10 or Eq. 10.13 from Eq. 10.11 one gets

$$\frac{u-U}{u_*} = 5.75 \log_{10} \frac{y}{R} + 3.75 \qquad (10.14)$$

This equation shows that for two pipes of same diameter and having same shear velocity, the velocity, difference (u – U) is the same at identical elevations irrespective of boundary roughness. Eqaution (10.14) is known as the *velocity defect law.*

10.5 Resistance of Smooth and Artificially Roughened Pipes

In Chapter 8, it was shown that for a steady uniform flow in a horizontal pipe, the pressure force must be balanced by the boundary shear. This leads to the equation

$$\tau_o = -\frac{\partial p}{\partial x}\frac{R}{2}$$

or

$$\tau_o = \frac{(p_1 - p_2)D}{4l}$$

Dividing both sides of the above equation by $\rho U^2/2$ where U is the average velocity, one gets

$$\frac{4\tau_o}{\rho U^2/2} = f = \left(\frac{p_1 - p_2}{l}\right)\frac{D}{\rho U^2/2} \qquad (10.15)$$

in which f is the dimensionless coefficient, commonly known as *Darcy – Weisbach resistance coefficient*. Equation 10.15 is commonly written in the form

$$(p_1 - p_2) = f\,\frac{l}{D}\,\frac{\rho U^2}{2} \qquad (10.16\ a)$$

or

$$h_f = \frac{f\,l\,U^2}{2g\,D} \qquad (10.16\ b^*)$$

and is known as Darcy-Weisbach resistance equation. It may be mentioned that Eq. 10.15 in the form $\tau_o = (f/4)(\rho U^2/2)$ is similar to Eq. 9.6 for average shear stress along a flat plate on which the boundary layer is developed, except that C_f is replaced by f/4. This is understandable because flow in a pipe is the case of a fully developed boundary layer.

---

*It may be noted that Eq. 10.16 b is many times written in the text books on Hydraulics in the form

$h_f = \frac{4f'lU^2}{2gD}$. It is evident that f′ = f/4.

It may be emphasised that even though Eq. 10.16 (b) contains gravitational acceleration g, the flow in pipes is not governed by gravity since there is no free surface. The term g is introduced in order to convert Δp into h_f.

Expression for shear velocity u_* can be obtained from Eq. 10.15 in the form

$$u_* = \sqrt{\frac{\tau_o}{\rho}} = U\sqrt{\frac{f}{8}} \tag{10.17}$$

In order to predict the loss of energy in pipe flow, one must predict Darcy-Weisbach resistance coefficient f, which is sometimes known as the friction factor. The dependence of friction factor f on the characteristics of the flow, the fluid and the boundary can be studied by dimensional analysis. It can be seen that pressure loss per unit length, $\Delta p/l$ depends on the average velocity of flow U, the fluid viscosity μ and the mass density of fluid ρ, and diameter of pipe the pipe wall roughness height k. Or

$$\frac{\Delta p}{l} = \phi_1 (U, D, k, \rho, \mu)$$

Choosing U, D and ρ as the repeating variables, the following functional relationship can be obtained

$$\frac{\Delta p}{l} \times \frac{D}{\frac{\rho U^2}{2}} = f = \phi_2\left(\frac{UD\rho}{\mu}, \frac{k}{D}\right) \tag{10.18}$$

It may be noted that f can be interpreted as a product of D/l and $\Delta p/(\rho U^2/2)$, the latter being Euler number. Since the pipe flow is governed by pressure, inertia, and viscous forces, one can expect Euler number (i.e. friction factor) to vary with Reynolds number. This fact is brought out in Eq. 10. 18. Some times k/D is written as R/k or D/k. The term k/D is commonly known as *relative roughness* since, other conditions remaining same, f is found to increase with increasing values of k/D. On the other hand, the term R/k is known as *relative smoothness*. Equation 10.18 is valid for laminar as well as turbulent flow in a pipe.

The actual relationship among the parameters, f, Re and R/k has been obtained from Nikuradse's data for flow through artificially roughened pipes.

The range of relative smoothness R/k studied by Nikuradse was from 15 to 507 and the observations were taken upto a Re value of 10^6. Although the sand coated pipes used by Nikuradse differ appreciably from the commercial pipes available in market, his data are extremely valuable since they provide a reliable basis for quantitative measurement of roughness effects. This has been achieved by introducing the concept of equivalent sand grain roughness which has been explained later. The entire available data were first plotted by Stanton with logarithmic co-ordinates as shown in Fig. 10.7.

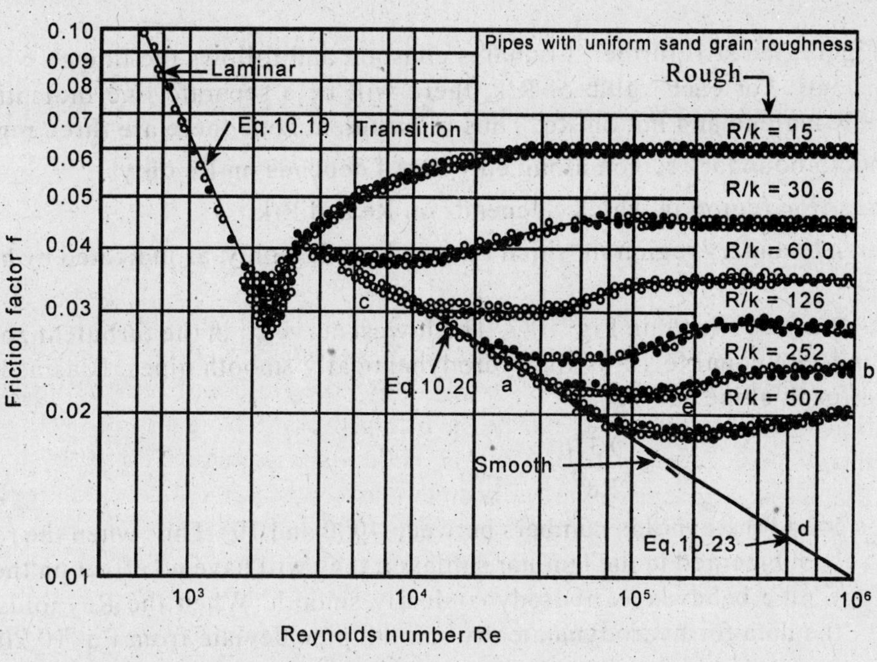

Fig. 10.7 General resistance diagram for pipe flow

It can be seen from Fig. 10.7 that in the laminar region i.e. upto Re equal to 2100, there is an inverse linear relation between f and Re indicating that friction factor f is a function of Reynolds number alone and that relative smoothes R/k has no effect. The stright line can be described by an equation

$$f = \frac{64}{Re} \tag{10.19}$$

This equation can also be obtained analytically from the Hagen-Poiseuille's equation. Equating h_f from Hagen-Poiseuille's equation with that from Darcy-Weisbach equation one gets,

$$h_f = \frac{32\,\mu\, l\, U}{\gamma\, D^2} = \frac{f\, l\, U^2}{2g\, D}$$

Solving for the friction factor one gets,

$$f = \frac{64\,\mu\, l\, g\, D\, U}{\gamma\, D^2\, l\, U^2} = \frac{64\mu}{\rho U D} = \frac{64}{Re}$$

As the Reynolds number increases to a value greater than 3500, a separate curve can exist for each value of R/k. In Fig. 10.7, consider the variation of f with Re for a given value of R/k say 252. After the flow becomes turbulent, the variation of f with Re is given by a curve ca which is a part of curve cd. If the Reynolds number lies between 3500 and the Reynolds number at a, the friction factor is independent of R/k. If Re is further increased, the variation of f follows the line along which f increases with increase in Re.

If Re is increased still further, f remains constant and follows the line eb which tends to be horizontal. For each value of R/k, there will be a separate line indicating that f depends on R/k alone and not on Re. Thus in turbulent zone there are three regions :

a. Smooth boundary region along cd where f depends on Re only

b. Transition region in which f depends on Re and R/k.

c. Rough boundary region in which f depends on R/k only, as indicated by horizontal lines.

These regions are shown in Fig. 10.7. The lowest curve cd in the turbulent zone which is straight upto Re equal to 10^5 is for hydrodynamically smooth pipes. Blasius has given an equation for this line as

$$f = \frac{0.316}{Re^{1/4}} \tag{10.20}$$

which holds good for Reynolds numbers between 4000 and 10^5. Thus when the roughness protrusions are submerged in the laminar sublayer, they will have no effect on the friction factor and the pipe behaves as hydrodynamically smooth. When the Reynolds number exceeds 10^5, the data for hydrodynamically smooth pipe deviate from Eq. 10.20.

Equations for friction can be obtained from the expressions for average velocity in turbulent flow, discussed earlier in this Chapter. Substituting $U\sqrt{f/8}$ for u_* in Eqs. 10.12 and 10.13 and simplifying the resulting equations, the friction factor equations become,

$$\frac{1}{\sqrt{f}} = 2.03 \log_{10} Re\sqrt{f} - 0.91 \qquad \text{for smooth pipe} \tag{10.21}$$

and

$$\frac{1}{\sqrt{f}} = 2.03 \log_{10} \frac{R}{k} + 1.68 \qquad \text{for rough pipe} \tag{10.22}$$

Actual experimental results indicate a slight difference in the numerical values of the constants obtained in the above equations. Thus, the equations which fit Nikuradse's data for the friction factors in turbulent flow are

for smooth pipes
$$\frac{1}{\sqrt{f}} = 2.0 \log_{10} Re\sqrt{f} - 0.8 \tag{10.23}$$

and for rough pipes
$$\frac{1}{\sqrt{f}} = 2.0 \log_{10} \frac{R}{k} + 1.74 \tag{10.24}$$

These are shown in the general resistance diagram. Equation 10.23 is found to be valid from Reynolds number 4×10^3 to a Reynolds number as high as 4×10^7. It may be noted that, Eq. 10.23, being implicit, can be solved for f only by trial and error method. The following empirical equation can be used alternatively for direct solution for f,

$$f = 0.0032 + \frac{0.221}{Re^{0.237}} \quad (10.25)$$

Another equation proposed by Jain for smooth pipes, which is explicit in nature is

$$\frac{1}{\sqrt{f}} = 1.8 \log_{10} Re - 1.5146 \quad (10.25a)$$

Since a pipe of a given roughness behaves as smooth at low Reynolds numbers and the same becomes rough at high Reynolds numbers, there must exist an intermediate transition zone in which the friction factor depends both on Reynolds number and the relative smoothness.

It can be seen that Eqs. 10.23 and 10.24 can be rearranged in the form

$$\frac{1}{\sqrt{f}} - 2\log_{10}\frac{R}{k} = \phi\left(\frac{Re\sqrt{f}}{R/k}\right) \quad (10.26)$$

where $\phi\left(\frac{Re\sqrt{f}}{R/k}\right) = 2\log_{10}\frac{Re\sqrt{f}}{R/k} - 0.80$ when pipe is smooth and 1.74 when pipe is

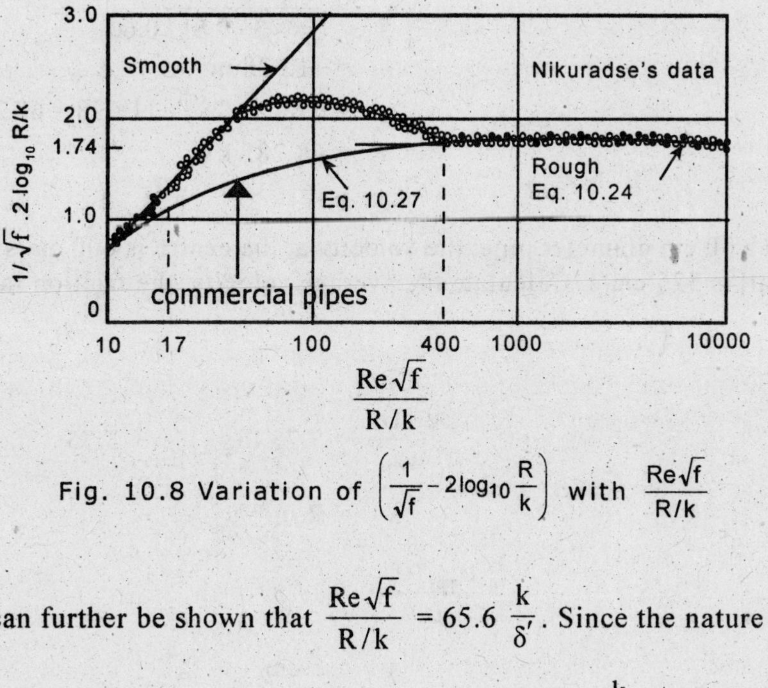

Fig. 10.8 Variation of $\left(\frac{1}{\sqrt{f}} - 2\log_{10}\frac{R}{k}\right)$ with $\frac{Re\sqrt{f}}{R/k}$

rough. It can further be shown that $\frac{Re\sqrt{f}}{R/k} = 65.6\frac{k}{\delta'}$. Since the nature of the boundary-smooth, rough or in transition-depends on the value of $\frac{k}{\delta'}$, it can be expected that a unique curve will define variation of $\left(\frac{1}{\sqrt{f}} - 2.0\log_{10}\frac{R}{k}\right)$ with $\frac{k}{\delta'}$ or $\frac{Re\sqrt{f}}{R/k}$ for Nikuradse's data over the entire range of roughness. Such variation is shown in Fig. 10.8. It should be noted that the transition of the curve begins when the ratio k/δ' is approximately 0.25 or $\frac{Re\sqrt{f}}{R/k}$ is about 17 and it ends when k/δ' is about 6.0 i.e. at a value of $\frac{Re\sqrt{f}}{R/k} \approx 400$.

Therefore a pipe will act as a smooth pipe if k/δ' is less than 0.25 and will act as rough when k/δ' is greater than 6.0, as mentioned in Chapter 9.

Example 10.1

What power is needed per km length of pipe to maintain a flow of 600 *l*/s water in a 60 cm diameter rough pipe. Take k to be 0.30 cm.

$$\frac{1}{\sqrt{f}} = 2\log_{10}\frac{30}{0.30} + 1.74$$

Solving for f, one gets f = 0.0304.

$$U = \frac{600 \times 10^{-3} \times 4}{\pi \times 0.60 \times 0.60} = 2.122 \text{ m/s}$$

Head lost $$h_f = \frac{0.0304 \times 1000 \times 2.122^2}{2 \times 9.81 \times 0.60}$$

$$= 11.628 \text{ m}$$

Power required $$= 0.60 \times 9787 \times 11.628 = 68\,281.94 \text{W}$$

or $$P = 68.282 \text{ kW}$$

Example 10.2

In turbulent flow in a 30 cm diameter pipe, the velocity at the centre is 600 cm/s and that at 5 cm from the wall is 525 cm/s. Calculate the average velocity, the friction factor and the discharge.

From Eq. 10.14

$$\frac{u - U}{u_*} = 5.75\log_{10}\frac{y}{R} + 3.75$$

when $$y = R,\ u = u_{max}$$

hence, $$\frac{u_{max} - U}{u_*} = 3.75$$

and when $$y = 5 \text{ cm}$$

$$\frac{u_5 - U}{u_*} = 5.75\log_{10}\frac{5}{15} + 3.75$$

Substituting the values of u_{max} = 600 cm/s and u_5 = 525 cm/s, the above two equations can be solved to obtain,

$$U = 497.8 \text{ cm/s and } u_* = 27.2 \text{ cm/s}$$

Since

$$u_* = U\sqrt{\frac{f}{8}},$$

$$f = \frac{8\times 27.2^2}{497.8^2} = 0.024$$

$$Q = \frac{\pi}{4} \times 30^2 \times 497.8$$

$$= 352\,000 \text{ cm}^3\text{/s} = 352 \; l\text{/s}$$

10.6 Commercial Pipes

Unfortunately the resistance diagram presented in Fig. 10.7 cannot be used for the commercial pipes because the nature of roughness in commercial pipes is very much different from that in the artificially roughened pipes. The pipes which are normally available for use are made of materials such as metal, wood, concrete etc.; therefore the surface irregularities in such pipes cannot be adequately described by sand grain diameter. Yet for a given pipe, one can find a uniform sand grain diameter such that, when the pipe is coated with these sand grains, it will yield the same limiting value (for rough condition) of friction factor as that given by the pipe. This *equivalent sand grain roughness* for any commercial pipe can be found experimentally by first computing the limiting value of friction factor f from a series of experiments and then substituting this value of f in Eq. 10.24 to obtain R/k and then k. In the transition region, when the friction factor is a function of both the Reynolds number and the relative smoothness, the result for commercial pipes and artificially pipes are different. The relationship between $Re\sqrt{f}/(R/k)$ and $\left(\frac{1}{\sqrt{f}} - 2\log_{10}\frac{R}{k}\right)$ for commercial pipes, as was obtained by Colebrook is shown in Fig. 10.8, which shows a large deviation in the transition zone from the curve for Nikuradse's data. The points for commercial pipes closely follow a smooth curve which is asymptotic to both the lines for smooth and rough pipes. For this curve Colebrook and White presented an empirical equation

$$\frac{1}{\sqrt{f}} - 2\log_{10}\frac{R}{k} = 1.74 - 2\log_{10}\left(1 + 18.7\frac{R/k}{Re\sqrt{f}}\right) \tag{10.27}$$

which can be used for obtaining friction factor values for the commercial pipes. This equation was later plotted by Moody in the form of Fig. 10.9 which is commonly known as Moody's diagram. Essentially Figs. 10.7 and 10.9 are similar except for the transition region.

Moody's diagram is frequently used for finding the friction factor value of commercial pipes, if the parameter R/k and Re are known. Values of k for some of the common pipe materials are given in Table 10.1. An explicit equation for f for commercial pipes covering both smooth and rough pipes, as given by Jain is

$$\frac{1}{\sqrt{f}} = 1.14 - 2\log_{10}\left[\frac{k}{2R} + \frac{21.25}{Re^{0.90}}\right] \quad (10.27\text{ a})$$

TABLE 10.1

Average Values of k for Different Materials

Pipe Material	*Value of k in mm*
Glass, drawn glass tubing	Smooth
Wrought iron, steel	0.045
Asphalted cast iron	0.120
Galvanised iron	0.150
Cast iron	0.260
Concrete	0.30 to 3.00
Riveted steel	0.90 to 9.00

It should be noted that the values of equivalent sand grain roughness indicated above correspond to materials which are new and clean. The value of k usually increases with use due to corrosion. Colebrook and White have given the following formula for evaluating the term k,

$$k = k_o + \alpha t$$

in which k is the equivalent sand grain roughness at any time t, k_o is the corresponding value of the new material and α is an experimental coefficient. Resistance measured on the same pipe at two different times will enable the estimation of α from which the resistance characteristics of the pipe can be predicted for any future time.

Environmental engineers more often use an empirical equation proposed by Hazen-Williams, than White- Colebrook equation, for designing pipe lines and sewers. In metric units this equation is

$$U = 0.85\, C_H\, R^{0.63}\, S^{0.45} \quad (10.28)$$

in which C_H is the coefficient, the values of which have been tabulated in Table 10.2.

TABLE 10.2

Average Values of C_H for Different Materials

Pipe Material	C_H
Concrete (regardless of age)	130
Cast iron :	
New	130
5 year old	120
20 year old	100
Welded steel (new)	120
Wood stave (regardless of age)	120
Vitrified clay	110
Riveted steel (new)	110
Brick sewers	100
Asbestos cement	140

Comparing this equation with Darcy-Weisbach equation, it can be seen that C_H is really a function of Reynolds number of flow and relative roughness. This fact is overlooked in values of C_H tabulated in Table 10.2. As a result Hazen Williams' equation, compared to White Colebrcok equation, yields errors upto ± 30 percent in the estimation of velocity and ± 60 percent in friction factor values for pipes commonly used in practice.

For this reason it is preferable to use Moody's diagram to determine friction factor for commercial pipes.

10.7 Turbulent Flow in Noncircular Conduits

In most of the problems of turbulent flow, the conduit carrying the flow is circular in shape and one can use Darcy-Weisbach equation along with the Moody's diagram to solve them. Problems of flow in noncircular conduits can also be solved by Darcy-Weisbach equation provided a suitable length dimension is used in place of the diameter D in Eq. 10.16 (b). It is a common practice to replace D by 4R in which R is the *hydraulic radius* defined as the ratio of cross-sectional area to wetted perimeter. Hydraulic radius is a characteristic length dimension, mostly used in open channel flow problems. For circular pipes, the hydraulic radius will be

$$R = \frac{\pi D^2}{4 \times \pi D} = \frac{D}{4}$$

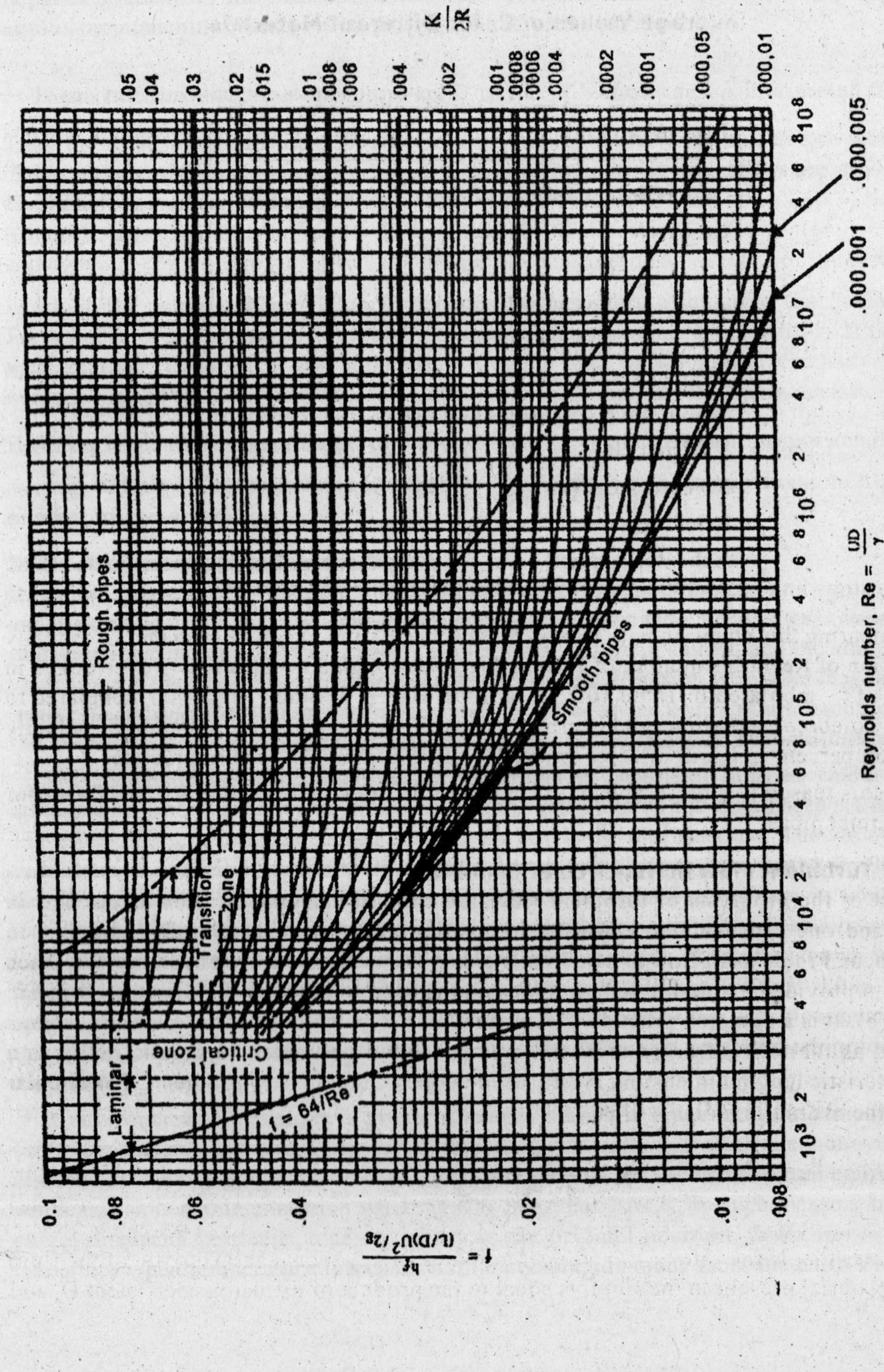

Fig. 10.9 Moody's diagram for fγ commerical pipes

Thus if D is replaced by 4R, Eq. 10.16 (b) takes a form

$$h_f = \frac{f\,l\,U^2}{2g\,(4R)} = \frac{f\,l\,U^2}{8gR}$$

For using Moody's diagram the Reynolds number can also be computed using 4R instead of D in the Reynolds number.

Jamil Malaika has conducted extensive experiments in rough non-circular conduits to investigate relationship between friction factor, relative roughness and form factor using conduits of four different shapes. Malaika found that a more appropriate length dimension characterising the boundary of non-circular conduits is the diameter of the inscribed circle d. If d is used in place of 4R, Eqs. 10.23, 10.24 and 10.27 can be modified for use in the case of noncircular conduits. These equations are :

Smooth conduit $$\frac{1}{\sqrt{f}} = 2\log R_d\sqrt{f} - 0.8 \qquad (10.29)$$

Rough conduit $$\frac{1}{\sqrt{f}} = 2\log\frac{d}{k} + 1.14 \qquad (10.30)$$

and transition $$\frac{1}{\sqrt{f}} = -2\log\left(\frac{2.51}{R_d\sqrt{f}} + \frac{1}{3.72d/k}\right) \qquad (10.31)$$

in which $R_d = \frac{Ud}{\nu}$, d being the diameter of an inscribed circle.

10.8 Turbulent Diffusion

As discussed earlier, turbulent flow is characterised by the presence of eddies which move in all the directions. As these lumps of fluid move across the flow they carry with them the associated quantities which may be momentum, kinetic energy, heat, suspended sediment, dissolved solids, etc. Therefore turbulent flow has a great ability for diffusion. Diffusion also takes place in laminar flow but it is due to molecular motion only and therefore it is very feeble. In turbulent flow the diffusion is several hundred times greater than in laminar flow because it is due to travel of eddies. Turbulent diffusion is responsible for spreading of smoke coming out of chimneys, suspension of sediment in flowing water and artificial mixing in many chemical processes.

By assuming that the general nature of two dimensional diffusion process due to turbulence eddies is similar to molecular diffusion in laminar flow (Boussinesq's assumption mentioned in Sect. 10.2), the basic equation for diffusion due to turbulence can be written as

$$N = -D_1\frac{d\theta}{dy} \qquad (10.32)$$

This states that N the rate of transfer per unit area of any local characteristic of the fluid or the material present in the fluid, is equal to the product of diffusion coefficient D_1 and negative gradient of the fluid characteristic θ in that direction. This general expression applies to momentum, heat, sediment, etc., in the turbulent fluid.

It can be seen that the dimensions of D_l are L^2/T which can be interpreted as $\frac{L}{T}L$. Thus the diffusion coefficient should be proportional to velocity and length which are characteristic of diffusion process. Since turbulent fluctuations and eddies are responsible for diffusion, one can write

$$D_l = \beta l \sqrt{v'^2} \tag{10.33}$$

in which the numerical coefficient β depends on the nature of quantity that is diffused. For transfer of momentum $\beta = 1$ and D_l is equal to eddy kinematic viscosity ε. If the flow were laminar, value of D_l for momentum transfer will be kinematic viscosity ν. The average size of the eddy can be assumed to be proportional to the characteristic size of flow, e.g. pipe diameter or depth of flow whereas $\sqrt{v'^2}$ can be taken proportional to the average velocity. Therefore one can write $D_l \sim UD$ or D_l/ν to be proportional to Reynolds number of gross flow.

10.9 Dispersion from Smoke Stacks

It is quite instructive to observe the smoke coming out from chimneys and smoke stacks and dispersing it into the atmosphere. A keen observer must have noticed various patterns of dispersion depending on the height of smoke stack, nature of smoke, and the atmospheric conditions. From the point of pollution control an ideal situation would be that in which smoke is carried downstream without its mixing in the lower layers of atmosphere, since this will protect the areas immediately downstream of smoke stack from pollution.

Two mechanisms are responsible for dispersion of pollutants such as smoke in the atmosphere. The average wind speed carries the pollutant in the downstream direction. The atmospheric turbulence causes it to spread vertically and laterally. The atmospheric turbulence is caused by two effects namely, due to velocity gradient in the vertical and due to temperature gradient. The latter turbulence is sometimes known as convective turbulence. If the atmosphere is dry and if the expansion or compression of an air parcel as it moves vertically, takes place at constant heat content, it can be shown that the temperature will decrease with increase in elevation at the rate of 1°C per 100 m. This is known as *dry adiabatic lapse rate* (DALR). It is the prevailing environmental lapse rate (ELR) in relation of DALR that governs the effect of temperature gradient on dispersion.

If environmental lapse rate is greater than dry adiabatic lapse rate, the atmosphere is said to be unstable and a small air parcel displaced vertically will continue to move in that direction. If the two gradients are equal, the atmosphere is said to be in neutral equilibrium whereas it is in stable condition when ELR is less than DALR. In such a case a small air parcel displaced vertically tends to return to the original position. *Inversion* is said to take place when temperature increases with increasing distance from the earth's surface ere ELR has opposite sign compared to that of DALR. This is the condition of strong tability which reduces vertical dispersion of pollutants. Inversion takes place during night vhen the earth's surface radiates heat into the atmosphere.

As the smoke or pollutant comes out from the stack and mixes with the surrounding air noving in the horizontal direction, both fluids have different momentum and heat content er unit mass. The plume moves vertically upward for some distance. In this process the lume slows down and gradually turns in the wind direction while still continuing to move pward. For turbulent flow the maximum rise Z_m of the plume is given by the empirical quation proposed by Holland,

$$Z_m = (3\, U_s R_s + 0.04H)/U \tag{10.34}$$

in which Z_m is in m, U_s and U are the stack velocity and wind velocity at the stack level n m/s, R_s is the radius of smoke-stack in m and H is the heat content of smoke at stack evel in kilocalories per second, see Fig. 10.10. After the plume becomes horizontal, the ynamics of plume spreading is governed by environmental turbulence and is predicted y diffusion equation. Various patterns of dispersion of pollutant are shown in Fig. 10.10

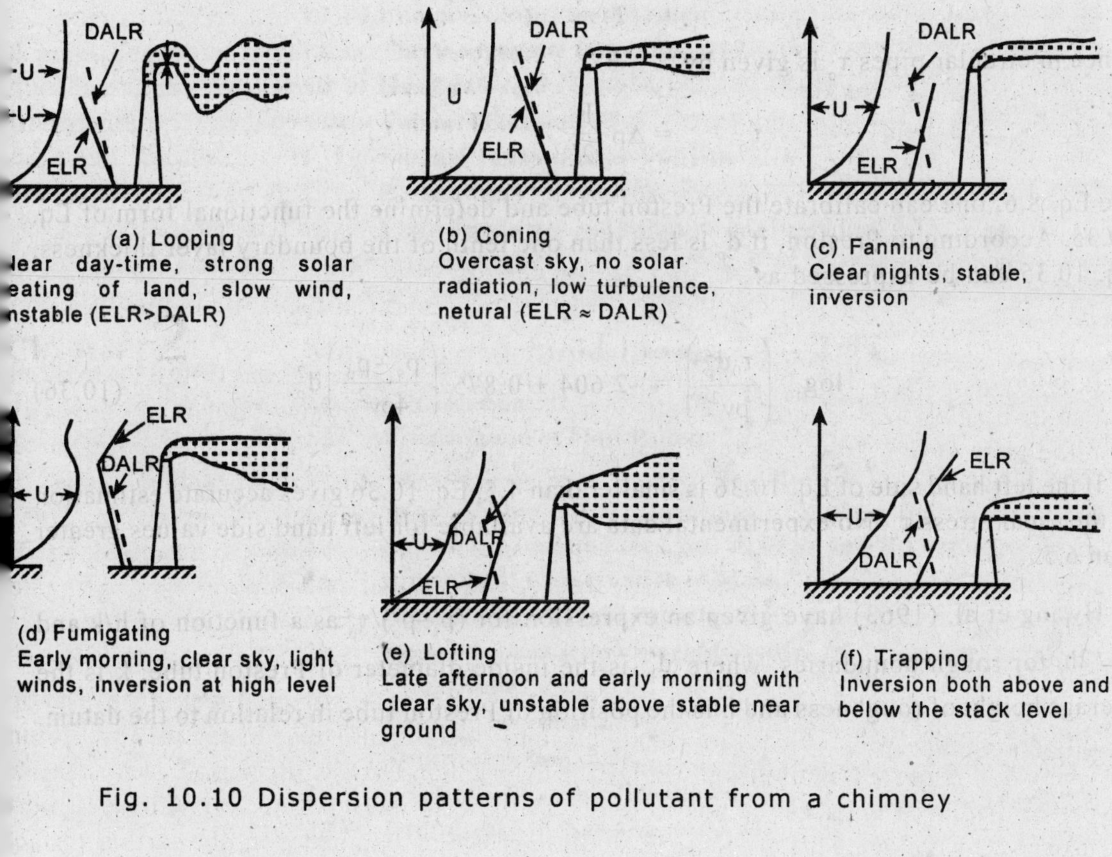

(a) Looping
lear day-time, strong solar eating of land, slow wind, nstable (ELR>DALR)

(b) Coning
Overcast sky, no solar radiation, low turbulence, netural (ELR ≈ DALR)

(c) Fanning
Clear nights, stable, inversion

(d) Fumigating
Early morning, clear sky, light winds, inversion at high level

(e) Lofting
Late afternoon and early morning with clear sky, unstable above stable near ground

(f) Trapping
Inversion both above and below the stack level

Fig. 10.10 Dispersion patterns of pollutant from a chimney

along with conditions under which they occur.

10.10 Preston Tube

Preston tube is a simple device to indirectly measure shear stress on a smooth or rough boundary in pipes, open channels and boundary layers. It consists of a total head tube of outside diameter d_p resting on the floor which measures $p_s = p + \frac{\rho u^2}{2}$, and a tube for measuring the ambient pressure as shown in Fig. 10.11. Then $(p_s - p)$ should depend on the boundary shear τ_o, ρ, d_p and ν, because the velocity distribution close to the wall is governed by law of the wall

$$u/u_* = f(u_* y/\nu)$$

and is independent of the pressure gradient and upstream disturbances in the flow over smooth boundaries. Therefore one can write

$$(p_s - p)d_p^{\,2} / \rho\nu^2 = f\left(\frac{\tau_0 d_p^2}{\rho\nu^2}\right) \tag{10.35}$$

Since in circular pipes τ_o is given by

$$\tau_o = \Delta p \frac{R}{2l}$$

see Eq. 8.6, one can calibrate the Preston tube and determine the functional form of Eq. 10.35. According to Preston, if d_p is less than one tenth of the boundary layer thickness, Eq. 10.35 can be expressed as

$$\log_{10}\left(\frac{\tau_0 d_p^2}{\rho\nu^2}\right) = -2.604 + 0.875\left(\frac{p_s - p_o}{4\rho\nu^2}\right)d_p^2 \tag{10.36}$$

If the left hand side of Eq. 10.36 is smaller than 4.5, Eq. 10.36 gives accurate estimation of the shear stress τ_o. No experimental data are available for left hand side values greater than 6.5.

Hwang et al. (1963) have given an expression for $(p_s - p_o)/\tau_o$ as a function of h/k and $d'_p/2h$ for rough boundaries, where d'_p is the inside diameter of Preston tube, k is the average height of roughness and h is the position of Preston tube in relation to the datum.

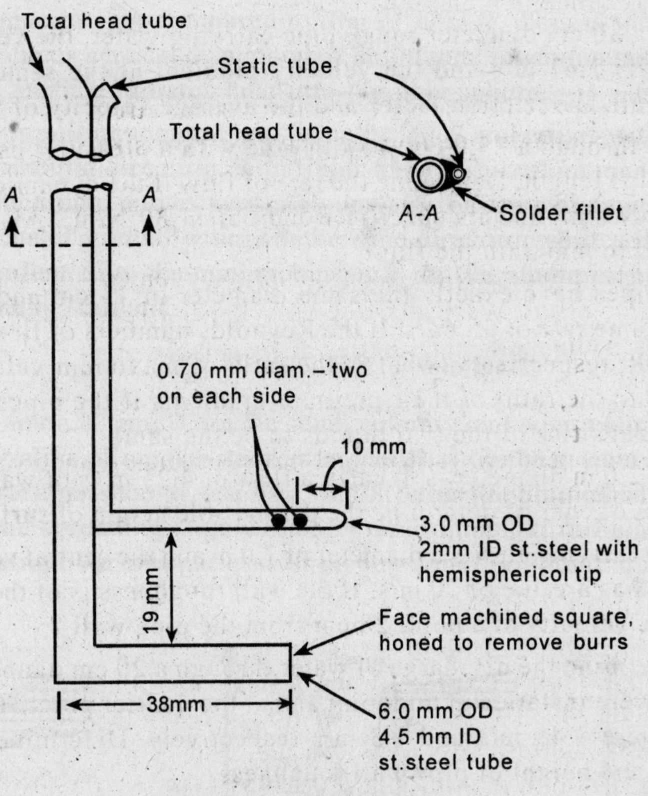

Fig. 10.11 Preston tube

PROBLEMS

0.1 Below are given the instantaneous values of velocity in m/s measured at given point in flow at the interval of one second,

13.10, 13.15, 13.05, 13.20, 12.95, 13.16, 13.02, 12.85, 12.85, 13.00,
12.97, 13.12, 13.09, 12.93, 13.11, 13.09, 12.81, 13.26, 13.00

Determine the time averaged velocity $\overline{u}$, $\overline{u'^2}$ and $\sqrt{\overline{u'^2}}/\overline{u}$

0.2 From the equations of velocity distribution for turbulent flow in pipes (smooth as well as rough) show that

$$\frac{u_{max}}{U} = 1.326\sqrt{f} + 1$$

0.3 For turbulent flow in a pipe, determine the value of y/R at which the average velocity and the local velocity will have the same magnitude.

0.4. A 300 m long 20 cm smooth pipe, carries oil at the rate of 2300 *l*/min. The oil has a relative density of 0.9 and a dynamic viscosity of 0.038 kg/m s. If a decrease in temperature causes the viscosity to increase to 0.380 kg/m s and the power input remains the same, what will be the changed rate of flow ?

10.5 In the case of a 30 cm diameter rough pipe carrying water, the velocity at 2.0 cm from the wall is 2.67 m/s and the velocity gradient at the same point 25.8 s^{-1}. stress at the wall, the friction factor and the average velocity of flow.

10.6 Air is pumped through a 25.0 cm smooth pipe with a pressure loss of 41.68 N/m^2 per 100 m of pipe length. Determine the rate of flow if the dynamic viscosity of air is 1.893×10^5 N s/m^2 and its specific weight is 11.80 N/m^3. Also determine the power required to maintain the flow.

10.7 Two smooth pipes have exactly the same diameter of 15 cm and carry different liquids at the same rate of 55.6 *l*/s. If the Reynolds numbers of flow in the pipe are 1000 and 50000 respectively, what is the ratio of maximum velocity in the two pipes ? Compute the ratio of their pressure gradients if the pipes are horizontal. Assume mass densities of the two liquids to be the same.

10.8 If a conduit of 2.0 m diameter is to carry a flow of 4.25 m^3/s of water at 20°C with a minimum loss of energy, determine the permissible height of surface protrusions.

10.9 A circular pipe carrying air has a diameter of 1.0 m and the central velocity observed by a pitot tube has a value of 20 m/s. If the wall roughness is of the order of 0.177 cm, what is the velocity at a point 28 cm from the pipe wall ?

10.10 In order to determine the discharge of water through a 20 cm diameter rough pipe, Prandtl tubes were installed at midpoint and at the quarter point. The velocities at these points were 1.45 m/s and 1.3 m/s respectively. Determine the discharge, friction factor and height of pipe wall roughness.

10.11 If sand grains of 0.076 cm diameter are cemented on the inner surface of a 10 cm pipe for test purposes, at what velocity of water the surface roughness will just begin to disturb the laminar sublayer ? At what velocity the pipe wall will behave as rough (Take $\nu = 1 \times 10^{-6} m^2/s$).

10.12 The shear at the channel bottom is many times determined by observing the velocities at two points in the vertical. Show that the expression for shear stress is

$$\tau_o = \frac{K^2 \rho (u_2 - u_1)^2}{5.29 (\log_{10} y_2 / y_1)^2}$$

in which K is Karman constant.

10.13 What size of galvanised iron pipe should be selected to convey water at the rate of 15 *l*/s at 20°C if the head loss is not to exceed 3.0 m for every 100 m of pipe length?

10.14 A smooth pipe carries 7 *l*/s of water at 20°C with a head loss of 7.5 cm per 10 m length. Determine the diameter of the pipe.

10.15 A 60 cm steel pipe is required to convey oil at the rate of 600 *l*/s to a distance of 80 km. Determine the required power input at 85% efficiency of' the pump. Take $\rho = 815$ kg/m^3 and $\mu = 1.92 \times 10^{-2}$ N s/m^2 for the oil.

10.16 Field tests on a 30 cm cast iron water main indicate that the wall roughness has increased to 1.5 mm after many years of service. If the water main now carries a flow of 225 *l*/s what increase in flow at the same power would result by replacing the line with a new cast iron pipe of the same diameter (Take $\rho = 998$ kg/m^3 and $\nu = 1 \times 10^{-6}$ m^2/s).

10.17 The pipe wall roughness height k for a new cast iron pipe is 0.26 mm. After three years of service it becomes 0.41 mm. What will be its value after 18 years ?

10.18 A domestic mixer is able to complete a certain mixing operation in 2 minutes. Estimate the time required for proper mixing if (i) size of blades is reduced to half and (ii) speed of rotation is tripled.

10.19 Consider a steady state case of sediment suspension in open channel flow. At any distance y from the boundary, the downward settling of sediment per unit area per unit time will be balanced by the rate of upward transfer per unit area due to turbulent diffusion. This is expressed by the equation

$$\omega\, c + D_s \frac{dc}{dy} = 0$$

where ω is fall velocity of sediment, C is concentration and D_s diffusion coefficient. Assuming D_s and ω to be constant, integrate the above differential equation and obtain expression for c.

10.20 Tests on a 500 mm diameter commercial pipe gave the following data for head loss in 100 m length of pipe:

Q *l*/s	40	200	400	800
h_f m	0.01	0.210	0.820	3.27

i. Determine equivalent sand grain roughness of pipe

ii. What is the maximum discharge at which the pipe will still act as smooth.

iii. At what minimum discharge the pipe will act as rough.

[illegible] new cast iron pipe of the same diameter. (Take ρ = 998 kg/m³ and [illegible])

10.17 Average wall roughness height k for a new cast iron pipe is 0.26 mm. After three years in service it becomes [illegible] mm. What will be its value after 18 years?

10.18 [illegible] reduced to half [illegible]

10.19 Consider a steady state case of sediment suspension in open channel flow. At any [illegible] the downward settling of sediment per unit area per unit time will be balanced by the vertical transfer per unit area due to [illegible]. This is expressed by the equation

[illegible]

where w is fall velocity of sediment, c its concentration and [illegible] diffusion coefficient. Assuming [illegible] and w to be constant, integrate the above differential equation and obtain expression for c.

10.20 Tests on a [illegible] mm diameter [illegible] pipe gave the following data for head loss in 100 m length of pipe:

[illegible]

Determine equivalent sand grain roughness of pipe [illegible] the pipe will still act as smooth.

[illegible] the pipe will act as rough.

[illegible]

Chapter Eleven

Problems in Pipe Flow

11.1 Introduction

In the chapters on laminar flow and turbulent flow, the basic laws governing resistance to flow through pipes have been discussed. Many of these laws can be applied in the solutions of the problems in pipe flow such as the prediction of discharge through pipe of given characteristics, the determination of pipe size necessary to carry a given discharge and the calculation of energy required to maintain a given flow. When the pipes flow partially full as in the case of sewer lines and culverts, the laws of open channel flow, (which are discussed later) can be applied. Most of the pipe flow problems can be solved by the application of the equations of energy and continuity and the law of frictional resistance.

The concepts of *hydraulic grade line and total energy line* are very useful in solving the pipe flow problems. The line of piezometric head, which has been defined and explained in Chapter 3, is the line which shows the sum of pressure head p/γ and potential head z along the pipe. It is commonly known as the *hydraulic grade line.* In other words, hydraulic grade line is a line joining all points indicated by the liquid rise in piezometers connected to the pipe line. When the pressure is less than atmospheric, the hydraulic grade line falls below the centre line of the pipe indicating a negative pressure. The slope of the hydraulic grade line is known as hydraulic gradient which for steady uniform flow, must equal h_f/l.

The *total energy line* is obtained by plotting the sum $\left(\frac{U^2}{2g}+\frac{p}{\gamma}+z\right)$ with reference to the some arbitrary datum as for the hydraulic grade line. The slope of energy grade line is always negative i.e. the total energy decreases in the direction of flow. It should be noted that while energy grade line continuously falls in the direction of flow, the hydraulic grade line may rise or fall in some reaches along the flow. The vertical distance between the energy grade line and the hydraulic grade line at any point indicates the velocity head of flow at that section. Such analysis is usually one dimensional in that the velocity is assumed to be constant over any cross section, and hence the kinetic energy correction factor α is normally taken as unity.

The resistance offered to flow is not only due to the boundary resistance but is also due to the non-uniformity in flow which may be caused due to the presence of fittings, transitions, bends, valves, etc. The non-uniformity causes considerable expenditure of energy which must be evaluated and taken into consideration in solving the pipe flow problems. The energy loss due to non-uniformity assumes greater importance when the pipe length is small than when it is large.

11.2 Energy Losses in Transitions

Transitions are sections of pipe which connect two pipes of different diameters by a gradual change in cross-section. Transition may be either convergent or divergent or they may be for a gradual change in the cross sectional shape e.g. from rectangular to circular shape and vice versa. There may be either acceleration or retardation of the flow due to the transitions. In a converging transition, the potential or pressure energy is converted into kinetic energy and the flow gets accelerated. Because the gradually accelerated flows have an inherent stability and since they are free from separation, the energy loss in gradually converging transitions is very small. It is however important that the boundary changes should be very gradual and that the pressure at any point does not reach the cavitation limits. In the diverging transitions, also known as conical diffusers, where retardation of flow takes place, the kinetic energy of flow is converted into pressure energy. If the total angle of expansion θ is larger than approximately 10°, the boundary layer ultimately separates resulting in the formation of eddies. The boundary causes frictional resistance also. Due to these factors, the energy loss in expanding transition is considerably more than that in a convergent transition.

The energy loss h_L in transitions depends upon the average velocity of flow U, the variables defining the geometry of the transition such as diameters before and after the transition, flare angle θ, etc., the pipe roughness k, and the fluid characteristics mass density ρ and the viscosity μ. The energy loss in a transition can be expressed in terms of a dimensionless parameter $\Delta p/(\rho U^2/2)$ (also known as pressure coefficient) or $h_L/(U^2/2g)$ where Δp is the drop in pressure. The pressure coefficient in the form of $\Delta p/(\rho U^2/2)$ can be used for gas flow while its other form, $h_L/(U^2/2g)$ may be used for flow of liquids. In the form of a functional relationship one can write,

$$\frac{h_L}{U^2/2g} \text{ or } \frac{\Delta p}{\rho U^2/2} = f\left(Re, \frac{k}{D} \text{ and geometry of transition}\right) \quad (11.1)$$

in which Re is the Reynolds number of flow, and D is the characteristic diameter. This is for Mach number less than 0.4. The geometry includes D_2/D_1 and θ, or D_2/D_1 and $L/(D_2-D_1)$.

The Reynolds number Re is important when the transitions are smooth and very long. In the case of long diffusers there is frictional resistance and also form resistance due to the boundary layer separation, both of which depend on the Reynolds number of flow. When the transition is abrupt and short such as a sudden expansion, the point of separation is fixed. Furthermore, the transition being short, the contribution of frictional resistance to the total resistance is very small and therefore one would expect $\Delta p/(\rho U^2/2)$ to be independent of Re and D/k and it should depend only on the geometry i.e. on the diameter ratio D_2/D_1. This is borne out by the experimental results. In order to reduce the losses it is necessary to round off the corners and streamline the transition.

The details of flow and energy loss in conical diffusers have been extensively studied by Gibson and Kalinske. It has been found that except for gradual expansions (total expansion angle between 5° and 10°) the frictional resistance is very small compared to form resistance due to boundary layer separation. As the expansion angle is increased the form loss increases rapidly. As can be seen from Fig. 11.1, the loss is maximum at an expansion angle of 60°. Apparently any further increase in expansion angle does not modify flow pattern so drastically as to change the value of K. For this reason, for expansion angle between 60° and 180°, K values depend primarily on A_2/A_1 ratios. It may also be mentioned that the pressure continues to rise a few pipe diameters downstream of section 2 due to readjustment of velocity distribution.

The diffuser performance can be improved by four methods, namely removing the low-energy flow near the wall by suction, re-energising the near wall flow by injecting high velocity fluid, by generating turbulence near the wall at the entrance by roughnesses or vortex generators or by provision of vanes.

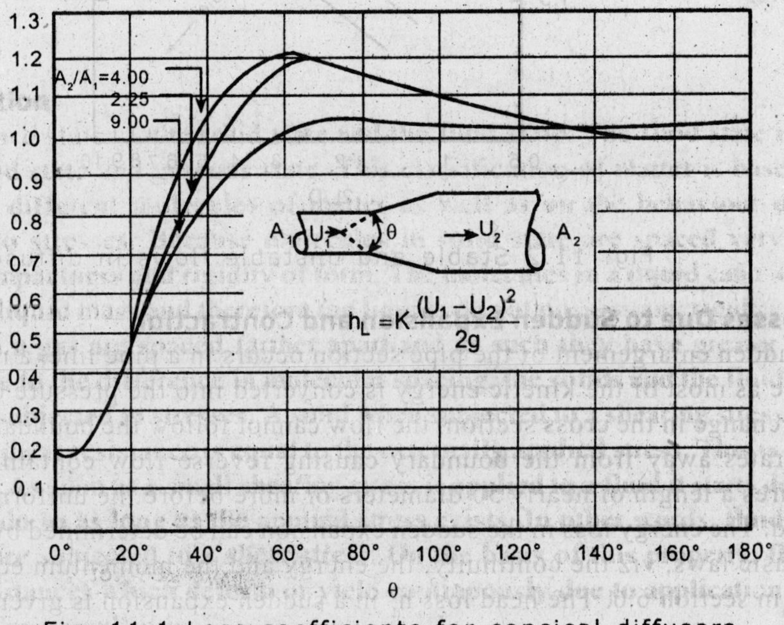

Fig. 11.1 Loss coefficients for concical diffusers

If the diffuser angle is large, if the boundary layer at the inlet is thin, or when flow entering the diffuser is unsymmetrical because of upstream flow geometry, the flow in wide angle diffusers is unstable, causing pressure fluctuations and clinging of jet alternately from one side to other. The frequency f of pressure fluctuations can be expressed in terms of Strouhal number S which is equal to $\frac{f D_1}{U_1}$; Figure 11.2 shows how S varies with area ratio A_2/A_1 and $2L/D_1$ where L is the diffuser length. Stable and unstable regions are shown in the Figure. Flow is without undesirable lateral fluctuations in stable region.

In the case of a gradual contraction or reducer, the energy loss is very small and can be neglected. The flow is almost irrotational because the fluid is being accelerated. The energy loss is given by formula,

$$h_f = 0.04\, U_2^2/2g \tag{11.2}$$

in which U_2 is the average velocity in the contracted section.

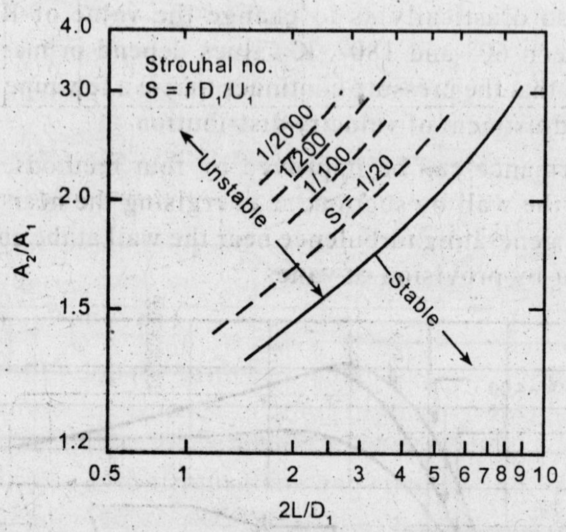

Fig. 11.2 Stable and unstable flows in diffusers

11.3 Losses Due to Sudden Expansion and Contraction

When a sudden enlargement of the pipe section occurs in a pipe line, a rapid retardation takes place as most of the kinetic energy is converted into the pressure energy. Because of sudden change in the cross section, the flow cannot follow the boundary and hence the flow separates away from the boundary causing reverse flow containing eddies. The flow requires a length of nearly 50 diameters or more before the uniform conditions are established. The energy loss in the sudden expansion can be determined by the application of three basic laws, viz the continuity, the energy and the momentum equations. This is presented in section 6.6. The head loss h_L in a sudden expansion is given by equation,

$$h_L = \frac{(U_1 - U_2)^2}{2g} = \left(1 - \frac{A_1}{A_2}\right)^2 \frac{U_1^2}{2g} \tag{11.3}$$

This equation is known as Borda-Carnot equation. The factor $\left(1 - \frac{A_1}{A_2}\right)^2$ depends only on the size of the two pipes. It is known as loss coefficient K and its values are given in

Table 11.1. Fig. 11.3 shows a sudden expansion in a pipe from area A_1 to area A_2. The energy grade line and the hydraulic grade line are also shown in the figure.

When the pipe discharges into a large reservoir, A_2 becomes infinite and the ratio A_1/A_2 is zero thus the value of loss coefficient is unity.

TABLE 11.1

Loss Coefficients for Sudden Expansion

A_1/A_2	0	0.1	0.2	0.3	0.4	0.5	0.6	0.7	0.8	0.9	1.0
K	1.0	0.81	0.64	0.49	0.36	0.25	0.16	0.09	0.04	0.01	0

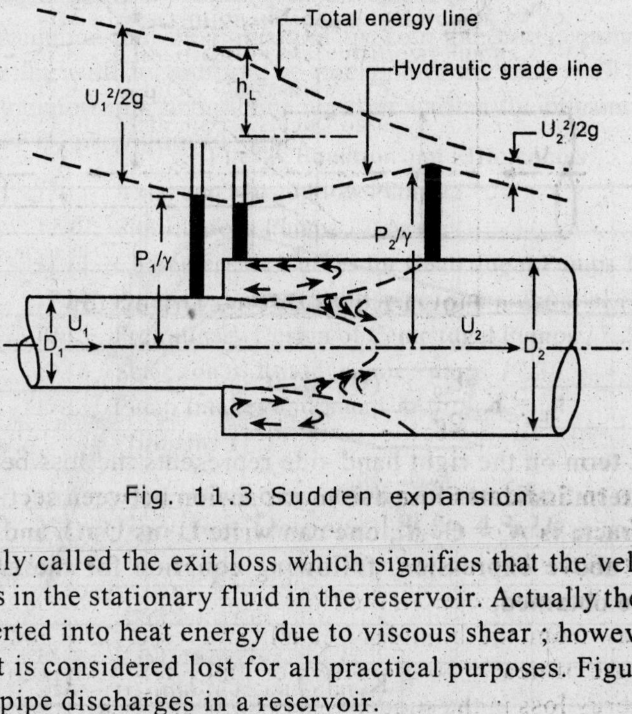

Fig. 11.3 Sudden expansion

This is commonly called the exit loss which signifies that the velocity head is lost while the jet diffuses in the stationary fluid in the reservoir. Actually the kinetic energy is not lost but is converted into heat energy due to viscous shear ; however since this heat cannot be utilised, it is considered lost for all practical purposes. Figure 11.4 shows the flow details when a pipe discharges in a reservoir.

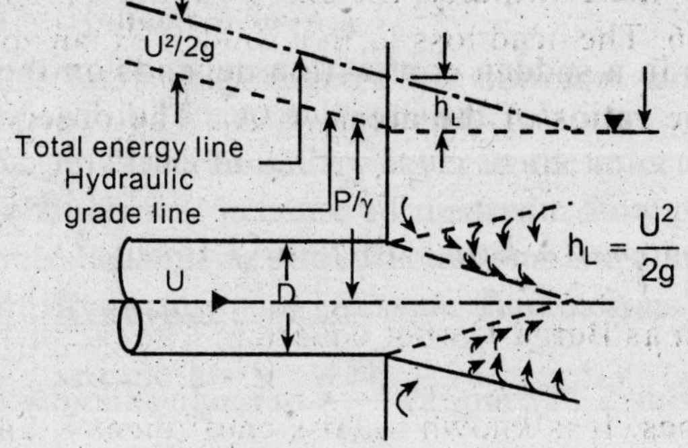

Fig. 11.4 Exit loss

In the case of sudden contraction illustrated in Fig. 11.5, the important feature is the formation of vena contracta and subsequent expansion of the jet. As the fluid is accelerated from section 1 to 0, the energy loss is relatively small; when the flow is decelerated from sections 0 to 2, the energy loss will be appreciable. There is also zone of stagnation where the boundary abruptly turns inside. The total loss of head between sections 1 and 2 will be,

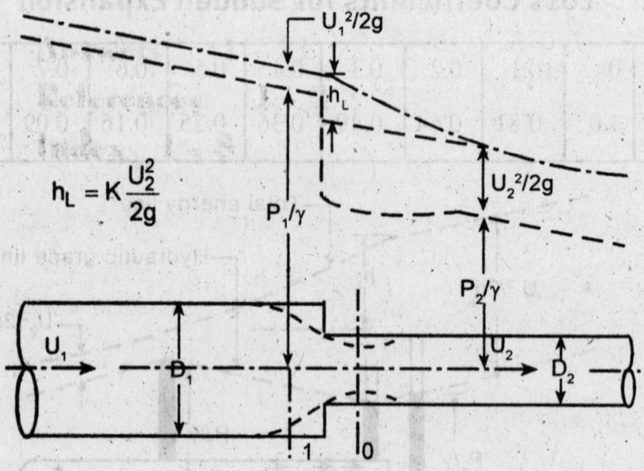

Fig. 11.5 Sudden contraction

$$h_L = K_1 \frac{U_0^2}{2g} + \frac{(U_0 - U_2)^2}{2g}$$

in which the first term on the right hand side represents the loss between sections 1 and 0 and the second term indicates loss due to expansion between section 0 and 2. Since the area at vena contracta is $A_0 = C_c A_2$, one can write U_o as U_2/C_c and with the value of U_0 subsituted in the above expression, following equation for the energy loss in sudden contraction can be obtained,

$$h_L = \left[\frac{K_1}{C_c^2} + \left(\frac{1}{C_c} - 1\right)^2\right]\frac{U_2^2}{2g} = K\frac{U_2^2}{2g} \tag{11.4}$$

Thus the energy loss in a sudden contraction depends on the coefficient of contraction which varies with the ratios of the areas A_2/A_1. The observed values of C_c and K are listed in Table 11.2.

TABLE 11. 2

The Coefficient of Contraction and Loss Coefficient for Sudden Contractions

$\frac{A_2}{A_1}$	0	0.1	0.2	0.3	0.4	0.5	0.6	0.7	0.8	0.9	1.0
C_c	0.617	0.624	0.632	0.643	0.659	0.681	0.712	0.755	0.813	0.892	1.0
K	0.50	0.46	0.41	0.3	0.30	0.24	0.18	0.12	0.06	0.02	0

When a pipe is connected to a reservoir, the value of A_2/A_1 is almost zero and thus loss coefficient will be 0.5 which is for a square or sharp entrance. Here K depends upon the type of entrance conditions also. For a rounded or bell mouthed entry the value of K is between 0.02 to 0.04 and for re-entrant mouthpiece entry the value is 0.8. Figure 11.6 shows different types of entrances and their K values. In most of the practical problems of pipe flow the entrance loss is taken as 0.5 $\frac{U^2}{2g}$ unless the conditions of entry are specified for adopting a smaller value.

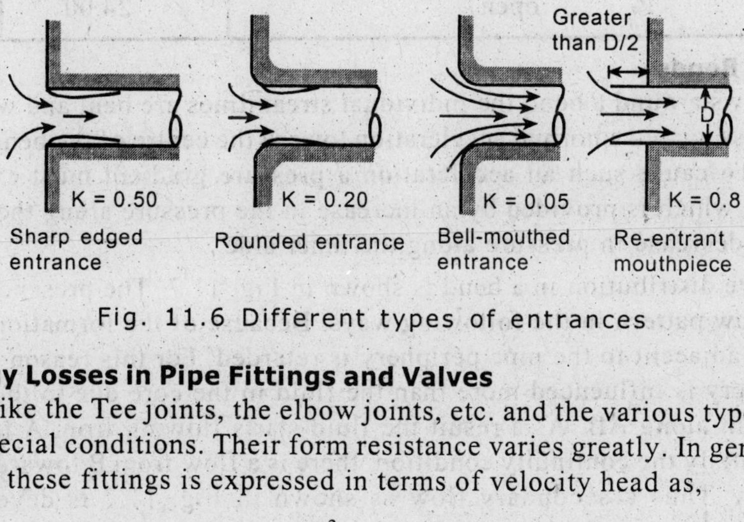

Fig. 11.6 Different types of entrances

11.4 Energy Losses in Pipe Fittings and Valves

Pipe fittings like the Tee joints, the elbow joints, etc. and the various types of valves are used under special conditions. Their form resistance varies greatly. In general the loss of energy due to these fittings is expressed in terms of velocity head as,

$$h_L = K \frac{U^2}{2g} \tag{11.5}$$

in which U is the average velocity of flow in the pipe in which the fittings are installed. Actual experimental measurements are necessary to determine the numerical value of K for each type of fitting and valve because the coefficient K varies with the geometry of the fitting and the Reynolds number. Some typical values of K are given in Table 11.3. These values are the averages of series of tests conducted, and therefore the K value of individual fitting may be slightly different than that presented in Table 11.3.

TABLE 11.3

Values of Loss Coefficient K due to fittings and Valves

Fitting or Valve	*K*
Standard Tee joint (branch flow)	1.80
Standard Tee joint (Line flow)	0.40
Standard 90° elbow	1.90
Medium sweep 90° elbow	0.95
Long sweep 90° elbow	0.60
Standard 45° elbow	0.42
Closed return bend	2.20
Globe valve fully open	10.00
Angle valve fully open	5.00
Switch valve fully open	2.40
Gate valve fully open	0.19
" ¾ open	1.15
" ½ open	5.60
" ¼ open	24.00

11.5 Flow in Bends

As the fluid flows around a bend the individual streamlines are bent and with these bent streamlines is associated a normal acceleration toward the centre of the bend as explained in Chapter 2. To cause such an acceleration a pressure gradient must exist along the radial direction which is provided by an increase in the pressure along the outer side of the bend and a decrease in pressure along the inner side.

The pressure distribution in a bend is shown in Fig. 11.7. The presence of viscosity modifies the flow pattern in the following ways. Because of the formation of boundary layer, the fluid adjacent to the pipe periphery is retarded. For this reason the fluid near the pipe periphery is influenced more than the fluid in the core due to the existence of pressure gradient along AB. As a result the fluid starts flowing from A to B along the pipe wall. To satisfy the continuity condition, there is a flow from B towards A along the radial direction. Thus a secondary flow as shown in Fig. 11.7 is developed and is superimposed on the main flow.

In bends of short radius there is a tendency of boundary layer separation along the inner wall of the bend. As the fluid separates away from the wall, vortices form which dissipate some energy. There is also a weak stagnation zone on the outer side. Sharper the bend more pronounced are the zones of separation and stagnation. As the actual flow area is reduced at the downstream of the bend due to separation and weak stagnation, the average velocity correspondingly increases thereby causing a further reduction in piezometric head in the direction of flow.

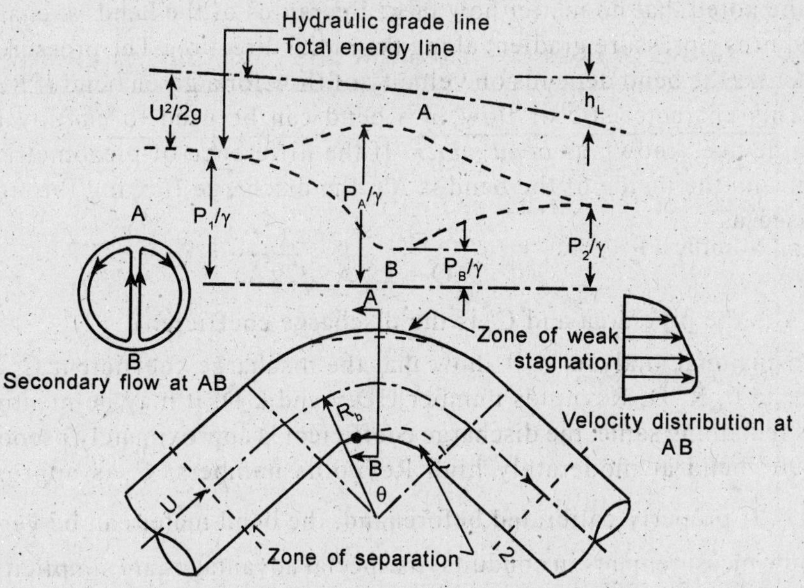

Fig. 11.7 Flow in a pipe bend

The energy loss in the bend is the sum of energy loss due to boundary friction and loss due to generation of turbulence and its dissipation which are the result of flow separation and secondary circulation. The loss coefficient K for the bend therefore depends on bend angle θ, centre line bend radius to pipe diameter ratio R_b/D, Reynolds number of the flow and relative roughness. If Reynolds number exceeds 10^5, K is found to be nearly independent of it. Fig. 11.8 shows variation of K with R_b/D and θ for smooth and rough pipes. For R_b/D greater than about 8, K becomes nearly independent of the former and depends on θ and pipe roughness.

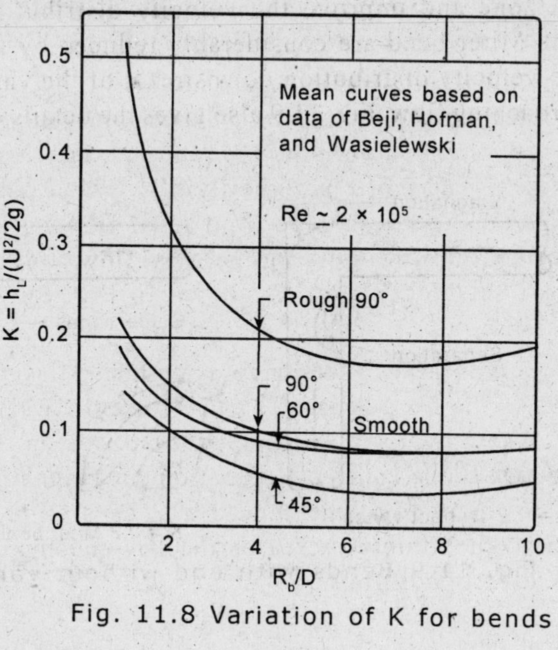

Fig. 11.8 Variation of K for bends

It may be noted that no matter how large the radius of the bend is, change in direction of flow requires a pressure gradient along the radial direction. The pressure or piezometric gradient across the bend depends on velocity of flow for a given bend if Reynolds number is large. This characteristic of flow in a bend can be used to employ bend as a flow measuring device, known as *bend meter*. If the difference of piezometric head between the outside and the inside of the bend is Δh, the discharge flowing through the bend can be expressed as

$$Q = C_d A \sqrt{2g \Delta h} \tag{11.6}$$

in which A is the pipe area and C_d is the discharge coefficient.

The dimensional analysis will show that the discharge coefficient C_d depends on the angle of bend θ, R_b/D, Reynolds number UD/ν and k/D. It may be mentioned that other conditions remaining same, the discharge coefficient is approximately proportional to angle θ. For a 90° bend at moderately high Reynolds numbers, C_d is approximately equal to $\sqrt{R_b/2D}$. If properly calibrated beforehand, the bend meter can be very conveniently used for flow measurements in conduits. Its special advantages are simplicity and economy. Any bend connected in pipe line can be used as a bend meter. It should, however be calibrated in place like other measuring devices and it should have at least twenty five diameters of straight pipe in the upstream and ten diameters on the downstream.

A special type of bend, known as Miter bend, is extensively used in large ducts such as wind tunnels and water tunnels where space does not permit a bend of large radius. The Miter bend has $(R_b/D) \approx 0$ and the loss coefficient is as high as 1.2. Such high bend loss is due to a relatively large zone of separation and subsequent expansion loss after the bend. It is found that by installing guide vanes as shown in Fig. 11.9. the value of loss coefficient can be reduced to 0.2. The curved guide vanes break up the spiral motion, reduce the separation zone and improve the velocity distribution downstream. Thus separation zones in the Miter bend are considerably reduced by the provision of guide vanes. In addition, the velocity distribution downstream of the vanes is nearly the same as that obtained in approaching flow. Fig. 11.9 also gives the details of vanes recommended for use.

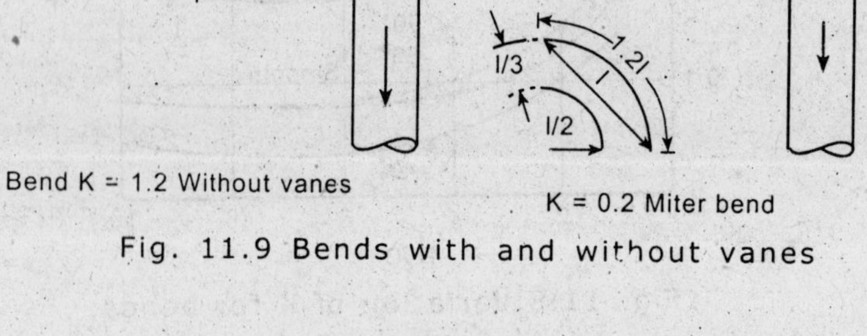

Fig. 11.9 Bends with and without vanes

The effect of the bend is felt certain distance upstream of the bend. As can be seen from Fig. 11.7, a certain length downstream of the bend is required for the stream lines to become parallel to the pipe wall and for the secondary flow to die out so that the original logarithmic velocity distribution is established again. If another bend is introduced in the pipe line before the flow regains its original characteristics, the flow in the second bend is affected by the upstream bend and the effect depends on the individual bend characteristics such as θ and R_b/D and dimensionless spacer length between the two bends L/D. In such a case if spacer length is smaller than the minimum length required for the flow to regain its original characteristics, $K \neq K_1 + K_2$ where K_1 and K_2 are individual bend loss coefficients and K is combined loss coefficient for the two bends. In fact in such a case $K > (K_1 + K_2)$.

11.6 Concept of Equivalent Length

It has been mentioned earlier that all types of energy losses in a pipe flow can be expressed as a constant times the velocity head, viz.

$$h_L = K\frac{U^2}{2g}$$

in which the value of K depends upon the type of nonuniformity. It is therefore possible to express the form effect in terms of an *equivalent length* of straight pipe which will result in the same energy loss at the same rate of discharge. In other words, two pipe systems are said to be equivalent in their lengths when the same discharge produces the same head loss in both the systems. For example, the form loss $K\frac{U^2}{2g}$ can be equated to the Darcy-Wesibach formula

$$K\frac{U^2}{2g} = f\frac{L_e U^2}{D\,2g}$$

from which one gets,

$$\frac{L_e}{D} = \frac{K}{f}$$

where L_e is the length of a pipe of diameter D and friction factor f in which for the same Q, h_L equals h_f. This implies that form loss is the same as the frictional loss which will take place in the pipe of length L_e for equal discharge.

Similarly, in two pipes of diameter D_1 and D_2 and friction factors f_1 and f_2, the loss of head is same for a given discharge then,

$$\frac{f_1 L_1 U_1^2}{2g D_1} = \frac{f_2 L_2 U_2^2}{2g D_2}$$

Since $$U = \frac{Q}{\pi D^2/4}$$

one can simplify the above expressions as

$$\frac{f_1 L_1}{D_1^5} = \frac{f_2 L_2}{D_2^5} \text{ or } L_2 = L_1 \frac{f_1}{f_2}\left(\frac{D_2}{D_1}\right)^5 \quad (11.9)$$

Thus, if 20 cm diameter pipe of 300 m length and $f_1 = 0.020$ is to be replaced by a pipe of 15 cm diameter with $f_2 = 0.018$, a pipe length of

$$L_2 = 300 \times \frac{0.020}{0.018}\left(\frac{15}{20}\right)^5 = 79.10 \text{ m}$$

is required. Thus 79.10 m of 15 cm pipes is equivalent to 300 m of 20 cm pipe.

The equivalent length method is specially useful where there are minor losses such as those due to bends, enlargements, etc. which can be readily expressed in terms of equivalent pipe lengths. Thus the compound pipe problem reduces to that of a single pipe of certain total length.

Example 11.1

Three pipes, 300 m of 30 cm, 150 m of 20 cm, and 200 m of 25 cm diameter are fitted between two reservoirs as shown in Fig. 11.10. The friction factors for these pipes are 0-019, 0.021 and 0.020 respectively. Determine the discharge if the difference in water surface elevations in the two reservoirs is 10 m.

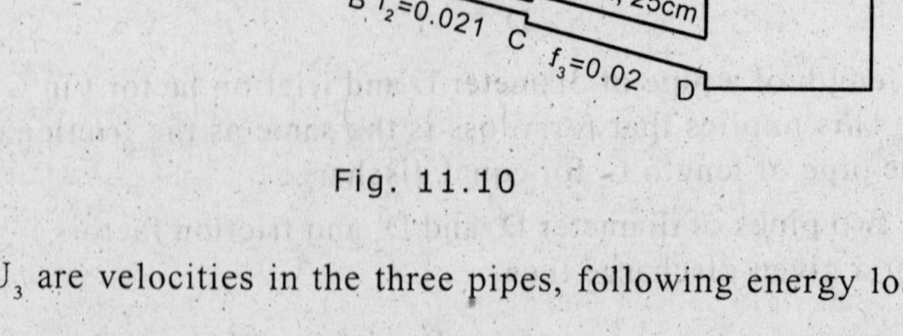

Fig. 11.10

If U_1, U_2 and U_3 are velocities in the three pipes, following energy losses will take place:

1. Entrance loss at A = $0.5 \dfrac{U_1^2}{2g}$

2. Friction loss in pipe 1 = $\frac{f_1 L_1 U_1^2}{2g D_1}$

3. Sudden contraction at B = K $\frac{U_2^2}{2g}$

4. Friction loss in pipe 2 = $\frac{f_2 L_2 U_2^2}{2g D_2}$

5. Loss due to sudden expansion at C = $\frac{(U_2 - U_3)^2}{2g}$

6. Friction loss in pipe 3 = $\frac{f_3 L_3 U_3^2}{2g D_3}$

7. Exit loss at D = $\frac{U_3^2}{2g}$

It would be necessary to express the three velocities in terms of any one.

From continuity $$\frac{U_2^2}{2g} = \frac{U_1^2}{2g}\left(\frac{D_1}{D_2}\right)^4 = \frac{U_1^2}{2g}\left(\frac{30}{20}\right)^4 = 5.063\ \frac{U_1^2}{2g}$$

Similarly, $$\frac{U_3^2}{2g} = \frac{U_1^2}{2g}\left(\frac{D_1}{D_3}\right)^4 = 2.074\ \frac{U_1^2}{2g}$$

The pipe areas A_1, A_2, and A_3 are 0.07 065 m², 0.03 142 m² and 0.04 906 m² respectively. The value of K for sudden contraction is 0.275 (by interpolation). Similarly the loss due to expansion has a value of $(U_2^2/2g) \times 0.129$. Thus Bernoulli's equation can be written as

$$10.0 = \frac{U_1^2}{2g}\left[0.50 + \frac{0.019 \times 300}{0.3} + 0.275 \times 5.063 + \frac{0.021 \times 150}{0.2} \times 5.063 + 0.129 \times 5.063 + \frac{0{,}02 \times 200}{0.25} \times 2.074 + 2.074\right]$$

∴ $10 = 136.545\ U_1^2/2g$

Simplifying one gets, $U_1 = 1.199$ m/s

Flow rate $Q = A_1 U_1 = 0.07\ 065 \times 1.199 = 0.0847$ m³/s

The problem can also be solved using the concept of equivalent length as indicated below. Choose the 30 cm pipe as standard and express the minor losses of pipe 1 in terms of equivalent length.

$$K_1 = 0.5$$

$$\therefore \quad L_{e1} = \frac{K_1 D_1}{f_1} = \frac{0.50 \times 0.3}{0.019} = 7.9 \text{ m of 30 cm pipe}$$

For pipe 2

$$K_2 = 0.129 + 0.275 = 0.404;$$

$$\therefore \quad L_{e2} = \frac{0.404 \times 0.2}{.021}$$

$$= 3.848 \text{ m of 20 cm pipe}$$

$$K_3 = 1.0; \text{ so } L_{e3} = 12.5 \text{ m of 25 cm pipe}$$

Now 30 cm pipe length for pipe 1 = 300 + 7.90 = 307.9 m

20 cm pipe of (150 + 3.848) = 153.848 m

$$L_{e1} = 153.848 \times \frac{0.021}{0.019} \times \left(\frac{30}{20}\right)^5$$

$$= 1291.26 \text{ m of 30 cm diameter pipe}$$

25 cm pipe of (200 + 12.5) = 212.5 m

$$L_{e1} = 212.5 \times \frac{0.02}{0.019} \times \left(\frac{30}{25}\right)^5$$

$$= 556.60 \text{ m of 30 cm diameter pipe}$$

Thus total length of 30 cm pipe = 307.90 + 1291.26 + 556.60

= 2155.76 m

$$\therefore \quad 10 = \frac{f_1 L_e U_1^2}{2g D_1} = \frac{0.019 \times 2155.76 \times U_1^2}{2 \times 9.81 \times 0.3}$$

$$\therefore \quad U_1^2 = \frac{10 \times 2 \times 9.81 \times 0.3}{0.019 \times 2155.76} = 1.436$$

$$U_1 = 1.199 \text{ m/s}$$

$$Q = 0.07065 \times 1.199 = 0.0847 \text{ m}^3/\text{s}$$

11.7 Solving Pipe Flow Problems

To understand the procedure for solving the pipe flow problems one must start with all the possible variables involved. These are, the kinematic viscosity of the fluid ν, the length of pipe l, the diameter D, the pipe wall roughness k, the discharge Q, and the energy loss h_f. Out of these six variables usually five are known and it is required to find the sixth one. In general, there are three categories of problems which are of practical interest, namely

i. Given ν, l, D, k and Q, to find h_f
ii. Given ν, l, D, k and h_f to find Q
iii. Given ν, l, k, h_f and Q to find D.

The problems in the first category are relatively simple and the unknown h_f can be directly evaluated. Since Q and D are known, the velocity can be found as $U = 4\,Q/\pi D^2$ and thus Reynolds number of flow can be computed as $Re = UD/\nu$. For the known values of Reynolds number and relative roughness k/D, the friction factor can be found from the Moody's diagram. The last step is to evaluate h_f from the Darcy-Weisbach equation,

$$h_f = \frac{f\,l\,U^2}{2g\,D}$$

The problems in the second category need to be solved by trial and error since both the average velocity U and the friction factor f are not known. Since the relative roughness k/D is known, assume a reasonable value of f from the Moody's diagram. As a first trial, the pipe can be assumed to act as a rough pipe. Using this limiting value of f, compute U from the Darcy-Weisbach equation. From the computed value of U, find the Reynolds number Re of flow and knowing Re and k/D, find the second approximate value of f. Repeat the procedure until no further refinement in the f value is possible. The discharge Q can then be found.

In the third category, the diameter D is unknown and therefore, k/D and Re cannot be obtained. It is desirable to reduce the unknowns U and D to one by rearranging the expressions for h_f and the Reynolds number. This can be clone as follows:

$$h_f = \frac{f\,l\,U^2}{2g\,D} = \frac{8\,f\,l\,Q^2}{\pi^2\,g\,D^5}$$

$$\therefore \quad D^5 = \frac{8\,f\,l\,Q^2}{g\,\pi^2\,h_f} = \left(\frac{8\,l\,Q^2}{g\,\pi^2\,h_f}\right) f = C_1\,f \qquad (11.10)$$

Similarly, $$Re = \frac{UD}{\nu} = \frac{4\,Q}{\pi\,D\nu}$$

$$\therefore \quad Re = \left(\frac{4Q}{\pi\,\nu}\right)\frac{1}{D} = C_2\,\frac{1}{D} \qquad (11.11)$$

The constants C_1 and C_2 in Eqs. 11.10 and 11.11 are known. Assuming an arbitrary value of f, obtain D from. Eq. 11.10 and with computed D, find Re from Eq. 11 .11. Now k/D and Re are known for finding f from the Moody's diagram. With the new value of f, repeat the procedure until no further improvement in the value of f is required. The corresponding D is the desired answer.

For obtaining direct-solution to all three types of problems the method of dimensional analysis is used. Variables ν, l, D, k, Q and h_f can be related by the following functional relationship.

$$\frac{k^3 gS}{\nu^2} = \phi\left(\frac{Q}{\nu k}, \frac{k}{D}\right)$$

in which $S = h_f/l$. Using curves from Moody's diagram, this functional relationship is shown to be rather simple. For values of Reynolds numbers between 4×10^3 and 7×10^7 and from completely smooth to completely rough pipes with k/D upto 0.04, it has been shown that

$$\left(\frac{Q}{\nu k}\right)\left(\frac{k}{D}\right)^{8/3} = 2.30\left(\frac{k^3 gS}{\nu^2}\right)^{0.517} \qquad (11.12)$$

Problems of all the three categories can he solved directly by making use of Eq. 11.12. The solutions for D or Q by the above equation yields values which are within ±3 percent of values obtained by use of Moody's diagram. However, solutions for S or h_f by these equations differ a maximum of ± 5.0 percent from those obtained by Moody's diagram. Since one does not have to use any design charts while using Eq. 11.12, use of Eq. 11.12 in solving pipe flow problems is very convenient.

In most of such problems, the minor losses are usually neglected and only the frictional loss is considered. If the pipe lengths are considerably large, the omission of minor losses does not affect the solution. However, when the pipe lengths are small, it is necessary to consider the minor losses also. For example if a pipe of length l and diameter D connects two reservoirs having a difference in elevation H, (see Fig. 11.10) the following equation can be set up;

$$H = \frac{U^2}{2g}\left(0.5 + \frac{f\,l}{D} + 1.0\right)$$

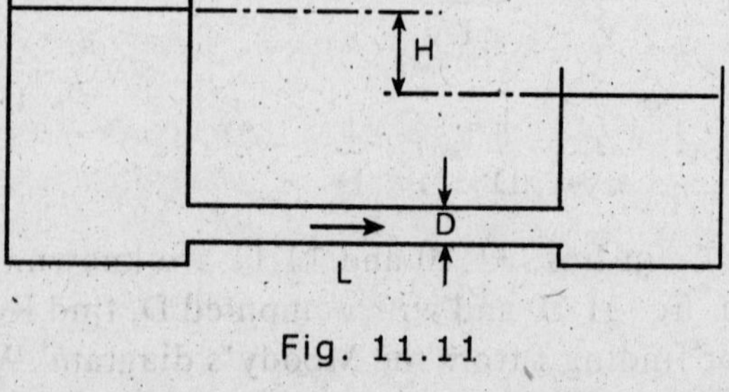

Fig. 11.11

It can be noticed that as l/D increases, the terms 0.5 and 1.0 become too small to influence the flow. If a friction factor of 0.03 is assumed, the omission of minor losses involves an error of 22 percent for l/D 100, 2.8 per cent for l/D = 1000 and 0.3 percent for l/D 10 000 respectively in the velocity computations.

Example 11.2

Water flows at 20°C through a 30 cm diameter riveted steel pipe (k = 3.0 mm) with a head loss of 6.0 m in a length of 300 m. Determine the discharge ?

Since the friction factor is not known it is necessary to assume a trial value of f. Assuming the pipe to act rough, Moody's diagram gives

$$f = 0.038 \text{ for } \frac{k}{D} = \frac{0.3}{30} = 0.01$$

Darcy-Weisbach equation can then be solved as

$$6.0 = \frac{0.038 \times 300 \times U^2}{2 \times 9.18 \times 0.3}$$

$$U = 1.760 \text{ m/s}$$

For this value of velocity, compute Reynolds number as

$$Re = \frac{1.760 \times 0.3}{1 \times 10^{-6}}$$

$$= 5.28 \times 10^5$$

From Moody's diagram the value of f can be found as f = 0.030 for Re = 5.28×10^5 and k/D = 0.01.

The discharge Q $= (\pi/4) \times 0.30^2 \times 1.760$

$= 0.124 \text{ m}^3/\text{s}$

For use of Eq. 11.12 calculate k^3gs/ν^2

which is 3297.4. Eq. 11.12 gives $(Q/kv)\,(k/D)^{8/3}$ as 193.67 and Q = 0.125 m^3/s

Example 11.3

Determine the suitable size of a cast iron pipe (k = 026 mm) to carry 200 *l*/s of kerosene ($\nu = 2.3 \times 10^{-6}$ m²/s), with an energy loss of 20 m in a length of 3000 m.

From Eq. 11.10,
$$D^5 = \left(\frac{8 l Q^2}{g \pi^2 h_f}\right) f = \frac{8 \times 3000 \times 0.20^2}{9.81 \times \pi^2 \times 20} f$$

$$D^5 = 0.496 f$$

From Eq. 11.11,
$$Re = \left(\frac{4Q}{\pi \nu}\right) \frac{1}{D} = \left(\frac{4 \times 0.20}{\pi \times 2.3 \times 10^{-6}}\right) \frac{1}{D}$$

$$Re = \frac{1.107 \times 10^5}{D}$$

If f = 0.02, D = 0.398 m, Re = 2.77×10^5, $\frac{k}{D} = \frac{.026}{39.8} = 0.00065$ and from Moody's diagram f = 0.019. Repeat the procedure with f = 0.019, D = 0.394 m. Re = 2.81×10^5 and

$k/D = 0.00065$. Therefore a size of 0.394 m, or approximately 40 cm diameter pipe may be adopted. Use of Eq. 11.12 gives $(Q/k\nu)\,(k/D)^{8/3}$ as 1.0447 and diameter as 0.402 m.

11.8 Siphons

A siphon is a conduit through which liquid can be transferred from a higher to a lower level over an intermediate higher elevation. The pressure is necessarily reduced at the intermediate section or the summit of the siphon since the hydraulic grade line for the flow is much below the summit. A siphon shown in Fig. 11.12 can be analysed by the application of Bernoulli's equation. Assuming the pipe to run full, one can apply Bernoulli's equation between sections 1 and 3 as

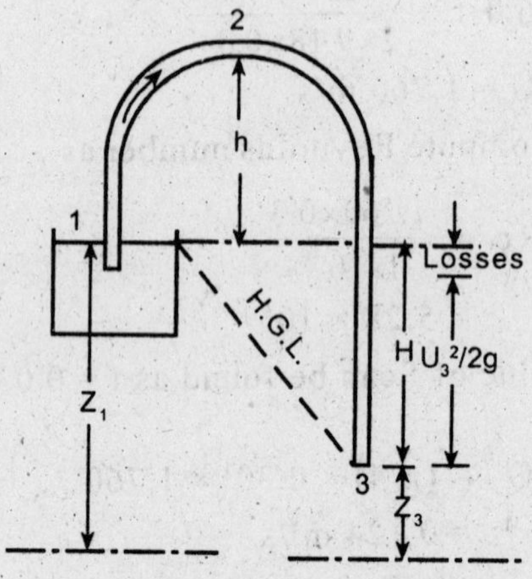

Fig. 11.12 Siphon

$$\frac{p_1}{\gamma} + z_1 + 0 = \frac{p_3}{\gamma} + z_3 + \frac{U^2}{2g} + \frac{f\,l\,U^2}{2gD} + K\,\frac{U^2}{2g}$$

Since the pressure at both sections is atmospheric, $\frac{p_1}{\gamma} = \frac{p_3}{\gamma}$ and $(z_1 - z_3) = H$; thus the expression can be simplified as

$$H = \frac{U^2}{2g}\left(1 + K + \frac{f\,l}{D}\right) \qquad (11.13)$$

in which K is the coefficient for the minor losses and f is the friction factor.

If it is required to find H for a given Q the procedure is simple and straight forward. However, if one wants to find Q under a given head H, the procedure involves trial and error solution if f is taken as unknown; i.e. a certain Q will have to be assumed, Reynolds number and k/D computed and f determined. Using Eq. 11.13, one now gets a better approximation of velocity. Again Re can be found and using Moody's diagram f is determined. Use of this in Eq. 11.13 yields U and Q. The pressure intensity at the summit section 2 can be found by the application of Bernoulli's equation between sections 1 and 2 with arbitrary datum through section 1. One can write,

$$\frac{p_1}{\gamma} = \frac{p_2}{\gamma} + \frac{U^2}{2g} + h + K'\frac{U^2}{2g} + \frac{f\,l'\,U^2}{2gD}$$

in which K′ is the minor loss coefficient between the two sections and l' is the length of siphon from section 1 to 2.

Solving for $\frac{p_2 - p_1}{\gamma}$ one gets

$$\frac{p_2 - p_1}{\gamma} = -h - \frac{U^2}{2g}\left(1 + K' + \frac{f\,l'}{D}\right) \tag{11.14}$$

It can be seen that when p_1 is the atmospheric pressure, the gauge pressure at section 2 is negative and it decreases with increasing h and ($U^2/2g$). If the value of p_2/γ (gauge) is equal to or less than vapour pressure of the liquid, air and other gases that are dissolved in the liquid are liberated and liquid is vaporized. These gases collect at the highest point and create pockets of air and consequently the liquid column is broken; the siphon then stops working. Thus theoretically the pressure at the summit must be greater than the vapour pressure of the liquid.

In practice, the pressure at the summit is not allowed to fall below 2 m of water (absolute). It must also be mentioned that to start the siphon, the air in the pipe must be removed by some means. The process is sometimes known as priming of syphon.

Example 11.4

A cast iron pipe of 15 cm in diameter connects the reservoirs having a difference in elevation of 15 m. The length of the pipe is 400 m and the summit which is 3 m above the reservoir is at a distance of 100 m from the upper reservoir. Neglecting minor losses, determine the discharge and the pressure at the summit. The friction factor for the pipe may be taken as 0.02.

Neglecting the term (1+K) in Eq. 11.12 one gets,

$$15 = \frac{0.02 \times 400 \times U^2}{2 \times 9.81 \times 0.15}$$

$$U = 2.35 \text{ m/s}$$

$$Q = \frac{\pi}{4} \times 0.15 \times 0.15 \times 2.35 = 0.0416 \text{ m}^3/\text{s}$$

Similarly for the pressure at the summit,

$$\frac{p_2}{\gamma} = -3 - \frac{(2.35)^2}{2 \times 9.81}\left(1 + \frac{0.02 \times 100}{0.15}\right)$$

$$\frac{p_2}{\gamma} = -7.03 \text{ m (gauge)}$$

If the friction factor were not known in this problem, the procedure would have been to assume a certain friction factor and then compute the velocity and Reynolds number. Then from Moody's diagram find the friction factor for the known pipe material and repeat the procedure if necessary.

11.9 Parallel Pipes

In order to increase the capacity of the system, many times a pipe line is supplemented by one or more pipes connected in parallel as shown in Fig. 11.13. In such a case, the following equations must be satisfied,

$$\left.\begin{aligned} Q &= Q_1 + Q_2 + Q_3 \\ h_f &= h_{f1} = h_{f2} = h_{f3} \end{aligned}\right\} \qquad (11.15)$$

in which Q is the total discharge, Q_1, Q_2 and Q_3 are the discharges in the three pipes respectively, h_f is the head loss between sections A and B, and h_{f1}, and h_{f2}, and h_{f3} are head losses in the three types which are equal to h_f. Two types of problems may arise in parallel pipe systems:

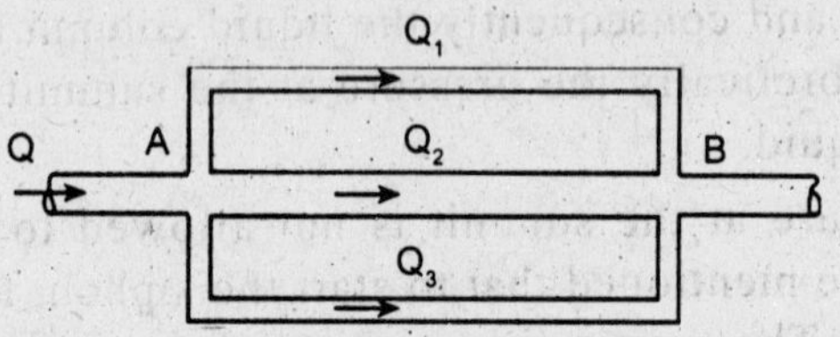

Fig. 11.13 Parallel pipes

i. to determine the total discharge Q in the system for a given head loss between sections A and B.

ii. to find the distribution of the discharge and head loss for a given total discharge Q.

Usually the pipe characteristics and fluid properties are known. The first type of problems is simple. Since the head loss in each pipe is known, it is not difficult to find the discharge in each pipe. The total discharge Q can be found by the summation of the individual discharges in the parallel pipes.

The problems in the second category can be solved by the following procedure :

i. Assume a certain discharge in one pipe, say Q_1' and compute the head loss h'_f with the assumed discharge.

ii. For this value of h_f' find Q_2' and Q_3' and also $\Sigma Q'_i = Q'_1 + Q'_2 + Q'_3$.

iii. Distribute the total given discharge Q in the same ratio as that of Q_1', Q_2', Q_3', to $\Sigma Q_i'$. In other words,

$$Q_1 = \frac{Q_1'}{\Sigma Q_i'} Q, \; Q_2 = \frac{Q_2'}{\Sigma Q_i} Q \text{ and } Q_3 = \frac{Q_3'}{\Sigma Q_i'} Q \qquad (11.16)$$

iv. Check the correctness of the discharges Q_1, Q_2 and Q_3 by computing the loss in each pipe.

In such problems the minor loses can either be completely neglected or could be added in the pipe lengths as the equivalent lengths.

Example 11.5

In Fig. 11.13, if a total flow of 4.0 m³/s takes place in the three pipes, determine the distribution of flow. The pipe lengths, diameters and friction factors are listed below :

1. l_1 = 1500 m, D_1 = 1.0 m and f_1 = 0.020
2. l_2 = 1200 m, D_2 = 0.8 m and f_2 = 0.020
3. l_3 = 1600 m, D_3 = 1.2 m and f_3 = 0.024

Assume $Q_1' = 1.4$ m³/s

Since $A_1 = 0.785$ m², $U_1' = \dfrac{1.4}{0.785} = 1.783$ m/s

$$h_f' = \frac{0.02\times1500\times1.783^2}{2\times9.81\times1.0} = 4.86 \text{ m}$$

Hence, $$4.86 = \frac{0.02\times1200\times U_2'^2}{2\times9.81\times0.8}$$

∴ $U_2' = 1.783$ m/s and $Q_2' = 0.896$ m³/s

Similarly, $U_3' = 1.725$ m/s and $Q_3' = 1.95$ m³/s

Thus, $\Sigma Q_i' = 1.400 + 0.896 + 1.950 == 4.246$ m³/s

Therefore,

$$Q_1 = \frac{1.4}{4.246} \times 4.0 = 1.320 \text{ m}^3/\text{s}$$

$$Q_2 = \frac{0.896}{4.246} \times 4.0 = 0.844 \text{ m}^3/\text{s},$$

and $$Q_3 = \frac{1.95}{4.246} \times 4.0 = 1.836 \text{ m}^3/\text{ s},$$

Also $U_1 = 1.320/(0.785 \times 1.0^2) = 1.682$ m/s

$$h_f = \frac{0.02\times1500\times1.682^2}{19.62\times1} = 4.320 \text{ m}$$

11.10 Branching Pipes

Many times problems involving flow between three or more reservoirs are encountered. These can be analysed as described below.

Suppose three reservoirs A, B and C are connected through a junction by three pipes 1, 2 and 3 as shown in Fig. 11.14. The friction losses h_1, h_2 and h_3 are known and it can be assumed that pipes are sufficiently long so that minor losses may be ignored. The problem then is to find the discharge through each pipe line for particular elevations of reservoirs when the pipe characteristics such as the length, diameter, wall roughness and the fluid characteristics such as the mass density and the viscosity are known. For solving the problems, Darcy-Weisbach equation must be satisfied for each pipe and the continuity equation must be satisfied so that the flow into the junction must equal the flow out of the junction. It can be seen from Fig. 11.14 that the flow will take place from reservoir A into the reservoir C. Whether the flow will be into the reservoir B or out of reservoir B depends on the piezometric head at the junction. If P is the piezometric head at the junction, one can see that $Q_1 = Q_2 + Q_3$ when P is greater than Z_2 and $Q_1 + Q_2 = Q_3$ when P is less than z_2.

In such problems usually the pipe lengths, diameters and the friction factor values are known. There can be three types of problems arising in such interconnected reservoirs.

i. Given the elevations of A and B and the discharge Q_1 in pipe 1, find the elevation of C and the discharges Q_2 and Q_3.
ii. Given the elevations of A and C and the discharge Q_2 in pipe 2, find the elevation of B and discharges Q_1 and Q_3.
iii. Given the elevations of all the there reservoirs A, B and C, to find the discharges Q_1, Q_2 and Q_3.

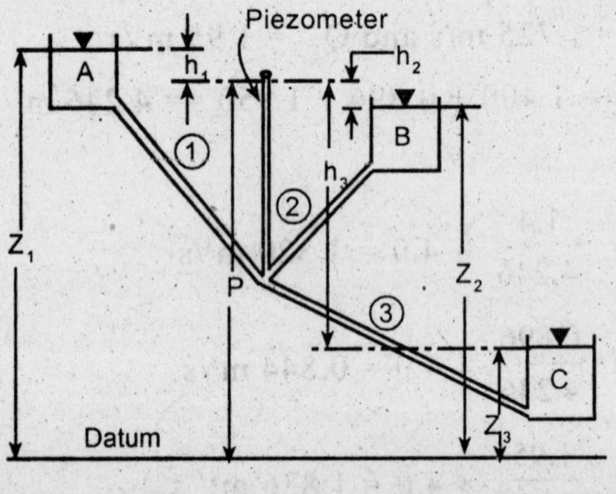

Fig. 11.14 Three interconnected reservoirs

In the first category since the elevation of A is known and the discharge Q_1 is known, piezometric head at the junction can be found out. Knowing the piezometric head at the junction, it is easy to find Q_2 and then Q_3 which in turn determines the elevation of reservoir C.

In the second category, $(h_1 + h_3)$ is known and $(Q_1 - Q_3)$ or $(Q_3 - Q_1)$ are known but the piezometric head at the junction cannot be directly determined. This needs trial solution. Assume P. For these values of h_1 and h_3 find the discharge Q_1 and Q_3. Then determine $(Q_1 - Q_3)$ and compare its magnitude with that of given Q_2. Repeat the procedure for other assumed elevations P until the two values are equal.

The third category of problems also are not amenable to direct solution. Assuming the elevation P, find h_1, h_2 and h_3 and then determine Q_1, Q_2 and Q_3. But it remains to be determined whether $Q_1 = Q_2 + Q_3$ or $Q_1 + Q_2 = Q_3$ because the flow may be into the reservoir B or out of the reservoir B. The elevation of P may be raised or lowered to satisfy the continuity equation for the given reservoir elevations. A plot as shown in Fig. 11.15 may be helpful and with three points, one can easily determine the exact position of P by parabolic interpolation.

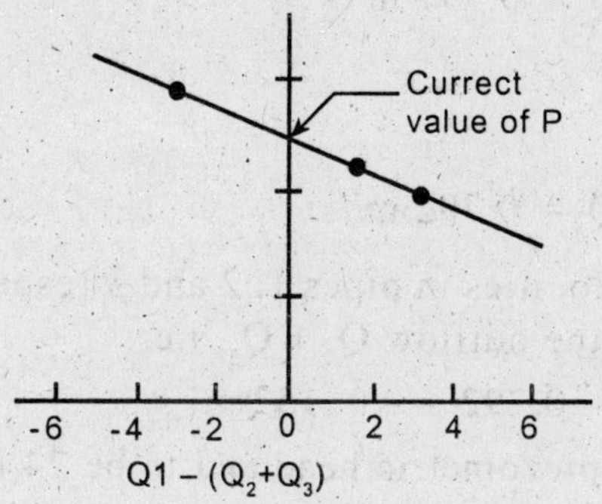

Fig. 11.15

Example 11.6

Find the discharges in the branching system shown in Fig. 11.16. Following are the pipe line data.

1. pipe 1 is 100 cm dia, 3000 m long and f = 0.015,
2. pipe 2 is 50 cm dia, 600 in long and f = 0.024,
3. pipe 3 is 60 cm dia, 1200 in long and f = 0.020,

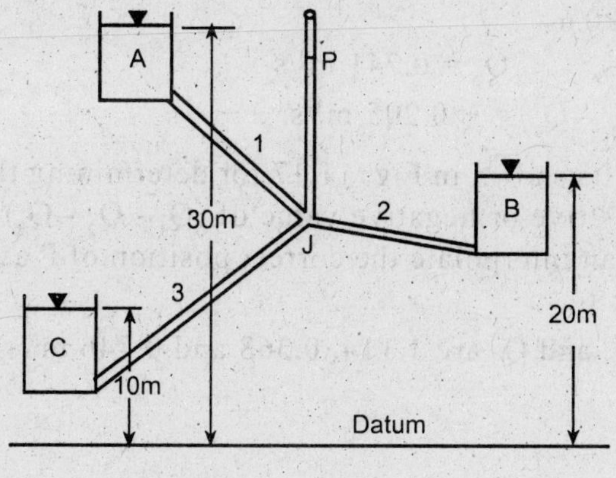

Fig. 11.16

Assume the piezometric head at J be 26 m. Then the Darcy-Weisbach equation for the three pipes can be written as

i. $4 = \frac{0.015 \times 3000 U_1^2}{2 \times 9.81 \times 1}$

$\therefore$ $U_1 = 1.321$ m/s and $Q_1 = 1.087$ m³/s

ii. $6 = \frac{0.024 \times 600 U_2^2}{2 \times 9.81 \times 0.5}$

$U_2 = 2.023$ m/s and $Q_2 = 0.397$ m³/s

iii. $16 = \frac{0.02 \times 1200 U_3^2}{2 \times 9.81 \times 0.6}$

$U_3 = 2.801$ m/s and $Q_3 = 0.792$ m³/s

in which U_1, U_2 and U_3 are velocities in pipes 1, 2 and 3 respectively. It can be seen that the inflow Q_1 is smaller than the outflow $Q_2 + Q_3$, i.e.

$$1.037 - 0.397 - 0.792 = -0.152 \text{ m}^3/\text{s}$$

As a second trial assume the piezometric head at J to be 24 m. Then

i. $6 = \frac{0.015 \times 3000 U_1^2}{2 \times 9.81 \times 1}$

$\therefore$ $U_1 = 1.617$ m/s, $Q_1 = 1.270$ m³/s

ii. $4 = \frac{0.024 \times 600 U_2^2}{2 \times 9.81 \times 0.5}$

$U_2 = 1.651$ m/s, $Q_2 = 0.324$ m³/s

iii. $14 = \frac{0.02 \times 1200 U_3^2}{2 \times 9.81 \times 0.6}$

$U_3 = 2.622$ m/s, $Q_3 = 0.741$ m³/s

In this case $Q_1 - Q_2 - Q_3 = +0.205$ m³/s.

A plot can be made its shown in Fig. 11.17 for determining the correct elevation at J. The abscissa shows positive or negative value of $(Q_1 - Q_2 - Q_3)$ against the elevation P. With two points, one can interpolate the correct position of P as 25.15 m above datum at which $(Q_1 - Q_2 - Q_3) = 0$.

The values of Q_1, Q_2 and Q_3 are 1.114, 0.368 and 0.746 m³/s respectively.

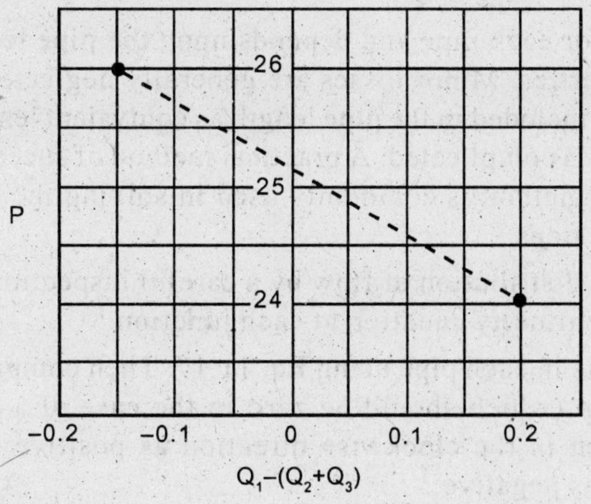

Fig. 11.17

11.11 Pipe Networks

The solution of pipe networks is probably the most complicated of all the problems in pipe flow. In a pipe network there are several interconnected pipes through which the flow to a particular outlet may come as shown in Fig. 11.18. Such networks exist in the municipal water distribution systems. It is difficult to predict the flow direction in any one pipe, say GD, by inspection. Nevertheless, however complicated the network may be, it must satisfy the following conditions

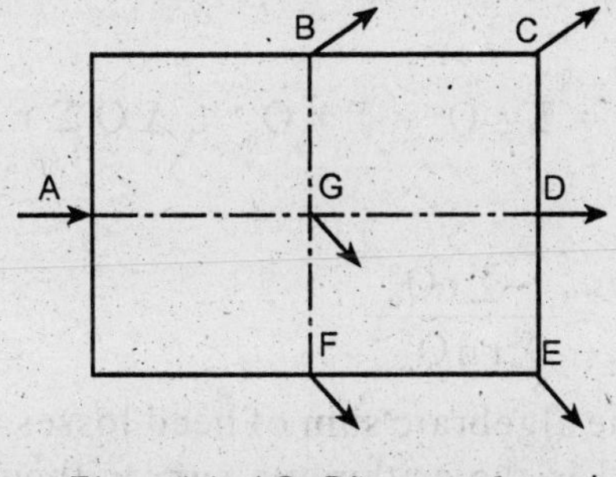

Fig. 11.18 Pipe network

i. The flow into any junction must equal the flow out of the junction;
ii. Darcy-Weisbach equation must be satisfied for each pipe ; and
iii. The algebraic sum of the head losses around any closed circuit such as BCDG will be zero when discharge distribution is correct.

The first condition is the continuity equation. The second condition states that proper relation between energy loss and discharge must be maintained for each pipe. The third condition implies that in any circuit such as BCDG the head loss from B to C must equal the summation of head losses along BG, GD and DC.

To simplify the solution, the friction factor f is expressed as a function of discharge Q for a given pipe and thus the Darcy-Weisbach relation can be written as,

$$h_f = r\,Q^n \tag{11.17}$$

in which r is a constant for each pipe and depends upon the pipe length, size, roughness as well as the fluid properties. Minor losses are generally neglected in solving network problems, but they can be included in the pipe length as equivalent length. Actual analytical solution of pipe networks is complicated. A practical method of successive approximation, known as Hardy – Cross method is commonly used in solving the network problems. It consists of the following steps :

1. Assume a reasonable distribution of flow by a careful inspection of the network such that it satisfies the continuity equation at each junction.
2. Compute the head loss in each pipe using Eq. 11.17. Then compute the total head loss around a certain loop (which should be zero in the case of a correct distribution). Consider losses taken in the clockwise direction as positive and those in counter clockwise direction as negative.
3. Adjust the flow in each loop by a corrective discharge ΔQ to balance the head loss i.e. to obtain $\Sigma\, r\, Q^n = 0$.

The value of ΔQ can be determined as follows. The discharge Q is the sum of assumed discharge Q_o and corrective flow ΔQ. Or

$$Q = Q_o + \Delta Q$$

Then

$$h_f = r\,Q^n = r\,(Q_o + \Delta Q)^n$$

$$= r\,[Q_o^{\,n} + n\,Q_o^{\,n-1}\,\Delta Q + ...]$$

and since ΔQ is small, its higher powers can be neglected. If this is the right correction, one must get $\Sigma h_f = 0$. Hence

$$\Sigma h_f = \Sigma\, r\, Q^n = \Sigma\, r\, Q_o^{\,n} + \Delta Q\, \Sigma\, r\, n\, Q_o^{\,n-1} = 0$$

and solving for ΔQ one gets,

$$\Delta Q = \frac{-\Sigma r Q_o^n}{\Sigma r n Q_o^{n-1}} \tag{11.18}$$

It should be noted that $\Sigma r\, Q_o^{\,n}$ is the algebraic sum of head losses with due regard to signs, while the denominator $\Sigma\, r\, n\, Q_o^{\,n-1}$ is the arithmetic sum without reference to sign. The direction of ΔQ will be counter clockwise when negative and clockwise when positive.

4. Use the procedure mentioned above to all other loops in the net work and determine the correction ΔQ for each loop.
5. Readjust the discharges in the loops taking into account the corrections computed above. Check if $\Sigma\, r\, Q^n = 0$; otherwise repeat the procedure until the corrections become negligible.

Example 11.7

Determine the distribution of discharge in the pipe network shown in Fig. 11.19. Assume $h_f = r\,Q^2$.

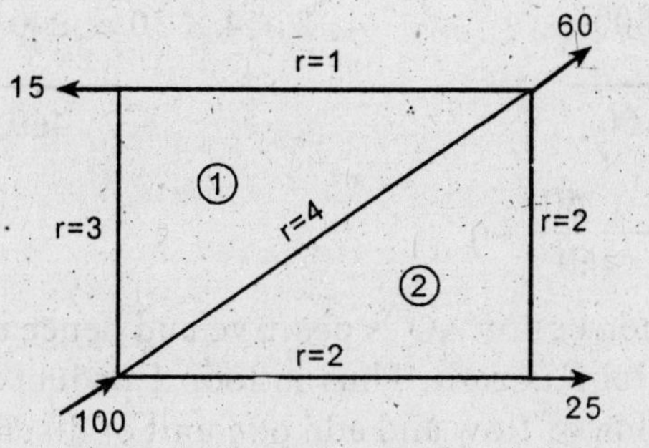

Fig. 11.19

Assume a suitable distribution of discharge as shown in Fig. 11.20 and compute the correction factors ΔQ for both the loops.

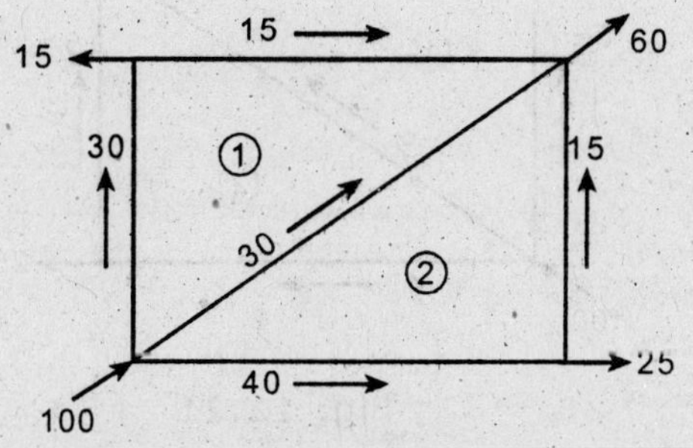

Fig. 11.20

(Clockwise direction + ve and counter clockwise-ve)

Loop 1

$\Sigma\, r\, Q^2$		$\Sigma\, 2r\, Q$	
$3 \times 30^2 =$	2700	$3 \times 2 \times 30 =$	180
$1 \times 15^2 =$	225	$1 \times 2 \times 30 =$	30
$4 \times 30^2 = -$	3600	$4 \times 2 \times 30 =$	240
	$-$ 675		450

$$\Delta Q = \frac{-(-675)}{450} \approx 1$$

Loop 2

Σ r Q^2		Σ 2r Q	
$2 \times 40^2 = -$	3200	$2 \times 2 \times 40 =$	160
$2 \times 15^2 = -$	450	$2 \times 2 \times 15 =$	60
$4 \times 30^2 =$	3600	$2 \times 4 \times 30 =$	240
	– 50		460

$$\Delta Q = \frac{-(-50)}{460} \approx 0$$

It can be seen that the correction ΔQ is positive and hence clockwise in loop 1 and the correction for the second loop is zero. Thus in loop 1 deduct one unit of discharge from pipes with negative direction of flow and add one unit of discharge in pipes with positive direction of flow. The discharge in the loop 2 is unchanged. The revised distribution of discharge is shown in Fig. 11.21.

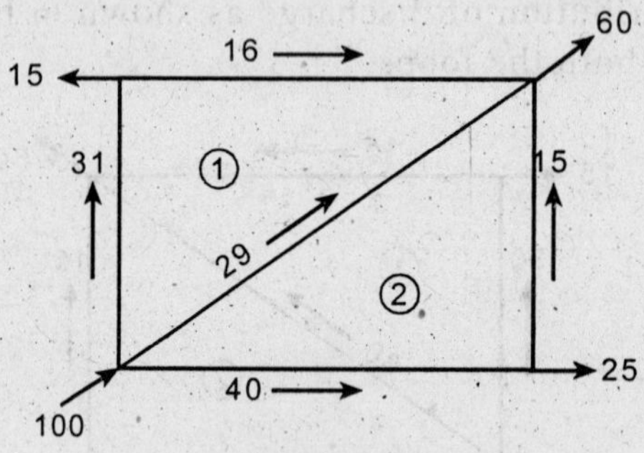

Fig. 11.21

Repeat the same procedure.

Loop 1

Σ r Q^2		Σ 2r Q	
$3 \times 31^2 =$	2883	$3 \times 2 \times 31 =$	180
$1 \times 16^2 =$	256	$1 \times 2 \times 16 =$	32
$4 \times 29^2 = -$	3364	$4 \times 2 \times 29 =$	232
	– 225		450

$$\Delta Q = \frac{-(-225)}{450} = 0.5$$

Loop 2

Σ r Q2	Σ 2r Q
$2 \times 40^2 = -\ 3200$	$2 \times 2 \times 40 = 320$
$2 \times 15^2 = -\ 450$	$2 \times 2 \times 15 = 60$
$4 \times 29^2 = +\ 3364$	$2 \times 4 \times 20 = 232$
$-\ 286$	612

$$\Delta Q = \frac{-(-286)}{612} < 0.5$$

It can be seen that the correction in the loop 1 is 0.5 and in the second one it is less than 0.5. It is left to the reader to solve the network for further accuracy. In all such problems requirement for accuracy should be set and computations performed till that accuracy is reached.

11.12 Resistance to Breathing

The discussion on pipe flow will not be complete without describing the human respiratory system and resistance during the breathing process. Human respiratory system can be divided into three regions : (i) the upper airways comprising nose, mouth, and all airspaces above and including the larynx, (ii) the tracheobronchial tree (or conducting airways) comprising the trachea and the bronchi to which it leads, down to airways about 0.05 cm in diameter, and (iii) gas exchanging region of the lung. The trachea is a circular tube about 1.8 cm in diameter and 12 cm long. It then bifurcates into two and the process continues twenty times. The average length of trachea or each generation reduces from 12 cm to 0.10 cm whereas their diameter reduces from 1.8 cm to 0.05 cm. The angle or bifurcation varies between 65° and 100°.

For a healthy person the rate of air flow varies from 0.50×10^{-3} m^3 /s to 2.0×10^{-3} m^3/s, the two figures representing fairly quiet breathing to fairly vigorous breathing. At these rates the Reynolds number in the breathing system ranges from about 9000 to 0.10 indicating that in some portions the flow is turbulent while in others it is laminar. In addition to frictional loss, there is also loss due to branching and flow establishment. However, it is very difficult to assess these losses separately. The difference of pressure Δp between outside and lungs is usually expressed as

$$\Delta p = K_1\left(\frac{dV\!\!\!/}{dt}\right) + K_2\left(\frac{dV\!\!\!/}{dt}\right)^2 \qquad (11.19)$$

Here $V\!\!\!/$ is volume of air present in the systems at any time and hence $\frac{dV\!\!\!/}{dt}$ represents volume rate of flow in m^3/s at any time, K_1 and K_2 are constants for the system for laminar and tubulent flow respectively. Using Hagen-Poiseuillle's equation K_1 can be shown equal to $128\ \mu\ l_1/\pi D_1^4$ which can be interpreted as pressure loss per unit volume rate. The resistance to turbulent flow $K_2\,(d\forall/dt)^2$ implies $K_2 = 8\,f\,l_2/g\pi^2 D_2^5$. Thus K_2 is constant if f, the Darcy-Weisbach friction factor, is constant. Here l_1, D_1, l_2, D_2 are some equivalent lengths and diameters. Since the pressure loss necessary to overcome the elastic forces in expansion is approximately proportional to volume of air $\forall$ present in the system at any time, the corresponding pressure loss can be expressed as $K\forall$. Hence, total pressure difference will be

$$\Delta p = K\forall + K_1\left(\frac{d\forall}{dt}\right) + K_2\left(\frac{d\forall}{dt}\right)^2 \qquad (11.20)$$

On the basis of this equation Otis, Fenn and Rahn have worked out experimentally the contribution of three sources of resistance to the muscular work done at different breathing rates and have shown that at a frequency of 15 breathings per minute the work done is minimum. Incidently this is close to normal breathing frequency in an adult.

PROBLEMS

11.1 At a section A in a horizontal pipe of 30 cm diameter carrying water, the pressure head is 30 m. At a distance of 60 m from A, the pipe suddenly reduces to 15 cm diameter and continues for 30 m when again it enlarges to its original size. If the velocity at A is 2.5 m/s, find the pressure head at the sections immediately downstream of sudden contraction and sudden enlargement. Draw the total energy and hydraulic grade line. Assume f to be 0.018 and 0.02 for the 30 and 15 cm pipes.

11.2 A vertical pipe carrying water upwards suddenly changes its diameter from 10 cm to 15 cm at a certain section. A differential manometer connected to points 2 m above and 2 m below the point of sudden enlargement shows a gauge reading of 5 cm of mercury the piezometric head being greater in 10 cm dia. pipe. If the friction factor values for the 10 cm and 15 cm pipes are 0.026 and 0.022 respectively, determine the flow rate through the pipe.

11.3 In the sudden enlargement shown in the figure, find the distance L when the pressure p_1 and p_2 at section 1 and 2 are equal. The diameter ratio D_2/D_1 is $\sqrt{2}$ and the friction factor is 0.02.

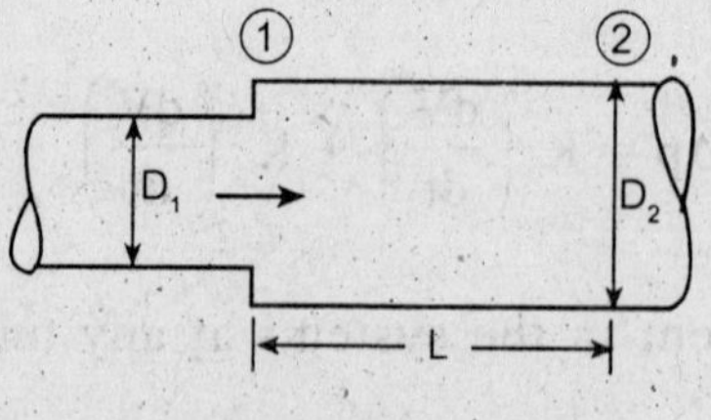

Prob. 11.3

11.4 A 30 cm horizontal water main enlarges to a 60 cm size through a 20° conical diffuser. When 280 l/s, flow through the pipe, the pressure in the smaller pipe is 137.29 kN/m². Neglecting the friction, calculate the pressure in the large pipe.

11.5 A sharp 90° bend is installed in a 5 cm pipe having a friction factor of 0.03. Calculate the head loss due to this bend if the average velocity of flow is 1.5 m/s. To what length of pipe does it correspond ?

11.6 Reservoirs A and B are connected with a pipe line composed of the following sizes :

a. a horizontal pipe 15 cm in diameter and 15 m long having its entry in the side wall of reservoir A at a depth of 3.5 m below the water surface,

b. a 90° bend directed downwards,

c. a 5 m long vertical pipe of 15 cm diameter,

d. a second 90° bend and

e. a horizontal pipe of 15 cm diameter, 4 m long having its outlet in reservoir B.

If the difference in elevations of the two reservoirs is 7 m, determine the rate of flow assuming a friction factor of 0.025, and K for bend as 1.90.

11.7 Find the discharge through the pipe line shown in the figure, if it discharges into the atmosphere. Take f to be 0.025 and the bend coefficient to be 0.060.

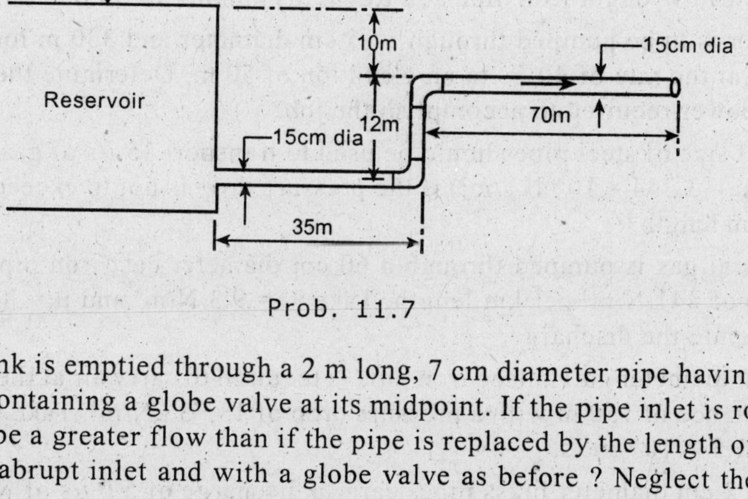

Prob. 11.7

11.8 A water tank is emptied through a 2 m long, 7 cm diameter pipe having an abrupt inlet and containing a globe valve at its midpoint. If the pipe inlet is rounded off, will there be a greater flow than if the pipe is replaced by the length of 9 cm pipe having an abrupt inlet and with a globe valve as before ? Neglect the frictional resistance.

11.9 A bend meter in 10 cm diameter pipe has a discharge coefficient of 0.90. What discharge of water through this meter is indicated when the attached differential manometer shows a difference of 30 cm of mercury ?

11.10 What energy must be supplied to pump 70 l/s of water from the lower reservoir to the upper reservoir shown in the figure ? Neglect minor losses and assume friction factors of 0.018 and 0.019 for the 20 cm and the 15 cm pipes. Draw the hydraulic grade line.

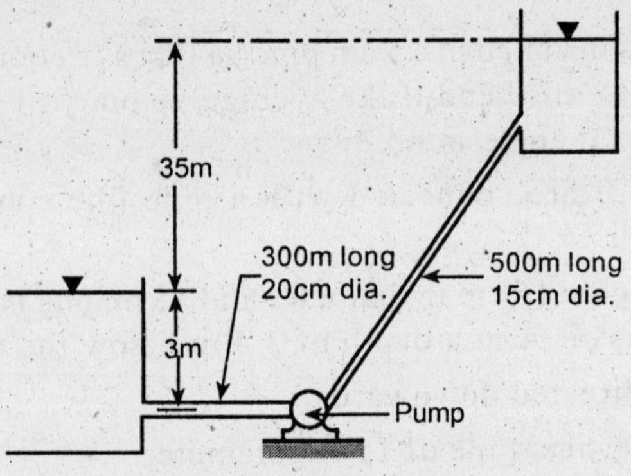

Prob. 11.10

11.11 A test in a horizontal 20 cm diameter pipe coated with uniform sand grains shows a pressure differential of 40 cm of mercury between two sections 65 m apart. If the water discharge is 95 *l*/s, what is the friction factor and the size of sand grains ? Take $\nu = 1 \times 10^{-6}$ m²/s.

11.12 What diameter of clean cast iron pipe has the same limiting friction factor as a 15 cm clean wrought iron pipe at a Reynolds number of 50 000 ?

11.13 Water is to be pumped through a 15 cm diameter and 350 m long clean cast iron pipe at the rate of 40 *l*/s to an elevation of 50 m. Determine the loss of head and the power required to accomplish the job.

11.14 What size of steel pipe should be used to transport 15 *l*/s of gasoline (R. D. = 0.7 and $\mu = 3.354 \times 10^{-4}$ N s/m²) if the pressure drop is not to exceed 34.323 kN/m² in 350 m length?

11.15 Natural gas is pumped through a 60 cm diameter cast iron pipe with a pressure drop of 441 N/m² per km length. Take $\gamma = 9.3$ N/m³ and $\mu = 8.55 \times 10^{-6}$ N.s/m². Compute the discharge.

11.16 What diameter galvanised iron pipe is required to carry air at the rate of 11.5 *l*/s to a distance of 150 m with a pressure drop of 13.73 kN/m². Take $\gamma = 11.7$ N/m³ and $\nu = 1.5 \times 10^{-5}$ m²/s.

11.17 Five 2 cm diameter brass pipes carry a discharge of 5.0 *l*/s of water between two reservoirs whose surface levels are constant. Find the diameter of a single brass pipe which will carry the same discharge between these reservoirs. Assume friction factor to be same in both the cases. Neglect the minor losses. Take water temperature to be 20°C.

11.18 In the pipe system shown in figure, water flows from the upper reservoir to the lower one if there is no pump. If a pump is introduced to maintain the same flow in the opposite direction, calculate the power needed by the pump. Assume $f = 0.018$.

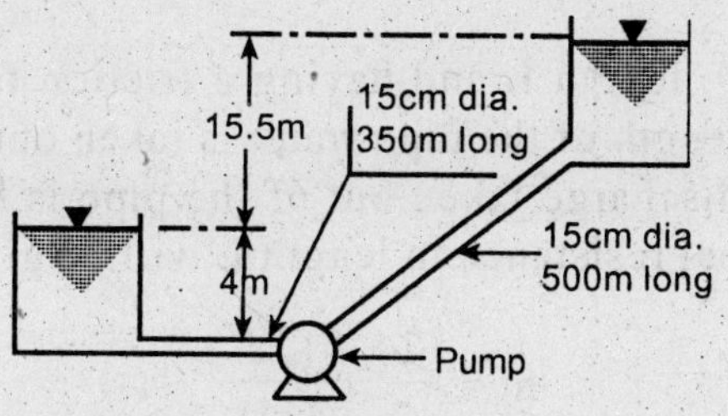

Prob. 11.18

11.19 Two reservoirs are connected by a 35 cm steel pipe line which rises above the level of the highest reservoir. Determine the discharge and the elevation of the highest point in the siphon if the pressure there is not be less than 2 m of water absolute. Assume f to be 0.024.

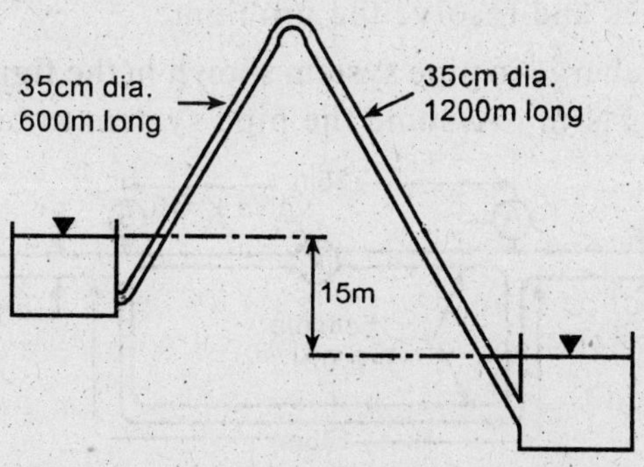

Prob. 11.19

11.20 Water is to be pumped through a 1.0 m riveted steel pipe (k = 3 mm) to a height of 24 m above the elevation of the pump. If the distance between the pump and the point of supply is 1000 m, what pressure should be maintained at the pump during a flow of 785 l/s such that the pressure at the point of supply is never less than atmospheric. Take ν to be 1.0×10^{-6} m²/s.

11.21 Compute the discharge through the siphon shown in figure. What are the pressures at A and just downstream of the globe valve? Assume f to be 0.02, and atmospheric pressure equal to 10.30 m of water.

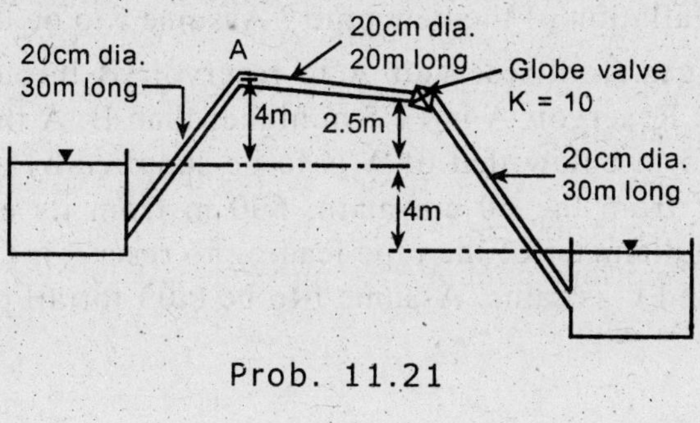

Prob. 11.21

11.22 A pipe of diameter D, length L and having a friction factor f, is connected to a reservoir. Along the length of the pipe water is taken out at a uniform rate in such a way that the total discharge taken out of the pipe is half of that which enters. Show that the frictional resistance in length L will be given by

$$h_f = \frac{7}{12} \frac{f L U^2}{2 g D}$$

in which U is velocity at the entrance.

11.23 Three new cast iron pipes 20 cm, 30 cm and 40 cm in diameters and 800 m, 1600 m and 2400 m long respectively are connected in parallel. What is the pressure drop and distribution of flow in the system for a flow of 550 *l*/s ? Hint : Assume pipes to act as rough and calculate f values. After determining the discharge, recompute f values and resolve the problem.

11.24 Determine the discharge in pipe system shown in the figure, for a pressure difference $(p_A - p_B) = 14.22$ kN/m². Assume the pipe system to be in a horizontal plane.

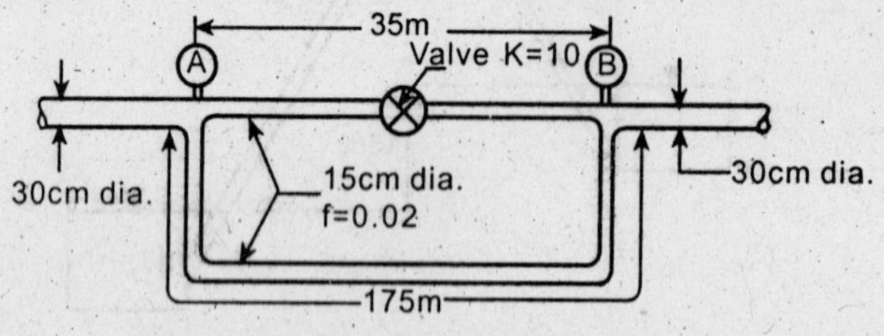

Prob. 11.24

11.25 Two pipes with the same friction factor of 0.02 and equal length of 350 m each are connected in parallel at their ends. They carry a total discharge of 30 *l*/s. If one pipe is 20 cm in diameter and the other is 30 cm in diameter, determine the discharge through each pipe.

11.26 A straight 30 cm pipe line 5.0 km long is laid between two reservoirs having a difference of 50 m in their water surface elevations. To increase the capacity of the system, an additional 2.5 km long 30 cm pipe is laid in parallel from the mid point of the original one upto the second reservoir. What is the increase in discharge due to the installation of the new pipe ? Assume f to be 0.02 for all pipes.

11.27 Water discharges from reservoir A to reservoir B through a 1500 m of 60 cm diameter pipe. Reservoir A is 12.5 m higher than B. A third reservoir C, with its free surface 25 m below that of A is to be supplied by a pipe line 1200 m long branching off from the 60 cm main, 600 m from its entrance at reservoir A. Determine the diameter of the pipe leading to reservoir C such that the flow into reservoirs B and C is same. Assume f to be 0.03 for all pipes.

11.28 Calculate the flow rate in each for the branching system shown in the figure. Take f to be 0.02 for all the pipes.

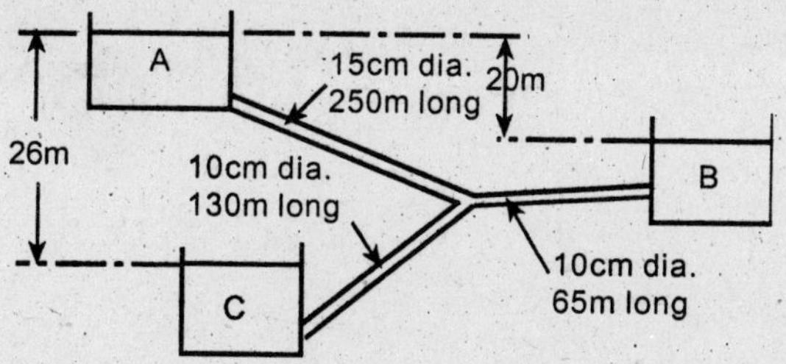

Prob. 11.28

11.29 Find the elevation of the water surface in reservoir B in problem 11.28 if there is no water flowing into or out of reservoir B.

11.30 Determine the distribution of flow in the pipe network shown in the figure. Assume n to be 2 in all cases.

11.31 Determine the distribution of flow in the pipe network shown in the figure. Assume n to be 2.

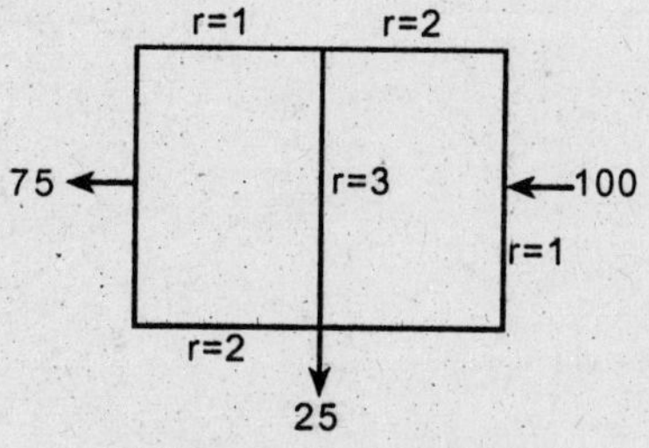

Prob. 11.30

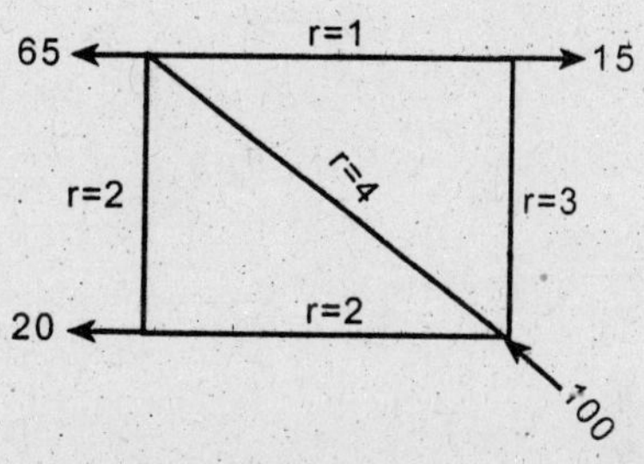

Prob. 11.31

11.32 Assuming n to be 2 for all pipes determine the distribution of discharge in all pipes, if the discharge in AB is 70 m³/s.

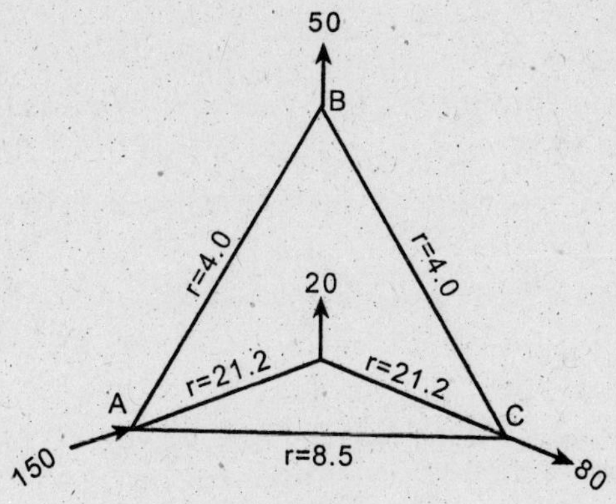

Prob. 11.32

CHAPTER TWELVE

FORCES ON IMMERSED BODIES

12.1 Introduction

In fluid mechanics, aeronautics and several other engineering fields, one is many times interested in studying the motion of discrete bodies in a fluid of large extent or flow of fluid around such bodies. The study of forces on tall buildings and bridges due to high velocity winds, problems concerning the motion of airplanes, submarines and torpedoes and the design of propellers, fans and turbines fall in this category.

Consider a body placed in an infinite fluid flowing at a steady uniform velocity. As long as the fluid is real, it will exert a force on the body in the direction of the motion; this is known as the *drag force*. The body, in turn, exerts a force on the fluid equal in magnitude to the drag force but opposite in direction. This is commonly known as the *resistance*. Suppose that a uniform velocity of equal magnitude and in the opposite direction is applied to the above case. The fluid then will be stationary and the body will be moving in the opposite direction. Such superposition does not have any dynamic effect on the motion. As such, the magnitude of drag or resistance remains the same whether the body is moving and the fluid is at rest or the fluid is moving and the body is at rest.

The total force exerted by the fluid on the body need not necessarily be in the direction of motion. In general, it can make a certain angle with the direction of motion. The component of this force in the direction of motion is known as the *drag*, F_D, while the component of this force in the direction perpendicular to the flow is known as *lift*, F_L. It may be mentioned that lift force occurs only when there is an asymmetry of fluid motion with respect to an axis of symmetry of the body parallel to the flow direction.

In the case of a symmetrical body, such as a sphere or a cylinder moving at a uniform velocity through an ideal fluid, the methods of hydrodynamics can be used to predict the pressure distribution and velocity distribution around the body. From this, one can find that the resultant force acting on the body is zero. For the steady flow of an ideal fluid around a sphere or a cylinder, therefore, both the drag and the lift are zero.

In nature there are several fluids of small viscosity such as air and water. However, if a sphere is moved through these fluids, at a uniform velocity, it is found that the sphere does experience a resistance to its motion. Therefore, it can be concluded that however small the viscosity may be, it must be modifying the flow pattern to such an extent as to cause drag. It has been shown in Chapter 9 that the real fluid sticks to the boundary and adjacent to the boundary, there is a thin layer of fluid which is retarded. The existence of no slip condition at the boundary, thus results in a velocity gradient and hence shear force is caused. Therefore, one way in which the presence of even a small viscosity modifies the flow pattern is by the development of the boundary layer. The second effect of viscosity is the separation of flow. If the surface along which the boundary layer forms curves away from the flow there is a tendency for the flow to separate. The separation of flow modifies the flow pattern drastically and thus changes the pressure distribution. This alters the drag appreciably. The third effect of viscosity is felt at very low Reynolds number when the viscous forces are much more important than the inertial forces. In such a case, the fluid is deformed in a very wide zone and the forces required for this deformation cause additional resistance.

DRAG ON IMMERSED BODIES

12.2 Types of Drag

Consider a body held in a stream of uniform velocity U_o and let F be the resultant force acting on the body. The total force can be resolved into two components F_D the drag force acting in the direction of motion and F_L the lift force acting in the direction perpendicular to that of motion (see Fig. 12.1). Since the velocities at various points near the surface of the body are different, application of Bernoulli's equation will show that pressure at these points also varies. As shown in the figure, two types of forces act at any point on the surface, the shear stress τ_o which acts tangential to the surface and the pressure force acting perpendicular to the surface.

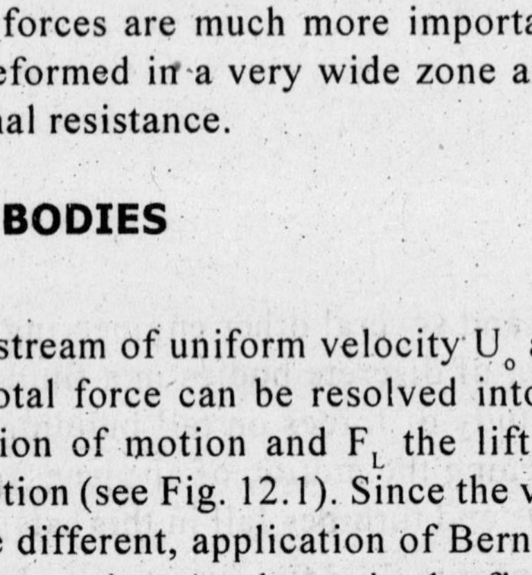

Fig. 12.1 Definition of drag and lift

Naturally, the drag force acting in the direction of motion is given by the summation of the components of shear force and pressure force acting over the entire surface of the body, in the direction of motion. In other words,

$$F_D = \text{Summation of } \tau_o \sin\theta\, \delta A + \text{Summation of } p \cos\theta\, \delta A$$

or
$$F_D = \int_A \tau_o \sin\theta\, \delta A + \int_A p \cos\theta\, \delta A \qquad (12.1)$$

in which $\int_A$ represents the summation over the entire surface. A similar expression can be written for the lift force F_L. The first term in above expression is the contribution of viscous shear to the drag. The second term gives the contribution due to pressure variation. The relative contribution of each of these to the total drag necessarily depends on the shape of the immersed body and on the flow and the fluid characteristics.

Thus in the case of a flat plate immersed in a fluid and held parallel to the direction of flow (see Fig. 12.2 a), $\int_A p \cos\theta\, \delta A = 0$ and hence the total drag is due to viscous shear. On the other hand, if the same plate is held perpendicular to the flow (see Fig. 12.2 b), $\int_A \tau_o \sin\theta\, \delta A = 0$ and the total drag is due to variation in the pressure. In between the two extremes, there are numerous body shapes for which, at high velocities, the contribution of viscous shear to the total drag varies within wide limits depending on the shape of the body and flow conditions.

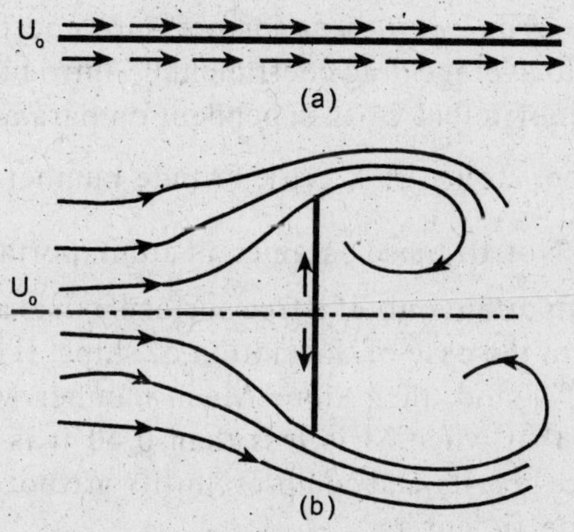

Fig. 12.2 Viscous shear on a flat plate held (a) parallel, and (b) perpendicular, to flow

12.3 Dimensional Analysis

In order to study the variation of drag and lift in generality, it is desirable to list the variables that may influence the phenomenon of forces acting on a submerged body and perform dimensional analysis. Considering the drag F_D, following are the variables which govern the variation of drag:

Characteristics of immersed body :	Characteristic length L (e.g. diameter of a sphere or cylinder), shape factor ξ.
Characteristics of fluid :	mass density ρ, coefficient of dynamic viscosity μ, gravitational acceleration g, coefficient of volume modulus of elasticity E.
Characteristics of flow:	average velocity U_o.

Hence $\quad F_D = f(L, \xi, \rho, \mu, g, E, U_o)$ (12.2)

Choosing U_o, L and ρ as the repeating variables, Eq. 12.2 can be written as

$$\frac{F_D}{L^2\left(\rho U_o^2/2\right)} = f\left(\xi, \frac{U_o L\rho}{\mu}, \frac{U_o}{\sqrt{Lg}}, \frac{U_o}{\sqrt{E/\rho}}\right) \quad (12.3)$$

The term $\frac{F_D}{L^2\left(\rho U_o^2/2\right)}$ can be interpreted as force per unit area divided by the dynamic head and is known as the *drag coefficient* (or pressure coefficient) designated by C_D. This coefficient is similar to average drag coefficient C_f introduced in Chapter 9. Equation 12.3 shows that the drag coefficient C_D is dependent on parameters describing geometry such as ξ, Reynolds number Re ($= U_o L \rho/\mu$), Froude number Fr ($= U_o \sqrt{Lg}$) and Mach number M ($= U_o/\sqrt{E/\rho}$). Not all these parameters are important in every problem. Thus the Froude number Fr is important only if a free surface exists and if waves are produced; therefore, Fr is important in the case of the motion of ships. If the velocity of the body is comparable to velocity of sound, then alone Mach number M needs to be considered. Experiments have shown that when M is less than 0.40 it is not important. Hence for majority of problems where gravity and compressibility are not significant, Eq. 12.4 gives the dependence of drag coefficient as

$$C_D = f(\xi \text{ and Re}) \quad (12.4)$$

The analysis of drag, when only the viscous and inertial forces are important, will now be discussed.

12.4 Deformation, Friction and Form Drags

The total drag is in fact sum of *deformation drag* and *form drag*. The deformation drag exists at very small velocities, or when the length dimensions (such as diameter of a disk or a sphere) are small and kinematic viscosity is large. In other words, the Reynolds number must be very small-less than approximately 0.20. At such values of Reynolds number, the inertial force can be neglected in relation to the viscous force and equations f motion can be solved for the steady state condition. Under such circumstance the iscosity influences the flow pattern considerably. In the words of Prandtl and Tietjens, The body pushes itself through the fluid which is deformed by it. The resistance caused y this is due primarily to the forces necessary for the deformation of various fluid articles".

Smaller the Reynolds number, greater is the distance from the body up to which eformation takes place. At large values of Reynolds number the deformation is confined the boundary layer. It must be remembered that the deformation drag itself consists of iction drag or surface drag at the boundary and the pressure drag due to variation of ressure caused by widespread deformation. The proportion of these two, for a given ody, is necessarily a function of Reynolds number. Indeed, it has been shown that in the ase of a sphere in the Stokes' range, one third of the total drag is due to pressure ifference and two third due to boundary shear. Considering a sphere and a disk of the ame diameter it has been found that, if Re is less than 0.10, the total drag of the sphere only slightly higher than that of disk. Realising that there is considerable difference etween the shape of a sphere and the shape of disk, the above observation regarding the tal drag at low Re shows that the deformation drag chiefly depends on the projected rea and not much on the actual shape of body.

As already mentioned, with the increase in Reynolds number, the extent of deformation ecreases and it is limited to a very thin boundary layer. With this thinning of the eformation zone, the contribution due to friction drag increases; on the other hand, the ontribution due to pressure variation in the deformation zone becomes almost negligible. hus for high Reynolds number, the direct action of the viscous deformation is the friction rag. While discussing the boundary layer theory methods have been developed for stimating the surface drag or friction drag. At such high Reynolds number if the boundary orm (i.e. shape of the body) is such that separation occurs, a low pressure area is created the rear portion of the body and this produces *form* drag. The form drag is therefore ue to the pressure difference between the front and the rear of the body. At moderately gh and high Reynolds numbers the proportion of friction drag and form drag in the total ag necessarily depends on the body shape and the Reynolds number. If the body is harp edged, the point of separation is almost fixed as in the case of a flat plate or disk eld at right angles to fluid motion. On the other hand in the case of well rounded bodies ch a cylinder and sphere, the location of the point of separation depends on the Reynolds umber. There is still another class of bodies such as airfoils for which the profile is such at the separation occurs only at the downstream end; as such the form drag constitutes very small fraction of the total drag in case of airfoils.

Of the three types of drag, namely deformation drag, friction drag and form drag, ome can be computed and others can be measured. Since the relative contribution of ese to the total drag depends on Reynolds number and body shape, problem of predicting e total drag on a body is not amenable to a complete analytical solution. On the other and, the conditions of similarity obtained from dimensional analysis are quite useful in nalysing the experimental data and drawing certain conclusions.

With this general discussion of the drag, the drag experienced by a sphere, cylinder, a flat plate and an airfoil will be discussed in detail. These cases clearly illustrate the importance of body shape and Reynolds number on variation of drag.

12.5 Drag on a Sphere

In order to appreciate the flow of a real fluid around a sphere it is necessary to know the analysis of steady flow of an ideal fluid around a sphere. Laplace's equation with the necessary boundary conditions can be solved for this case and an expression can be obtained for velocity distribution around the sphere. Application of Bernoulli's equation then yields the pressure distribution. Since the flow pattern is symmetrical the pressure distribution is also symmetrical on the front and rear of the sphere, see Fig. 12.3 (a). If this pressure distribution is integrated over the surface and its component taken in the direction of' motion, it yields zero, indicating no resistance due to pressure difference. In other words there is no form drag. Since there is no viscosity, there is neither deformation drag nor friction drag, thus indicating that there is no total drag.

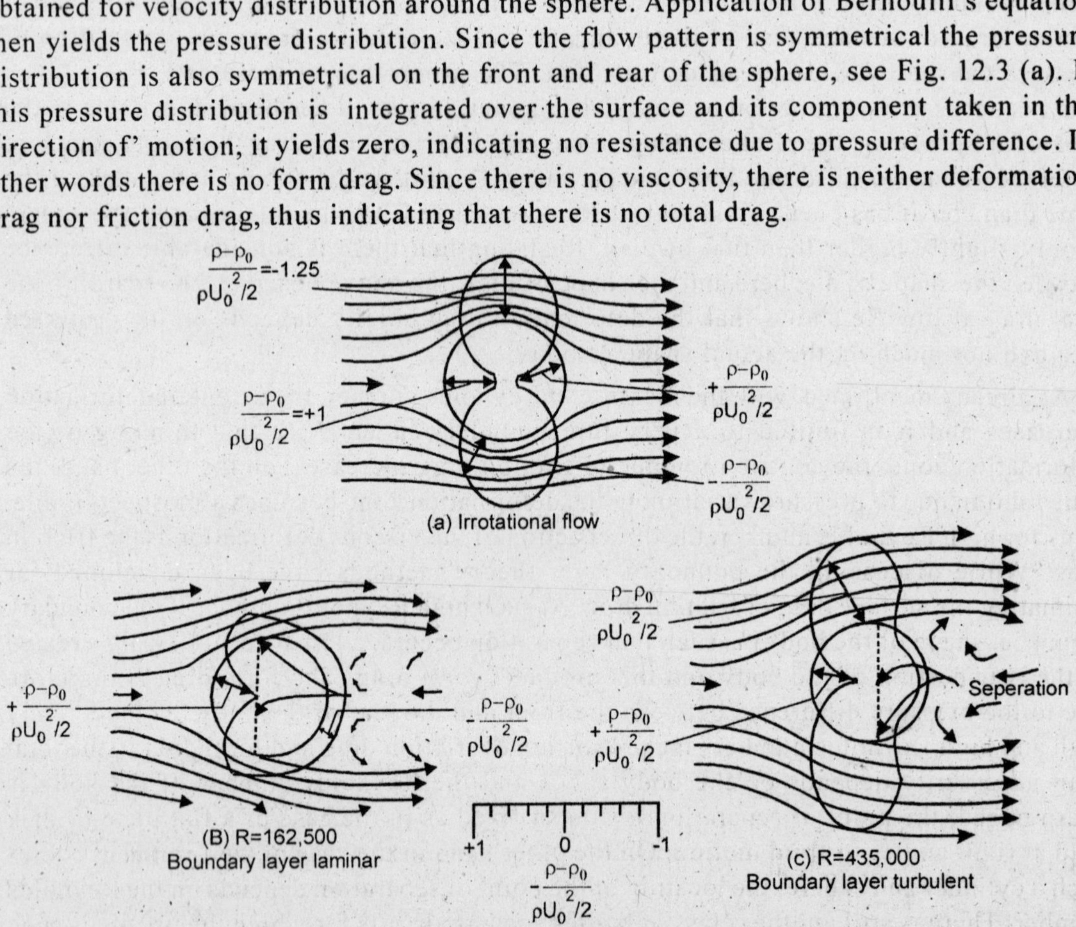

Fig. 12.3 Mean flow pattern and pressure distribution for flow past a sphere

In general, consideration of steady flow of an ideal fluid around immersed symmetrica bodies with axis of symmetry parallel to flow leads to zero resistance, except in thos cases where vortex trails exist in the wakes of the body. This inability of the theory o ideal fluids to yield results approximating those observed in experiments is known a *D'Alembert's Paradox.*

However, when the fluid possesses some viscosity, the flow pattern and the resultin pressure distribution are entirely different. If Reynolds number defined as $U_0 D\rho/\mu$, i very small–less than 0.20–the viscous forces are much more important than the inertial forces. Therefore, Navier-stokes equations can be integrated after neglecting the convective acceleration terms. This yields an expression for the drag on the sphere as

$$F_D = 3\pi\, D\, \mu\, U_o \tag{12.5}$$

or

$$C_D = \frac{F_D/\left(\pi D^2/4\right)}{\rho U_o^2/2} = \frac{24}{Re} \tag{12.6}$$

Thus for such low values of the Reynolds number, the drag coefficient is inversely proportional to the Reynolds number. It can be shown that out of the total drag $3\pi D\mu U_o$, the contribution due to pressure difference (because of the deformation) is $\pi\, D\mu\, U_o$ and he contribution of the surface drag is $2\pi D\mu\, U_o$.

Experiments have shown that upto a Reynolds number 0.20, Stokes' law predicts the drag coefficient accurately provided the sphere is in motion in an infinite fluid. However, proximity of the boundary increases the resistance. In such a case, the drag coefficient is given by the equation.

$$C_D = \frac{24}{Re}\left\{1 + 2.1\frac{D}{D_1}\right\}$$

where D_1 is the diameter of the container in which a sphere of diameter D is moving. With the increase in Reynolds number, the deformation drag decreases and so does the influence of the boundary proximity.

In 1927, Oseen pointed out that it is only in the vicinity of the sphere that the acceleration terms omitted by Stokes are very small compared to the viscous terms. Far away from the sphere opposite is the case. Improving Stokes' analysis by taking into account certain inertial terms, Oseen proposed the equation

$$C_D = \frac{24}{Re}\left\{1 + \frac{3}{16} Re\right\} \tag{12.7}$$

Thus the inclusion of inertial terms increases the drag coefficient over and above that given by Stokes' law. However, as can be seen from Fig. 12.4, Oseen's solution does not follow experimental trend and the upper limit of applicability of Oseen's solution is Reynolds number equal to two, or at most 4 to 5.

As Reynolds number is further increased, the region in which the viscous deformation takes place is reduced considerably and is restricted to the laminar boundary layer. Furthermore, the boundary layer which is laminar increases in thickness and separates somewhere upstream of the point of maximum cross section. The separation produces a wake behind the body, which is laminar for low values of the Reynolds number; the flow in the wake becomes unstable and continuous eddies are shed behind the body.

When the boundary layer is laminar, typical pressure distribution around a sphere is a shown in Fig. 12.3 (b). It can be seen that the pressure distribution in the zone o accelerating flow is almost the same as that in the potential flow. Since the lamina boundary layer can stand only small adverse pressure gradients, the boundary laye separates at an angle of 80°. For Reynolds numbers between 0.50 and 10^4, the followin empirical equation gives variation of C_D for sphere,

$$C_D = \frac{24}{Re} + \frac{3}{\sqrt{Re}} + 0.34 \quad (12.8$$

with the increase in Reynolds number the point where $\frac{\Delta p}{\rho U_o^2/2}$ is maximum negative moves slightly downstream. When there is a separation of flow, the contribution of frictio drag to the total drag is much smaller as compared to the contribution of form drag Because of this, it may be expected that in the range of Reynolds numbers 10^3 to 10 Reynolds number will have very small influence of C_D. Indeed, within this range C increases from 0.40 to 0.50 only. This small increase in C_D is due to the development c the boundary layer and change in the character of the wake.

However, with further increase in Reynolds number, the boundary layer cannot remai laminar. With the onset of turbulence in the boundary layer, the velocity distribution change drastically, there is an energy transfer within the boundary layer and this decreases th tendency for separation. As a result, the turbulent boundary layer can travel furthe downstream before it separates. The separation now occurs at approximately 110°. Thi shift in the point of separation reduces the size of the wake and changes the pressur distribution so as to cause a reduction in C_D from 0.50 to 0.20. Typical pressure distributio around a sphere with turbulent boundary layer is shown in Fig. 12.3 (c). The Reynold number at which the boundary layer changes from laminar to turbulent is known as *Critica Reynolds number* and for a sphere it varies from 2×10^5 to 4×10^5. The actual value c critical Reynolds number depends on factors such as roughness of the surface and characte of turbulence in the stream. Complete variation of C_D with Re for a sphere is shown in Fig. 12.4

The drag coefficients of a sphere and a cylinder are affected by surface roughnes and tubulence in the free stream. If the surface is made rougher, C_D is slightly increase due to increase in friction. Secondly, because of increase in roughness the laminar boundar layer changes into turbulent boundary layer at somewhat lower Reynolds number. Thirdl the reduction in C_D is smaller for rougher sphere or cylinder. With the increase in turbulenc intensity, the critical Reynolds number is reduced. The drag coefficient is also increase with increase in free stream turbulence.

Even though Fig. 12.4 clearly depicts the variation of C_D with Re, it cannot be use directly in several problems in which the primary interest is to find velocity for give diameter, force and fluid properties. Since the velocity occurs in both Re and C_D, on must assume a velocity and check whether it is correct. This difficulty is overcome b using a scale with $F_D/\rho v^2$ as the parameter, see Fig. 12.4. For the known value of $F_D/\rho v$ the intersection of this line with C_D– Re curve will give the correct value of Re fro which velocity can be known. By using Re and $F_D/\rho v^2$ scales one can also determine D directly for known values of F_D, U, ρ and μ.

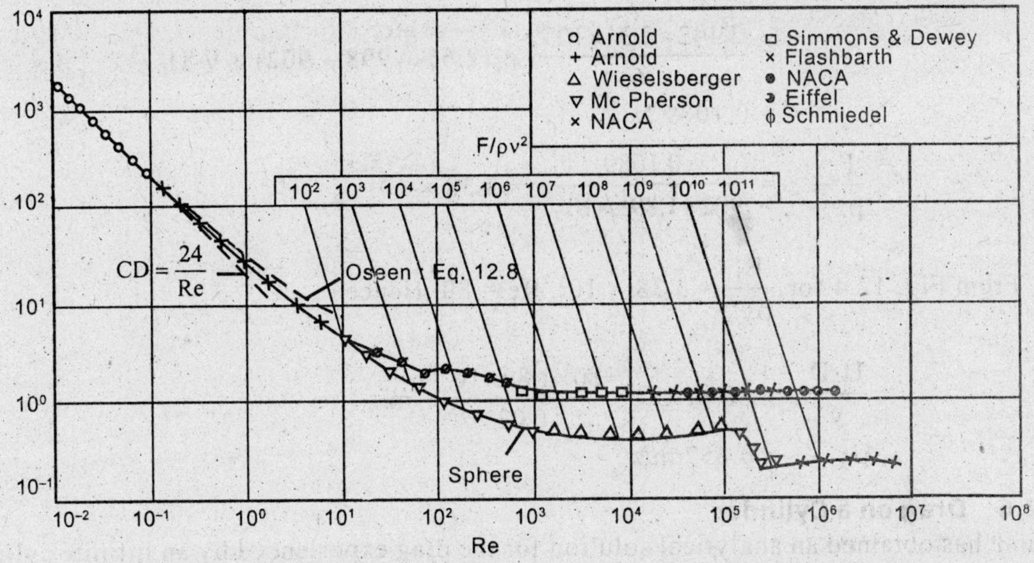

Fig. 12.4 Variation of C_D with Re for spere and disk

Example 12.1

A 1.5 mm diameter aluminium ball of relative density 2.80 falls in an oil of mass density 902.2 kg/m³ at a terminal velocity of 0.30 cm/s. Determine the dynamic viscosity of oil.

Initially assume that the Reynolds number for this case is very small and hence within Strokes' range. Substituting $F_D = \pi D^3 (\gamma_s - \gamma)/6$ in Eq. 8.23 one gets

$$\mu = \frac{D^2}{18U_o}(\gamma_s - \gamma)$$

$$= \frac{1.5^2 \times 10^{-6}}{18 \times 0.30 \times 10^{-2}} (2.80 \times 998 - 902.2) \times 9.81$$

$$= \frac{1.5^2 \times 10^{-4}}{5.4} \times 9.81 \times 1092.2 = 0.7767 \text{ kg/m s}$$

One must check whether with this viscosity the Reynolds number is within Strokes' range.

$$\frac{U_o D\rho}{\mu} = \frac{0.3 \times 10^{-2} \times 1.50 \times 10^{-3} \times 902.2}{0.7767} = 5.23 \times 10^{-3}$$

Hence the assumption is justified.

Example 12.2

Determine the fall velocity of a sphere 2.30 cm in diameter having a relative density 2.65 in an oil of mass density 902 kg/m³ and kinematic viscosity 1.89×10^{-4} m²/s.

$$F_D = \frac{\pi D^3}{6} (\gamma_s - \gamma)$$

$$= \frac{3.142 \times 2.3^3 \times 10^{-6}}{6} \times (2.65 \times 998 - 902) \times 9.81$$

$$= 0.1089 \text{ N}$$

$$\therefore \quad \frac{F_D}{\rho v^2} = \frac{0.1089}{902 \times 1.89^2 \times 10^{-8}} = 3.38 \times 10^3$$

From Fig. 12.4 for $\frac{F_D}{\rho v^2} = 3.38 \times 10^3$, Re = 80. Hence

$$\frac{U_o D}{\nu} = 80 \text{ or } U_o = \frac{80 \times 1.89 \times 10^{-4}}{0.023} \text{ m/s}$$

$$\therefore \quad U_o = 0.657 \text{ m/s}$$

12.6 Drag on a Cylinder

Lamb has obtained an analytical solution for the drag experienced by an infinite cylinder placed in a uniform stream, with its axis perpendicular to the direction of fluid motion. This is expressed in terms of C_D and Re as

$$C_D = \frac{10.9/\text{Re}}{(0.87 - \log_{10} \text{Re})}$$

However, such an analytical solution is valid for Re less than 0.20, and experimental points start deviating from the theoretical curve for Reynolds numbers greater than 0.20 or so. As in the case of a sphere, the drag coefficient of a cylinder also decreases with increase in Reynolds number. With the increase in Reynolds number, the inertial forces become more important and cannot be neglected from the analysis. In such case, when Reynolds number is still relatively small i.e., upto 2 or 3, Oseen's approximate method can be extended for the case of cylinder also.

With the increase in the Reynolds number, asymmetry is introduced in the flow pattern with respect to an axis perpendicular to the direction of flow. At Reynolds number value of 4.0, very weak vortices are formed on the downstream side of the cylinder (see Fig. 12.5). Together, these two vortices form the wake. In this region there is an inflow along the axis of the wake and a flow in the general direction of motion in the outer portions. At a Reynolds number value of approximately 20, the wake and hence the vortex pair is quite distinct. With the increase in the Reynolds number, the vortices become more and more elongated in the direction of flow. For an infinite cylinder in infinite fluid, when Reynolds number is between 25 and 30, these vortices become unsymmetrical, they leave the cylinder and slowly move in the downstream direction. The flow patterns around cylinder for various Reynolds number values are shown in Fig. 12.5.

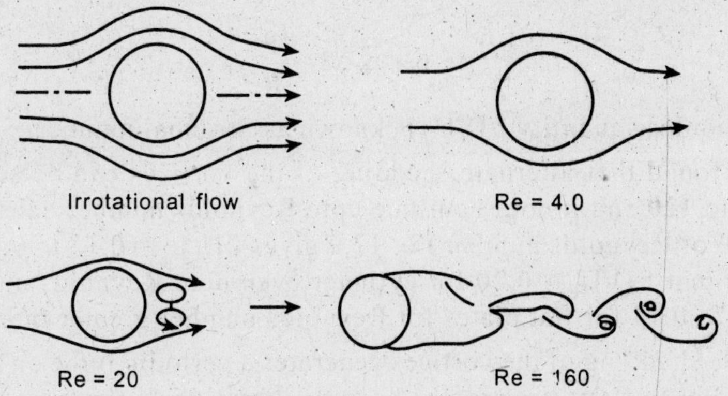

Fig. 12.5 Flow around an infinite cylinder

Karman Vortex Trail : When the Reynolds number exceeds approximately 30, the two vortices in the wake elongate to such an extent as to become unstable and are washed down. Now two more vortices form and replace the old one. Under such circumstances the wake consists of a series of vortex pairs moving in the downstream direction with very small velocity. Karman was the first to give explanation of this phenomenon and hence this is commonly known as *Karman Vortex Trail*. Karman suggested that there are two possibilities of the vortex configuration as shown in Fig. 12.6 (i) and (ii).

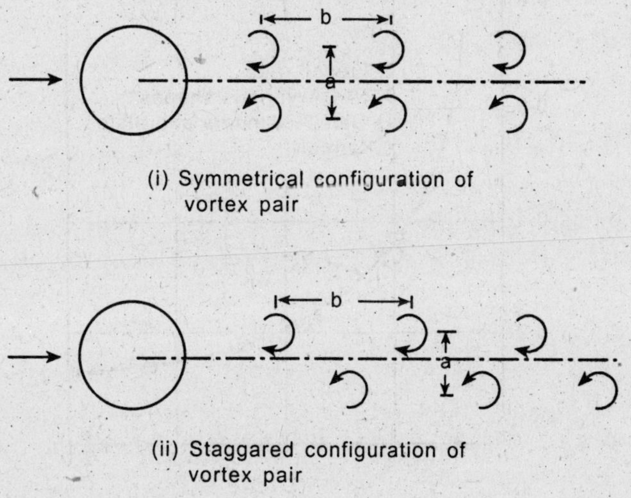

Fig. 12.6 Possible vortex configurations in Karman vortex trail

A theoretical analysis of stability of vortices of these two configurations revealed that the configuration (i) is unstable while the configuration (ii) is also unstable except when $a/b = \cos h^{-1} \sqrt{2} = 0.281$. These vortices move with a velocity $u_v = \Gamma/b\sqrt{8}$ in which Γ is the circulation. Experiments conducted by Hoffman and others have confirmed the validity of the above expression. The frequency with which the vortices are shed from one side of the cylinder is given by the parameter $(U_o - u_v)/b$. Taylor has shown that the frequency f is given by the expression

$$\frac{f\,D}{U_o} = 0.198\left\{1-\frac{19.7}{Re}\right\} \tag{12.9}$$

The dimensionless quantity $f\,D/U_o$ is known as Strouhal number.

It has been found that alternate shedding of the vortices can be seen upto Reynolds number equal to 120 and it does continue upto Reynolds number equal to about 20 000. Over this range of Reynolds number Eq. 12.9 gives $f\,D/U_o = 0.17$ to 0.20. Recent studies have indicated that $f\,D/U_o = 0.20$ for cylinder even upto Reynolds number value of 10^5 and it is equal to 0.14 for flat plates for Reynolds number greater than 10^3.

The alternate shedding of the vortices generates a periodic force on the cylinder which acts perpendicular to flow direction and causes vibration. If the frequency of this lateral force is equal to the natural frequency of the cylinder, there is tendency for resonance. Such considerations are important in the aerodynamic stability of suspension bridges. Since for two dimensional bodies C_D is a function of Reynolds number, and for different body shapes C_D will be different for same Reynolds number, it seems logical that Strouhal number S should be function of C_D. That such is indeed the case is shown in Fig. 12.7 where S is plotted against C_D. The relation between S and C_D is expressed very well by the equation

$$S = 0.21/C_D^{0.75} \tag{12.10}$$

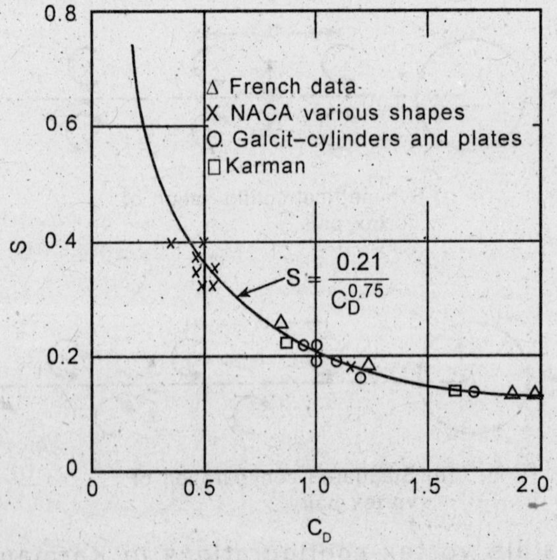

Fig. 12.7 Variation of Strouhal number with C_D for two dimensional bodies

Electrical cables stretched across transmission towers vibrate in the lateral direction at high frequency in strong winds and create a musical sound. Further, if the natural frequency of the system is close to imposed frequency, resonance leads to harmful effects

The variation of C_D with Reynolds number for a cylinder follows a pattern similar to that of a sphere at high Reynolds number values. There is slight increase in C_D between

Re values 10^3 to 10^5. At about 3×10^5 Reynolds number, the boundary layer changes from laminar to turbulent and there is drop in C_D from 1.20 to 0.33. With a further increase in Reynolds number, the drag coefficient C_D increases gradually.

Example 12.3
What is the frequency of vortex shedding for a 3.0 mm diameter wire in 100 km/hr wind in air at 20°C ?

Since $$U_o = \frac{100 \times 1000}{3600} \; 27.78 \text{ m/s}, \; \rho = 1.208 \text{ kg/m}^3$$

and $$\mu = 1.85 \times 10^{-5} \text{ kg/m s},$$

$$\frac{U_o D \rho}{\mu} = \frac{27.78 \times 0.003 \times 1.208}{1.85 \times 10^{-5}} = 5.44 \times 10^3$$

$$\therefore \quad f = 0.198 \times \frac{27.78}{0.003}\left(1 - \frac{19.7}{5.44 \times 10^3}\right) = 1827 \text{ Hz}$$

12.7 Drag on Flat Plate

The drag on a flat plate held at right angles to the flow is of interest because unlike in the case of a cylinder or sphere, the point of separation in the case of a flat plate is fixed. Fig. 12.8 (a) shows the stream line pattern for irrotational motion which is symmetrical on the upstream and downstream side of the plate. In such a case separation does not take place. Further, because of the symmetrical flow pattern the pressure distribution is also symmetical and no pressure drag results. However, due to presence of viscosity, the flow pattern for real fluids is markedly different as can be seen from Fig. 12.8 (b). At the edge of the plate the stream lines separate. This is necessitated by the fact that if the stream lines were to follow the irrotational flow pattern around the edge, it would mean a zero radius of curvature and a pressure intensity of minus infinity. This is not physically possible. Separation increases the radius of curvature of streamlines clinging to the boundary and causes a less extreme but constant pressure drop on the downstream of the plate, see Fig. 12.8 (c). In the case of such a plate the drag coefficient C_D is a function of Reynolds number, only at low and moderate values of Reynolds number. However, once Reynolds number exceeds about 10^3, C_D assumes a constant value of 1.90 if the plate is infinitely long. If the ratio of length of the plate to width is not very large, the flow is not truly two dimensional and hence the drag coefficient will be smaller. Figure 12.9 shows the variation of C_D with b/L for high values of Re.

Historically several theoretical estimates of C_D have been made for a two dimensional flow past a plate. Amongst these, mention may be made of the approach made by Helmholtz and Kirchhoff. Realising that the motion downstream of the plate is highly rotational, they introduced the concept of vortex sheet along the separating stream line and showed that the drag coefficient for the plate should be 0.88. Even though this value is much lower than 1.90, both have the same order of magnitude.

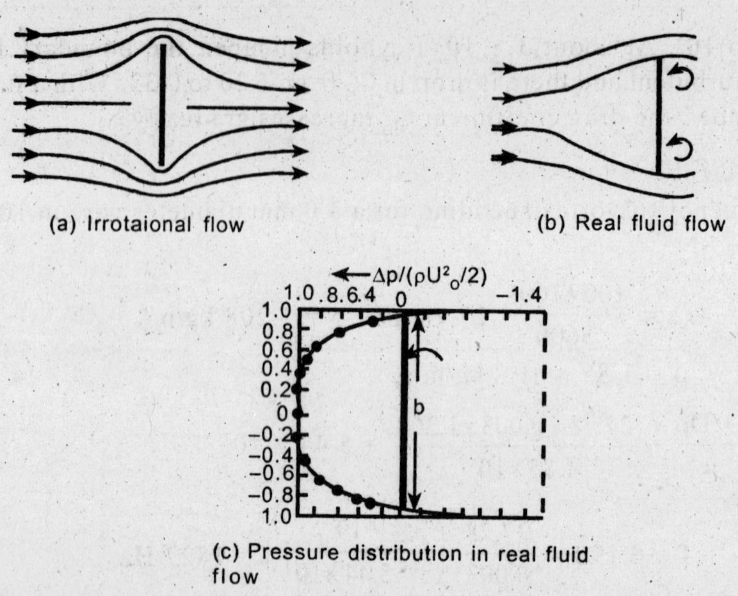

Fig. 12.8 Flow around a flat plate held perpendicular to flow

The variation of C_D with Re for the case of a disk follows a trend similar to the one for flat plate held perpendicular to flow. However, because of the three dimensional character of the flow, the limiting drag coefficient is 1.10 which is much smaller than the drag coefficient for a plate, see Fig. 12.4. Further, at Reynolds number of 300, C_D shows a peak for the disk. This is due to change in pattern of vortex system behind the body.

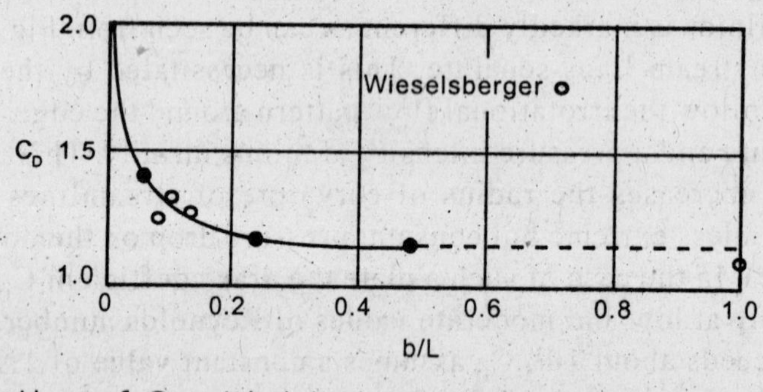

Fig. 12.9 Variation of C_D with b/L for a rectangular plate held perpendicular to the flow

12.8 Drag on an Airfoil

As the last example of drag on immersed bodies consider the case of flow around an airfoil shown in Fig. 12.10. Because of the efficient streamlining of the body, separation occurs only at the extreme rear of the airfoil. As a result, for relatively high values of Reynolds number the major contribution to the total drag is of the friction drag and contribution of form drag is comparatively very small. Figure 12.10 shows the measured pressure distribution and the predicted pressure distribution using the theory of irrotational flow. It can be seen that two pressure distributions agree very well except at the trailing edge. In the case of airfoils the drag coefficient will necessarily depend on Reynolds number and shape; but a sudden drop in C_D as in the case of a sphere or cylinder cannot be expected since the change from laminar to turbulent boundary layer does not alter the wake size significantly to vary the contribution of form drag. Further, since major drag is due to friction, C_D will continually decrease with increase in Reynolds number.

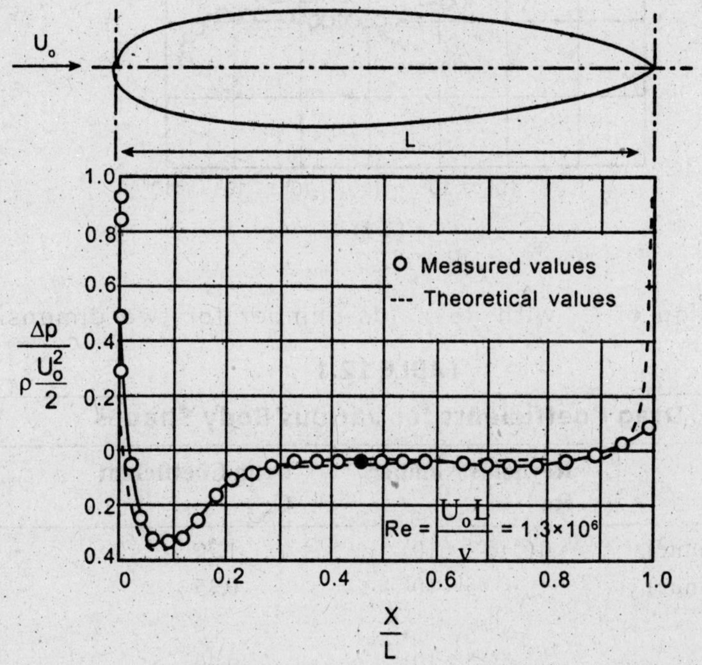

Fig. 12.10 Pressure distribution around an airfoil

Figures 12.4 and 12.11 give variation of C_D with Re for disk and sphere and three dimensional bodies respectively. Table 12.1 gives C_D values for several geometric shapes of bodies while Table 12.2 lists drag coefficients of practical body shapes.

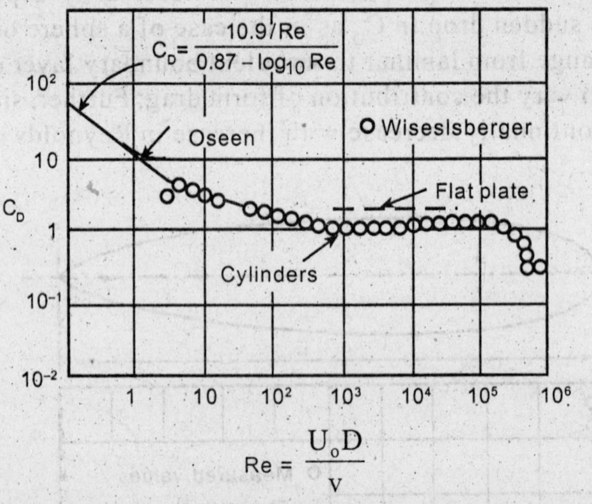

Fig. 12.11 Variation of C_D with Reynolds number for two dimensional bodies

TABLE 12.1

Drag Coefficients for Various Body Shapes

Body profile		Reynolds Number Re	Drag Coefficient C_D
Circular Cylinder (Infinite)		10^4 to 2×10^5	1.20
Circular Cylinder (Infinite)		5×10^5	0.35
Elliptic Cylinders			
2 : 1		5×10^4	0.46
		5×10^5	0.60
4 : 1		2.5×10^4 to 10^5	0.32
8 : 1		2.5×10^4	0.29
		2×10^5	0.20
Triangular cylinders 120°	→ ▶	10^4	2.00
120°	→ ◀	10^4	1.72
60°	→ ▶	10^4	2.20
60°	→ ◀	10^4	1.39
30°	→ ▶	10^4	1.80
30°	→ ◀	10^5	1.00
Hemispheres (hollow) → ◗		10^3 to 10^5	0.34
	→ ◖	4×10^4	2.30
Semitubular Cylinder	→ ⊃	4×10^4	1.12
	→ ⊂	3.5×10^4	2.00
Square Cylinders	→ ■	$10^4 + 10^5$	1.60

[Data taken from W.F. Lindsey NACA Tech. Report 619,1938 (U.S.A.)]

TABLE 12.2

Drag Coefficients of some Practical Bodies

Body profile	Drag coefficient
1. Empire State Building, New York, about 380 m high	1.30 to 1.50 (depending on wind direction)
2. "Trylon" slender pyramidal building 206 m high with 20 m wide base	0.80 to 1.43 (depending on wind direction)
3. Wind resistance of several ships	0.20 to 0.70
4. A man falling down vertically	1.0 to 1.30
5. Volkswagen passenger car	0.50
6. Minibus	0.73
7. Nonstremlined railway engine with five bogies	1.90

(see Section 12.10) Eq. 12.3 takes the form

12.9 Effect of Free Surface on Drag

When the effect due to compressibility can be neglected

$$C_D = f(\xi, \text{Re}, \text{Fr})$$

Hence for geometrically similar bodies with free surface flows the drag coefficient will depend on both the Reynolds number and the Froude number. This occurs in the case of ships moving over the water surface for which the total drag is the sum of friction drag, form drag and drag due to surface waves. Since the ships are streamlined, the form drag is very small and within the small range of Reynolds number it can be assumed to remain constant. The friction drag along the surface of ship can be adequately computed on the basis of boundary layer theory developed in Chapter 9. The difference between the total drag and the friction drag is commonly known as *residual drag* which is made up of small form drag and the wave drag. The residual drag is essentially a function of Froude number and has to be determined by model studies.

Example 12.4

The total resistance and power required for a prototype ship are to be deduced from 1:16 scale model tested under the following conditions:

area = 0.40 m², length = 3.0 m, velocity = 3.5 m/s, ρ for water = 998 kg/m³, ν at 20°C = 1×10^{-6} m²/s, total resistance in model = 10.0 N.

For model

$$\text{Re}_L = \frac{3.0 \times 3.5}{1 \times 10^{-6}} = 1.05 \times 10^7$$

$C_f = 0.455 / [\log (1.05 \times 10^7)]^{2.58} = 0.00298$

Frictional force $F_{fm} = 0.00298 \times 0.4 \times \dfrac{998 \times 3.5^2}{2}$

$= 7.286$ N

Residual force $= (10.000 - 7.285) = 2.714$ N

For prototype $U = 3.5 \sqrt{16} = 14.00$ m/s

$L = 3 \times 16 = 48$ m

$A = 0.40 \times 16^2 = 102.4$ m^2

$Re_L = (14.0 \times 48/1 \times 10^{-6}) = 6.72 \times 10^8$

$C_f = 0.455/[\log (6.72 \times 10^8)]^{2.58} = 0.00165$

$F_{fp} = (0.00165 \times 102.4 \times 998 \times 14.0^2)/2$

$= 16\ 524.98$ N or 16.525 kN

Force scale $= \rho_r l_r^3$ $= 1 \times 16^3 = 4096$ as per Froude's law.

Residual force $F_p = 4096 \times 2.714 = 11\ 116.544$ N or

$= 11.117$ kN

Total force $= 11.117 + 16.525 = 27.642$ kN

Power $= 27.642 \times 14$

$= 387.00$ kW

12.10 Effect of Compressibility on Drag

The effect of compressibility on the drag can be considered in terms of velocity of the body relative to the velocity of sound $C \left(= \sqrt{\dfrac{E}{\rho}} \right)$ in the fluid. From Eq. 12.3 it can be seen that when free surface does not exist. C_D is given by

$$C_D = f(\xi, Re, M)$$

in which M is the Mach number ($= U_o / \sqrt{E/\rho}$). As long as Mach number is smaller than approximately 0.40, the effects of compressibility are found to be negligible. The effects become significant when the velocity of the body is about the same as the velocity of sound in the fluid. If Mach number is less than one, the flow is called *subsonic* while if Mach number exceeds one, the flow is known as *supersonic* flow. Flow characteristics change markedly depending on whether the flow is subsonic or supersonic.

As the body moves through the fluid, the forces are transmitted through the fluid in the form of spherical pressure wave travelling at the velocity of sound. However, in subsonic flows, since the velocity of flow is less than the velocity of sound, the pressure wave is always ahead of the body. In other words, when the body arrives at a particular point, the pressure wave has already passed through that point and thus the fluid is given a chance to condition itself to the oncoming body. On the other hand, in the case of supersonic flows, the velocity of the body is greater than the velocity of pressure wave. Hence the body always leaves behind the pressure wave it has created. Consider a body moving at supersonic velocity (see Fig. 12.12). In the time the body moves from X to Y through a distance $U_0\,\Delta t$, the pressure wave is moving at velocity C (C being less than U_0); hence it will travel a distance $C\Delta t$ in the form of a spherical surface. While the body is moving from X to Y it will be creating other pressure waves also. Consider the pressure waves created by the body when it was at X_1 midway between X and Y. During the time the body reaches from X_1 to Y (i.e., in time $\Delta t/2$) the pressure wave will cover a $C\Delta t/2$ distance in the form of a spherical wave. As can be seen from Fig. 12.12 tangents YO and YO_1 can be drawn through Y touching the wave fronts the body has generated because of its motion. Naturally

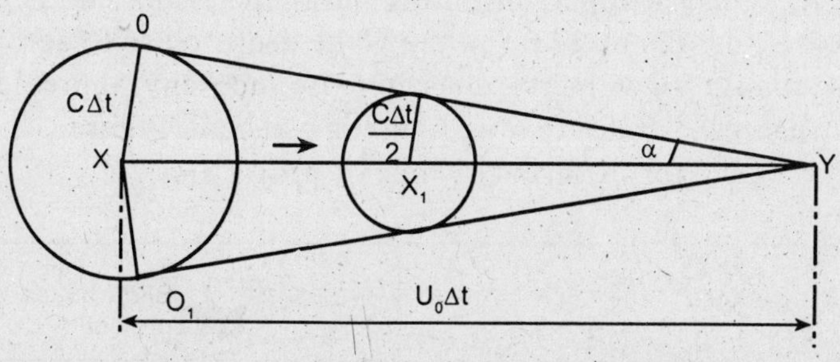

Fig. 12.12 Travel of pressure waves at supersonic speeds

$$\sin \alpha = \frac{C\Delta t}{U_0 \Delta t}$$

$$\alpha = \sin^{-1} C/U_0 = \sin^{-1}\left(\frac{1}{M}\right) \qquad (12.11)$$

The angle α is known as *Mach angle*. Note that in case of supersonic flow, all the activity is restricted to the cone generated by the tangent line YO. This tangent line is in fact the wave front of what is known as a *shock wave*. Actually a shock wave is a form of discontinuity and in real fluids it has a finite thickness. Conditions, within the shock wave have been a subject of considerable study (see Chap. 14). The resistance of bodies in high velocity flow depends on the shape, Reynolds number and the Mach number. However, since the Reynolds number values are usually quite large, effects of shape and compressibility are considerably more significant than viscous effects. It is important to note that form of the bodies which gives minimum drag when viscosity is important is not necessarily the best shape when compressibility is an important factor. In the case of tapered-nose projectiles in supersonic flow, the shock wave starts from the front corner and is essentially a straight line. On the other hand if the nose of the projectile is blunt, the wave front is slightly curved and it starts from a point little upstream of the nose, see Fig 12.13. In the latter case, just in front of the body there is a high pressure region.

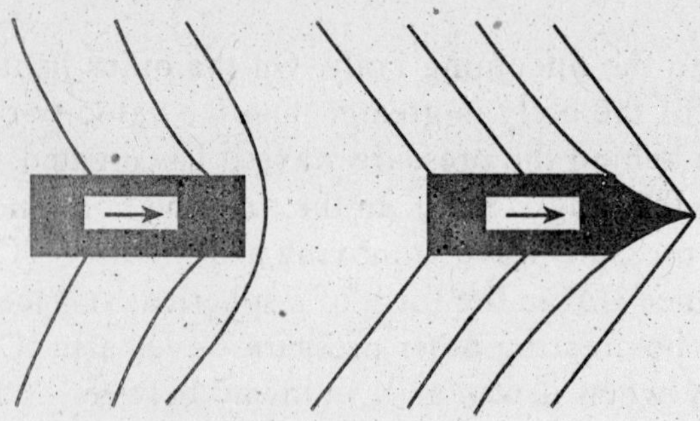

Fig. 12.13 Shock wave pattern for blunt and sharp-nosed projectiles

The shape of the tail end of projectile is extremely important in the subsonic flow since the drag can be reduced at subsonic velocities by streamlining the tail end of the projectile. But it has been found that in supersonic flow the shape of tail end is not very important. At supersonic velocities, the pressure in the wake drops close to zero and thus there is a vacuum. Further change in velocity does not produce any appreciable change in the pressure and as a result the pressure drag remains constant. Figure. 12.14 shows variation of C_D with Mach number for different shapes of projectiles.

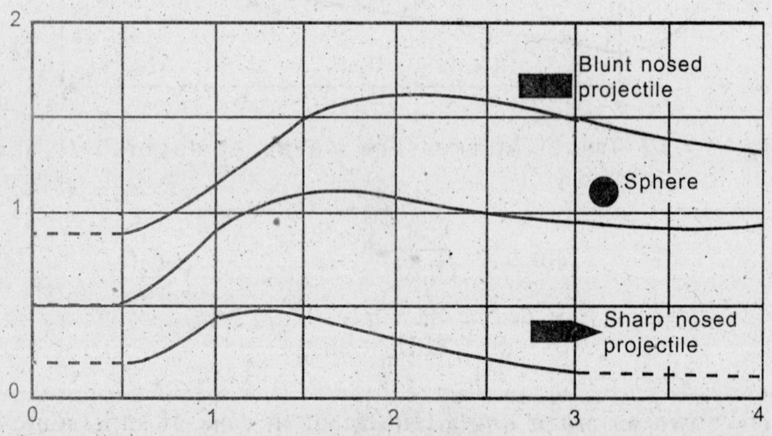

Fig. 12.14 Variation of C_D with Mach number for various bodies

LIFT ON IMMERSED BODIES

12.11 Development of Lift

As mentioned earlier, the total force exerted by the fluid on the body can be resolved into two components - one in the direction of motion known as drag and the other perpendicular to the direction of motion, known as lift. When the body is symmetrical with respect to its axis parallel to the direction of motion, as in the case of a sphere or a cylinder, the resultant force exerted by the fluid on the body is in the direction of motion. In this case the lift is zero. However, if the axis of symmetry of the body makes an angle with the direction of motion, the resultant force acting on the body has the lift component. This is illustrated in

Fig. 12.15 by considering flow around a symmetrical airfoil. The study of lift force acting on bodies and the study of its variation with flow, fluid and body characteristics is important in several problems in the design of hydraulic machinery, aeronautics etc. In fact designing body shapes which will give minimum drag and maximum lift is one of the primary concerns in aeronautical engineering.

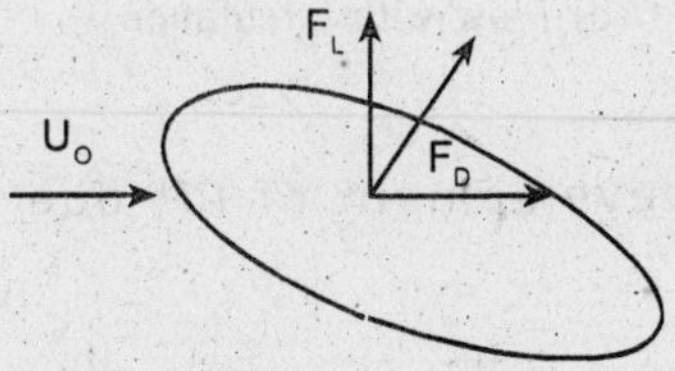

Fig. 12.15 Drag and lift on airfoil

In order to study the development of lift, consider steady irrotational flow around two dimensional circular cylinder (see Fig. 12.16 (a)). Because of the symmetry of flow pattern with respect to the axis ab, the pressure distribution on the upper and lower halves of the cylinder is identical. As a result there is no lift force acting on the cylinder. Consider again the flow pattern around the same cylinder caused by a constant circulation (refer Sec. 2.9), see Fig. 12.16 (b). Here the stream lines will be a series of concetric circles. If these two flow patterns are superimposed one over the other, an unsymmetrical flow pattern results as shown in Fig. 12.6 (c). In the upper half portion the direction of flow being the same, the stream lines will be crowded thereby showing an increase in the velocity. In the lower half the two motions are in the opposite direction; hence streamlines will be spaced farther apart thereby showing a decrease in the velocity. Application of Bernoulli's equation will show that the pressure on the lower portion is greater than the pressure on the upper portion of the cylinder. As a result there will be a lift force at right angles to the direction of flow. However the flow pattern is still symmetrical about an axis perpendicular to the flow direction. As such the pressure distribution must be symmetrical about this axis and there is no drag on the cylinder. Thus it is possible to explain the existence of lift on the basis of ideal flow theory. An expression for the magnitude of this lift force can be obtained as follows.

Using the methods of hydrodynamics it can be shown that if U_0 is the free stream velocity, the velocity at any point on the surface of the cylinder in case (a) is given by

$$u = 2\,U_0 \sin\theta \qquad (12.12)$$

in which u is the tangential velocity at an angle θ, see Fig. 12.16 (a). Similarly if Γ is the constant circulation, the velocity on the surface of the cylinder due to circulation, u_e is given by (see Fig. 12.16 b)

$$u_c = \frac{\Gamma}{2\pi r} \qquad (12.13)$$

in which r is the radius of the cylinder. Therefore, the resultant velocity in superimposed flow is

$$u = 2\,U_0 \sin\theta + u_c$$

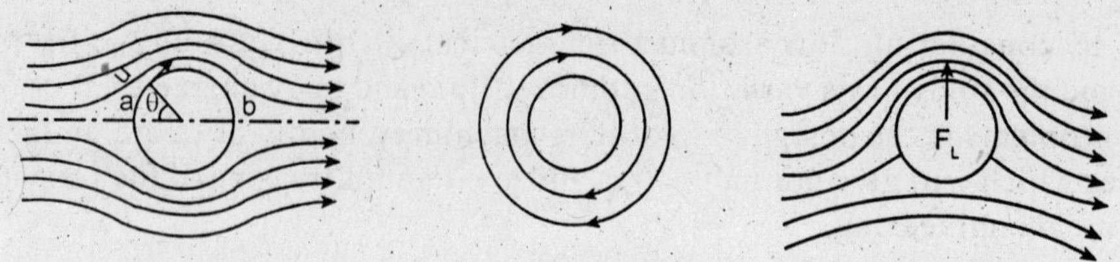

(a) Irrotational flow (b) Flow with circulation (c) Irrotational flow and circulatory flow superimposed

Fig. 12.16 Develepment of lift due to circulation

or

$$\frac{u}{U_o} = 2\sin\theta + \frac{u_c}{U_o} \qquad (12.14)$$

for a given value of u_c/U_o, substitution of u = 0 in the above equation gives the location of stagnation points. Equation 12.14 shows that in the upper portion u/U_o, is greater than one and hence the velocity is increased. Similarly there is a decrease in velocity in the lower portion of the cylinder. Let p_0 be the pressure in the ambient flow. Application of Bernoulli's equation between any point in the unaffected flow and a point on the surface of cylinder yields,

$$p - p_o = \Delta p = \frac{\rho}{2}(U_o^2 - u^2) \qquad (12.15)$$

The lift force acting on an area Lr dθ, in which L is length of cylinder, is Lr dθ Δp sin θ as can be seen in Fig. 12.17. The total lift force F_L is given by

$$F_L = \int_0^{2\pi} Lr\,\Delta p \sin\theta\, d\theta \qquad (12.16)$$

Substitution of the value of Δp from Eq. 12.15 into Eq. 12.16 and subsequent integration gives

$$F_L = L\rho U_o \Gamma \qquad (12.17)$$

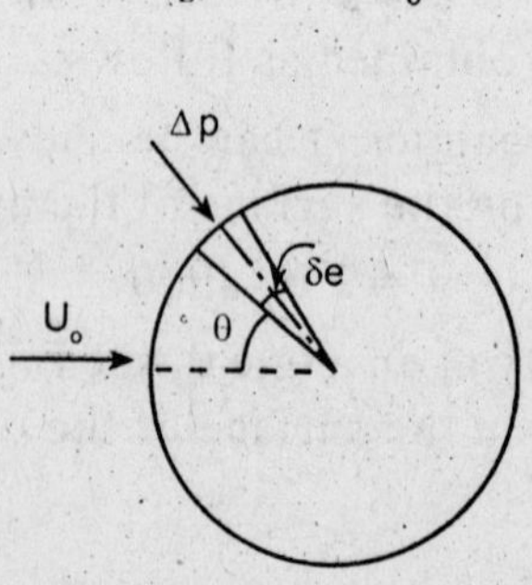

Fig. 12.17 Definition sketch

That such a force perpendicular to the direction of motion can be created by imposing circulation or due to spinning was first discovered by a German scientist Magnus in 1852 and hence this phenomenon is known as *Magnus effect*. In the same manner a lift force can be generated on a sphere if circulatory flow is superimposed on rectilinear motion. This is known as *Robin effect*. This has applications in many games such as table tennis, cricket and tennis.

Equation 12.17, even though developed for a circular cylinder, is found to hold good for a variety of shapes of bodies about which circulation is supposed to take place. This has been achieved through the process of conformal transformation and this was first done by a German scientist Kutta in 1902 and Russian scientist Joukowsky in 1906 independently. Hence Eq. 12.17 is commonly known as Kutta-Joukowsky equation for lift.

Similar to the definition of drag coefficient, the *lift coefficient* can be defined as,

$$C_L = \frac{F_L / \text{area}}{\rho U_o^2 / 2} \tag{12.18}$$

in which the area is the projected area of the body at right angles to the direction of lift. Hence for the cylinder, combining Eqs. 12.13, 12.17 and 12.18. one gets

$$C_L = 2\pi \frac{u_c}{U_o}$$

Figure 12.18 shows the comparison of theoretical and experimental results obtained by Ackeret using air as the fluid.

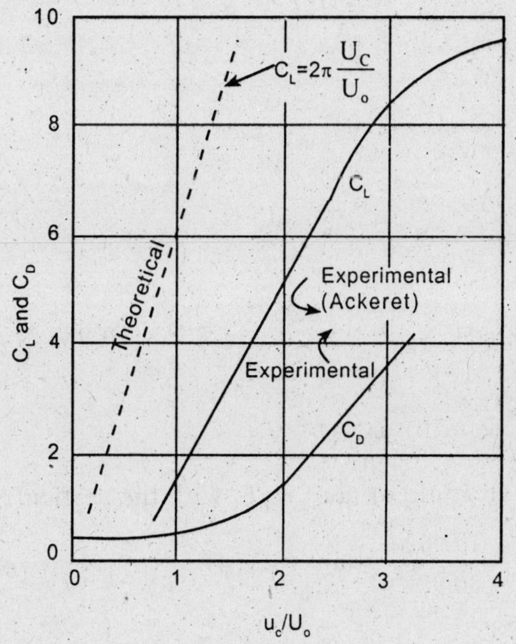

Fig. 12.18 Variation of C_L with u_c/U_o for rotating circular cylinder

The discrepancy between the theoretical and experimental values of C_L is primarily due to the effect of viscosity. However, despite this discrepancy, the theory of irrotational flow does give a qualitative explanation for the existence of lift.

Example 12.5

A circular cylinder 2.0 m in diameter and 12 m long is rotated at 360 rpm with its axis perpendicular to the air stream having a velocity of 37.7 m/s. Assuming ρ to be 1.236 kg/m³ determine (i) circulation (ii) theoretical lift (iii) position of stagnation points (iv) actual lift, drag, and the direction of resultant force.

$$u_c = \frac{\pi DN}{60} = \frac{3.142 \times 2 \times 360}{60} = 37.7 \text{ m/s}$$

Hence $$\frac{u_c}{U_o} = \frac{37.7}{37.7} = 1.0$$

(i) Circulation $\Gamma = 2\pi r\, u_C = 2 \times 3.142 \times 1.0 \times 37.7 \text{ m}^2/\text{s}$

$= 236.91 \text{ m}^2/\text{s}$

(ii) Theoretical lift

$$F_L = L\rho U_o \Gamma = 12.0 \times 1.236 \times 37.7 \times 236.91$$

$$= 132\ 472 \text{ N or } 132.472 \text{ kN}$$

(iii) Position of stagnation points

when $\frac{u}{U_O} = 0$, Eq. 12.14 becomes $2 \sin\theta = -1$

$$\therefore \quad \theta = \sin^{-1}\left(-\frac{1}{2}\right)$$

$$\therefore \quad \theta = -30^\circ \text{ and } +210^\circ$$

(iv) Actual lift and drag

From Fig.12.18, for $\frac{u_c}{U_o} = 1$, $C_L = 1.47$, $C_D = 0.52$

Hence $$F_L = 1.47 \times 2 \times 12 \times \frac{1.236}{2} \times 37.7^2 = 30\ 988 \text{ N}$$

and $$F_D = F_L \frac{C_D}{C_L} = 10\ 962 \text{ N}$$

The resultant force will make an angle of $\tan^{-1} F_D/F_L$ with the vertical

or $$\alpha = \tan^{-1}\frac{10\ 962}{30\ 988} = \tan^{-1}(0.354)$$

$$\therefore \quad \alpha = 19.28'$$

12.12 Lifting Vanes

Many times vanes as shown in Fig. 12.19 are used in order to produce lift as they move through a fluid, Such vanes are called *lifting vanes*. The lifting vanes are generally characterised by the geometric chord C and angle of attack θ_o between the geometric chord and the direction of flow. The lifting vanes can be symmetrical or unsymmetrical as shown in Fig. 12.19. The unsymmetric shape with cambering has been evolved in order to eliminate separation of the boundary layer forming on the surface. Figure 12.20 shows the effect of superposition of circulation on irrotational flow around the lifting vane. It can be seen from this figure that by properly adjusting the circulation, it is possible to make the streamline at the trailing edge tangential. It has been shown that the circulation required to do this is given by

$$\Gamma = \pi \, C \, U_o \sin \theta_o \qquad (12.19)$$

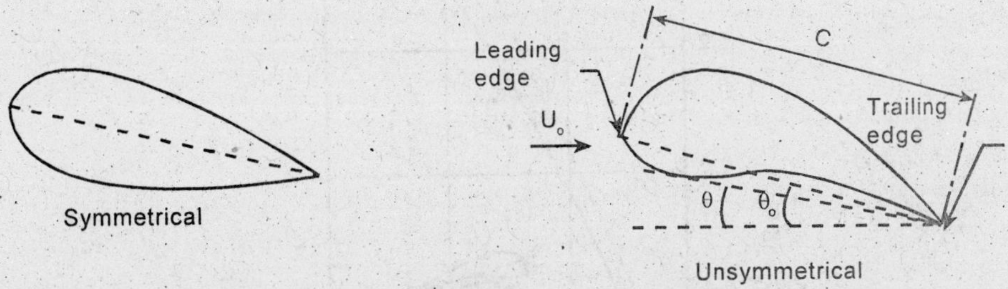

Fig. 12.19 Typical lifting vanes

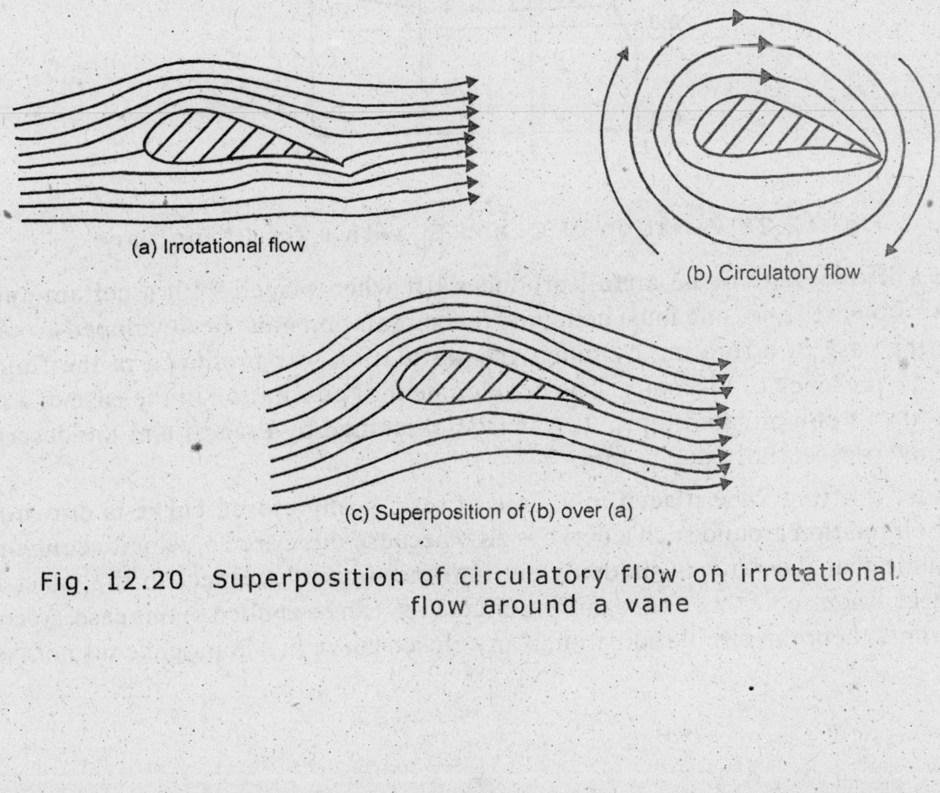

Fig. 12.20 Superposition of circulatory flow on irrotational flow around a vane

Hence the lift force becomes (see Eq. 12.17).

$$F_L = \pi \, CL\rho \, U_o^2 \sin \theta_o \qquad (12.20)$$

and
$$C_L = \frac{F_L / CL}{\rho U_o^2 / 2}$$

or
$$C_L = 2\pi \sin \theta_o \qquad (12.21)$$

Figure 12.21 shows the variation of C_D and C_L with θ for a very long lifting vane. The agreement between theoretical and observed C_L values is much better for lifting vane than for the cylinder. With the increase in value of θ, the difference between theoretical and observed values of C_L increases because of the separation at the leading edge of the vane, a phenomenon known as *stall*.

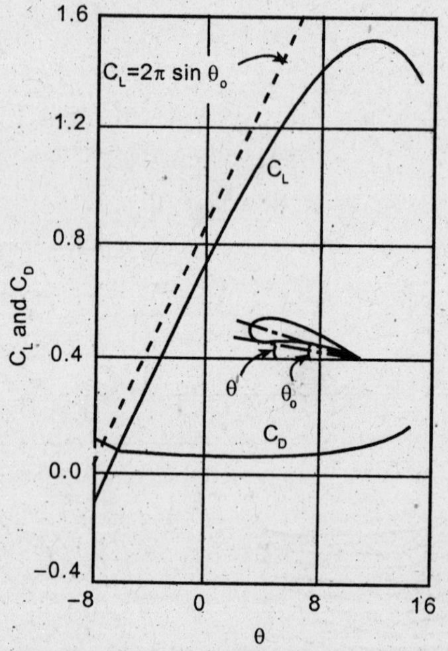

Fig. 12.21 Variation of C_L and C_D with θ for lifting vane

Since a lifting vane or an airfoil produces lift when placed with a certain angle of attack in a flowing fluid, one must conclude that circulation must be developed around the vane. In the case of a rotating cylinder, the circulation was produced in the fluid as a result of the presence of viscosity. The development of circulation in the case of a lifting vane is rather a complicated topic. It was first explained by Prandtl and the description given below is essentially due to him.

Consider a lifting vane placed in a fluid at rest. If any closed curve is drawn in the fluid, the circulation around such a curve is zero because there are no velocity components. Now assume that the fluid is suddenly set into motion with respect to the vane. If the fluid is ideal, Thomson's theorem regarding circulation can be applied in this case. According to Thomson's theorem, circulation around any closed curve in a homogeneous nonviscous fluid is constant for all the time. For this reason, in the case of ideal fluid past the vane, the circulation around the vane must be zero. This contradiction in the existence of circulation around the vane is explained on the basis of a surface of discontinuity at the trailing edge of the vane.

When the vane makes an angle with the direction of flow, the flow pattern in Fig. 12.20 shows that the underside of trailing edge of the vane has a much larger velocity than the upper side of the trailing edge. Since these two velocities are markedly different just downstream of the trailing edge, a surface of discontinuity is formed which gives rise to a vortex or eddy because of the inherent instability of the surface of discontinuity. This vortex is known as the *starting vortex*. This vortex increases in size to such an extent that a finite velocity is produced at the trailing edge. Thus the generation of circulation around the vane is essentially due to the formation of the starting vortex. Once the starting vortex is formed, it is accompanied by the generation of circulation around the vane, the magnitude of the circulation being the same as that of the circulation of the starting vortex and the direction is opposite, see Fig. 12.22. For a curve which surrounds the vane as well as starting vortex, the total circulation is thus zero. In this way the presence of circulation around the vane does not violate Thomson's theorem.

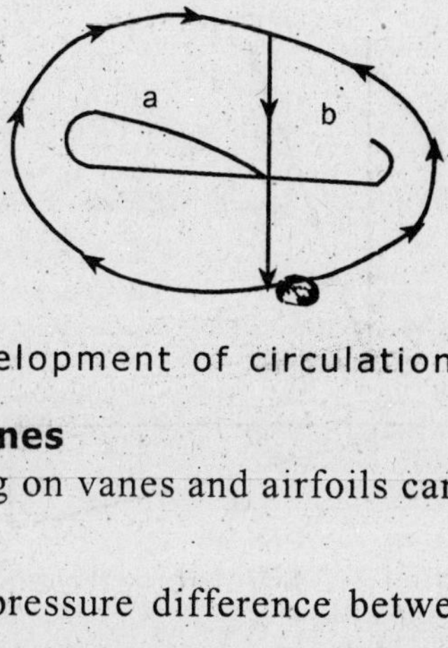

Fig. 12.22 Development of circulation around vane

12.13 Drag on Airfoils and Vanes

As done by Prandtl, the total drag on vanes and airfoils can be divided into three parts :

a. skin friction or friction drag,

b. form drag which is due to pressure difference between upstream and rear of the vane, and

c. pressure drag which is due to three dimensional nature of airfoil or vane. This is commonly known as *induced drag*, see Fig. 12.23.

Whenever lift force exists, the pressure on the upper face of airfoil is smaller than the pressure on the lower face. This causes an upward flow around the sides of the airfoil if length to chord ratio L/C known as aspect ratio, is small. These are called *tip vortices*. These vortices cause a downward velocity on the top of the vane, the effect of which is to make the relative velocity between fluid and vane inclined downwards as shown in Fig. 12.24. This in effect reduces the angle of attack and therefore causes a decrease in lift. The true lift, by definition, is always at right angles to the relative velocity U and hence it can now have a component in the horizontal direction i.e., in the direction of U_0. This is known as the *induced drag* F_{Di}. The magnitude of F_{Di} is given by

$$F_{Di} = F_L \sin \beta \approx F_L \cdot \beta$$

as long as β is small. It has been shown that for airfoils the induced drag coefficient C_{Di} is given by

$$C_{Di} = \frac{C_L^2}{\pi L / C} \tag{12.22}$$

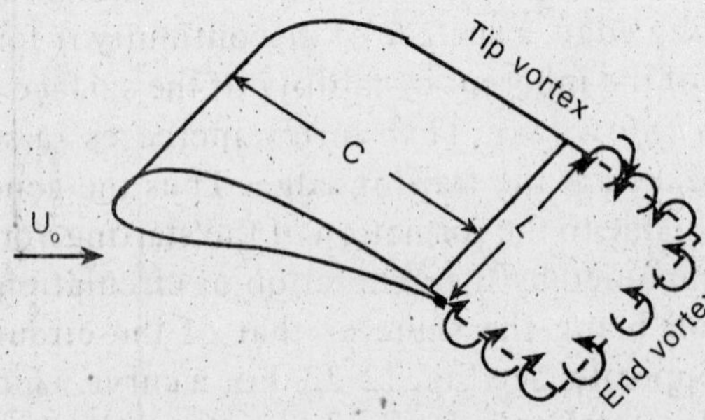

Fig. 12.23 Vortex system in three dimensional flow around an airfoil

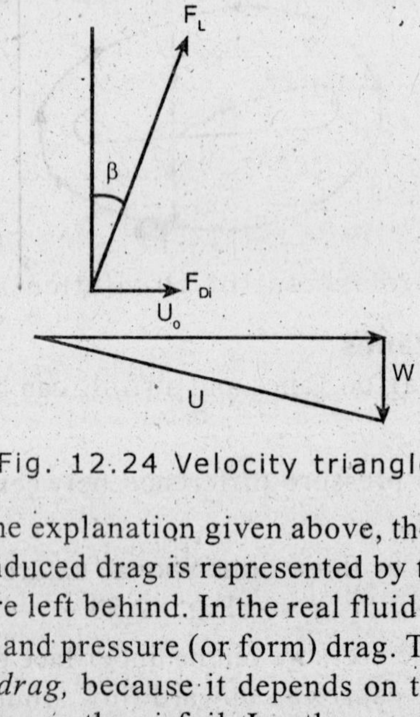

Fig. 12.24 Velocity triangle

It should be noted that in the explanation given above, the existence of drag in an ideal fluid has been proved. This induced drag is represented by the kinetic energy supplied to the trailing vortices as they are left behind. In the real fluid the total drag will be the sum of induced drag, friction drag and pressure (or form) drag. The summation of latter two is commonly known as *profile drag,* because it depends on the shape and not on the plan form or aspect ratio of the vane or the airfoil. In other words,

$$C_D = C_{Do} + C_{Di} \tag{12.23}$$

in which C_{Do} is the profile drag for two dimensional wing.

12.14 Polar Diagram for Airfoils

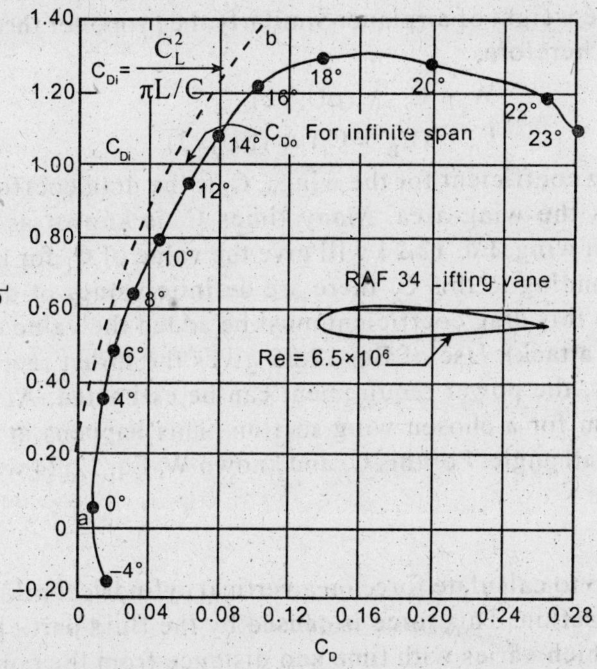

Fig. 12.25 Polar diagram for RAF-34 lifting vane with aspect ratio of six

It can be seen that the drag coefficient as well as the lift coefficient for airfoils and vanes depend primarily on the angle of attack. To represent this variation, C_D and C_L values can be plotted against the angle of attack. This was done in the earlier stages. Otto Lilienthal suggested plotting C_L as a function of C_D with angle of attack as the third variable for a given airfoil. Such a diagram is known as the *polar diagram*, see Fig. 12.25. For a given aspect ratio L/C, Eq. 12.22 can be used to plot relation between C_L and C_{Di} as shown by the curve ab. With the increase in L/C, C_{Di} decreases and becomes zero when L/C is equal to infinity i.e. for a two dimensional airfoil, curve ab will be vertical and coincide with the Y axis. For any angle of attack the profile drag C_{Do} is partly experimentally determined and partly computed from boundary layer theory and added to C_{Di} to give the drag coefficient. The drag coefficient thus obtained is plotted against C_L and the angle of attack which will give maximum lift and minimum drag i.e. C_L/C_D maximum is given by drawing a tangent to the curve passing through point of zero C_L. The point of tangency gives the required angle of attack.

12.15 Effects of Compressibility on Lift

Experiments have shown that lift coefficient C_L increases with increase in Mach number as long as the Mach number is smaller than a critical value (around 0.80 to 0.90). With further increase in Mach number, there is a sudden decrease in C_L due to formation of shock waves.

12.16 Airplane Mechanics

When an airplane is travelling through air and when it is level, the total lift on the airplane wings must balance the weight of airplane. Similarly the propeller thrust must be equal to the total drag force. Therefore,

Weight $$W = C_L A (\rho U_o^2/2) \qquad (12.24)$$

Thrust $$F_D = (C_D + C_f) A (\rho U_o^2/2) \qquad (12.25)$$

in which C_D is the drag coefficient for the wings, C_f is the drag coefficient for the rest of the airplane and A is the wing area. Many times C_f is known as the *parasite drag coefficient*. For a given wing, Eq. 12.24 will give the value of C_L for known values of W, ρ, U_o and A. Corresponding to this C_L there are definite values of drag coefficient and the angle of attack. To this drag coefficient must be added the value of C_f (which varies slightly with angle of attack). Use of Eq. 12.25 gives the thrust required. Knowing the thrust and the velocity, the power requirement can be estimated. At the take-off stage, C_L should be maximum for a chosen wing section. This happens at an angle of attack slightly less than the stall angle. For this C_L and known W, Eq. 12.24 will give the take-off speed of the airplane.

12.17 Wave Forces

In several cases one has to calculate force on a vertical cylindrical pile or similar element subjected to the wave action. This force is caused by the fluid particle velocity u in the horizontal direction which varies with time and distance from the boundary. Because of the unsteady character of motion, the force on the cylindrical pile is partly due to steady state drag and partly due to fluid acceleration. Morrison has proposed the following equation for force F due to unidirectional sinusoidal wave on a unit length of vertical circular cylinder of diameter D;

$$F = D\, C_D \frac{\rho}{2} u \,|\, u \,|\, + \rho\, C_M A \frac{du}{dt} \qquad (12.26)$$

where C_D and C_M are the coefficients of drag and inertia and $A = \pi D^2/4$. Under the wave fluid particles move in elliptic orbits in a vertical plane and hence u varies with t and z, the vertical distance from the boundary. For this reason it can be + ve, -ve or zero. Writing u^2 as $u\,|\,u\,|$ in the above equation provides for changes in direction of F with change in direction of u. This formula is physically correct in the two extreme cases viz, for steady flow when du/dt is zero, and acceleration from rest when u is zero; here $C_M = 2.0$. Normally C_D and C_M are assumed to be constant over the wave cycle. However C_D and C_M depend on Re, relative roughness k/D and Keulegan-Carpenter number $K_o = u_m T/D$ where u_m is the maximum velocity in the sinusoidal flow of period T, and on t/T. In general, recommended value of C_D is between 0.6 and 1.0 while that of C_M between 1.5 and 2.0. The velocity u and acceleration du/dt to be used in Morrison's equation are obtained from wave theory. These are:

$$\left.\begin{aligned} u &= \left(\frac{\pi H}{T}\right)\frac{\cosh(2\pi z/\lambda)}{\sinh(2\pi h/\lambda)}\cos(2\pi t/T) \\ \frac{du}{dt} &= \left(\frac{2\pi^2 H}{T^2}\right)\frac{\cosh(2\pi z/\lambda)}{\sinh(2\pi h/\lambda)}\sin(2\pi t/T) \end{aligned}\right\} \qquad (12.27)$$

where H is the wave height, λ is the wave length, h is the depth of flow and T is the wave period, see Fig. 12.26. These equations give good approximation of particle velocity and acceleration for small H/λ and h/λ greater than about 0.20. It can be seen that since u and du/dt depend on t, the total force on cylinder length dz will vary with time. When $u = 0$, $2\pi t/T = \pi/2$ and at that time du/dt is maximum. Thus minimum drag and maximum inertia are out of phase by 90°.

At any time total force on length dz is

$$dF = \left[\frac{1}{2}C_D\,\rho\,D\,u\,|u| + C_M\,\rho\frac{\pi D^2}{4}\frac{du}{dt}\right]dz \qquad (12.28)$$

Substitution of values of u and du/dt from Eq. 12.27 and subsequent integrations from z = 0 to h yields the total force on the cylindrical pile at any time t. To find the maximum force this expression for F must be differentiated with respect to t and result equated to zero. This gives the condition for F to be maximum, which when substituted in the expression for F yields its maximum value.

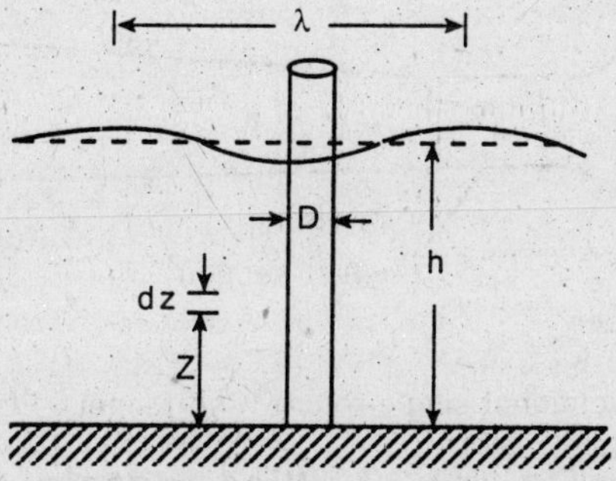

Fig. 12.26 Definition sketch

12.18 Wind Tunnels

The wind tunnel is an indispensable device for conducting tests to measure forces (drag and lift) and moments on bodies kept in an air stream such as spheres, cylinders, airfoils and buildings, and for testing aircraft and its components. Wind tunnels are also used for environmental studies related to diffusion of smoke and pollutants, and building comforts. At present there are a large number of wind tunnels in the world, many of them are for subsonic work and others for high speed testing. Wind tunnels are economical and accurate means of fluid mechanics research. We will briefly discuss here the basic aspects of subsonic wind tunnels. Two basic types of wind tunnels, namely open circuit and closed circuit tunnels are shown in Fig. 12.27. The open circuit wind tunnel sucks air from the atmosphere which passes through honey comb, and entrance cone and then passes through the test section where the model is kept. The air then passes through the diffuser section into atmosphere. The suction is caused by an exhaust fan or propeller.

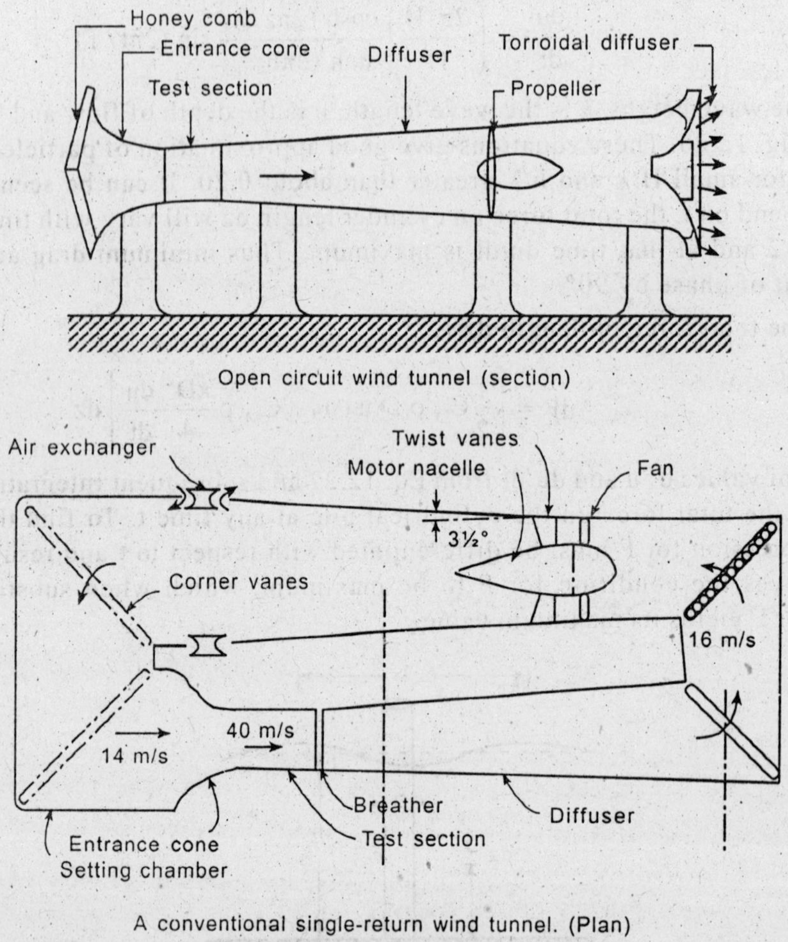

Fig. 12.27 Wind tunnels

The simplest form of closed circuit single-return wind tunnel consists of entrance cone, test section, diffuser, vanes at the corners, fan, and air-exchangers which allow air to enter and leave the tunnel. A lot of thought goes into the design of wind tunnels so that air enters and leaves the test section smoothly, has a low level of turbulence, air temperature remains fairly constant and energy requirement is low. Special attention is given to the determination of the size and length of the test section, inlet transition, diffuser length, corner vanes and the honey-comb at the entrance.

The quantities that need to be measured in the wind tunnel include pressure, pressure difference, average velocity and velocity distribution, boundary shear, turbulence level and drag, lift and moments on the body. The wall pressure can be measured using a piezometer connected to U-tube manometer. The pressures at a number of points on a body can be measured using variable-angle inclined multitube manometer. The mean velocity can be measured using a total head tube, or mean velocity hot wire anemometer; the hot wire anemometer can also be used to measure turbulence velocity components and turbulent shear. The boundary shear can be measured by Preston tube. The drag, lift and moments are measured using a force balance. The flow pattern around the body can be visualized by introducing smoke.

PROBLEMS

12.1 A body having a projected area of 1.30 m^2 experiences a drag of 201 N when travelling through air at a velocity of 90 km/hr with the projected area perpendicular to the direction of travel. If ρ is equal to 1.208 kg/m^3, determine the drag coefficient.

12.2 Water flows around a very long cylinder which has its axis perpendicular to the direction of flow. Determine the drag on the cylinder if the velocity of water is 5.0 m/s and diameter of the cylinder is 0.30 in. Take the drag coefficient as 0.30.

2.3 A lead sphere of 25 mm diameter, weighing 111.8 kN/m^3 falls at a constant velocity under the action of gravity, in a thick oil. If the value of C_D is 29.4 and relative density of oil is 0.93, determine the velocity at which the sphere is falling.

2.4 A steel sphere having a relative density of 7.96 and a sphere of magnesium (relative density 1.82) fall freely in water and glycerine respectively at 20°C. What will be the ratio of their diameters for attaining dynamic similarity ?

2.5 Determine the bending moment at the base of a 40 m high chimney of average diameter 2.5 m if the wind velocity is 25 m/s. Take ρ to be 1.208 kg/m^3 at 20°C.

2.6 A steel ball of relative density 7.85 and 1.50 mm diameter falls at a velecity of 50 mm/s through an oil of relative density 0.61. What is the kinematic viscosity of the oil ?

2.7 Air at velocity of 40 km/hr flows past a rectangular sign board 1.5 m × 0.75 m in size held normal to flow direction. If air temperature is 20°C (ρ = 1.208 kg/m^3) determine the drag force on the board.

12.8 Determine the maximum load that can be carried by a 6.0 m diameter parachute if the maximum permissible velocity of descent is 7.0 m/s.

12.9 An automobile with a projected area of 2.4 m^2 and which is perfectly streamlined travels in air at 20°C at maximum speed of 120 km/hr. What is the power required to overcome the air frictional resistance ? Take C_D to be 0.30.

12.10 A sphere of 12.5 mm diameter rises in an oil with a speed of 36.5 mm/s. Determine the specific weight of the ball if the mass density of the oil is 920 kg/m^3 and μ is given as 0.340 N s/m^2.

12.11 A cylinder 1.0 m in diameter and 10.0 m length is kept in a uniform stream of water having 10 m/s velocity. The cylinder axis is perpendicular to flow and the cylinder is rotated about its axis at 300 rpm. Determine (a) circulation (b) position of stagnation points (c) lift force per unit length and (d) lift coefficient. (Neglect the effects of viscosity).

12.12 In problem 12.11 determine the speed of rotation of the above cylinder which yields only a single stagnation point.

12.13 A cylinder of 0.50 m diameter is rotated at 550 rpm in an air stream of velocity 39 km/hr. If it develops a lift of 95.6 N per meter length of the cylinder, determine the ratio of actual to theoretical lift.

12.14 Wings of an airplane are replaced by two cylinders 1.2 m in diameter and 4.0 m in length each and it is proposed to make use of the lift caused by their rotation to lift the airplane. If the speed of airplane is 400 km/hr and the cylinders are rotated at 2100 rpm, determine how much weight can be lifted and what power will be required to overcome the rotor friction.

12.15 A kite weighs 13.34 N and has a dimension 1.20 m × 0.75 m. When the kite assumes an angle of 10° to the horizontal, the string attached to it makes an angle of 45° with the horizontal and has a tension of 33.05 N. If the wind velocity is 38.5 km/hr and ρ for air is 1.268 kg/m^3, find the drag and lift coefficients.

12.16 For RAF – 34 wing of aspect ratio 6 and chord of 2.0 m, determine the lift if it is travelling at 250 km/hr at such an angle of attack that the ratio of lift to drag on the wings is maximum. Under such condition determine the induced drag coefficient. Finally determine the total drag.

12.17 An airplane weighing 22 555 N has a wing area of 22.5 m^2 and a span of 12 m. What is the lift coefficient if the plane travels at 320 km/hr in the horizontal direction ? Also compute the theoretical value of circulation and angle of attack, measured from zero lift axis.

12.18 An airplane fitted with RAF-34 wings has total wing area of 25 m^2 and an aspect ratio of 6, and it travels at 400 km/hr horizontally. If the parasite drag coefficient for the rest of the plane is 0.01 find the horse power required if the plane weighs 138.273 kN.

12.19 Integrate Eq. 12.28 with respect to z and show that the total force on the cylindrical pile is given by

$$F = \left[C_D \rho D \frac{\pi H^2 \lambda}{16T}\left(\frac{\sin(4\pi h/\lambda) + (4\pi h/\lambda)}{\sinh^2(2\pi h/\lambda)}\right)\right]\cos^2\frac{2\pi t}{T}$$

$$+ \left[\frac{C_M \rho D^2 \pi^2 H \lambda}{4T^2}\right]\sin(2\pi t/T)$$

12.20 If A and B represent quantities in the [ ] brackets in the above equation in problem 12.19, show that F is maximum when

$$\sin(2\pi t/T) = \frac{B}{2A}$$

CHAPTER THIRTEEN

Flow in Open Channels

13.1 Introduction

Attention has been drawn in the previous Chapters mainly to the flows in conduits in which the fluid does not come in contact with another fluid. On the other hand there are several practical cases of flow, in which two fluids of different mass densities come in contact with each other. The common examples of this type of problems are the flow in canals, the flow in rivers and the flow in conduits running partially full. The less known but equally important are density currents, dust laden winds, etc. (see Fig. 13.1) which also fall in this category. The main characteristic of all these flows is that the pressure intensity at all points on the interface is the same. In the case of liquid flow in open channels, the interface is the free surface and the pressure on the free surface is atmospheric. The free surface in the open channel itself represents the hydraulic grade line for the flow. It should be evident that the force causing the flow is derived from the component of submerged weight of the heavier fluid prism in the direction of flow and hence the longitudinal bed slope of the channel plays an important part in the study of these types of problems. If γ and γ_1 respresent the specific weights of the two fluids, $(\gamma - \gamma_1)$ is the effective specific wheight. In the case of open channel flow where the lighter fluid is air and heavier one is water, γ_1 the weight of air being very small $(\gamma - \gamma_1)$ is very nearly equal to γ which is the specific weight of water.

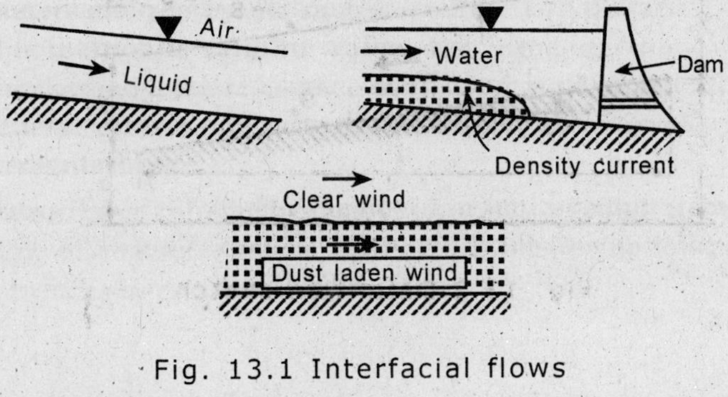

Fig. 13.1 Interfacial flows

Open channels may either be natural channels like the streams or artificial channels built for some specific purpose like navigation, irrigation or power generation. Natural channels usually have irregular cross-section and the roughness of the bed and sides also varies considerably from smooth to very rough. On the other hand, the artificial channels have fairly well defined hydraulic properties viz., cross-section, bed slope and roughness and therefore, solutions of problems in artificial channels are less complicated.

In Chapter 2, the flow in general has been classified as steady, unsteady, uniform and non-uniform depending upon the variations of the flow parameters with respect to time or with respect to space. In open channels the major variables are the depth and velocity of flow, and their variation with time or space determines whether the flow is steady or unsteady and uniform or non-uniform. If the depth of flow at a certain section does not vary with time, it is a steady flow; otherwise it is unsteady. Uniform flow is that in which at a given time, the depth of flow is same at every section of the channel. On the contrary, if the depth of flow varies from section to section at a given time, the flow is non-uniform or varied. *Varied flow* can be further classified as *gradually varied* or *rapidly varied.* In gradually varied flow, change in the depth of flow takes place gradually in a long reach of the channel while in rapidly varied flow the change in the depth of flow occurs in a relatively short distance. Flow upstream of a dam, as shown in Fig. 13.1, is gradually varied flow. *Rapidly varied* flow is a local phenomenon like a hydraulic jump in which the depth of flow changes in a very short distance, see Fig. 13.24. Flow over spillway, flow in a bend, flow at sudden expansion or contraction in a channel are some examples of rapidly varied flow.

13.2 Steady Uniform Flow

In order to obtain a truly uniform flow, it is necessary that the channel cross-section should be uniform and that the channel is laid on constant bed slope. A channel with a constant bed slope and having the same cross-section at various distances along its length is known as *prismatic channel.* Since the depth of flow is constant in the uniform flow reach, it follows that the average velocity is also constant. Figure 13.2 shows a short reach of steady uniform flow in a prismatic channel. Applying Bernoulli's equation between sections 1 and 2 and assuming energy correction factor to be unity, one can write,

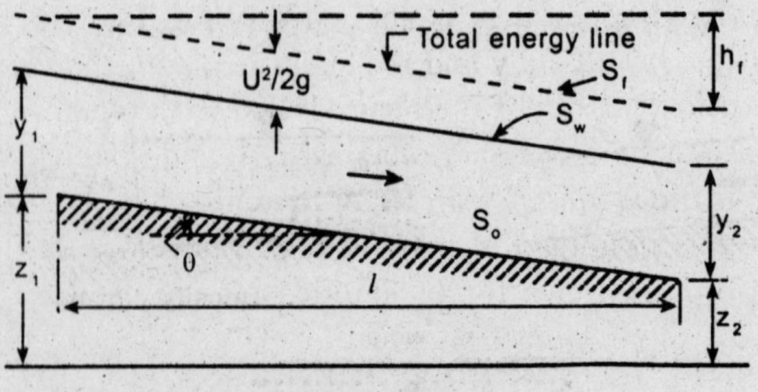

Fig. 13.2 Definition sketch

$$\frac{U_1^2}{2g} + y_1 + z_1 = \frac{U_2^2}{2g} + y_2 + z_2 + h_f$$

which h_f is the energy loss between sections 1 and 2. Since y_1 and y_2 are the same, the lues of $U_1^2/2g$ and $U_2^2/2g$ will also be same. The inclination of energy line is thus the me as that of the free surface. The channel bed slope S_o is $(z_1 - z_2)/l$ which is the same that of the slope of energy line S_f because $h_f = z_1 - z_2$ and the depth of flow and velocity two sections are the same. It can therefore, be concluded that in uniform flow the ope of the energy line S_f, the slope of free surface S_w and the slope of the channel bed are the same i.e. $S_f = S_w = S_o$. The depth of flow under these conditions is known as, e *uniform or normal depth* y_o.

Since the velocity of flow does not change along the length of the channel in uniform ow, there is no acceleration and hence the summation of the components of all the ternal forces in the direction of flow must be zero. In other words, the weight component the liquid prism in the direction of flow is equal to the shear resistance offered by the annel perimeter, the pressure force on either side of the liquid prism being the same. tially some distance is required on the upstream side for attaining this condition of lance. In this region the flow is gradually varied. Consider a short reach of length l in ich uniform flow has been established, see Fig. 13.3.

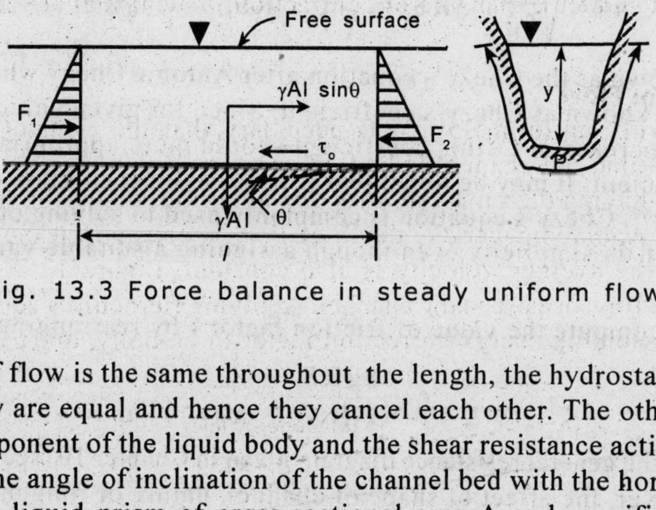

Fig. 13.3 Force balance in steady uniform flow

As the depth of flow is the same throughout the length, the hydrostatic forces F_1 and F_2 the liquid body are equal and hence they cancel each other. The other forces are those the weight component of the liquid body and the shear resistance acting against the flow ection. If θ is the angle of inclination of the channel bed with the horizontal, the weight nponent of the liquid prism of cross-sectional area A and specific weight γ will be $A\,l \sin\theta$). Similarly, if P is the *wetted perimeter* or the channel perimeter in contact with liquid and τ_o is the average boundary shear, the total resistance to flow will be $\tau_o\,Pl$. ce there is no acceleration, these two forces should balance. Hence

$$\gamma A l \sin\theta = \tau_o P l$$

$$\tau_o = \gamma \frac{A}{P} \sin\theta$$

It may be noted that for very small values of θ, sin θ can be taken as the slope of the channel; it is also equal to water surface slope or energy gradient for uniform flow. The term A/P is known as the *hydraulics radius* and is commonly designated by R. The above expression can be written as

$$\tau_o = \gamma\, R\, S_o \qquad (13.1$$

in which S_o is the bed slope. It may be noted that for uniform flow, since $S_o = S_w = S_f$, any one of these three can be, used in Eq. 13.1. A similar analysis can be conducted for non-uniform flow and it can be shown that $\tau_o = \gamma\, R\, S_f$.

Hydraulic radius R is an important characteristics and is very commonly used as length parameter in open channel problems. It may be noted that as the channel become wider, the hydraulic radius increases and approaches the depth of flow. In other word for very wide channel R ≈ depth of flow. Similarly for channels of very small width an large depth R is nearly equal to half the width.

Earlier in Chapter 10, the shear stress τ_o was related to ρ and U by the equatio

$\tau_o = \frac{f}{4}\frac{\rho U^2}{2}$ in which U is the average velocity. Equating the two expressions for τ_o, on gets,

$$U = \sqrt{\frac{8\gamma}{f\rho}}\sqrt{R\,S_f} = \sqrt{\frac{8g}{f}}\sqrt{R\,S_f} = C\sqrt{R\,S_f} \qquad (13.2$$

Equation 13.2 is known as the Chezy's equation after Antonie Chezy who developed it i 1769. The term C is known as Chezy's coefficient. Since for given values of R and S_f, increases with the increase in C, this coefficient should more appropriately be called a the discharge coefficient. It may be noted that C is not a dimensionless coefficient but has dimensions of $g^{1/2}$. Chezy's equation is commonly used in solving open channel flo problems because of its simplicity even though assigning a suitable value to C is rath difficult.

It is possible to compute the value of friction factor f by rearranging Eq. 13.2 as

$$f = \frac{8\,g\,R\,S_f}{U^2}$$

and a plot similar to the general resistance diagram given in Chapter 10 (see Fig. 10.7 or 10. can be made. However, the effect of shape of channel, nature of roughness and presen of free surface, in general complicate the variation of f. It should be remembered that f open channels the length characteristic in Reynolds number is the hydraulic radius. Ma investigators have studied the variation of friction factor with Reynolds number Re, f various channel shapes and roughness patterns. In general, for laminar region, which upto a Re value of 500, the friction factor and Reynolds number are related as

$$f = \frac{K}{Re}$$

The value of K varies between 14 and 60 depending upon the channel shape. The fully developed turbulent flow is obtained when the Reynolds number exceeds a value of 2000. After the establishment of fully developed turbulent flow, one can have either a smooth ransition or rough boundary depending on the values of Reynolds number and relative oughness parameter. If one assumes that the flow in open channels does not have any effect of waves, Moody's diagram can be used for determination of f. In such case Re = (4UR/ν), relative roughness will be k/4R and $f = 8gRS_0/U^2$ where R is the hydraulic adius.

Many attempts have been made towards the determination of Chezy's C, notable amongst hem being the formulae of Ganguillet and Kutter (Eq. 13.3) and Manning (Eq. 13.4). The formulae involve another empirical constant n, known as *roughness coefficient* or *esistant coefficient* which varies widely depending on the channel surface and its conditions. The two formulae are

$$C = \frac{23 + \dfrac{0.00155}{S_o} + \dfrac{1}{n}}{1 + \left(23 + \dfrac{0.00155}{S_o}\right)\dfrac{n}{\sqrt{R}}} \qquad (13.3)$$

$$C = \frac{R^{1/6}}{n} \qquad (13.4)$$

n which R is in m. Using Manning's value for Chezy's C, Eq. 13.2 can be written in the orm,

$$C = \frac{1}{n} R^{2/3} S_0^{1/2} \qquad (13.5)$$

which is commonly known as Manning's equation for average velocity in uniform flow. This equation is for the metric system of units. Stickler has found that for hydrodynamically ough plane boundaries, Manning's n is related to the nature of material forming the hannel perimeter according to the equation

$$n = \frac{d_{50}^{1/6}}{21} \qquad (13.6)$$

n which d_{50} is in meters and represents such a size that fifty percent of the bed material s finer than d_{50}. This relation is valid for values R/d_{50} ranging from 5 to 500. In natural igid boundary open channels, the resistance coefficient n depends on the depth of flow, channel shape, vegetative growth, presence of fine suspended material, existence of bends, nd other channel irregularities.

Several investigators have collected valuable information about the variation of n with hanges in the nature of channel surface. Table 13.2 lists some typical values of n for different types of surfaces encountered in practice.

TABLE 13.1*

Average Values of Manning's Roughness Coefficient

Type of channel	*Value of n*
1. Closed conduits flowing partly full	
a. vitrified clay	0.014
b. concrete sewer, smooth inside	0.013
c. glazed brickwork	0.013
2. Lined channels	
a. cement lined, smooth surface	0.011
b. cement concrete finish	0.015
c. brick in cement mortar	0.018
d. concrete on neatly excavated rock	0.020
e. cement rubble masonry	0.020
f. concrete on irregular excavated rock	0.027
3. Excavated channels	
a. earthen channels neatly excavated	0.018
b. well maintained channels	0.020
c. alluvial channels	0.01– 0.04 (Varying)
4. Natural streams	
a. clean and straight	0.030
b. clean straight with boulders	0.035
c. with weeds, deep pools, etc.	0.075 to 0.150

*(Adapted from Chow)

It is not difficult to get steady uniform flow in artificial channels such as lined irrigatio canals, flumes, etc., where a controlled discharge is allowed to flow into the channe Such steady uniform flow seldom occurs in natural channels. However, uniform flo condition is a very basic condition and therefore its knowledge is essential in the solutio of most of nonuniform flow problems. Therefore computation concerning uniform flo forms an important part of analysis of open channel flow. In such problems one has t deal with the following variables : discharge Q, average velocity of flow U, normal dept y_o, slope S_o, resistance coefficient n or C, and geometric elements of the channel e.g. be width and side slope.

TABEL 13.2

Types of Uniform Flow Problems

No.	Given	To find
i.	y, n, S_o and channel shape and dimensions	Q, U
ii.	Q, y_o, S_o, and channel shape and dimensions	n, U
iii.	Q, y_o, n, and channel shape and dimensions	S_o, U
iv.	Q, n, S_o, and channel shape and dimensions	y_o, U
(v)	Q, n, S_o, and channel shape	y_o and channel dimensions

The equations connecting these variables are the continuity equation Q = AU and the resistance equation such as Manning's or Chezy's. Five categories of problems can be encountered in practice which are listed in Table 13.2.

The problems of the first, second and third category can be solved directly without any difficulty. The problems of the fourth category involve some difficulty. Consider a rectangular channel of width B. The continuity and Manning's equation can be combined to give

$$Q = \frac{By_o}{n}\left(\frac{By_o}{B+2y_o}\right)^{2/3} S_o^{1/2}$$

which must be solved for y_o when Q , n, B and S_o are known. The corresponding equation for trapezoidal channel is

$$Q = \frac{(B+z\,y_o)y_o}{n}\left[\frac{(B+z\,y_o)y_o}{B+2\,y_o\sqrt{(1+z^2)}}\right]^{2/3} S_o^{1/2}$$

in which B is bed width and z hor : 1 vert is the side slope. These equations must be solved by trial and error to obtain y_o. One must assume y_o and compute the right hand side. If this does not equal Q, assume another value of y_o. It can however be seen that these equations can be written as $Q\,n/S_o^{1/2} = AR^{2/3}$ when $y = y_o$. Therefore a graph can be prepared between y and $AR^{2/3}$ and one can read the value of $y = y_o$ from this graph, such that $AR^{2/3} = Q\,n/S_o^{1/2}$. Here A is the flow area.

The quantity $AR^{2/3}$ is known as the *section factor* for uniform flow computation and is denoted by Z_o. For any channel Z_o will be a unique function of the flow depth y For rectangular channel of width B the expression for Z_o is

$$Z_o = B\,y\left\{\frac{B\,y}{B+2y}\right\}^{2/3}$$

which can be written in demensionless form as

$$\frac{Z_o}{B^{8/3}} = \frac{y}{B}\left\{\frac{y/B}{1+2\,y/B}\right\}^{2/3}$$

$$= (y/B)^{5/3} \,/\, [1+2y/B]^{2/3}$$

For trapezoidal channel of bed width B and side slope z hor : 1 vertical. one gets

$$\frac{Z_o}{B^{8/3}} = \{1 + z\,(y/B)\}\,\frac{y}{B}\left[\frac{\{1+z(y/B)\}\,y/B}{1+2(y/B)\sqrt{(1+z^2)}}\right]^{2/3}$$

$$= \left[\left(1+z\frac{y}{B}\right)\frac{y}{B}\right]^{5/3} \Bigg/ \left[1+2\frac{y}{B}\sqrt{1+z^2}\right]^{2/3}$$

It can be seen that when $z = 0$, the equation for $Z_o/B^{8/3}$ for trapezoidal channel reduces to that for rectangular channel. One can in fact plot $Z_o/B^{8/3}$ as a function of y/B with z as a third parameter and use it for determination of normal depth.

The problems of the fifth category are encountered in irrigation engineering, where the channel shape is governed by such factors as whether it is a lined or unlined channel, or what is the stable side slope for a given material. The other factor which governs the width to depth ratio is cost. Thus the channel section can be designed as the most economical which yields a condition that hydraulic radius equals half the depth. Practising engineers have recommended the following bed widths for trapezoidal lined channels.

Q m³/s	120	100	60	30	20	5	1.5
B m	9.9	8.2	4.8	3.5	2.75	1.9	1.3

Example 13.1

What size of a sewer pipe should be laid at a slope of 0.0001 to carry a discharge of 650 *l*/s when flowing half full ? The sewer is circular and the roughness coefficient n has value of 0.015.

If the diameter of the pipe is d then area and hydraulic radius will be $(\pi/8)d^2$ and d/4 respectively. From the Manning's equation

$$0.65 = \frac{1}{0.015} \times \left(\frac{\pi}{8}d^2\right)\left(\frac{d}{4}\right)^{2/3} (0.0001)^{1/2}$$

$$0.65 = \frac{1}{0.015} \times \frac{\pi}{8} \times \left(\frac{1}{4}\right)^{2/3} \times 0.01 \times d^{8/3}$$

or $$d^{8/3} = \frac{0.65\times0.015\times8}{\pi\times0.01\times0.397} = 6.24$$

$$= (6.24)^{3/8} = 1.985 \text{ m}$$

Adopt a pipe of 2 m diameter

Example 13.2

Determine the normal depth in a 3.0 m wide rectangular channel carrying 1.50 m^3/s discharge. The channel slope is 0.0004 and Manning's n of 0.013.

$$Q = \frac{By_o}{n}\left(\frac{By_o}{B+2y_o}\right)^{2/3} S_o^{1/2}$$

or $$\frac{Q\,n}{B^{5/3}\,S_o^{1/2}} = \frac{y_o^{5/3}}{(B+2y_o)^{2/3}}$$

Substituting the values of Q, n, S_o and B, one gets

$$0.0781 = y_o^{5/3} / (3.0 + 2\,y_o)^{2/3}$$

Solving this equation by trial and error, one gets

$$y_o = 0.581 \text{ m}$$

Example 13.3

For a channel section shown in the accompanying figure, determine the discharge in m^3/s if $S_o = 0.0004$ and n = 0.02.

The channel section is such that there is considerable variation in depth across the width. Therefore, it is inaccurate to determine the hydraulic radius R as total area divided by total perimeter. Instead it is more logical to divide the area into A_1, A_2 and A_3, and obtain R_1, R_2 and R_3. Then compute the discharge in each area and add them to get the total discharge Q.

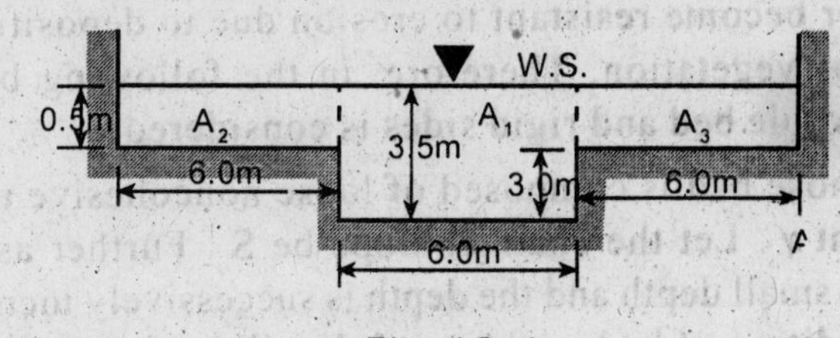

Fig 13.4

$\therefore$ $A_1 = 6 \times 3.5 = 21 \text{ m}^2$

$A_2 = A_3 = 6.0 \times 0.5 = 3.0 \text{ m}^2$

$$P_1 = (6.0 + 3.0 + 3.0) = 12.0 \text{ m}$$

$$P_2 = P_3 = 6 + 0.5 = 6.5 \text{ m}$$

$$\therefore \quad R_1 = \frac{21}{12} = 1.75 \text{ m}; \quad R_2 = R_3 = \frac{3.0}{6.5} = 0.461 \text{ m}$$

$$\therefore \quad Q_1 = \frac{1}{.02}(6 \times 3.50)(1.75)^{2/3}(0.0004)^{1/2}$$

$$= 30.50 \text{ m}^3/\text{s}$$

$$Q_2 = Q_3 = \frac{1}{.02}(3.0)(0.461)^{2/3}(0.0004)^{1/2}$$

$$= 1.79 \text{ m}^3/\text{s}$$

$$\therefore \quad Q = Q_1 + Q_2 + Q_3 = 30.50 + 1.79 + 1.79 = 34.08 \text{ m}^3/\text{s}$$

In order to get an idea about the inaccuracy involved in using the total area, let us find the discharge Q taking the entire section.

$$\therefore \quad A = 21.0 + 3.0 + 3.0 = 27.0 \text{ m}_2$$

$$P = 0.50 + 6.0 \times 3.0 + 6.0 + 3.0 + 6.0 + 0.50 = 25.0 \text{m}$$

$$\therefore \quad R = \frac{27}{25} = 1.01 \text{ m}$$

$$\therefore \quad Q = \frac{27}{0.02}(1.08)^{2/3}(0.0004)^{1/2} = 28.422 \text{ m}^3/\text{s}$$

Thus an error of 16.6% will be made in estimating Q if the area is not subdivided into nearly uniform sections.

13.3 Steady Uniform Flow in Alluvial channels

The flow in alluvial channel differs from that in rigid boundary open channels in that the sediment particles constituting the bed and sides of the former are capable of undergoing motion under certain flow conditions. The sediment in the range of sands usually has no cohesion. However, even if the banks are made of such loose noncohesive material in the beginning, the banks later become resistant to erosion due to deposition of fine material on it or due to growth of vegetation. Therefore, in the following brief discussion, an alluvial channel with movable bed and rigid sides is considered.

Consider a channel whose bed is composed of loose noncohesive material of uniform size d and specific weight γ_s. Let the channel slope be S_0. Further assume that uniform flow is established at very small depth and the depth is successively increased by increasing the discharge and the condition of bed is observed. It will be found that for small depths, the sediment particles on the bed do not move and the bed remains plane. This condition can be described as *plane bed without motion* and for all practical purposes its resistance can be predicted from the analysis presented in section 13.2. As the depth is increased.

the average shear stress acting on the bed, γRS_o, also increases. This causes an increased drag force on each particles. In fact the particles on the bed are subjected to (i) a drag force in the direction of flow, (ii) a lift force in the vertically upward direction, and (iii) the submerged weight of the particle acting downwards. When the resulting downward force multiplied by the static coefficient of friction is equal to drag on each particle, the particle just starts moving. This hydraulic condition is commonly known as the condition of *incipient motion*. From the analysis it can be shown that the condition of incipient motion can be expressed in the functional form as

$$\frac{\tau_{oc}}{(\gamma_s - \gamma)d} = f\left(\frac{u_{*c}d}{\nu}\right)$$

in which τ_{oc} is the critical shear stress at which the particles of diameter d and specific weight γ_s will just start moving in a liquid of specific weight γ and kinematic viscosity ν; also $u_{*c} = \sqrt{\tau_{oc}/\rho}$. The inclusion of $(u_{*c}d/\nu)$ can be appreciated if one recalls that the velocity at the level of particle on which the drag depends is a function of this parameter. This functional relationship has been evaluated by Shields and is shown in Fig. 13.5. This diagram is usually known as Shields' diagram. It can be seen that when $(u_{*c}d/\nu)$ is greater than 400, the sediment is of size greater than 4.0 mm and in such a case, $\tau_{oc}/(\gamma_s - \gamma)\, d = 0.056$. However for finer material, for given values of d, γ_s and ν, τ_{oc} can be determined from Fig. 13.5 only by trial and error procedure. This can be avoided if one forms a new dimensionless parameter by combining $[\tau_{oc}/(\gamma_s - \gamma)d]$ and $(u_{*c}d/\nu)$ which does not contain shear τ_{oc}. Thus,

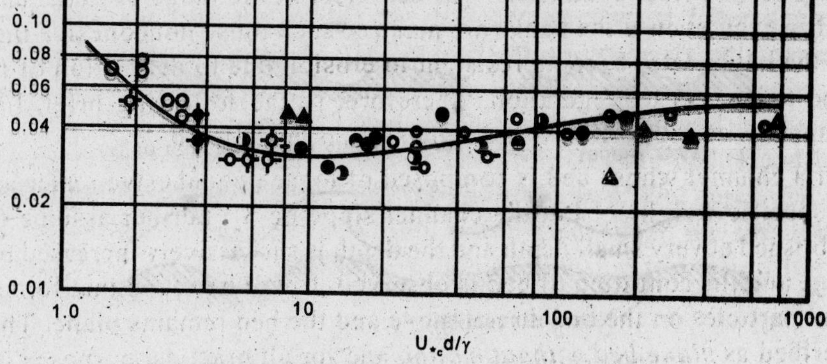

Fig. 13.5 Shields' diagram

$$\frac{(\gamma_s-\gamma)d}{\tau_{oc}}\,\frac{u_{*c}^2 d^2}{v^2}=\frac{d^3(\gamma_s-\gamma)}{\rho v^2}$$

Therefore from Shields' diagram one can prepare a graph between $\tau_{oc}/(\gamma_s - \gamma)d$ and $(\gamma_s - \gamma)d^3/\rho v^2$ which can be used to obtain critical shear stress directly for fine as well as coarse materials. Knowledge of critical shear stress is quite essential in problems related to scour, sediment transport and alluvial channel design. Recent studies by Yalin and Karahan, who have plotted additional data on shields' curve, indicate that the limiting value of $\tau_{oc}/(\gamma_s - \gamma)d$ at values of $u_{*c}d/v$ greater than 70 is 0.045.

If the average shear stress τ_o on the bed of an alluvial channel exceeds the critical shear stress τ_{oc} for the material forming the bed, the particles will start moving in the downstream direction. As a result, the bed no longer remains plane. In fact the bed and water surface can assume different configurations depending on the flow condition. These different bed and water surface configurations are called *regimes of flow*.

Once the shear stress slightly exceeds the critical shear stress, the bed is covered with unsymmetrical undulations which are small in size and three dimensional in nature. These are formed for relatively finer material and are called *ripples*. Further increase in shear stress (which can be effected by increasing discharge) causes ripples to grow in size. These are called *dunes*. With ripples on the bed, the water surface may be plane or choppy, but with dunes there is small depression over the crest and rise over the trough. The flow is also characterised by large eddies or boils caused by the separation on the downstream of each dune. When the shear is further increased, the dunes are flattened and elongated, and there is a tendency for the bed to become *plane*. Further increase in shear stress produces sinusuoidal waves on bed and water surface which may remain stationary or move slowly. They are known as *standing waves*. Slight increase in flow may cause these undulations to move slowly in the upstream direction; during this process their amplitude increases and they break. They are then called *antidunes*. These regimes are shown in Fig. 13.6.

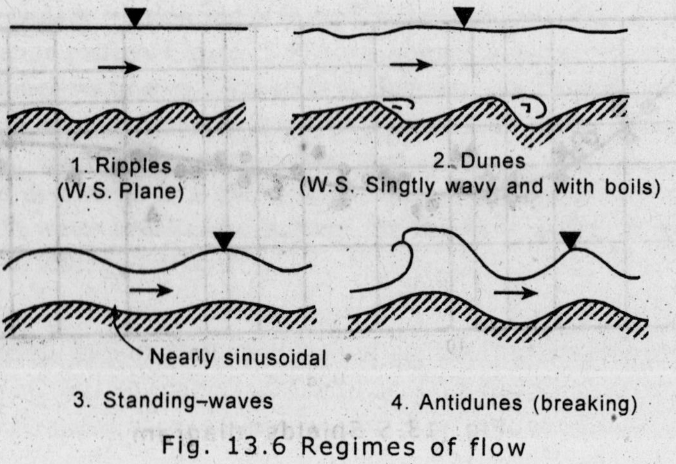

Fig. 13.6 Regimes of flow

Thus it can be seen that, as the discharge increases in a given channel, the bed and water surface undergo significant changes which must reflect in the variation in Manning's n or Chezy's C. That such is indeed the case can be seen from Fig. 13.7 in which the variation of n with $\tau_o/(\gamma_s - \gamma)d$ is shown for flume data. It can be seen that n may vary by as much as 300 percent. Therefore, in the study of uniform flow in alluvial channels, it becomes necessary to predict the regime of flow and resistance coefficient at different flow conditions.

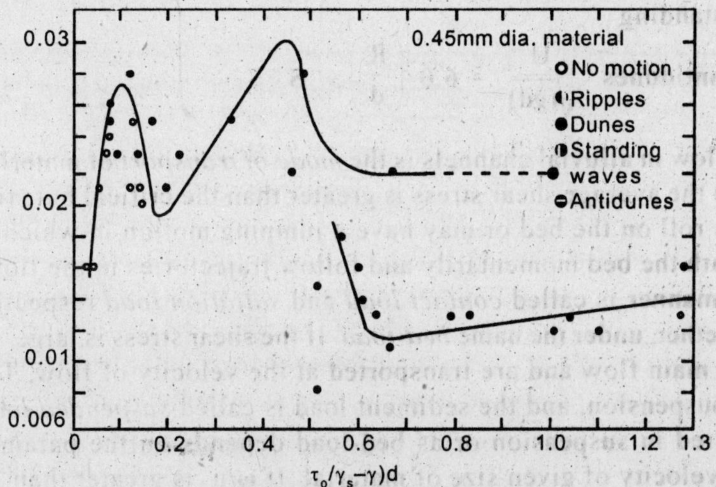

Fig. 13.7 Variation of n in alluvial channels

For a channel with a given slope and d, the depth at which sediment starts moving can be determined from Shields' diagram. Whether the flow will have ripple-dune regime or plan bed-standing wave regime or will have antidunes can be predicted from the following equations.

Ripples and dunes : $S_o < 0.014 \left(\frac{R}{d}\right)^{-0.45} \left(\frac{\gamma_s - \gamma}{\gamma}\right)$

Plane bed, standing waves : $0.014 \left(\frac{R}{d}\right)^{-0.45} \left(\frac{\gamma_s - \gamma}{\gamma}\right) < S_o < 0.066 \left(\frac{R}{d}\right)^{-0.55} \left(\frac{\gamma_s - \gamma}{\gamma}\right)$

Antidunes : $S_o > 0.066 \left(\frac{R}{d}\right)^{-0.55} \left(\frac{\gamma_s - \gamma}{\gamma}\right)$

The analysis of resistance to flow in alluvial channels is too involved to be discussed here. However it can be appreciated that when the regime of flow is either plane bed with transport or transition regime involving standing waves, n or C will be closer to rigid bed channels with grain roughness of size d. On the other hand in ripple and dune regimes, because of separation of flow behind each undulation, the form resistance will be appreciable and hence n will be much larger or C smaller. As a first approximation the following equations may be recommended

$$\left.\begin{array}{ll} \text{Ripples-dunes} & \dfrac{U}{\sqrt{(gd)}} = 6.50\left(\dfrac{R}{d}\right)^{0.50} S_o^{0.40} \\[2ex] \text{Plane bed, standing} & \\ \text{waves and antidunes} & \dfrac{U}{\sqrt{(gd)}} = 6.0\left(\dfrac{R}{d}\right)^{2/3} S_o^{1/2} \end{array}\right\} \quad (13.7)$$

Other aspect of flow in alluvial channels is the *mode of transport* of material dislodged from the bed. When the average shear stress is greater than the critical but still small, the individual particles roll on the bed or may have a jumping motion in which the particle may lose contact with the bed momentarily and follow trajectories in the flow. Sediment transported in this manner is called *contact load* and *saltation load* respectively, and is usually grouped together, under the name *bed-load.* If the shear stress is large, the particles are carried into the main flow and are transported at the velocity of flow. This mode of transport is called suspension, and the sediment load is called *suspended load.* Whether the material is carried in suspension or as bed-load depends on the parameter ω/u_* in which ω is the fall velocity of given size of material. If ω/u_* is greater than 2.0 and τ_o is greater than τ_{oc} the material is transported as bed-load. On the other hand if ω/u_* is less than 2.0 the sediment is transported in suspension.

There are several bed-load equations which can be used to estimate the bed-load transport rate. Among them mention can be made of the empirical equation proposed by Meyer-Peter and Müller, namely

$$\phi = 8\,(\tau_*' - 0.047)^{3/2} \quad (13.8)$$

in which $$\phi = \frac{q_B}{\gamma_S}\sqrt{\frac{\rho}{\rho_s-\rho}}\left(\frac{1}{gd_a^3}\right)^{1/2}$$

and $$\tau_*' = \frac{\tau_o}{(\gamma_s-\gamma)d_a}\left(\frac{n_s}{n}\right)^2$$

Here q_B is bed-load transport rate in wt/width/time, d_a is arithmetic mean diameter of bed material, n_s is Strickler's value of Manning's roughness coefficient and n is Manning's roughness coefficient for the flow. Strickler's n_s is obtained as

$$n_s = d_{90}^{1/6} / 26$$

where d_{90} in m is the size such that ninety percent of the material is finer than this size. In fact τ_*' is dimensionless shear corresponding to grain roughness, emphasising thereby that of the total shear τ_o on the bed, only a fraction of it is responsible for sediment transport as bed-load. Equation 13.8 also shows that when τ_*' is less than 0.047 there will be no bed-load transport, a fact supported by Yalin and Karahan's work.

The suspended material is maintained in suspension due to turbulence. If the material is extremely fine, it will be distributed almost uniformly in the vertical. However coarser material will have higher concentration near the bed and smaller near the water surface. The basic differential equation giving the distribution of suspended load in the vertical is

$$\omega C + \varepsilon_s \frac{\partial C}{\partial y} = 0$$

where C is the concentration of suspended sediment of fall velocity ω at a distance y above the bed and ε_s is sediment diffusion coefficient. Assuming that ε_s is equal to momentum transfer coefficient ε_m which can be determined from Karman-Prandtl analysis of velocity distribution in turbulent flow, the above equation can be integrated to yield

$$\frac{C}{C_a} = \left(\frac{D-y}{y} \frac{a}{D-a}\right)^{\omega/u_*K} \qquad (13.9)$$

in which C_a is the concentration at a given distance "a" above the bed, u_* is the shear velocity and K is Karman constant. If one knows C_a at a given distance "a" above the bed, Eq. 13.9 can be used to determine concentration at any other level. The total suspended load transported by the stream per unit width per unit time will be $\int Cu\,dy$. The integral can be evaluated knowing variation of C and u with y. The limits of integration are taken as 2d and D, since it is assumed that the bed-load will be transported in the layer of thickness 2d. It may be mentioned that value of K can be taken as 0.40.

13.4 Velocity Distribution in Open Channels

The velocity in an open channel is not uniformly distributed over the cross-section. This nonuniformity is due to the existence of free surface and fricitional resistance along the channel perimeter. In addition, the unusual shape of the channel and the presence of bends also cause non-uniformity in velocity profiles. As in the case of pipes, the velocity distribution in the vertical for turbulent flow in straight open channels is found to be logarithmic. A typical velocity distribution in a vertical is shown in Fig. 13.8. In a straight reach of the channel, the maximum velocity occurs at a distance of (0.05 to 0.25) times the depth below the free surface. The average velocity of flow over a cross-section can be computed from the measured velocity profiles at different verticals. It is observed that the velocity at a depth of 0.6 y_0 from the free surface is very close to mean velocity of flow in any vertical. A better method of obtaining the average velocity is by taking the mean of the velocities observed at 0.2 depth and at 0.8 depth from the free surface. The velocity distribution in open channels is usually measured either with the help of a current meter or with a Prandtl pitot tube.

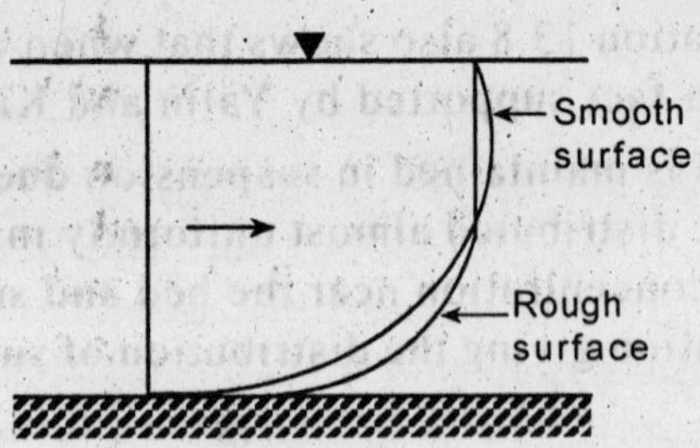

Fig. 13.8 Velocity distribution over smooth and rough surfaces

Keulegan has derived equations for average velocity for turbulent flow in open channels using Prandtl's velocity distribution laws. The equations obtained by Keulegan for the average velocity are,

$$\left.\begin{aligned} &\text{Smooth boundary} \quad \frac{U}{u_*} = \left(3.25 + 5.75 \log_{10} \frac{R u_*}{\nu}\right) \\ &\text{Rough boundary} \quad \frac{U}{u_*} = \left(6.25 + 5.75 \log_{10} \frac{R}{k}\right) \end{aligned}\right\} \qquad (13.10)$$

in which u_* is the shear velocity, R is the hydraulic radius and k is the equivalent sand grain roughness. The above equations were derived by Keulegan using Nikuradse's and Bazin's data. Similarity between Eqs. 13.10 (a) and (b) and Eq. 10.12, 10.13 (which are for turbulent flow in pipes) may be noted.

In very wide channels the velocity distribution in the major area of the cross-section is similar to that in a rectangular section of infinite width. In such channels the sides have very little effect on the flow. Furthermore, the hydraulic radius in such channels is very nearly equal to the depth or flow. In channels which are not sufficiently wide and in channels with irregular shape, the velocity is not uniformly distributed over the cross-section. This is mainly due to boundary friction and effect of channel shape which generates and modifies secondary circulation pattern. Figure 13.9 shows lines of constant velocity, commonly known is *isovels* for channel-section on Tisza river in Hungary. Noteworthy is the concentration of isovels at places where channel shape has acute curvature. Such detailed velocity measurements are taken by current meter and then graphically integrated over cross-section to determine the discharge at a given stage. From such measurements a curve can be prepared between water level and discharge for the river at the section. Such a curve is known as stage-discharge curve.

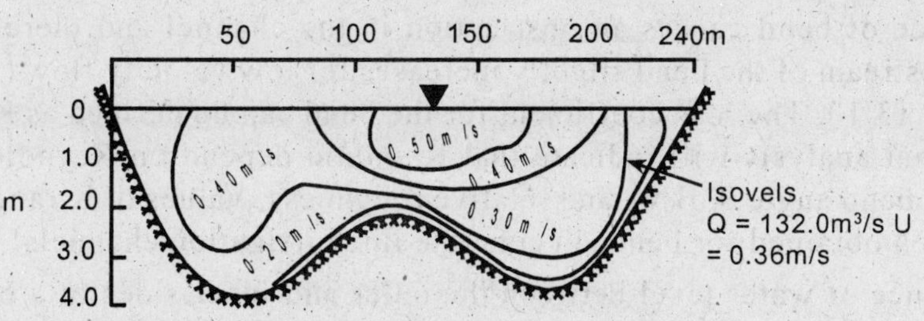

Fig. 13.9 Isovels in a natural stream

Since the velocity distribution in the vertical is not uniform, one has to apply correction factors while computing the energy and the momentum. If the actual velocity profile is known, the energy and the momentum correction factors can be computed. Experiments have indicated that for turbulent flow in prismatic channel the energy correction factor α varies from 1.03 to 1.36 and the momentum correction factor β varies from 1.01 to 1.12. It may be mentioned that the higher values of α and β correspond to narrow channels. Approximate values of α and β can be found from the following equation,

$$\left.\begin{aligned} \alpha &= 1 + 3\varepsilon^2 - 2\varepsilon^3 \\ \beta &= 1 + \varepsilon^2 \end{aligned}\right\}$$

in which $\varepsilon = (u_{max}/U) - 1$. Here u_{max} is the maximum velocity and U is the average velocity in any vertical. These expressions for α and β have been obtained on the basis of logarithmic velocity distribution laws. For the sake of simplicity α and β are assumed to be unity unless the problem calls for an accurate evaluation of energy and momentum fluxes.

The presence of bends in open channels complicates the flow pattern as well as the velocity distribution. Bends are required to be introduced in open channel alignments to negotiate natural obstructions in the way of the channel. Since the streamlines for flow in a bend are curved in plan, there is normal acceleration directed towards the centre of the bend. To have such an acceleration a resultant force must act in that direction which is provided by rise of water surface on the outside of the bend, see Fig. 13.10. The normal acceleration together with the velocity variation in vertical caused by effect of viscocity, make the fast moving surface layers shift towards the outer bank while the slow moving bottom layers go towards the inner bank. This sets the secondary or spiral flow as shown in the figure. For such a flow to develop a certain minimum distance from the beginning of the bend is necessary . Therefore if the bend is quite short, such a spiral motion cannot be developed fully; in such a case smaller velocities will prevail near outer bank and higher near inner bank as in the case of free vortex motion. However in a longer bend the velocity distribution approximating forced vortex motion will prevail. Other characteristic of flow in a bend is the separation zone near the inner bank; the extent of this zone increases as r_c/B decreases. Here r_c is center line radius of the bend.

The presence of bend causes an obstruction in the channel and therefore the water level on the upstream of the bend slightly increases for low velocity flow (i.e. subcritical flow), see Fig. 13.10. The loss coefficient for the bend can be defined as $K = h_L/(U^2/2g)$. The dimensional analysis will indicate that K should depend on Reynolds and Froude numbers, r_c/B, bend angle θ, B/y_o, and relative roughness. Values of K ranging from 0.50 to 0.1 have been obtained for bends in concrete lined irrigation channels.

The difference of water level between the outer and inner sides of a bend is usually known as *superelevation.* The expression for superelevation can be obtained by application of Euler's equation of motion in the radial direction viz.

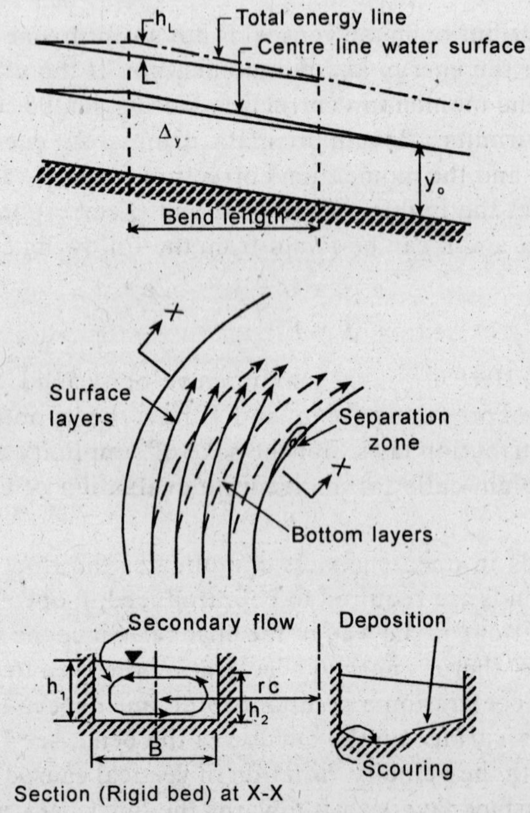

Fig. 13.10 Flow around a bend in an open channel

$$\frac{\partial p}{\partial r} = \frac{\rho U_1^2}{r}$$

where U_1 is the average velocity in the vertical at a radial distance r. Substitution of $p = \gamma h$ and subsequent integration yields

$$(h_2 - h_1) = \int_{r_1}^{r_0} \frac{U_1^2}{gr} dr$$

where r_i and r_o are the inner and outer radii of the bend. Assuming a velocity distribution law $U_1 = f(r)$, one can get an expression for superelevation $(h_2 - h_1)$. The following expression is found to give reasonably accurate results,

$$(h_2 - h_1) = \frac{B}{r_c}\left[\frac{1}{1+\frac{B^2}{12r_c^2}}\right]\frac{U^2}{g} \qquad (13.11)$$

Here U is the average velocity in the channel. In the case of an alluvial bend, the bed material moves towards the inner bank because of the direction of secondary flow near the bed. As a result there is scour near the outer bank and deposition near the inner bank. The superelevation in alluvial channel bends is somewhat smaller than that in rigid boundary bend for other conditions remaining the same.

13.5 Channel of Efficient Cross-Secion

A channel section is known as efficient when it can pass a maximum discharge for given values of cross-sectional area, resistance coefficient or Manning's n and slope. It can be seen from Chezy's or Manning's equation that the velocity of flow will be maximum when the hydraulic radius is maximum or wetted perimeter is minimum. At places where the channel excavation costs are very high, it is desirable to adopt channels of efficient cross section in order to keep the construction and excavation costs low.

The dimensions of an economical section can be obtained for trapezoidal channel of bed width B and side inclination θ. If the water depth in the channel is y (see Fig. 13.11), the following relations for area A and wetted perimeter P can be written.

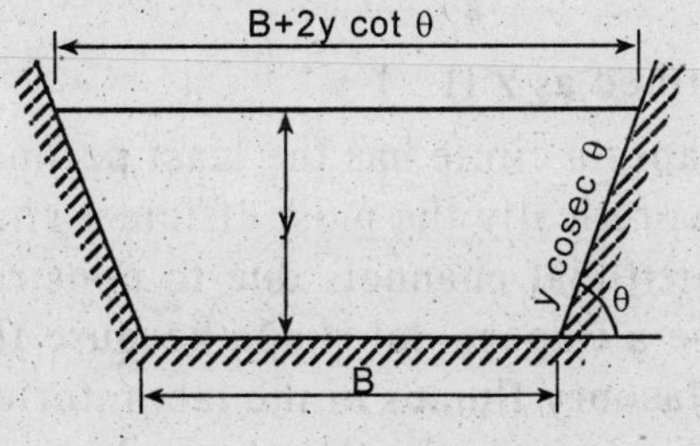

Fig. 13.11 Definition sketch

$$A = B\,y + y^2 \cot\theta$$

$$P = B + 2\,y \operatorname{cosec}\theta$$

The first equation can be solved for bed width B to obtain

$$B = \frac{A}{y} - y\cot\theta$$

and the wetted perimeter P can be expressed as a function of A, y and θ as

$$P = \frac{A}{y} - y \cot \theta + 2y \operatorname{cosec} \theta$$

Assuming the area A and angle θ to be constant, the wetted perimeter equation can b differentiated with respect to y and equated to zero for obtaining condition of minimum I

$$\frac{dP}{dy} = -\frac{A}{y^2} - \cot \theta + 2 \operatorname{cosec} \theta = 0$$

or

$$A = y^2 (2 \operatorname{cosec} \theta - \cot \theta)$$

The perimeter and hydraulic radius R can then be computed as

$$P = y (2\operatorname{cosec} \theta - \cot\theta) - y \cot \theta + 2y \operatorname{cosec} \theta = 2y (2 \operatorname{cosec}\theta - \cot\theta)$$

and

$$R = \frac{A}{P} = \frac{y^2(2\operatorname{cosec}\theta - \cot\theta)}{2y(2\operatorname{cosec}\theta - \cot\theta)} = \frac{y}{2}$$

Thus it can be seen that for a trapezoidal channel to be most efficient it is necessar that hydraulic radius R is equal to half the depth of flow. Rectangular channel is a specia case of trapezoidal channel when the angle θ is 90° and it can be found that in an efficier rectangular channel the flow depth will be half the bed width B in addition to the hydrauli radius R being half of flow depth.

In a similar manner, the optimum inclination of the sides can be obtained as 60° for given area and flow depth. On the other hand, if area and bottom width are constant, most efficient section is obtained when

$$A = \frac{y^2}{z}$$

where z is the side slope defined as z H : 1 V

Of all the geometrical shapes a circle has the least perimeter for a given area. Henc a semicircular channel is theoretically the most efficient channel; but this shape cannc be commonly adopted for artificial channels due to construction difficulties. Channe excavated in earth must have a trapezoidal shape because the earthen sides will not b stable if they are vertical. Masonry flumes in the laboratories carrying small discharge can be made rectangular in shape. Semicircular channels can be either of some metal lik steel, cast iron or reinforced concrete.

Example 13.4

Determine the efficient section of a trapezoidal canal to carry 12.75 m³/s of water a velocity of 1.0 m/s. The channel sides have a slope of 2 H : 1 V. Find the necessary be slope for the canal if the roughness coefficient has a value of 0.025.

For economical section

$$R = \frac{A}{P} = \frac{By + 2y^2}{B + 2y\sqrt{5}} = \frac{y}{2}$$

From this one gets $B = 2y\sqrt{5} - 4y$

Since the velocity is given as 1.0 m/s, the area A will be 12.75 m².

Or $By + 2y^2 = 12.75$

$$B = \frac{12.75 - 2y^2}{y}$$

Equating the two expressions for B one gets

$$2y\sqrt{5} - 4y = \frac{12.75 - 2y^2}{y}$$

Solving for y one gets y = 2.265 m

$$\therefore \quad B = \frac{12.75 - 2(2.265)^2}{2.265} = 1.09 \text{ m}$$

Design the canal with B = 1.09 m and y = 2.265 m.

The bed slope required can be found from the Manning's formula as,

$$1.00 = \frac{1}{0.025}\left\{\frac{2.265}{2}\right\}^{2/3} S_o^{1/2}$$

or $S_o = 0.00053$

3.6 Specific Energy and Critical Depth

t was mentioned earlier that free surface in the case of open channel flow represents he hydraulic gradient. Bernoulli's equation for uniform flow can be written as,

$$\left(\frac{U^2}{2g} + y + z\right)_1 = \left(\frac{U^2}{2g} + y + z\right)_2 + h_f$$

n which h_f is the energy loss in a certain distance *l* under consideration. It is assumed hat the energy correction factor α is unity and that the pressure variation in the vertical s hydrostatic. The term ($U^2/2g + y + z$) represents the total energy per unit weight of the luid. Many problems in open channel flow can be solved by considering the energy with he channel bed as the datum, which is known as *specific energy* or *specific head*. The oncept of specific energy, which was first introduced by Bakhmeteff in 1918, has proved ery useful for open channel flow problems. Specific energy H at any section is the sum f the depth of flow at that section and the velocity head; or

$$H = \frac{U^2}{2g} + y = \frac{Q^2}{2gA^2} + y \tag{13.12}$$

ince U = Q/A. Equation 13.12 indicates that for a given discharge the specific energy is function of depth of flow alone. For a given discharge when the specific energy H is plotted against the depth of flow y (using same scale for both) a very useful diagram is obtained which is known as *specific energy diagram* (see Fig. 13.12). At any point on the curve, the ordinate represents the depth of flow while the abscissa indicates the specific energy which is the sum of the depth of flow and the velocity head. The curve has two limbs, the lower limb becomes asymptotic to the specific head axis while the upper limb becomes asymptotic to a 45° line through origin along which the depth of flow is equal to the specific head. It can be seen from Fig. 13.12 that there is one point on the curve which has a minimum specific energy. The depth at which the specific energy is minimum for a given Q is called *critical depth* y_c. For any other value of the specific energy, there are two possible depths, one greater than the critical depth and the other smaller than the critical depth. These two depths at a given specific energy are called the *alternate depths*. For depths of flow greater than the critical depth, the specific energy increases with the increase in depth, and for depths smaller than the critical depth, the specific energy increases with decrease in depth. The condition of flow above the critical depth is known as *subcritical* or *tranquil* and that below the critical depth it is known as *supercritical or rapid*.

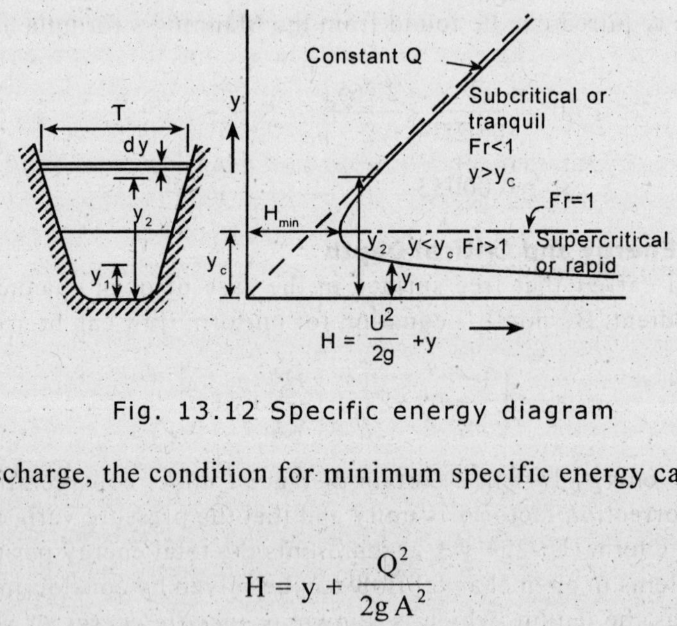

Fig. 13.12 Specific energy diagram

For a given discharge, the condition for minimum specific energy can be obtained as follows :

Since
$$H = y + \frac{Q^2}{2g A^2}$$

and Q is constant,

$$\frac{dH}{dy} = 1 - \frac{Q^2}{g A^3} \frac{dA}{dy}$$

This must be zero for H to be a minimum. Hence

$$\frac{dA}{dy} = \left(\frac{g A^3}{Q^2}\right)_{\text{critical}}$$

In the channel section if T is the top width of flow then

$$dA = T\,dy \quad \text{or} \quad \frac{dA}{dy} = T \qquad \text{(Fig. 13.12)}$$

With this value of dA/dy, the above equation can be written as.

$$\frac{Q^2}{g} = \left(\frac{A^3}{T}\right)_{critical} \qquad (13.13)$$

Thus in a prismatic channel carrying a given discharge Q, the area A and the top width T satisfy Eq. 13.13 when the flow is critical.

A rectangular channel is a simplified case of the prismatic channel discussed above, in which the top width T and bed width B are equal and the area A is By. Using the discharge per unit width q, Eq. 13.13 can be written as,

$$\frac{q^2 B^2}{g} = \frac{B^3 y_c^3}{B}$$

or

$$\frac{q^2}{g} = y_c^{\,3} \qquad (13.14)$$

It may be noted that y_c has been used instead of y since Eq. 13.14 indicates critical condition in rectangular channel. Equation 13.14 can also be written as,

$$y_c = \sqrt[3]{q^2/g} \qquad (13.15)$$

Equation 13.15 is important in the study of critical flow in rectangular channels as one can determine the critical depth y_c directly if the discharge per unit width is known. Equation 13.13 yields another important relation if it is rearranged as

$$\frac{Q^2}{A^2}\,\frac{1}{g}\,\frac{T}{A} = 1$$

Defining A/T as the *hydraulic mean depth* D, one can write the above relation as

$$\left(\frac{U^2}{gD}\right)_c = 1 \qquad (13.16)$$

since Q/A = U. This equation for, rectangular channels is

$$Fr = \left(\frac{U}{\sqrt{gy}}\right)_c = 1 \qquad (13.17)$$

in which Fr is the Froude number. It may thus be noted that at critical flow, Froude number is unity. It follows that for subcritical or tranquil flow for which y is greater than y_c, Froude number is less than unity and for supercritical or rapid flow for which y is less than y_c, Fr is greater than unity. These conditions have also been indicated in Fig. 13.12.

Up till now the conditions for variation of specific energy for a given discharge have been considered. These can occur in channels if the discharge per unit width is maintained constant and the channel bed is raised or lowered. On the contrary, if the specific head is kept constant and the discharge q is changed, one can investigate the optimum conditions for a maximum discharge. A situation of this type may occur in portions of channels where the bed width is decreased whereby the discharge per unit width is increased. For a rectangular channel, the specific energy equation (Eq. 13.12) can be written as,

$$H = y + \frac{q^2}{2g\,y^2} \tag{13.18}$$

Rearranging Eq. 13.18, and solving for q one gets,

$$q = \sqrt{2g(y^2H - y^3)} \qquad (13.18\ a)$$

For a given specific head H, the condition for the discharge q to be maximum is obtained by setting dq/dy = 0. Hence

$$\frac{dq}{dy} = \frac{\sqrt{2g}}{2}\ \frac{(2yH - 3y^2)}{\sqrt{(y^2H - y^3)}} = 0$$

or

$$H = \frac{3}{2}\,y \tag{13.19}$$

Substitution of Eq. 13.19 in Eq. 13.18 yields $q^2/g = y^3$ indicating that for maximum q for a constant H the conditions of critical flow will be obtained. Equation 13.19 can be written using y_c instead of y in the following two forms for the condition of constant H,

$$\left.\begin{aligned} H &= \frac{3}{2}\,y_c \\ \text{or} \qquad y_c &= \frac{2}{3}\,H \end{aligned}\right\} \tag{13.20}$$

An analysis similar to that given in Eqs. 13.18 to 13.19 can be performed for nonrectangular channels and it can be shown that for given specific energy, Q will be maximum when $U^2/gD = 1$ i.e. when flow is critical.

A relation between q and y for a given H can be plotted using Eq. 13.18 (a). This is shown in Fig. 13.13 and is known *as discharge diagram.* Similar to Fig. 13.1.2 it can be seen that in the diagram in Fig. 13.13 there are two values of y for a certain q as along as q is less than q_{max} at which there is a unique value of y. It is evident that this unique value of depth at maximum q is the critical depth y_c. For depths smaller than y_c the flow is supercritical while for depths greater than y_c the flow is subcritical.

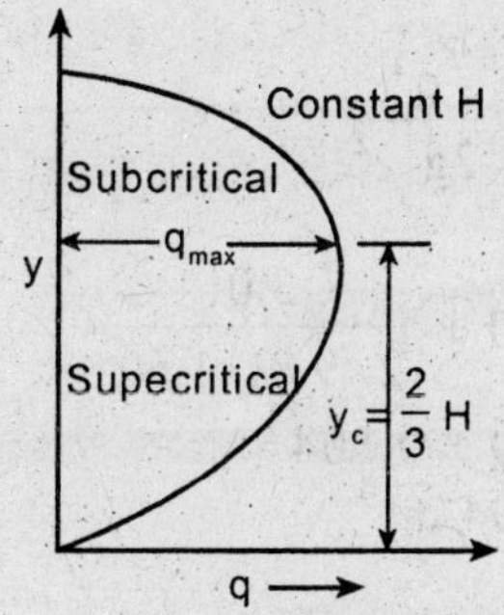

Fig. 13.13 Discharge diagram

Example 13.5

A trapezoidal channel has a bottom width of 6.0 m and side slopes of 1:1. If the depth of flow is 1.5 m at a discharge of 15.0 m³/s, determine the specific energy and the critical depth

$$A = (6.0 + 1.50) \times 1.50 = 11.25 \text{ m}^2$$

$$H = y + \frac{1}{2g}\left(\frac{Q}{A}\right)^2$$

$$= 1.5 + \frac{1}{2\times 9.81}\frac{(15)^2}{(11.25)^2} = 1.591 \text{ m}$$

For critical conditions,

$$\frac{Q^2}{g} = \frac{A^3}{T} = \frac{(6y_c + y_c^2)^3}{6+2y_c}$$

$$\frac{15^2}{9.81} = \frac{(6y_c + y_c^2)^3}{(6+2y_c)}$$

Solving by trial and error one gets $y_c = 0.818$ m

Since the depth of flow is greater than 0.818 m, the flow is subcritical.

Example 13.6

A 5.0 m wide rectangular channel carries 15.0 m³/s discharge at a depth of 1.5 m. (i) What is the critical depth ? (ii) What is the specific energy ? (iii) Is the flow subcritical or supercritical ? (iv) What is the depth alternate to 1.5 m ?

$$q = \frac{Q}{B} = \frac{15.0}{5.0} = 3.0 \text{ m}^3\text{/s m}$$

or $$y_c = \sqrt[3]{\frac{q^2}{g}} = \sqrt[3]{\frac{9.0}{9.81}} = 0.972 \text{ m}$$

$$H = y + \frac{q^2}{2g\,y^2}$$

$$= 1.50 + \frac{3.0^2}{2\times 9.81\times 1.50^2}$$

$$= 1.50 + 0.204$$

$$= 1.704 \text{ m}$$

Since $$F_r = \frac{U}{\sqrt{gy}} = \frac{q}{y\sqrt{gy}}$$

$$= \frac{3.0}{1.5\times\sqrt{9.81\times 1.50}}$$

$$\doteq 0.521$$

Hence the flow is subcritical

For the depth of 1.5 m the specific energy is 1.704 m. Hence

$$1.704 = y + \frac{q^2}{2g\,y^2}$$

$$\therefore \quad 1.704 = y + \frac{0.459}{y^2}$$

The solution of this equation when $y < 0.972$ m is needed. By trial and error the alternate depth comes out to be 0.665m.

Broad-Crested Weir

Specific energy concept finds application in the analysis of flow over a broad-crested weir. Broad-crested weir is an overflow structure with a horizontal crest over which the stream lines can be assumed to be straight and parallel to weir crest. Figure 13.14 shows a suppressed broad-crested weir. It is used as a flow measuring device in open channels; some times it is also used to control the hydraulic jump by maintaing a certain depth upstream of it. Its length in the direction of flow L, is usually such that $2 \le L/H_1 \le 12.5$, where H_1 is the specific energy upstream of the weir with weir crest as the datum. If the length L is greater than 12.5 H_1, the friction along the weir length cannot be neglected. On the other hand if it is less than $2H_1$, the stream lines may be curved on the weir and therefore pressure distribution there will not be hydrostatic. Considering that for given flow conditions on the upstream, the height of the weir W is such that critical flow prevails on the crest, one can get the discharge equation for the weir as follows.

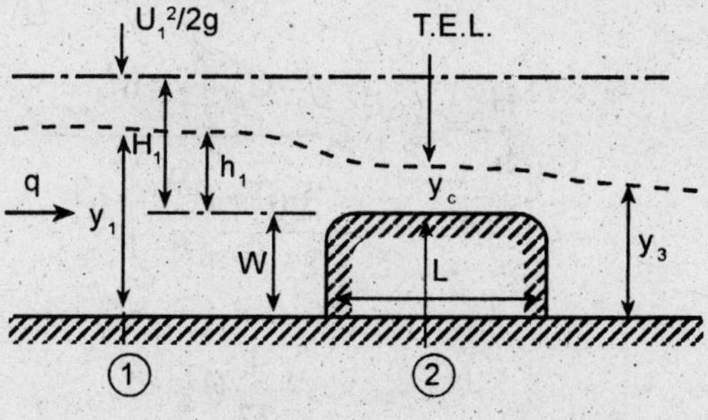

Fig. 13.14 Broad crested weir

Assume the velocity distribution to be uniform and the pressure distribution to be hydrostatic at sections 1 and 2; further assume that, the flow being converging, and sections 1 and 2 being sufficiently close, the energy loss between the two sections is negligible. Hence one can write

$$y_1 + \frac{U_1^2}{2g} = W + y_c + \frac{U_c^2}{2g}$$

or

$$H_1 = y_c + \frac{U_c^2}{2g}$$

$\therefore$

$$U_c = \sqrt{2g(H_1 - y_c)}$$

and

$$q = y_c U_c = y_c \sqrt{2g(H_1 - y_c)}$$

Since $y_c = 2/3\ H_1$, the above becomes

$$q = \frac{2}{3}\sqrt{\frac{2}{3}g}\ H_1^{3/2}$$

or

$$Q = \frac{2}{3}\sqrt{\frac{2}{3}g}\ B\ H_1^{3/2} \qquad (13.21)$$

in which B is the width of weir, It is convenient to write Eq. 13.21 in terms of h_1 instead of H_1. In fact if one writes

$$Q = \frac{2}{3} C_d B \sqrt{\frac{2}{3}g}\ h_1^{3/2}$$

then $C_d = (H_1/h_1)^{3/2}$. However

H_1/h_1 can be written as

$$H_1 = h_1 + \frac{Q^2}{2g\,B^2\,(h_1 + W)^2}$$

$$\frac{H_1}{h_1} = 1 + \frac{C_d^2 \frac{8}{27} g h_1^3}{2g\left(1+\frac{W}{h_1}\right)^2 h_1^3}$$

$$= 1 + \frac{\frac{4}{27} C_d^2}{\left(1+\frac{W}{h_1}\right)^2}$$

$$\therefore \quad C_d = \left(\frac{H_1}{h_1}\right)^{3/2} = \left[1+\frac{\frac{4}{27} C_d^2}{\left(1+\frac{W}{h_1}\right)^2}\right]^{3/2}$$

When the velocity of approach is small, the above equation gives C_d values close to unity. It may be mentioned that the analysis presented above does not take into account the effects of surface tension and viscosity on the discharge coefficient. However these effects, are of secondary importance in most of the practical cases.

If the downstream depth is small, it will not affect the flow over the broad-crested weir and the above equations will be applicable. Such free flow condition can be assumed to exist if $(y_3 - W)$ is less than 0.80 h_1.

13.7 Open Channel Transitions

A channel transition is a structure with varying cross section which connects two open channels (which may or may not have the same shape) having uniform flow. Various types of transitions are used in practice, some of which are

1. a transition from a wider to a narrower channel,
2. a gradual rise in the bed of a prismatic channel,
3. combination of the above two,
4. a transition from a narrower channel to a wider channel,
5. a gradual depression in the bed of a prismatic channel; and
6. a gradual contraction followed by a gradual expansion in a prismatic channel.

Of these six types, the first three types of transitions can be easily analysed with the help of the specific energy diagram and the discharge diagram. The assumption is made in such a case that, since transition is of contracting type and its length is small, there is no energy loss.

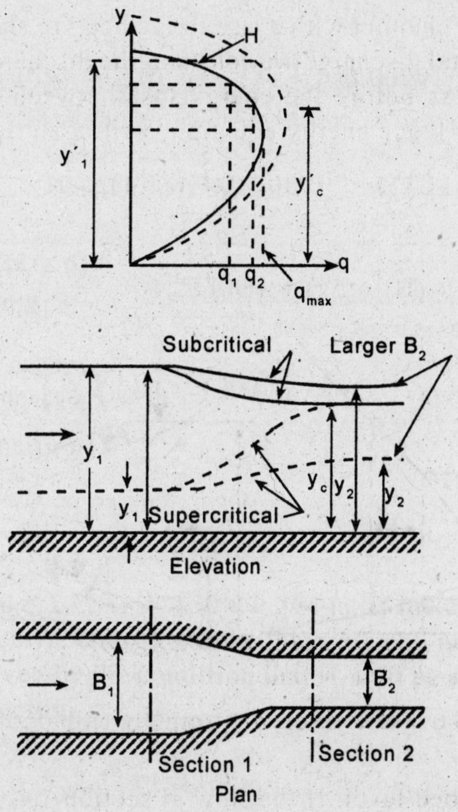

Fig. 13.15 Transition with reduction in channel width

Consider a rectangular channel in which only the width is reduced, see Fig. 13.15. Since the flow is converging between sections 1 and 2, it can be assumed that no energy loss takes place between these sections. In addition, since there is no change in the channel bed elevation, the specific energy can be assumed to be constant and only the discharge per unit width is changing. Fig. 13.15 shows flow in a contracting channel, in which the effect of channel width at the contracted section, and the nature of flow (subcritical or supercritical) at the upstream section on the flow are illustrated. When the depth y_1 is greater than y_c, the reduction in channel width causes an increase in the unit discharge and hence the depth at section 2 becomes smaller than y_1 but is greater than y_c. If B_2 is reduced further, q_2 increases and y_2 decreases. If the reduction of width B_2 is continued, a condition can be reached when $q_2 = q_{max}$ and y_2 equals y_c. If width at section 2 is reduced further, q_2 becomes greater than q_{max} for given H, and hence the flow cannot take place through the contraction unless upstream depth is increased to y_1' and H to H′. The discharge diagram for specific energy H′ is shown by the dotted line. With this energy H′ the flow at section 2 will be critical. If the flow at section 1 is supercritical, the depth y_2 will be greater than y_1 but less than y_C. If the width B_2 is reduced further, the depth at section 2 can become critical. Any further reduction in B_2 causes radical changes in flow at the upstream section.

The flow conditions in a channel with a rise in the bed are shown in Fig. 13.16. Since the channel width and the total discharge are constant, the discharge per unit width remains the same at two sections. As before the energy loss between the two sections can be neglected since it is small. Hence energy equation, written between two sections, yields

$$\frac{q^2}{2g y_1^2} + y_1 = \frac{q^2}{2g y_2^2} + y_2 + \Delta z$$

or $$(H_1 - \Delta z) = H_2$$

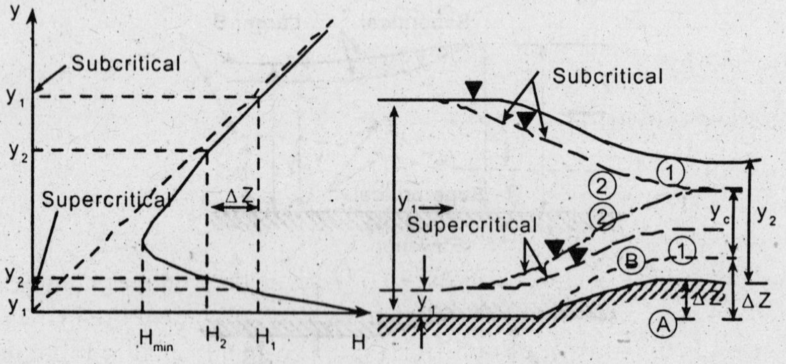

Fig. 13.16 Flow over a hump in the channel bed

where Δz is the rise in the bed level. If the flow at section 1 is subcritical with specific energy H_1, one can find $H_2 = (H_1 - \Delta z)$ and determine the subcritical depth y_2 corresponding to this H_2. It will be found that the depth y_2 is less than y_1. As Δz is increased, y_2 will decrease and when $(H_1 - \Delta z) = H_{min}$, the depth at section 2 will be critical. Any further increase in Δz will make $(H_1 - \Delta z)$ to be less than H_{min} and hence the flow cannot take place without altering the depth at section 1. As a result the depth at section 1 will increase to y_1' such that it gives the specific energy H_1' greater than H_1 and $(H_1' - \Delta z) = H_{min}$. Therefore the depth at section 2 will be critical.

If the depth at section 1 is supercritical, the water surface on the hump will show a rise; but the depth will be less than critical depth. As Δz is increased, y_2 will approach y_c. If Δz is such that $(H_1 - \Delta z)$ is less than H_{min}, the flow cannot take place with the given upstream conditions. In such a case there are radical changes in the character of flow at section 1 which includes formation of hydraulic jump.

Example 13.7

Uniform flow occurs in a 5.0 m wide rectangular channel at a depth 2.0 m. The channel is concrete lined (n = 0.015) and is laid at a bed slope of 0.0009. Calculate how much rise must be provided in the channel bed in order to obtain critical flow. In case critical depth is to be obtained without rise in the channel bed, what width in the transition will have to be provided ?

$$Q = \frac{1}{0.015}\,(5.0\ \times 2.0)\left\{\frac{5.0\times2.0}{9.0}\right\}^{\frac{2}{3}}\ (0.0009)^{1/2}$$

$$= \frac{1}{0.015}\times 10\times(1.11)^{2/3}\,(0.0009)^{1/2} = 21.11\ m^3/s$$

$$y_c = \sqrt[3]{\frac{(21.44/5.0)^2}{9.81}} = 1.233\ m$$

Minimum specific energy $= \frac{2}{3}\times 1.233 = 1.850$ m

Specific energy before transition

$$H_1 = 2 + \left(\frac{21.44}{2\times5}\right)^2\frac{1}{2\times9.81} = 2.234\ m$$

Rise which can be provided = 2.234 – 1.850 = 0.384 m. If the channel is to be contracted without rise in bed, the specific energy will be the same and hence the critical depth for the contracted section is given by the condition that H_1 will be equal to minimum specific energy in the contracted section.

$$y_c = \frac{2}{3}\times 2.234 = 1.49\ m$$

$$2.234 = 1.49\ + \left(\frac{21.44}{B_2\times1.49}\right)^2\frac{1}{2\times9.81}$$

$$B_2 = 3.75\ m$$

Example 13.8

In a 3.5 m wide rectangular channel, water flows at a depth of 2.0 m and a velocity of 2.5 m/s. If the channel width is reduced to 2.2 m and the bottom elevation is raised by 30 cm at a given section, to what extent will the surface elevation be affected by this change?

$$Q\ = UA = 2.5\times3.5\times2.0 = 17.5\ m^3/s$$

$$F_r = \frac{U}{\sqrt{gy}} = \frac{2.5}{\sqrt{9.81\times2.0}} = 0.565$$

Therefore, there will be a drop in water surface in the contracted portion. If q_2 is the discharge per unit width in the contracted portion,

$$q_2 = \frac{17.5}{2.2} = 7.95\ m^3/s\ m$$

$$\therefore \qquad y_c = \left[\frac{(7.95)^2}{9.81}\right]^{1/3} = 1.86 \text{ m}$$

and
$$H_{min} = \frac{3}{2} \times 1.86 = 2.79 \text{ m}$$

$$H_1 = 2 + \frac{2.5^2}{2 \times 9.81} = 2.318 \text{ m}$$

As the H in the channel before transition is 2.318 m which is less than 2.79 m, the contraction will cause a rise in water surface on the upstream side. The readjustment in flow will be such that, in the contracted portion the depth will be critical and specific energy minimum. Thus for obtaining the depth of flow on the upstream side, one can write the values of the total energies in the channel and the contraction as.

$$y_1 + \frac{(17.5)^2}{(3.5 \times y_1)^2 \, 2g} = 2.79 + 0.30$$

or
$$y_1^3 - 3.09 y_1^2 + 4.44 = 0$$

Solving by trial $\qquad y_1 = 2.275$ m

The water surface will rise by 27.5 cm in the channel.

The analysis of expanding transitions with subcritical flow is not so straight forward as that of contracting transitions. However certain basic considerations can be discussed. Consider an expanding transition in a rectangular channel, see Fig. 13.17. For given widths B_1 and B_2, there is bound to be separation of the flow unless a fairly long transition length is provided. Provision of such a long transition (i.e. small angle of divergence θ) leads to an uneconomic design of transition. Inadequate length and/or improper shape of boundary can lead to separation of flow and consequent increased loss of energy, nonuniform and many times unsymmetric velocity distribution across the width at the downstream end of transition, and greater scour in the down-stream channel if it is unlined. In an expanding transition, because of conversion of kinetic energy to potential energy, the water surface has a tendency to rise unless it is supressed by change in bed profile. It is desirable to have a gradual and uniform rise in the water surface.

These objective can be achieved by providing a transition of adequate length, equal to the length of separating stream line and conforming to the shape of separating stream line. The length of such a transition should be $2L/(B_2 - B_1)$ equal to 6 to 8. This length can be reduced to 6.0 by providing roughness at the sides and bottom near the entrance to the transition. The roughness helps in creating larger eddies at the boundary of diffusing jet which helps in the rapid expansion of the latter. In practice $2L/(B_2 - B_1)$ equal to 4.0 is many times used. The equation of separating stream line is given in Fig. 13.17. In order to reduce the transition length and to avoid separation, guide vanes or baffle blocks are also used in some cases.

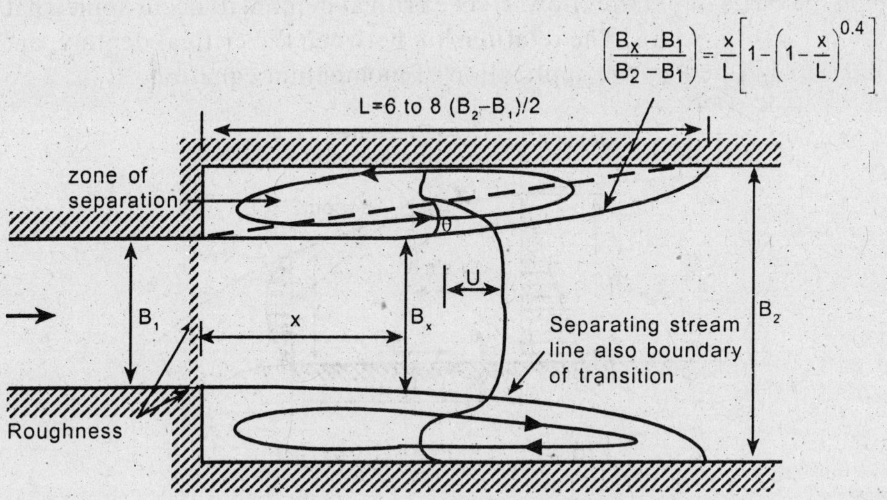

Fig. 13.17 Expanding transition

The energy loss in a sudden expansion in a horizontal rectangular open channel can be obtained by using energy and momentum equations and assuming that the boundary friction is negligible. The resulting expression for head loss h_L is

$$h_L = \frac{U_1^2}{2g}(1 - B_1/B_2)^2 \left[1 + \frac{2\,Fr_1^2 (B_1/B_2)^3}{(1 - B_1/B_2)}\right] \qquad (13.22)$$

which can be approximated to

$$h_L = \frac{U_1^2}{2g}(1 - B_1/B_2)^2$$

for F_{r1} less than 0.5 and B_1/B_2 less than 0.60.

13.8 Free Overfall

Figure 13.18 shows the essential features of a free overfall i.e. a channel followed by a sudden drop. This case is important from basic considerations as well as from practical point of view. As the flow approaches the sudden drop or brink, it is rapidly varying and is characterised by appreciable curvature of stream lines, therefore the pressure distribution in the vicinity of the drop is non-hydrostatic. This type of flow occurs in drop structures used in Irrigation engineering and understanding the basic characteristics of flow is essential for their design. Lastly, such an overfall acts as a control section and has a unique relationship between the discharge and depth at the overfall; hence it can be used as a flow measuring device.

As the flow approaches the end of the channel, the depth decreases and at the brink the depth should be such that the specific energy is minimum, that is the critical depth should prevail. However, it has been found that the brink depth is less than the critical depth. This can be explained from the fact that the flow being characterised by appreciable curvature, the actual specific energy at the brink is different from the specific energy computed on the basis of parallel flow. Hence critical depth will occur somewhat upstream, say at section 1 in Fig. 13.18. The relationship between the critical depth y_c and the brink depth y_b can be obtained by the application of momentum equation.

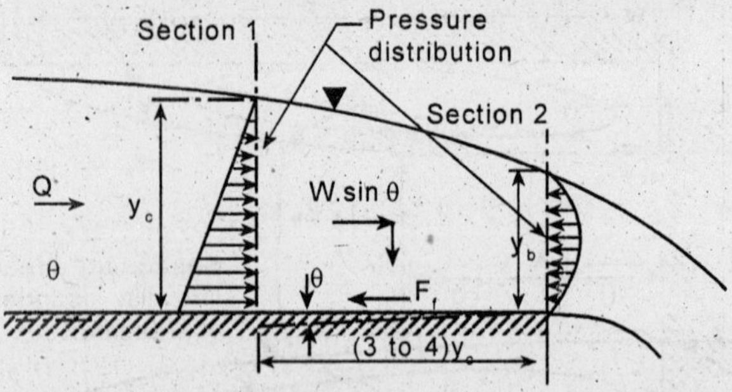

Fig. 13.18 Free overfall

Consider a rectangular prismatic channel with small slope, carrying a constant discharge Q. Assume uniform velocity distributions at section 1 and 2, and hydrostatic pressure variation at section 1. The momentum equation between sections 1 and 2 takes the form

$$q\rho\,(U_c - U_b) = \tfrac{1}{2}\,\gamma\, y_b^2\, K_b - \tfrac{1}{2}\gamma\, y_c^2 + W \sin\theta - F_f$$

in which q = Q/B, W is the weight of water per unit width between the two sections, and K_b is a coefficint which takes into account the fact that pressure distribution at section 2 is nonhydrostatic. Since the channel slope is very small, and sections 1 and 2 are sufficiently close, the last two terms on the right hand side can be neglected. The discharge q can be related to y_e through the energy equation as

$$y_c^3 = q^2/g$$

Combining these two equations and assuming $K_b = 0$ for simplicity. one gets

$$y_b/y_c = 2/3$$

Experimental investigations by Rouse, as well as the use of relaxation techniques by Southwell and Vaisey have yielded 0.715 and 0.705 values respectively for y_b/y_c. The discrepancy between the observed and computed values using the simplified approach given above is primarily due to the assumptions made in the derivation. It can be seen that the pressure force at section 2 is not zero as assumed in the above analysis. Actually for small slopes K_b is 0.30. Similarly since velocity distributions at both the sections are assumed uniform the momentum correction coefficients have been taken as unity. In actual practice β at section 1 is slightly greater than unity, but its value at section 2 can be of the order of 1.07 to 1.20, depending on channel slope. Assuming $y_b = 0.715\, y_e$, one can write

$$y_b = 0.715\sqrt[3]{\frac{q^2}{g}}$$

$$\therefore \qquad Q = B\,q = 1.654\, g^{1/2}\, y_b^{3/2}$$

where B is the channel width. Thus a single measurement of y_b at the overfall is adequate to determine the discharge in the channel.

Using manning's equation it can be shown that y_b/y_c will be a function of S_0/S_c where S_c is the critical slope (slope at which critical depth is equal to normal depth). That this is indeed the case has been shown by the experimental results of Delleur. Variation of y_b/y_c with S_0/S_c as obtained from experimental data for smooth and rough channels is given in table below.

TABLE 13.3

Variation of y_b/y_c with S_o/S_c

S_o/S_c	−10	−5.0	0	3.75	5.0	7.0	10	15
y_b/y_c	0.76	0.75	0.71	0.60	0.55	0.50	0.45	0.40

Analysis similar to the one given above has been carried out for trapezoidal channels as well as circular channels. For a prismatic channel of any shape, it can be shown that

$$\frac{A_b}{A_c} = \frac{D_c}{D_c + Z_c} \tag{13.23}$$

in which A_b and A_c are the areas of cross-section at brink and critical depth sections, D_c is the hydraulic mean depth at critical section and Z_c is the depth of centroid of A_c below the water surface.

13.9 Gradually Varied Flow

Gradually varied flow has been defined earlier as a steady nonuniform flow in which the depth of flow varies gradually along the length of the channel. There are many cases of gradually varied flow which are of interest to engineers. Flow upstream of a weir, dam or sluice gate, flow downstream of a sluice gate and flow in channels with changes in bed slope are a few typical cases of gradually varied flow. In all such problems, the prediction of the free surface profile for given condition of flow is of great significance. When a dam or a weir is constructed across a river, one is interested in the variation of the depth of flow at different sections along the river on the upstream of the weir or the dam; similarly on the downstream of a sluice gate one is interested in finding the exact position of a hydraulic jump if it can form. Such types of problems can be solved by writing the differential equation for the water surface profile and then integrating it to find the distance required for a certain change in depth to take place.

The differential equation for gradually varied flow can be obtained from the basic energy equation after making the following assumptions :

. the resistance law for steady gradually varied flow is the same as that for steady uniform flow, except that one must replace S_0 by S_f in either Manning's or Chezy's equation, and C or n are not function of x;

. the channel bottom slope is very small;

. the channel is prismatic;

4. the water surface curvature is very small so that the pressure distribution in any vertical is hydrostatic; and
5. the energy correction factor α is unity.

In a short reach of gradually varied flow in a prismatic channel (see Fig. 13.19) one can write the energy equation as

$$E = \frac{Q^2}{2gA^2} + y + z$$

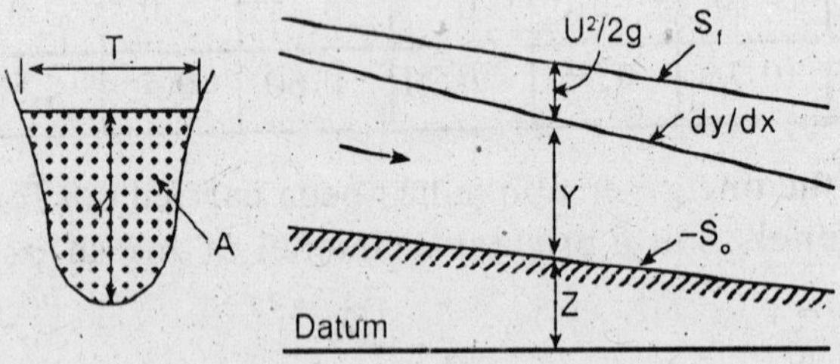

Fig. 13.19 Gradually varied flow

Differentiating each term of the above equation with respect to x, where x is measured along the channel bottom, the following differential equation can be obtained

$$\frac{dE}{dx} = -\frac{Q^3}{gA^3}\frac{dA}{dx} + \frac{dy}{dx} + \frac{dz}{dx}$$

In the above differential equation, dE/dx is the slope of the total energy line $-S_f$, dz/dx is the channel bed slope $-S_o$, (the negative sign for S_f and S_o indicates the decrease in E and z with increase in x) and dy/dx is the slope of the free surface. The term dA/dx can be written as (dA/dy) × (dy/dx) in which dA/dy is the water surface width T. Substitution of these terms in the differential equation yields,

$$-S_f = -\frac{Q^2T}{gA^3}\frac{dy}{dx} + \frac{dy}{dx} - S_0$$

Solving for dy/dx, the following differential equation for the free surface slope is obtained.

$$\frac{dy}{dx} = \frac{S_0 - S_f}{1 - \frac{Q^2T}{gA^3}} = \frac{S_0 - S_f}{1 - Fr^2} \qquad (13.24)$$

since

$$\frac{Q^2T}{gA^3} = \frac{U^2}{gD} = Fr^2$$

Equation 13.24 is the basic differential equation for gradually varied flow from which the shape of all surface profiles can be obtained.

In order to classify the water surface profiles, the channel bed slopes are categorised into different types. The channel bed slope on which the uniform flow depth y_0 and critical depth y_c are the same is called *critical* slope S_c. The channel bed slope is *mild* when the bed slope S_0 is less than critical slope. A *steep* slope is that bed slope which is greater than the critical slope. Application of Manning's or Chezy's equation will indicate that y_c is less than y_0 when the slope is mild and y_0 is less than y_C when it is steep. When the bed slope is zero, it is said to be a *horizontal* floor. An *adverse* slope is that in which $S_0 < 0$ and is positivie. The water surface profiles occurring on these slopes are designated as M curves on mild slope, S on curves on steep slope, C curves on critical slope, H curves on horizontal floor and A curves on adverse slope. The water surface profiles on the above mentioned slopes are further classified depending upon the position of water surface relative to critical depth y_0 and normal depth y_0. The entire region above channel bed can be divided in three zones. In zone 1 the given depth y lies above y_0 and y_c ; in zone 2 the given depth y_c lies between y_0 and y_c and in zone 3 y lies below y_0 and y_c. Three such zones are possible for mild and steep slopes and the corresponding three surface profiles are designated as M_1, M_2, M_3 and S_1, S_2, S_3 on the mild and steep slopes respectively. On the critical slope the normal depth y_0 and the critical depth y_c being the same, only two zones having the given depth y either above the critical depth or below the critical depth are possible resulting in either C_1 or C_3 curves. For the horizontal slope the normal depth is infinite while that for a channel with adverse slope it is imaginary and thus only two types of curves H_2, H_3 and A_2, A_3 are possible on these two slopes. Thus it can be seen that in all twelve surface profiles are possible as shown in Fig. 13.20.

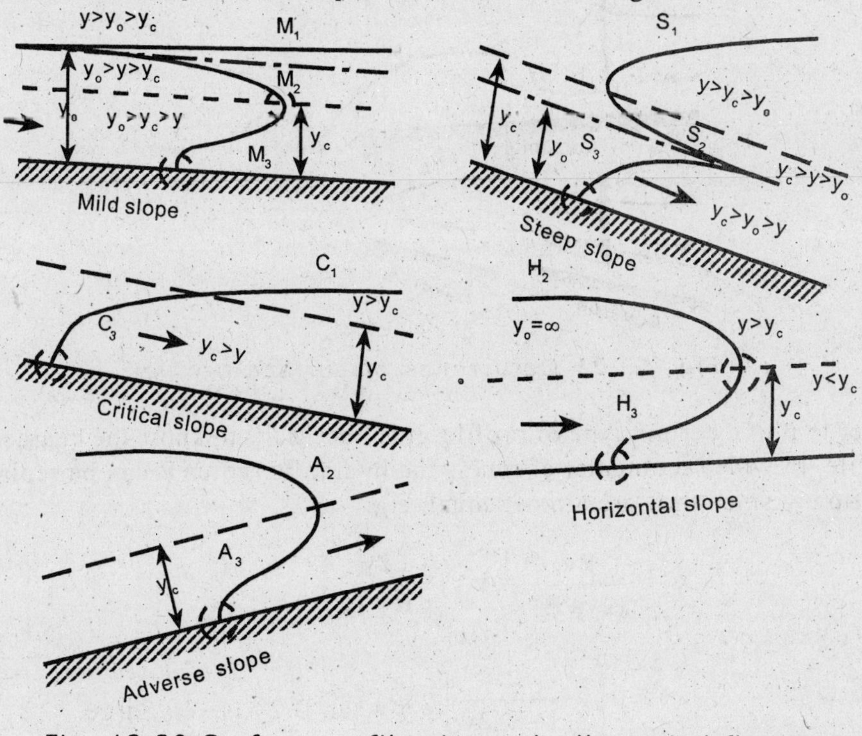

Fig. 13.20 Surface profiles in gradually varied flow

13.10 Characteristics of Surface Profiles

The various surface profiles shown in Fig. 13.20 can be classified as *backwater curves* or *drawdown curves* depending on whether the depth of flow increases or decreases in the direction of flow. A close study of Fig. 13.20 will indicate that all the surface profiles with subscript 1 and 3 (M_1, S_1, C_1, M_3, S_3, C_3, A_3 and H_3) are backwater curves while those with subscript 2 (M_2, S_2, A_2 and H_2) are drawdown curves. Fig. 13.21 shows the occurrence of different surface profiles in practical situations.

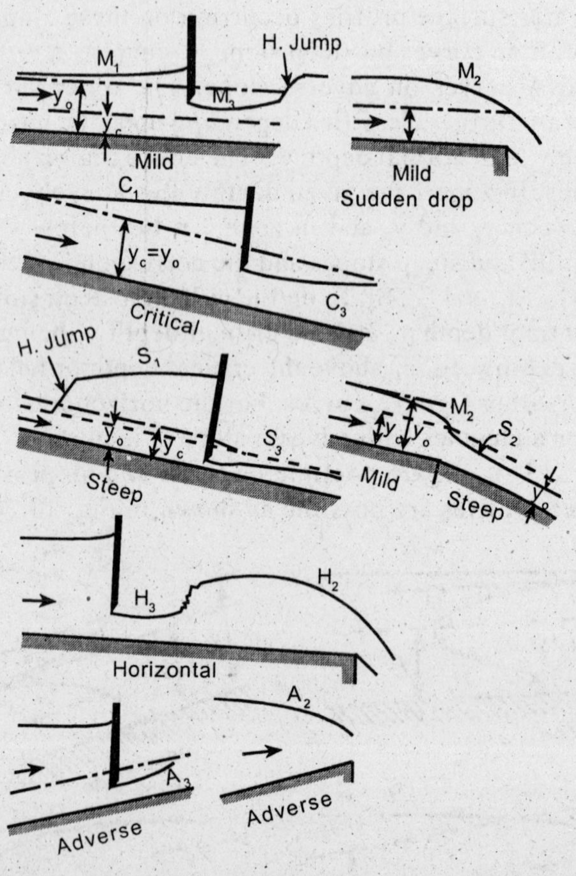

Fig. 13.21 Occurrence of surface profiles

In order to plot a certain type of profile, it is necessary to know the characteristics of each profile. In wide rectangular channels the hydraulic radius R can be replaced by the depth of flow y since they are almost equal, e.g.

$$R = \frac{By}{(2y+B)} = y\left(1-\frac{2y}{B+2y}\right)$$

$$= y\left(1-\frac{1}{1+B/2y}\right) \approx y \text{ when } B/2y \text{ is very large.}$$

Since the flow is assumed to be steady and nonuniform, one can write Manning's equation as

$$q = \frac{1}{n} y_o^{5/3} S_o^{1/2} = \frac{1}{n} y^{5/3} S_f^{1/2}$$

It may be noted that the hydraulic radius has been replaced by the depth of flow assuming a wide rectangular channel and n is assumed to be the same for the uniform and nonuniform flows. Therefore,

$$\frac{S_f}{S_o} = \left(\frac{y_o}{y}\right)^{10/3}$$

If Chezy's equation is used instead of the Manning's, the value of S_f/S_o is equal to $(y_o/y)^3$. In the same manner one can express Fr^2 as

$$Fr^2 = \frac{U^2}{gy} = \frac{q^2}{gy^3} = \left(\frac{y_c}{y}\right)^3$$

Thus the general varied flow equation 13.24 can be written as,

$$\left.\begin{aligned} \frac{dy}{dx} &= S_o \frac{1-\left(\frac{y_o}{y}\right)^{10/3}}{1-\left(\frac{y_c}{y}\right)^3} \\ \text{or} \quad \frac{dy}{dx} &= S_o \frac{1-\left(\frac{y_o}{y}\right)^3}{1-\left(\frac{y_c}{y}\right)^3} \end{aligned}\right\} \qquad (13.25)$$

The trend of the profiles can be examined with the help of Eq. 13.25.

(a) *Mild slope*

There are three zones on the mild slope viz. $y>y_o>y_c$, $y_o>y>y_c$ and $y_o>y_c>y$. In the first zone, M_1 curve will form and its shape and end conditions can be found from Eq. 13.25. The given depth y, at the extreme ends of the curve can be $y \rightarrow y_o$ on the upstream side and $y \rightarrow \infty$ on the downstream side. Equation 13.25 will show that when $y > y_o > y_c$, (dy/dx) is positive and as $y \rightarrow y_o$, $(dy/dx) \rightarrow 0$, also as $y \rightarrow \infty$, $(dy\ dx) \rightarrow S_o$. This indicates that M_1 curve meets the y_o line asymptotically on the upstream side and it tends to be horizontal on the downstream side. In the second zone i.e. when $y_o>y>y_c$, (dy/dx) is negative and as $y \to y_o$, $(dy/dx) \to 0$ and as $y \to y_c$, $(dy/dx) \to \infty$ indicating that M_2 curve meets y_o line asymptotically on the upstream and it meets the y_c line normally on the downstream. In the third zone, $y_o > y_c > y$ and (dy/dx) is positive. As $y \to y_c$, $(dy/dx) \to -\infty$ and as $y \to 0$, $(dy/dx) \to \infty$, indicating that M_3 curve meets the y_c line and the channel bed line normally. The trend of these curves can be seen in Fig. 13.20.

(b) *Steep slope*

On the steep slope also there will be three curves S_1, S_2 and S_3 in zones $y > y_c > y_o$, $y_c > y > y_o$ and $y_c > y_o > y$ respectively. In the first zone (dy/dx) is positive and as $y \to y_c$, $(dy/dx) \to \infty$, and when $y \to \infty$, $(dy/dx) \to S_o$; i.e., the S_1 curve meets the y_c line normally and on the downstream it tends to be horizontal.

In the second zone (dy/dx) is negative and the end condition will show that S_2 curve meets y_c line normally on upstream side and on the downstream side it meets the y_o line asymptotically. The slope of the S_3 curve is positive; it meets the channel bed normally and is asymptotic to the y_o line.

(c) *Critical slope*

On the critical slope, only C_1 and C_3 curves are possible as discussed earlier. Considering C_1 curve, it can be seen that as $y \to \infty$, $(dy/dx) \to S_o = S_c$ and as $y \to y_c$, $(dy/dx) \to S_o = S_c$. Use of Manning's equation for resistance will yield the value (dy/dx) as $(10/9)S_o$ when $y \to y_c$. For the C_3 curve as $y \to 0$, $(dy/dx) \to S_o = S_c$ and $y \to y_c$, $(dy/dx) \to S_o = S_c$. The C_1 and C_3 curve will be straight lines if Chezy's equation is used in obtaining dy/dx in Eq. 13.25; instead if Manning's equation is used, C_1 and C_3 will be curved. However for all practical purposes these differences are minor.

(d) *Adverse and Horizontal slopes*

On the adverse slope the normal depth concept cannot be applied, while in the case of horizontal channel the normal depth will be infinite. Hence the curves A_1 and H_1 do not exist. For investigating the trend of the curves, Eq. 13.25 cannot be used because S_o is positive on adverse slope and S_o is equal to zero on horizontal slope. In order to get over this difficulty, Eq. 13.25 can be expressed as,

$$\frac{dy}{dx} = \frac{S_o - U^2/C^2 y}{1-(y_c/y)^3}$$

(dy/dx) is negative on the adverse slope under the condition $y > y_c$ and it is positive when $y < y_c$. Thus A_2 curve tends to be horizontal when $y \to \infty$ and it meets the y_c line and the channel bed normally since $(dy/dx) \to \infty$ as $y \to y_c$ and as $y \to 0$.

For the horizontal channel (dy/dx) is negative for the H_2 curve and it is positive for the H_3 curve. The H_2 curve is a drawdown curve and it meets the y_c line vertically; the H_3 curve meets the y_c line and the channel bed vertically.

In order to determine the type of profile on a particular channel bed, the following procedure may be adopted :

1. Compute y_0 and y_c for the given discharge and plot the lines representing channel bed and, normal and critical depths.
2. Comparing the normal depth with the critical depth, determine whether the channel slope is mild, critical, steep, adverse or horizontal.
3. Locate the *control section*. A control section is defined as one at which there is a fixed relationship between the depth and the discharge. Sharp and broad-crested weirs, sluice gate, abrupt change in bed slope, sudden fall and section where critical depth occurs, act as control sections. The control section influences the variation of depth-either on the upstream side or on the downstream side, depending on whether the flow is subcritical or supercritical. In subcritical flow a disturbance can travel upstream (U is less than $\sqrt{gy}$); therefore what happens in the upstream channel is governed by the downstream control. In supercritical flow the disturbance cannot travel upstream (U is greater than $\sqrt{gy}$); therefore what happens in downstream channel is governed by upstream control. Knowing y_0, y_c and the depth at the control section, determine the type of the curve.
4. If the depth at the nonuniformity is above the critical depth, it is governed by a downstream control and if it is less than the critical depth it is governed by an upstream control. Thus with the values of the given depth y, normal depth y_0 and critical depth y_c known, the appropriate surface profile can be sketched.
5. If in any reach the supercritical depth has to meet the subscritical depth, there will be a hydraulic jump. Hydraulic jump will form when a steep floor meets a mild floor or when a sluice gate is installed on a steep or mild floor. On the steep floor the jump will occur on the upsteeam of the sluice gate while on a mild floor it will form on the downstream of the sluice gate. This is indicated in Fig. 13.21.

13.11 Integration of the Varied Flow Equation

In practical problems, it is often required to find the distance upto which a certain nonuniformity extends in an open channel. For example the construction of an overflow dam across a river having a mild slope causes a gradual reduction in the depth of flow in the upstream direction resulting in an M_1 curve. In such a case, one may be required to estimate the distance on the upstream side, where a certain depth of flow occurs on M_1 curve. Similarly, when a hydraulic jump forms downstream of a sluice gate installed on a mild slope, it is many times required to find the length of the M_3 curve in order to locate the exact position of the hydraulic jump. To solve problems of this nature, it is necessary to integrate the varied flow equation. The method of integration varies depending on particular requirement of the problem. These methods can be classified into the following categories :

(a) Step method,

(b) Graphical method, and

(c) Direct method of integration.

The step method of integration is very simple and the accuracy of the method can be increased to the required degree by choosing small depth increments. Graphical method of integration is a very powerful method applicable to prismatic as well as nonprismatic channels; however it is rather laborious. There are several methods of directly integrating the differential equation for gradually varied flow; out of these only Bresse's method and Chow's method are discussed here.

(a) *Step Method*

In the step method of integration the entire length of the surface profile is considered to be composed of small lengths ΔL such that the condition of flow on either side of ΔL are known. Consider a short reach of a channel as shown in Fig. 13.22. The energy equation for the two sections at the either end of the reach ΔL can be written as.

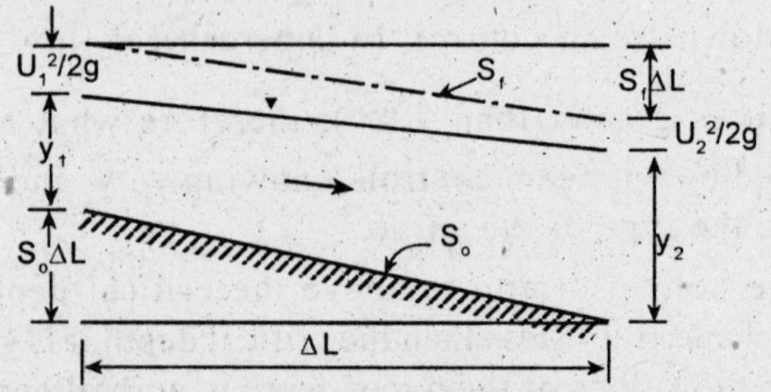

Fig. 13.22 A Channel reach with nonuniform flow

$$S_o\Delta L + H_1 = H_2 + S_f\,\Delta L$$

in which H_1 and H_2 are the specific energy values at the either end of reach and $(S_o\Delta L)$ is the rise in the channel bed at section 1 while $S_f\Delta L$ is the energy loss in distance ΔL. Solving the above expression for ΔL one gets,

$$\Delta L = \frac{H_2 - H_1}{S_o - S_f} \tag{13.26}$$

which is the equation for the step method of integration. For computing ΔL, the channel shape, the discharge Q the bed slope S_o, roughness coefficient n and one of the depths (the one at the control section) must be known. In Fig. 13.22 if it is assumed that the control is at section 2, the depth of flow y_2 and $U_2^2/2g$ will be known. The bed slope of the channel S_o is also known. In order to obtain distance ΔL. one can assume a small change in depth Δy to take place in ΔL, and knowing y_1 ($y_1 = y_2 - \Delta y$) one can compute H_1. The S_f in Eq. 13.26 is normally taken as average of the energy slopes at sections 1 and 2, i.e., $S_f = (S_{f1} + S_{f2})/2$. Unless detailed information concerning variation of C or n with the depth of flow is available, they are assumed to be constant. Knowing the terms S_f, S_o, H_1 and H_2, ΔL can be computed. The computations are now repeated for the next reach. The accuracy of the step method depends on the depth increments chosen. The procedure of step method of computation is illustrated in Example 13.9.

Example 13.9

A rectangular channel is 20 m wide and carries a discharge of 65 m³/s. It is laid at a slope of 0.0001. At a certain section along the channel length, the depth of flow is 2.0 m. How far upstream (or downstream) will the depth be 2.60 m ? Take Manning's n as 0.02.

The depth of uniform flow y_o can be computed as

$$65 = \frac{1}{0.02} \times (20\, y_o) \left(\frac{20\, y_o}{20+2y_o} \right)^{2/3} (0.0001)^{1/2}$$

$$\therefore \quad y_o = 3.70 \text{ m}$$

The critical depth y_c can be computed as

$$y_c = \left[\frac{(65/20)^2}{9.81} \right]^{1/3} = 1.021 \text{ m}$$

Since the given depth values are between y_o and y_c the free surface will indicate a M_2 curve and the depth of 2.6 m will occur upstream of the given depth 2.0 m. For computation of the length of the curve, a table can be set up with depth increments of 0.2 m and breaking the reach in three short distances.

Table of computation for Example 13.9

y m	A m²	U m/s	$U^2/2g$ m	H m	R m	S_f	$\overline{S_f}$	ΔH m	ΔL m	ΣL m
2.0	40	1.625	0.135	2.135	1.667	0.000 534				
							0.000 466	0.176	480.1	
2.2	44	1.477	0.111	2.311	1.803	0.000 397				480.1
							0.000 351	0.183	729.1	
2.4	48	1.354	0.094	2.494	1.935	0.000 304				1209.2
							0.000 271	0.196	1146.2	
2.6	52	1.250	0.080	2.680	2.064	0.000 238				2355.4

Total reach length is 2355.4 m

(b) *Graphical Method of Integration*

The graphical Method of integration of varied flow equation is quite powerful in that it can be used for prismatic as well as nonprismatic channels of any shape and slope. Hence it can be used for natural channels. Consider Eq. 12.22 namely

$$\frac{dy}{dx} = \frac{S_o - S_f}{1 - \frac{Q^2 T}{g A^3}}$$

It can be easily seen that for a given discharge and channel shape, A, T as well as S_f are functions of y. Hence one can write

$$dx = f(y)\,dy$$

in which $f(y) = (1 - Q^2T/gA^3)/(S_o - S_f)$. Let y_1 and y_2 be the depths of flow at sections distant x_1 and x_2 from the control section. Then one can write

$$(x_2 - x_1) = \int_{x_1}^{x_2} dx = \int_{y_1}^{y_2} f(y)\,dy$$

Thus, if one prepares a curve of f(y) versus y and determines the area under the curve between $y = y_1$ and $y = y_2$ it will give the longitudinal distance. $(x_2 - x_1)$ required for this change in the depth of flow. If y_1 and y_2 do not differ much, one can approximately write

$$(x_2 - x_1) = \frac{f(y_1)+f(y_2)}{2}\,(y_2 - y_1)$$

in which $f(y_1)$ and $f(y_2)$ are values of f(y) at $y = y_1$ and $y = y_2$.

Example 13.10

Solve Example 13.9 by graphical method of integration.

The problem is solved in a tabular form shown below.

A plot of f(y) against y is shown in Fig. 13.23 from which one can find the area under the curve f (y) between y = 2.0 m and y = 2.6 m which is 2385.3 m. This is the required distance.

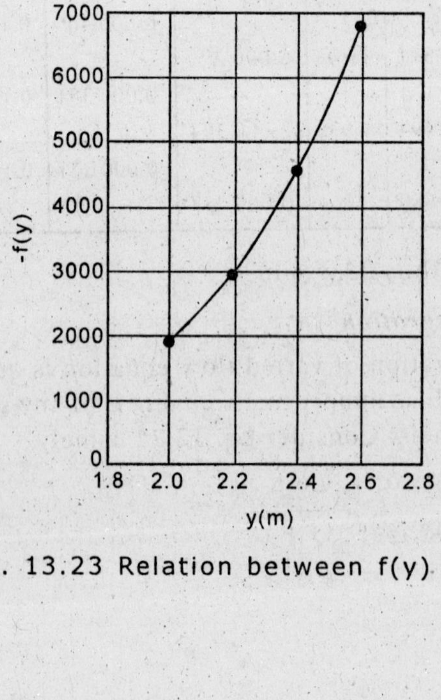

Fig. 13.23 Relation between f(y) and y

Table of Computation for Example 13.10

y	T	A	P	R	$R^{4/3}$	$\frac{Q^2T}{gA^3}$	$1-\frac{Q^2T}{gA^3}$	$S_f=\frac{n^2Q^2}{A^2R^{4/3}}$	S_o-S_f	-f(y)
m	m	m^2	m	m						
2.0	20.0	40.0	24.0	1.667	1.978	0.1348	0.8652	0.00534	-0.000434	1984
2.2	20.0	44.0	24.4	1.802	2.191	0.1012	0.8983	0.000397	-0.000297	3014
2.4	20.0	48.0	24.8	1.935	2.412	0.0780	0.9220	0.000304	-0.000204	4520
2.6	20.0	52.0	25.2	2.061	2.521	0.0614	0.9386	0.000238	-0.000138	6801

(c) *Bresse's Method*

Bresse's method of integrating the varied flow equation is applicable in the case of infinitely wide rectangular channels. This method makes use of the Chezy's formula and is convenient for computation as the result obtained from Bresse's method are fairly close to the observed values when the channels are wide and flat. The general varied flow equation

$$\frac{dy}{dx} = S_o \frac{1-(y_o/y)^3}{1-(y_c/y)^3} \qquad (13.25)$$

can be rearranged using a variable u to indicate the ratio y/y_o as

$$dx = \frac{y_o}{S_o}\left[1-\left(1-\frac{y_c^3}{y_o^3}\right)\frac{1}{1-u^3}\right]du$$

in which $u = \frac{y}{y_o}$ and $y_o\,du = dy$. Integrating the above equation, one gets

$$x = \frac{y_o}{S_o}\left[u-\left\{1-\left(\frac{y_c}{y_o}\right)^3\right\}\int\frac{du}{1-u^3}\right] + \text{constant}$$

The distance x can be calculated if the value of the integral $\int\frac{du}{1-u^3}$ is known. Usually tables are available giving the numerical value of this integral for various values of u. It can also be calculated from the expression

$$\int\frac{du}{1-u^3} = \frac{1}{6}\log_e\frac{u^2+u+1}{(u-1)^2} - \frac{1}{\sqrt{3}}\cot^{-1}\frac{2u+1}{\sqrt{3}}$$

The ratio of critical depth to normal depth in a rectangular channel can be expressed as

$$\left(\frac{y_c}{y_o}\right)^3 = \frac{C^2 S_o}{g}.$$

in which C is the Chezy's coefficient. Substituting the above expression in expression for x and writing the integral du/(1 – u³) as ϕ (u), Bresse's solution for varied flow equation is,

$$(x_2 - x_1) = \frac{y_o}{S_o}\left\{(u_2 - u_1) - \left(1 - \frac{C^2 S_o}{g}\right)\{\phi(u_2) - \phi(u_1)\}\right\} \tag{13.27}$$

in which u_2 and u_1 are the values of u at x_2 and x_1 respectively. The function ϕ (u) has been tabulated and listed in reference 23, and Appendix III.

(d) *Chow's Method*

Combining Manning's or Chezy's equation with continuity equation one can write $Q = (AR^{2/3} S_o^{1/2})/n$ or $CA\sqrt{RS_o}$. The quantity $(AR^{2/3}/n)$ or $CA\sqrt{R}$ depends only on the depth of flow for a channel of given characteristics and is usually called *conveyance* K. If K_o and K are the conveyance values under uniform and nonuniform conditions respectively, then one can express S_f/S_o as $(K_o/K)^2$. Next consider the term Q^2T/gA^3. If $\sqrt{A^3/T}$ is called the *section factor* Z, then Q^2/g can be designated as Z_c^2 since at critical depth $Q^2/g = (A^3/T)_c$. Therefore Q^2T/gA^3 can be expressed as $(Z_c/Z)^2$. Therefore Eq. 13.25 can be expressed as

$$\frac{dy}{dx} = S_o \frac{1-(K_o/K)^2}{1-(Z_c/Z)^2}$$

For any channel K^2 and Z^2 can usually be expressed as $K^2 \sim y^N$ and $Z^2 \sim y^M$ where M and N are constants depending on channel shape. Hence the above equation can be written as

$$\frac{dy}{dx} = S_o \frac{1-(y_o/y)^N}{1-(y_c/y)^M}$$

The values of M and N for different channel shapes are listed below. Note that the values of N listed below are for definition of K based on Manning's equation.

Channel Shape	*M*	*N*
Wide Rectangular	3.00	3.33
Narrow and deep rectangular	3.00	2.00
Triangular	5.00	3.33
Trapezoidal (varying side slope and y/B)	3.00 to 5.00	3.33 to 5.30

Substituion of $u = y/y_o$ in the above equation and subsequent simplification yields

$$dx = \frac{y_o}{S_o}\left[1 - \frac{1}{(1-u^N)} + \left(\frac{y_c}{y_o}\right)^M \frac{u^{M-N}}{(1-u^N)}\right] du$$

On integration this gives

$$x = \frac{y_o}{S_o}\left[u - \int \frac{du}{1-u^N} + \left(\frac{y_c}{y_o}\right)^M \int \frac{u^{M-N}}{1-u^N} du\right] + C_1$$

in which C_1 is the constant of integration. Further substitution $V = u^{N/J}$ and $J = N/(N - M + 1)$ converts the second integral on the right hand side to the same form as the first one. Hence one can write

$$(x_2 - x_1) = (y_o/S_o)\,[\,(u_2 - u_1) - \{F\,(u_2, N) - F\,(u_1, N)\} + \left(\frac{y_c}{y_o}\right)^M \frac{1}{(N-M+1)} \{F(V_2, J) - F\,(V_1, J)\}\,] \tag{13.28}$$

in which $F(u, N) = \int_0^u \frac{du}{1-u^N}$

It can be seen that F(u, N) and F(V, J) are the same functions except that the variables have been changed. The varied flow function F(u, N) has been tabulated for various values of u and N and given in Appendix III. It may be noted that the integral occurring in Bresse's method is a special case of F when N equals three.

Example 13.11

A wide rectangular channel carries 4.40 m³/s m discharge at a slope of 0.0001 when Manning's n is 0.02. At a certain section in the channel the depth of flow is 2.0. How far upstream or downstream will be the depth 2.6 m?

First determine y_o and y_c

$$4.40 = \frac{1}{0.02}\, y_o^{5/3}\, (0.0001)^{1/2}$$

$$y_o = 3.687 \text{ m}$$

Also $$y_c = \sqrt[3]{(4.4)^2/9.81} = 1.254 \text{ m}$$

Since y_o is greater than y_c the slope is mild. Further since the depth 2.0 m and 2.6 m lie between y_o and y_c the surface profile is M_2. Therefore the depth 2.6 m will occur upstream of the section where the depth 2.0 m occurs.

For wide rectangular channel N = 3.33, M = 3.0

and $J = N/(N - M + 1) = \dfrac{3.33}{1.33} = 2.510, \quad \dfrac{N}{J} = \dfrac{3.33}{2.51} = 1.327$

$$u_1 = \frac{2.0}{3.687} = 0.542 \qquad u_2 = \frac{2.6}{3.687} = 0.705$$

$$V_1 = (0.542)^{1.327} = 0.442 \qquad V_2 = (0.705)^{1.327} = 0.626$$

Referring to the table of varied flow function, one gets

$$F(u_1, N) = F(0.542, 3.33) = 0.557$$
$$F(u_2, N) = F(0.705, 3.33) = 0.762$$
$$F(V_1, J) = F(0.442, 2.51) = 0.460$$
$$F(V_2, J) = F(0.636, 2.51) = 0.695$$

Hence using, Eq. 13.28, one gets

$$(x_2 - x_1) = \frac{3.687}{10^{-4}}\left[(0.705-0.542)-(0.762-0.557)+\left(\frac{1.254}{3.687}\right)^3 \times \frac{1}{1.33}(0.695-0.460)\right]$$

$$= 3.687 \times 10^4 \, [0.163 - 0.205 + (0.0296 \times 0.235)]$$
$$= -1292 \text{ m}$$

If the channel is not prismatic, then the total energy loss between two sections is due to frictional resistance along the boundary and due to form loss because of expansion, contraction, bends etc. In such case energy equation between two sections (see Fig 13.22) can be written as

$$Z_1 + y_1 + \frac{U_1^2}{2g} = Z_2 + y_2 + \frac{U_2^2}{2g} + \overline{S}_f \Delta L + h_L$$

in which the form loss h_L, is usually expressed as $K(\,|\,U_1^2 - U_2^2\,|\,)/2g$. Value of K for expanding flow varies between 0.2 to 0.5; corresponding value for contracting flow will be much smaller say about 0.10. One must make a proper choice of K based on previous experience. One can now use the step method known as *standard step method* for computing the surface profile. For a given ΔL, y_1 is assumed and total energies E_1 and E_2 computed. Knowing U_1 and U_2, S_{f1}, S_{f2} and $\overline{S_f}$ can be computed. Also for assumed value of y_1, h_L is computed. If $E_1 = E_2 + \overline{S_f}\,\Delta L + h_L$ then assumed value of y_1 is correct. Otherwise choose a new value of y_i and repeat the calculations. After correct value of y_i is obtained, similar calculations are performed for the next section. Tabular form for performing the calculations is given below

ΔL	y	Z	A	U	$\frac{U^2}{2g}$	E	R	S_f	$\overline{S_f}$	$\overline{S_f}\,\Delta L$	h_L	$E + h_L + \overline{S_f}\,\Delta L$	Remarks

If may be mentioned that $\overline{S_f}$ can be calculated either as an average of S_{f1} and S_{f2} or for average of velocities at two sections and average of the two hydraulic radii. It has been found that the first method is more appropriate for computation of M_1 and S_2 profiles while the latter method is preferable for M_2, M_3, S_1 and S_2 profiles.

13.12 Hydraulic jump

A brief mention has been made about hydraulic jump in the introductory part of this chapter as a phenomenon by means of which flow passes abruptly from a supercritical state to a subcritical state. At the section of hydraulic jump, there is a sharp curvature to the water surface caused by rise in the depth of flow in a short reach. A roller is formed in this reach and there is large scale turbulence resulting in a considerable loss in energy. Hence a hydraulic jump is made use of for the dissipation of energy of high velocity flows. A typical example of this is the formation of hydraulic jump at the toe of a spillway or a weir (see Fig. 13.26) where the incoming water has an excess kinetic energy which, if not adequately dissipated, would damage the downstream side of the structure. Other possible situations for the hydraulic jump formation are (a) when a steep slope meets a mild, a horizontal or an adverse slope, (b) when a sluice gate is introduced on a mild or a steep slope, see Fig. 13.21.

The reason for the occurrence of a hydraulic jump below a sluice gate on the mild slope can be visualised by the study of the specific energy diagram and the M_3 curve forming below the sluice gate. In M_3 curve the depth of flow continuously increases while the specific energy decreases as can be seen in Fig. 13.12. If this decrease in energy were to continue upto the critical depth at which the specific energy is minimum, subsequent increase in energy would be required as the flow depth has to change from critical depth to the normal depth of flow in the downstream channel. But since the energy gradient is much steeper than the bed slope of the channel, it is not possible for the depth to increase from y_c to y_o in a short distance. Therefore, the depth directly increases from supercritical to subcritical flow without reaching y_C and a hydraulic jump forms. A similar explanation can be presented for the jump formation upstream of a sluice gate on the steep slope.

In order to relate the conditions of flow before and after the hydraulic jump, one can use the momentum equation considering the portion of hydraulic jump as the control volume. The following assumptions are made in the analysis:

1. The length of the jump is small so that frictional resistance at the boundary is small and can be neglected.
2. Uniform flow exists before and after the jump and that the pressure distribution is hydrostatic before and after the jump.

3. The channel is horizontal or has a very gentle slope so that the weight component of the prism of water in the direction of flow is negligibly small.
4. Velocity distribution is assumed to be uniform so that $\alpha = \beta = 1.0$.

Consider a hydraulic jump in any prismatic channel as shown in Fig. 13.24. The symbols y, U, A and Z indicate depth of flow, average velocity, cross-sectional area and the depth of centroid of the area A below the free surface respectively. Subscript 1 and 2 indicate the values before and after jump respectively. Other terms have their usual meaning. Because of the assumptions mentioned above, the only external force causing a change in momentum between sections 1 and 2 is the pressure force. Hence the momentum equation takes the form,

$$\gamma A_2 \bar{Z}_2 - \gamma A_1 \bar{Z}_1 = \rho Q (U_1 - U_2) \tag{13.29}$$

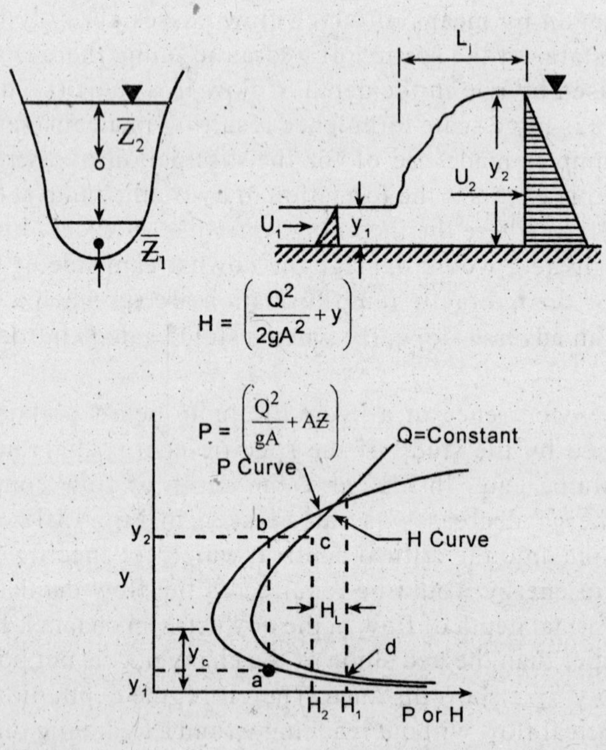

Fig. 13.24 Hydraulic jump in a prismatic channel

This equation can be rewritten as

$$\frac{Q^2}{gA_1} + A_1 \bar{Z}_1 = \frac{Q^2}{gA_2} + A_2 \bar{Z}_2 \tag{13.30}$$

indicating that the sum of momentum and pressure force at the two sections is constant.

The sum $\left(\frac{Q^2}{gA} + A\bar{Z}\right)$ is called the *specific force* P and it can be plotted against the depth of flow to yield a specific force diagram for a constant discharge, see Fig 13.24. If this plot of specific force is superimposed on the specific energy diagram, it will be seen that both P and H attain a minimum value at critical depth y_c. In fact it can be analytically shown that for a given discharge the specific force is minimum at critical depth y_c; similarly for a given specific force, the discharge is maximum at y_c. The critical depth, obtained from specific energy and specific force considerations are equal if $\alpha = \beta = 1$ and pressure distribution is hydrostatic.

It may be noted that since there is energy loss due to hydraulic jump, the two depths before and after the jump will not indicate the same specific energy. The energy loss involved can be found from the plots of P and H versus y. As the specific force P is same before and after the jump, any vertical line ab on the P curve indicates the two depths y_1 and y_2 before and after the jump. Horizontal lines from a and b cut the specific energy diagram at points d and c as can be seen in the figure indicating the specific energy values before and after jump. The horizontal distance between points d and c is the energy loss due to hydraulic jump. The depths y_1 and y_2 before and after the jump are known as the *conjugate* depths as against the alternate depths which indicate the same specific energy.

A relation between the conjugate depths y_1 and y_2 can be obtained for rectangular channels very conveniently. Substituting in Eq. 13.29. $\bar{Z}_1 = \frac{1}{2}y_1$, $\bar{Z}_2 = \frac{1}{2}y_2$ and $Bq = Q$, B being the width of the channel, $A_1 = By_1$ and $A_2 = By_2$, one gets,

$$\left.\begin{aligned} \frac{1}{2}(y_2^2 - y_1^2) &= \frac{q^2}{g}\left(\frac{y_2 - y_1}{y_1 y_2}\right) \\ \text{or} \quad y_1 y_2 (y_1 + y_2) &= \frac{2q^2}{g} \end{aligned}\right\} \quad (13.31)$$

Eq. 13.31 is the momentum equation for hydraulic jump in rectangular channels. From Eq. 13.31 one can get relation between conjugate depths y_1 and y_2 as

$$\left.\begin{aligned} y_2 &= -\frac{y_1}{2} \pm \sqrt{\frac{y_1^2}{4} + \frac{2q^2}{gy_1}} \\ y_1 &= -\frac{y_2}{2} \pm \sqrt{\frac{y_2^2}{4} + \frac{2q^2}{gy_2}} \end{aligned}\right\} \quad (13.32)$$

The negative sign before the square root gives unrealistic values of y_1 or y_2 and therefore only a positive sign is taken to evaluate the conjugate depth. From Eq. 13.32 one can write the ratio of conjugate depths as a function of Froude number at sections 1 as

$$\frac{y_2}{y_1} = \frac{1}{2}\left[\sqrt{(1+8Fr_1^2)}-1\right] \tag{13.33}$$

A plot of Eq. 13.33 is shown in Fig. 13.25 with experimental data from various sources. It can be seen that experimental data agree well with Eq. 13.33.

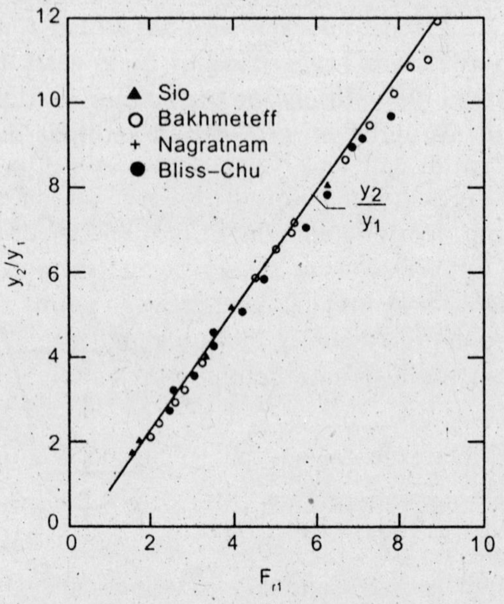

Fig. 13.25 Variation of y_2/y_1 with Fr_1 for hydraulic jump in rectangular channels

Once the conjugate depths are known, it is easy to find the energy loss H_L in the hydraulic jump as

$$H_L = \left(y_1+\frac{U_1^2}{2g}\right)-\left(y_2+\frac{U_2^2}{2g}\right) \tag{13.34}$$

From Eqs. 13.31 and 13.34 one can obtain a relation for energy loss in terms of velocities as

$$H_l = \frac{(U_1-U_2)^3}{2g(U_1+U_2)} \tag{13.35}$$

It can also be shown that

$$H_l = \frac{(y_2-y_1)^3}{4y_1 y_2} \tag{13.35 a}$$

In the problems concerning the design of stilling basins of the hydraulic structures, one must know 1. the length of the hydraulic jump - a distance, from the front for the jump to the end of the roller. The investigations have shown that it is rather easy to define where the jump begins, but rather difficult to identify its end. Dimensional considerations along with experimental evidence show that $L_j/(y_2 - y_1)$ is a function of Fr_1, channel roughness and channel geometry. In general $L_j/(y_2 - y_1)$ decreases as Fr_1 increases and its value can range from about 4.5 to 8.75 for Fr_1 lying between 1.75 and 12. The following table lists the average values of two parameters.

Fr_1	1.75	3	5	7	9	12
$L_j/(y_2-y_1)$	8.75	6.50	5.50	5.00	4.75	4.50

The U.S. Bureau of Reclamation has given the following formula for L_j

$$L_j = 6.9\,(y_2 - y_1) \tag{13.36}$$

In the light of above discussion. the approximation involved in Eq. 13.36 should be noted.

Example 13.12

For a hydraulic jump formed downstream of a dam, the discharge q is 17.93 m²/s m and energy loss in the jump is 17.52 m. Determine the depths before and after the hydraulic jump.

Since initial conditions are not known, the problem must be solved by trial and error by assuming various values of y_1, and computing H_L. For assumed y_1, compute $Fr_1 = q/\sqrt{gy_1^3}$. Using Eq. 13.33 determine y_2 and use Eq. (13.35 a) to find H_L. The value of y_1 which gives the correct H_L is the solution. This is done in a tabular from as shown below.

y_1 m	Fr_1	y_2/y_1	y_2 m	H_L m
0.5	16.190	22.400	11.020	54.690
1.0	5.700	7.608	7.608	9.481
0.75	8.814	11.974	8.981	20.695
0.78	8.310	11.263	8.707	18.33
0.80	8.000	10.825	8.660	17.520

Hence y_1 = 0.80 m and y_2 = 8.66 m.

Example 13.13

A discharge of 705 m³/s flows over a spillway and then passes on a 50 m wide concrete apron (n = 0.015). The velocity of water at the toe of the spillway is 10 m/s. A hydraulic jump forms on the horizontal apron due to a tail water depth of 4.5 m in the channel below. Find the exact position of the hydraulic jump and the total length of the apron such that the jump remains entirely over the apron.

$$\text{Discharge per unit width} = \frac{705}{50} = 14.1 \text{ m}^3/\text{s m}$$

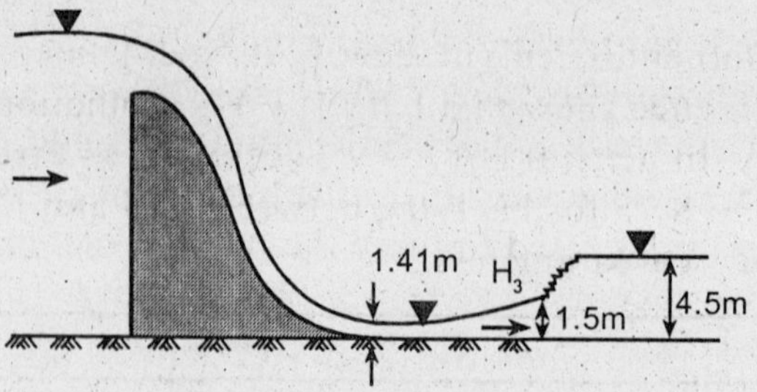

Fig. 13.26 Hydraulic jump below a spillway

Depth of flow at the toe $= \frac{14.1}{10.0} = 1.41$ m

Depth before the jump corresponding to $y_2 = 4.5$ m is

$$y_1 = -\frac{4.5}{2} + \sqrt{\frac{2\times14.1^2}{9.81\times4.5}+\frac{4.5^2}{4}} = 1.50 \text{ m}$$

Therefore, the water depth will rise from 1.41 m to 1.50 m before the jump takes place The distance required for the change in the depth from 1.41 m to 1.50 m can be found by step method.

$$U_1 = 10 \text{ m/s}, \quad \frac{U_1^2}{2g} = 5.10 \text{ m}$$

$$R_1 = \frac{50\times1.41}{52.82} = 1.332 \text{ m}$$

$$U_2 = \frac{14.1}{1.5} = 9.4 \text{ m/s}, \quad \frac{U_2^2}{2g} = 4.5 \text{ m}$$

$$R_2 = \frac{50\times1.5}{53} = 1.415 \text{ m}$$

$$S_{f1} = \frac{U_1^2 n^2}{R_1^{4/3}} = \frac{10^2\times0.015^2}{1.332^{4/3}} = 0.0154$$

$$S_{f2} = \frac{U_2^2 n^2}{R_2^{4/3}} = \frac{9.4^2\times0.015^2}{1.415^{4/3}} = 0.0125$$

$$\therefore \quad \bar{S}_f = \frac{(0.0154+0.0125)}{2} = 0.0139$$

Hence $\quad x = \frac{(1.50+4.50)-(1.41+5.10)}{0.0139} = \frac{0.51}{0.0139}$

$= 36.70$ m

The jump will form at it distance of 36.70 m from the toe. The approximate length of jump is 6.9 (4.5 – 1.5) = 20.70 m. Hence, total length of the apron = 36.70 + 20.70 = 57.40 m.

In many situations the tail water depth is not adequate and hence the jump moves downstream. Since ideally one would like the jump to occur at a predetermined position, various artificial devices are used to force the jump to take place at a fixed place. These are provisions of a – ve step, or a + ve step or baffle blocks. These are shown in Fig. 13.27.

The negative step is used when the tail water depth is greater than adequate. In such a case the relation between y_2/y_1 and Fr_1 is also dependent on $\Delta z/y_1$. This can be derived by using continuity and momentum equation. Consider case II in Fig. 13.27. In the momentum equation, one must take into account the additional force on the fluid in the flow direction exerted by the step and which is shown by the trapezium. Hence

$$q = U_1 y_1 = U_2 y_2$$

and

$$\tfrac{1}{2}\gamma y_1^2 + \Delta z \tfrac{1}{2} [\gamma y_1 + \gamma(y_1 + \Delta z)] - \tfrac{1}{2} \gamma y_2^2 = q \rho (U_2 - U_1)$$

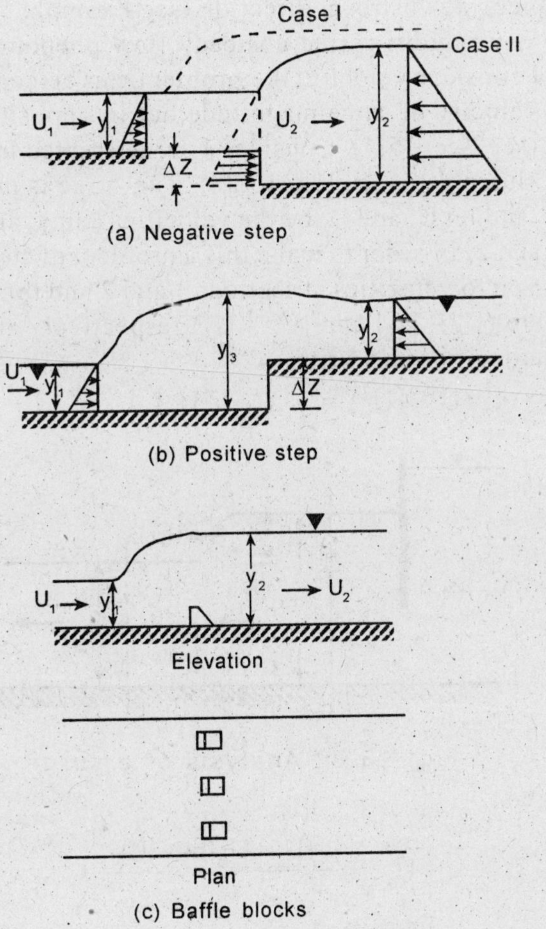

Fig. 13.27 Artificial devices to fix location of a jump

The second equation can be simplified and combined with continuity equation to get

$$Fr_1^{\,2} = \{(y_2/y_1)^2 - (1 + \Delta z/y_1)^2\}/2\,(1 - y_1/y_2) \qquad (13.37)$$

Similarly a relation can be obtained between Fr_1, $\Delta z/y_1$, and y_2/y_1 for case I. A positive step is recommended when the tail water depth is smaller than the conjugate depth. If the step were not provided the jump moves downstream. An analysis similar to one given above can be carried out for this case. However, in such an analysis, two uncertainties exist, namely location of jump in relation to the position of step and force exerted by vertical face of step on the fluid, the latter depending on the location of jump.

The baffle blocks serve nearly the same function as positive step. The force exerted by them on the fluid reduces the conjugate depth and hence they are used when downstream water depth is inadequate.

13.13 Surges and Waves in Open Channels

A surge represents an abrupt change in the depth of flow caused by regulation of a sluice gate fixed in the channel; surges also occur in tidal rivers. A hydraulic jump which moves either in the upstream or downstream direction (see Example 15.1) is a familiar example of a surge. A surge is a rapidly varied unsteady flow phenomenon. However, when the surge is moving at a constant velocity, the problem can be converted into one of steady flow by applying a velocity of same magnitude but in opposite direction to the fluid as well as to the surge (see Sec. 15.4). Consider a surge created in a rectangular channel by suddenly opening a sluice gate (see Fig. 13.28). The surge is moving to the right with an absolute velocity U_w and let U_1 and U_2 be the velocities and y_1 and y_2 be the corresponding depths at sections 1 and 2. In order to make this a problem of steady flow, apply a velocity U_w in opposite direction to velocities at sections 1 and 2 and the surge. Thus the velocities at sections 1 and 2 are $(U_1 - U_w)$ and $(U_2 - U_w)$ respectively and the surge is stationary. From continuity equation one can write,

$$y_2\,(U_2 - U_w) = y_1\,(U_1 - U_w)$$

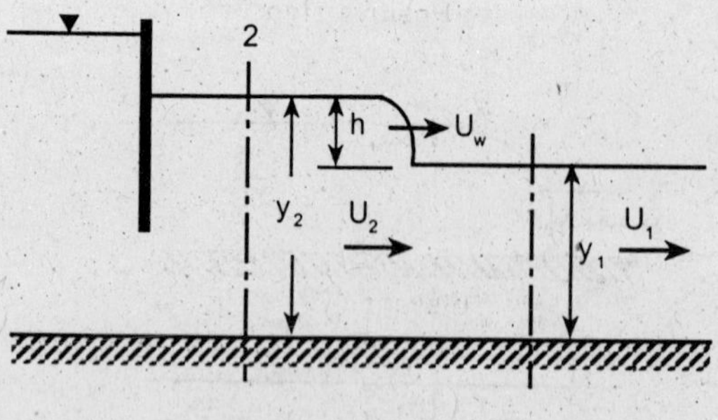

Fig. 13.28 Analysis of a surge

Solving for U_2 one gets

$$U_2 = \frac{y_1(U_1 - U_w) + y_2 U_w}{y_2} \qquad (13.38)$$

Since there is change in momentum due to this surge, one can write the momentum equation as,

$$\frac{1}{2}\gamma(y_2^2 - y_1^2) = \rho\, y_2 (U_2 - U_w)\,[(U_1 - U_w) - (U_2 - U_w)]$$

or

$$\frac{1}{2}\gamma(y_2^2 - y_1^2) = \rho\, y_2 (U_2 - U_w)(U_1 - U_2) \tag{13.39}$$

Substituting the above value of U_2 from Eq. 13.38 in Eq. 13.39 and simplifying one gets,

$$(U_w - U_1)^2 = \frac{gy_2}{2y_1}(y_2 + y_1) \tag{13.40}$$

Solving for U_w the following relation can be obtained

$$U_w = \sqrt{\frac{gy_2}{2y_1}(y_2 + y_1)} + U_1 \tag{13.41}$$

Equation 13.41 is the expression for the absolute velocity of the surge. The *celerity of the wave* C is defined as the velocity of the wave relative to the velocity of flow and hence $C = (U_w - U_1)$.

$$C = \sqrt{\frac{gy_2}{2y_1}(y_2 + y_1)} \tag{13.42}$$

Suppose the height of the surge is h which is equal to $(y_2 - y_1)$. Then one can replace y_2 by $(y_1 + h)$ in Eq. 13.42 to yield,

$$C = \sqrt{\frac{g(y_1 + h)(2y_1 + h)}{2y_1}}$$

Simplifying the above expression one gets

$$C = \sqrt{gy_1}\,\sqrt{1 + \frac{3}{2}\left(\frac{h}{y_1}\right) + \frac{1}{2}\left(\frac{h}{y_1}\right)^2}$$

If $h < y_1$ term $\frac{1}{2}(h/y_1)^2$ becomes sufficiently small and it can be neglected. Thus the celerity equation simplifies to

$$C = \sqrt{gy_1}\,\sqrt{1 + \frac{3}{2}\left(\frac{h}{y_1}\right)}$$

or

$$C \simeq \sqrt{gy_1}\left(1 + \frac{3}{4}\frac{h}{y_1}\right) \tag{13.43}$$

When the ratio h/y_1 is very small, one can even neglect the term $\frac{3}{4}\, h/y_1$ to yield.

$$C \simeq \sqrt{gy_1} \tag{13.44}$$

This simplification was suggested by Lagrange and hence Eq. 13.44 is sometimes known as Lagrange's equation for celerity of a small wave.

In the case of a stationary hydraulic jump, the absolute velocity U_w is zero. Hence substitution of $U_w = 0$ in Eq. 13.40 and subsequent simplification yields Eq. 13.32 or Eq. 13.33. Hence the stationary hydraulic jump is a special case of a surge.

The above analysis has been carried out for the case of a rectangular channel. Application of the same principles for a surge in a prismatic channel will yield the following relation for C,

$$C = (U_w - U_1) = \sqrt{\frac{(A_2\bar{Z}_2 - A_1\bar{Z}_1)g}{A_1\left(1 - \frac{A_1}{A_2}\right)}} \qquad (13.45)$$

which is a counterpart of Eq. 13.42. Here $\bar{Z}_1$ and $\bar{Z}_2$ are positions of centroids of areas A_1 and A_2 below the water surface. The above analysis neglects boundary friction, which is not very important in short channels. However in long natural streams friction becomes important. This causes change in the surge profile.

Example 13.14

A steady flow occurs in a rectangular channel at a depth of 1.5 m and a velocity of 2.0 m/s. The sides of the channel are 3 m high and the channel is 1000 m long. The flow is suddenly stopped at the downstream end by means of a gate. Due to the surge produced, will the water spill over the sides ? How much time will be required for the surge to reach the upstream end of the channel ?

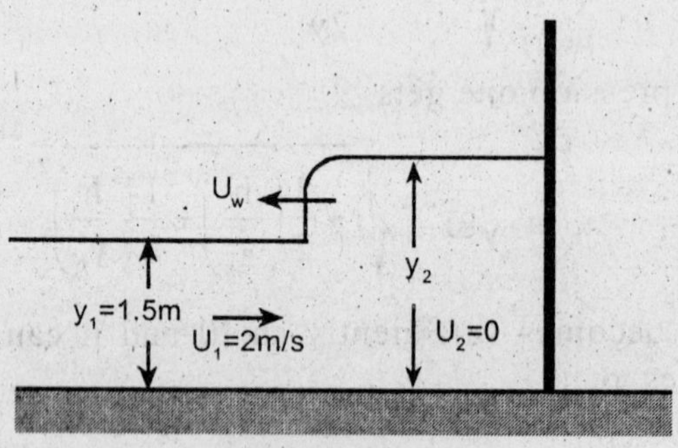

Fig. 13.29

In this problem the surge is moving in the opposite direction to flow (see Fig. 13.29). Therefore, to make it a case of steady flow apply a velocity U_w in the direction opposite to that of surge. The velocities before and after surge will then be $(U_1 + U_w)$ and $(U_2 + U_w)$ respectively. The continuity equation in this case is

$$y_1 (U_1 + U_w) = y_2 (U_2 + U_w)$$

and the momentum equation is

$\frac{1}{2}\gamma(y_2^2 - y_1^2) = \rho y_1 (U_1 + U_w)[(U_1 + U_w) - (U_2 + U_w)]$ As the flow is completely stopped the velocity $U_2 = 0$. Therefore, the two equations will be

$$1.5\,(2.0 + U_w) = y_2 U_w$$

and
$$\tfrac{1}{2} \times 9.81\,(y_2^2 - 1.5^2) = 1.5\,(2.0 + U_w)\,(2.0)$$

Substituting the value of U_w from the continuity equation in momentum equation, one gets,

$$4.905\, y_2^3 - 7.360\, y_2^2 - 17.060 y_2 + 16.56 = 0$$

This can be solved by trial and error process. It may be noted that an approximate value of y_2 can be obtained by Eq. 13.44 and the continuity equation. The surge velocity $U_w \doteqdot \sqrt{9.81 \times 1.5} = 3.83$ m/s and substituting this value in the continuity equation one can get $y_2 = 2.383$ m. This approximate value helps in the trial solution. By trial the value of y_2 in the momentum equation works out to be 2.30m. The velocity of the surge is therefore 3.75 m/s.

Since $y_2 = 2.30$ m the canal will not over flow as the height of the sides is 3.0 m. Time required for the surge to reach the upstream end is 1000/3.75 = 266.5 s or 4.45 minutes.

A *wave* is defined as a variation of velocity with time which travels through a fluid medium. The characteristics of waves depend on the fluid properties influencing the motion. Thus, there are capillary waves, gravity waves, and elastic waves. The capillary waves, as well as gravity waves require existence of a free surface or an interface between liquid and a gas, or two liquids. The elastic waves can be propagated through liquids and gases alike, regardless of whether or not the fluid is confined by solid boundaries. The viscosity of liquid opposes the fluid deformation and it gradually reduces the mechanical energy of the wave through transformation into heat.

Hydraulic engineers encounter a great variety of water waves. Waves generated by wind in oceans, flood waves in rivers, tidal waves, oscillations in harbours, moving hydraulic jumps, waves generated by moving ships in channels, tsunami waves generated by earthquakes, and waves generated by underwater nuclear explosions are some of the examples. All these are gravity waves. The gravity waves can be broadly classified into oscillatory waves and translatory waves. *Oscillatory waves* are periodic in character, imparting to the liquid an undulating motion with both horizontal and vertical components without causing any permanent discharge or mass transport. Waves caused by dropping a stone in calm water are oscillatory in nature. In such a case it can be seen that any floating material oscillates up and down as the wave passes, but remains at the same location. A *translatory wave* involves, by definition, a transport of fluid in the direction in which the wave travels. A moving hydraulic jump sometimes known as tidal bore, is a translatory wave.

An oscillatory wave can be either progressive or standing. A simple oscillatory progressive wave having a sine profile can be represented by the equation

$$\eta = a \sin \frac{2\pi}{\lambda}(x - Ct) \qquad (13.46)$$

in which "a" is the amplitude, λ is the wave length, C is the wave velocity in the positive x direction, and η is the elevation above the undistributed water level; see Fig. 13.30. The term λ/C gives the time required for one wave to pass past a particular section and is known as *wave period* T, whereas C/λ is the number of waves passing a fixed section per unit time and is known as *frequency*.

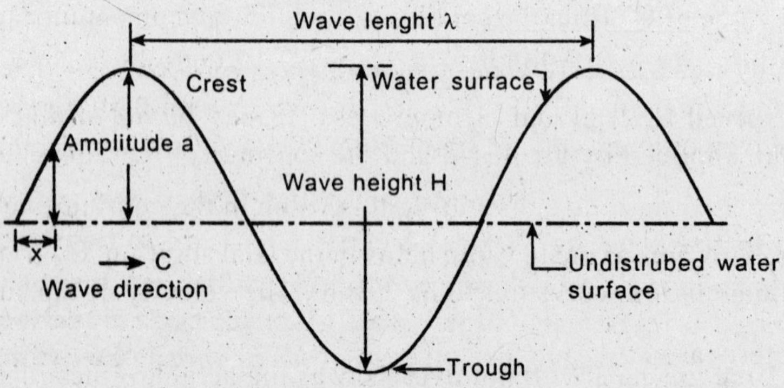

Fig. 13.30 Wave characteristics

Two progressive waves of the same amplitude and the same period travelling in opposite directions can be superposed. Thus

$$\eta = \eta_1 + \eta_2$$

$$= a \sin \frac{2\pi}{\lambda}(x - Ct) + a \sin \frac{2\pi}{\lambda}(x + Ct)$$

$$\therefore \quad \eta = 2a \cos \frac{2\pi t}{T} \sin \frac{2\pi x}{\lambda} \tag{13.47}$$

This is the equation of a *standing wave* whose amplitude is a function of time, see Fig. 13.31. This wave does not move in x direction; for given value of x, the water surface moves up and down.

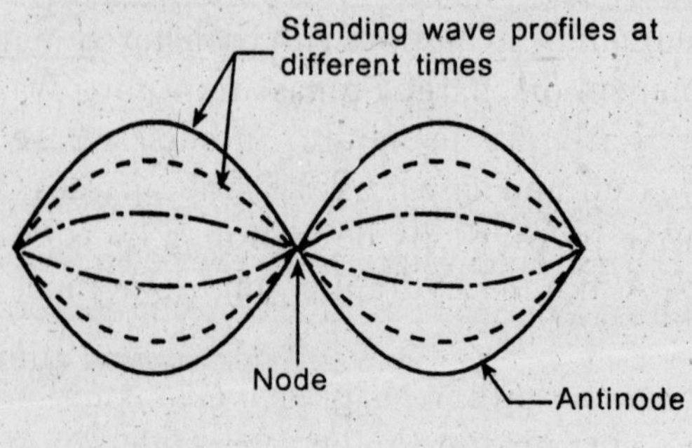

Fig. 13.31 Standing wave

The effect of surface tension on wave motion is very little or negligible unless the wave length is very small. The viscous effects in damping are also very small and can be neglected. In such cases the wave motion can be considered to be irrotational motion of a inviscid fluid. For this case the wave velocity C is related to the depth of flow h and wave length λ by the relation,

$$C^2 = \frac{g\lambda}{2\pi} \tanh \frac{2\pi h}{\lambda} \tag{13.48}$$

Waves governed by Eq. 13.48 are many time known as *Stokian waves*. Stokian theory is valid when a/λ and a/h are small. If h/λ is much smaller than 0.50, the waves are called *shallow water waves* or *long waves* ; then $\tanh 2\pi h/\lambda \approx 2\pi h/\lambda$ and hence

$$C^2 = \frac{g\lambda}{2\pi} \frac{2\pi h}{\lambda} = gh$$

$$\therefore \quad C = \sqrt{gh} \tag{13.49}$$

In shallow water waves the fluid particles can be shown to follow elliptic orbits in the plane of the wave. The vertical amplitude of the orbit becomes zero near the bed but not the horizontal one. If h/λ is greater than 0.50, the wave is called *deep water wave* or *short wave*. Then one can write

$$\tanh \frac{2\pi h}{\lambda} \approx 1.0$$

hence $$C^2 = \frac{g\lambda}{2\pi}$$

or $$C = \sqrt{\frac{gy}{2\pi}} \tag{13.50}$$

Thus C is proportional to square root of wave length in case of deep water waves. In deep water waves the liquid particles can be shown to follow circular orbits, its radius decreasing with increasing depth. These are shown in Fig. 13.32.

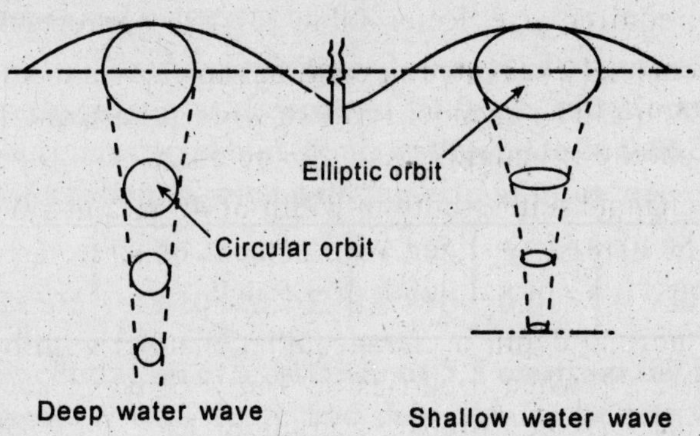

Fig. 13.32 Orbits of fluid particles in waves

PROBLEMS

13.1 From the basic principles discussed in Chapter 2, show that the continuity equation for open channel flow is given by

$$\frac{\partial A}{\partial t} + U\frac{\partial A}{\partial x} + A\frac{\partial U}{\partial x} = 0$$

What form will it take if there is inflow from the side at the rate of q m^3/s m ?

13.2 Show that for narrow deep rectangular channels R is approximately equal to B/2.

13.3 Prepare a graph showing variation of R/D with y/D for a circular channel; here D is the pipe diameter and R is the hydraulic radius.

13.4 Show that for channels with large slope, the pressure variation with depth is given by

$$p = \gamma y \cos^2 \theta$$

13.5 A cement lined laboratory channel of rectangular shape is laid at a bed slope of 0.0004. If it is 1.5 m wide, what discharge can be expected at uniform depth of 0.60 m in the channel ? Take n to be 0.011.

13.6 At what slope should a 0.50 m diameter vitrified clay pipe be laid in order to carry a discharge of 150 *l*/s when running half full ? Assume n to be 0.014.

13.7 Water flows at a uniform depth of 1.25 m in a rectangular channel 4 m wide laid at a slope of 1 in 1000. Compute the average shear stress on bottom of the channel.

13.8 A rectangular channel which is 5.0 m wide is laid at a slope of 0.000 09. Determine its discharge capacity in *l*/s when the normal depth is 2.1 m and the Manning's n has a value of 0.013.

13.9 A discharge of 40.0 m^3/s flows in a trapezidal channel with bottom width 4.0 m and side slopes 2 hor : 1 vert. If the normal depth at bottom slope of 0.0016 is 2.0 m, determine the values of n and C. Is the flow subcritical or supercritical ?

13.10 A circular pipe of reinforced concrete is to be used as a storm drainage conduit. It has to carry a discharge of 2.5 m^3/s at a slope of 1 in 2500, when running 0.9 full. Determine the required size. Refer Table 13.1 for appropriate value of n.

13.11 A trapezoidal channel excavated in earth has to carry a discharge of 5.0 m^3/s at a velocity of 0.75 m/s. The channel is 5.0 m wide at base and has side slope of 1:1. At what slope should it be laid? Take n to be 0.02.

13.12 A trapezoidal channel with a bottom width of 40 m and side slope 1:1 has a bed slope of 1 in 5000. If it is lined with cement concrete (n = 0.015) what is its carrying capacity at a normal depth of 3.5 m ?

13.13 Determine the normal depth in a trapezoidal channel with bottom width of 40 m and side slopes 2 : 1 when it carries 60.0 m^3/s of water at a slope of 1 in 5000. Take n to be 0.015. (Note : prepare a graph of $AR^{2/3}$ vs y. The normal depth will be that value of y at which $AR^{2/3} = Qn/S^{1/2}$).

13.14 Determine the normal depth in a triangular channel with apex angle of 90° when it carries a discharge of 1.5 m^3/s at a slope of 0.0001. Take Manning's n as 0.015.

13.15 Prove that the friction factor in the Darcy-Weisbach resistance equation is related to Manning's n by the formula

$$f = 8\ g\ n^2/R^{1/3}$$

13.16 The cross section of a channel is as shown in the figure. If S = 0.0004 and C = 80, determine Q.

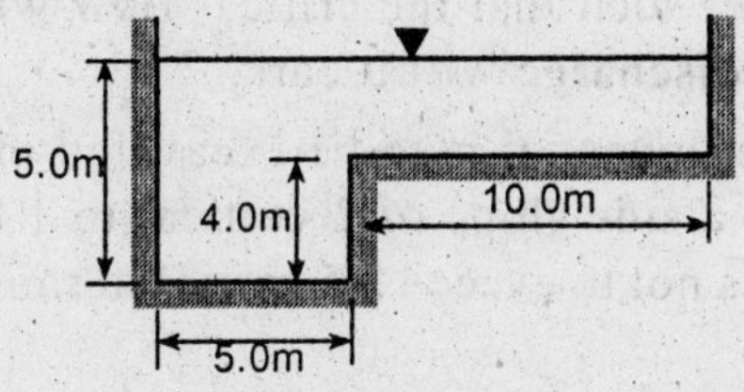

Prob. 13.16

13.17 The Tigris river at Mosul is nearly rectangular in shape with width of 300 m and bed material of median size 18 mm. The river has a bed slope of 0.005. At a depth of 2.0 m will the bed material move ? Determine the discharge.

13.18 From Shields' diagram prepare a curve showing variation of $\tau_{oc}/(\gamma_s - \gamma)d$ with $(\gamma_s - \gamma)\ d^3/\rho\nu^2$.

13.19 Making use of Shields' diagram or curve from problem 13.18 determine critical tractive stress for 0.40 mm sand of relative density 2.65 when the water temperature is 20°C.

13.20 What regime of flow will prevail in a wide channel with 0.40 mm sandy material with a slope of 0.0005 at 1.0 m, 3.0 m and 8.0 m depths ?

13.21 A 2.0 m wide rectangular channel has bed material with d_a = 2.0 mm and d_{90} = 4.5 mm. It carries a discharge of 3.2 m^3/s at a depth of 1.0 m when the channel slope is 0.0023. Using Meyer-Peter and Müller's bed load equation, determine the rate of bed load carried by the channel and express it in N/s.

13.22 A 1.22 m wide rectangular channel with bed composed of sand of 0.18 mm diameter carries 0.20 m^3/s discharge at a depth of 21.0 cm and slope of 0.001 35. The suspended load concentration at mid-depth was found to be 0.062 percent by weight. The velocity distribution measured with the help of pitot tube is given below

y cm	0.60	1.25	1.85	3.35	7.35	14.85	19.50
u m/s	0.348	0.506	0.610	0.702	0.890	0.915	0.930

Determine the concentration at a distance of 5.5 cm from the bed. Also compute concentration variation with depth and then obtain the rate of suspended load transport using method of graphical integration. Take fall velocity of sediment as 2.0 cm/s.

13.23 Determine the super elevation in a rectangular channel bend when the channel width is 4.0 m, centre-line radius of bend is 8.0 m and it carries a discharge of 5.0 m^3/s at a depth of 1.25 m.

13.24 A rectangular concrete lined channel with a bed width of 10 m has a bend of centre-line radius 80 m. When the depth in the channel is 2.5 m, a super elevation of 6.0 cm was observed in the bend. Estimate the discharge. If Manning's n = 0.016, what is the channel slope ?

13.25 A very wide rectangular channel has a roughness coefficient n = 0.02. Determine the slope of this channel such that the critical flow will be obtained at a normal depth of 1.50 m. What discharge will it carry ?

13.26 A hydraulically efficient channel is to be excavated in rock to carry 100 m^3/s of water. The channel has a side slope of 2 vertical to 1 horizontal and the average velocity in the channel is not to exceed 2.5 m/s. Determine its dimensions assuming n to be 0.02.

13.27 For an open channel with circular cross-section, show that maximum discharge will occur at a depth 0.95 diameter of channel (use Chezy's equation).

13.28 Show that triangular channel section is most efficient when its central angle is 90°.

13.29 For a rectangular channel, show that Q is maximum at the critical depth when specific force P is constant.

13.30 Show that for a rectangular channel carrying constant discharge, the specific force is minimum when the depth is critical.

13.31 For a circular conduit flowing partially full, show that the condition

$$\frac{Q^2}{gD^5} = \frac{\theta - \sin\theta\cos\theta}{64\sin\theta}$$

is satisfied when the depth is critical.

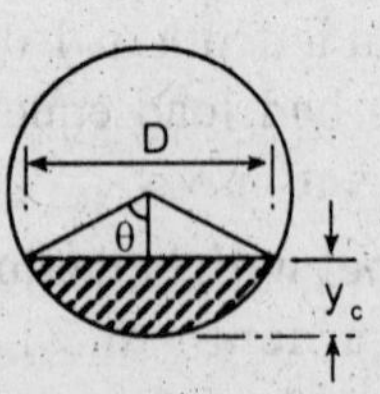

Prob. 13.31

13.32 In a wide rectangular channel the velocity distribution is given by $u/u_m = (y/D)^{1/n}$, where u_m is the surface velocity and D is the depth of flow. Obtain the energy and momentum correction factors α and β.

13.33 A trapezoidal canal 5 m wide at the base has side slope of 1 : 1. It carries a discharge of 2.5 m^3/s. Prepare a specific energy diagram for depths of flow varying from 0.53 to 3.5 m. From the diagram find the value of critical depth, minimum specific energy, and a depth alternate to 1.5 m.

13.34 A rectangular channel 4.0 m in width has a normal depth of 0.50 m when the channel slope is 0.0049 and n has value of 0.013. Determine,

i. discharge per metre width ;

ii. whether the flow is laminar or turbulent ;

iii. whether the flow is rapid or tranquil ;

iv. specific energy and specific force ;

v. critical depth, and

vi. depth alternate to 0.50 m.

13.35 A parabolic channel defined by the equation $x^2 = 4y$ carries a discharge of 3.0 m³/s. Determine the critical depth.

13.36 Find the diameter of a circular conduit carrying a discharge of 0.50 m³/s if the flow is to be critical when the conduit is running half full.

13.37 A canal has a bed width of 7.0 m and side slope of 2 horizontal to 1 vertical. Assuming Manning's n to be 0.025, calculate

i. bed slope required for a normal depth of 1.2 m at a discharge of 10 m³/s;

ii. critical depth and critical slope at a discharge of 10 m³s.

13.38 A trapezoidal canal with side slope of 2 horizontal to 1 vertical has to carry a flow of 17.0 m³/s. If the bottom width is 4 m, calculate depth and longitudinal slope required to maintain the critical depth. Adopt C to be 100 in Chezy's equation.

13.39 Using Eq. 13.13, show that the critical depth in a triangular channel with an apex angle 2θ is given by the formula

$$y_c = \sqrt[5]{\frac{2Q^2}{g \tan^2 \theta}}$$

13.40 A trapezoidal channel 40.0 m wide at the base and with 2 : 1 side slope carries a discharge of 150.0 m³/s. Prepare a specific energy diagram for the depths of flow between 0.50 m and 5.0m. From the diagram determine the value of critical depth, minimum specific energy and the depth alternate to 0.50 m.

13.41 Using Manning's equation obtain the condition for velocity to remain constant for various normal depths for a channel with constant S and n.

13.42 Show that the height of broad crested weir required for obtaining critical flow on the weir is given by

$$\frac{W}{y_1} \geq \frac{1}{3}\left(1+\frac{1}{2}Fr_1^2\right)$$

13.43 For a triangular broad crested weir flowing free, show that the discharge is given by

$$Q = \frac{16}{25} \tan\theta \sqrt{\frac{2}{5} g} \; H_1^{5/2}$$

in which θ is half the apex angle.

13.44 A 5 m wide rectangular flume (n = 0.012) is laid at a slope of 0.0004 and carries a discharge of 15.0 m³/s. To what width should it be narrowed in order to obtain critical depth at the contracted section without affecting the conditions at upstream end ?

13.45 Uniform flow occurs at depth of 1.5 m in a long 3 m wide rectangular channel laid at a slope of 0.001. If Manning's n is given as 0.015, calculate (i) the minimum height of the hump on the floor to produce critical depth, and (ii) the width a contracted section which will produce critical depth without increasing the upstream depth of flow.

13.46 For the purpose of discharge measurement, the width of a rectangular channel is reduced from 2.75 m to 2.15 m and the floor is raised by 30 cm at a given section When the approaching depth of flow is 2 m, what rate of flow will be indicated by a drop of 15 cm in the water surface elevation at the contracted section ?

13.47 Uniform flow occurs at a depth of 1.3 m in a rectangular canal of 3.0 m width laid at a slope of 0.0004. To what width can the canal be narrowed to cause critical flow in the contracted section? If the width is reduced to 1.5 m, what depth of the flow, can be expected at the contracted section and on the upstream side where the width is 3.0 m. Take n to be 0.014.

13.48 A 3.5 m wide rectangular channel carries a discharge of 10 m³/s at a depth of 1.75 m. If the width is to be reduced to 2.25 m at a given section, what change in bottom elevation at that section will maintain the water surface at the same level as before ?

13.49 In a 3.5 m wide rectangular canal laid at a slope or 0.0036, uniform flow occurs at depth of 2 m. There is a flexible hump on the floor which can be raised or lowered Find how high can the hump be raised without causing afflux ? If the upstream depth of flow is to be raised to 2.3 m, how high should the hump be placed ? Adopt Manning's n as 0.015.

13.50 Calculate the discharge over a 4 m long broad crested weir if the depth of flow over the crest is 0.5 m. Take C_d to be 0.97.

13.51 Sketch the flow profiles in the following cases

i. mild slope to steep slope,

ii. mild slope to horizontal slope.

iii. mild slope to adverse slope,

iv. steep slope to mild slope,

v. steep slope to horizontal slope.

13.52 A 7.0 m wide rectangular channel consists of three reaches of different bed slopes which are in continuation one after another. The first reach has a slope of 0.01 and is 150 m long, the second one has a slope of 0.0004 and is 500 m long and the third one has a bed slope of 0.0036 and is 300 m long. For a discharge of 15 m^3/s and n of 0.015 plot the water surface profiles.

13.53 The value of Chezy's C for a wide rectangular channel carrying a discharge of 5.30 m^3/s m is 60.0. If the channel slope abruptly changes from 0.0009 to 0.0049, determine the lengths of surface profiles using step method. Make computations upto y/y_o equal to 0.990 and 1.001 respectively.

13.54 A trapezoidal channel with bottom width of 30.0 m, and side slopes 1:1 has a bottom slope of 0.0004. It discharges 175.0 m^3/s of water into a large reservoir where the depth of flow is 7.50 m. Determine the depth of flow 11.30 km upstream if n has a value of 0.022. Use graphical integration method.

13.55 In order to decrease the average velocity of flow, a low overflow dam is installed at the end of a long rectangular channel. The channel is 3.25 m wide and its bed slope is 0.001. If the depth just upstream of the dam is 2.5 m for a discharge of 9 m^3/s, how far upstream the back-water will cause a velocity reduction of 20% ? Assume n to be 0.014 and use single step method.

13.56 A sluice gate discharges 8.0 m^3/s m of water in a wide rectangular horizontal channel. The gate opening is 0.75 m and the coefficient is 0.60. Assuming Chezy's C to be 75 and using the step method, determine how far downstream of the vena contracta the depth of flow will be 1.50 m.

13.57 Solve Problem 13.56 using graphical integration method.

13.58 A wide rectangular channel carrying 5.0 m^3/s m has a bottom slope of 0.000 266 and Manning's n of 0.015. If the channel is followed by a sudden drop, determine how far upstream from the drop the depth of flow will be 2.40 m. Use step method.

13.59 Solve Problem 13.58 using Bresse's method.

13.60 Solve Problem 13.58 using Chow's method.

13.61 Show that in the case of wide rectangular channel with horizontal floor,

$$x = \frac{C^2}{g}\left(y - \frac{y^4}{4y_c^3}\right) + \text{constant}$$

13.62 A 4 m wide long rectangular channel carries a flow of 7.5 m^3/s, bottom slope changing abruptly from 0.01 to 0.0001. Assuming Manning's n to be 0.015, examine conditions of flow.

13.63 Show that the specific force P for a trapezoidal channel of bed width B and side slopes z : 1 can be expressed in terms of three dimensionless parameters

$$\frac{Pz^2}{B^3},\ \frac{z^3Q^2}{gB^5} \text{ and } \frac{zy}{B} \text{ as}$$

$$\frac{Pz^2}{B^2} = \frac{z^3 Q^2}{gB^5}\left[\frac{1}{(1+zy/B)(zy/B)}\right] + \frac{z^2 y^2}{B^2}\left(\frac{1}{2}+\frac{1}{3}\frac{zy}{B}\right)$$

13.64 For the case of hydraulic jump in a rectangular channel, complete the following table :

y_1 m	U_1 m/s	q m³/ms	y_2 m	U_2 m/s	H_L m
0.20			1.204		
		2.50		2.50	
		50			59.5

13.65 A hydraulic jump occurs in a rectangular channel and the depths of flow before and after jump are 0.5 m and 2.0 m respectively. Calculate the critical depth and the energy loss in the jump.

13.66 In the case of' a hydraulic jump in a rectangular channel show that

i. $$H_L = \frac{(y_2-y_1)^3}{4y_2 y_1}$$

ii. $$a^3 = \frac{(x-1)^9}{33x^4(x+1)}$$

in which $a = H_L/y_c$ and $x = y_2/y_1$

13.67 For hydraulic jump in a rectangular channel show that

$$Fr_2^2 = \frac{8\,Fr_1^2}{\left(\sqrt{1+8\,Fr_1^2}-1\right)^3}$$

13.68 Show that for hydraulic jump in a rectangular channel

$$\frac{H_L}{H_1} = \frac{8\,Fr_1^4+20\,Fr_1^2-(8\,Fr_1^2+1)^{3/2}-1}{8\,Fr_1^2\left(2+Fr_1^2\right)}$$

13.69 Show that in the case of a hydralic jump in a triangular channel, the depths y_1 and y_2 are related by the equation

$$\frac{1}{3}\left(\frac{y_2^3}{y_1^3}-1\right) = Fr_1^2\left(1-\frac{y_1^2}{y_2^2}\right)$$

in which $Fr_1^2 = Q^2/gA_1^2y_1$.

13.70 At the bottom of a spillway the velocity of water is 12.0 m/s and the depth of flow is 1.5 m. If the available tail water depth is 5 m, find the position of the jump with repect to the toe of the spillway. What should be the approximate length of the stilling basin ? Assume the floor downstream of spillway to be horizontal and take n to be 0.014.

3.71 A river flowing towards the sea at the velocity of 2.5 m/s and a depth of 2.0 m encounters an incoming tide which increases its depth to 4.0m. This creates a surge travelling upstream in the river. Estimate the celerity of surge. What speed and direction will the flow have downstream of the surge ?

3.72 The depth and velocity of flow in a rectangular channel are 1.0 m and 1.75 m/s respectively. If the rate of inflow at the upstream is doubled, what will be the height and the absolute velocity of the resulting surge ?

3.73 Find the velocity of propagation of waves of wave length 150 m travelling in 30 m deep water. What will be their velocity if the depth is 500 m ?

3.74 A floating piece of wood is found to come on the crest 20 times per minute in deep sea. Determine the wave length and velocity of propagation of waves.

3.75 Using Moody's friction factor diagram find the values of f and C for 3.0 m wide rectangular channel carrying a discharge of 6.0 m^3/s at a depth of 1.50 m. Assume water temperature to be 20°C and roughness height as 2.00 mm.

23.71 A river flowing towards the sea at the velocity of 2.5 m/s and 3.0 m depth is [illegible] tidal [illegible], which increases its depth to [illegible] m. This causes a surge travelling upstream in the river. Estimate the velocity of surge. What speed and direction will the flow have downstream of the surge?

23.72 The depth and velocity of flow in a rectangular channel are 1.0 m and 2.0 m/s respectively. If the rate of inflow at the upstream is suddenly [illegible], find the height and the absolute velocity of the resulting surge.

23.73 The phase velocity of propagation of waves in water found 150 m/s in deep water. What will be the wave velocity in the depth 5.500 m?

[illegible] A floating piece of wood is found to come on the crest 20 times per minute in deep sea. Determine the wave length and velocity of propagation of waves.

23.74 Using Moody's friction factor diagram find the values of f and C for a 2 m wide rectangular channel carrying a discharge of 4.5 m^3/s at a depth of 1.5 m. Assume water temperature to be 20°C and roughness height as 2.00 mm.

Chapter Fourteen

Compressible Flow

14.1 Introduction

In the case of compressible fluids, there occurs volume change which can influence the fluid motion appreciably. Such a case, where there is appreciable volume change, needs to be analysed taking into account the compressibility of the fluid. In previous chapters it has been tacitly assumed that these volume changes are small and hence the problems have been analysed on the assumption that fluid under consideration is incompressible. Problems involving large volume change include flights of airplanes and projectiles, flow of gases through orifices and nozzles, problems in accoustics and problems involving flow of gases in machines such as compressors. These large volume changes occur under the following conditions;

1. whenever there is a great change in the elevation as in the case of flights of air planes at varying altitude and in meteorology;
2. when gases move at very high velocities. This occurs when bodies such as projectiles or jet planes travel in air at very high velocities or when two regions, between which there is a pressure difference comparable with the absolute pressure, are connected by a tube; and
3. when large accelerations occur. This occurs in the case of fluids (either moving or stationary) when solid body in contact with it moves with large accelerations- e.g. water hammer and acoustical problems.

14.2 Basic Relationships

It has been mentioned that a gas can be compressed or expanded in two different ways. When a gas is compressed, heat is produced. If sufficient time is allowed for heat to diffuse in the surrounding and retain its original temperature, the gas is compressed at constant temperature and the process is known as *isothermal*. Isothermal process is governed by Boyle's law according to which for a given mass of gas

$$pv = p_1 v_1 = \text{constant}$$

On the other hand, if the gas is not given sufficient time to attain the temperature of its surrounding, then compression or expansion takes place at constant heat content and is known as adiabatic process. If the process is *adiabatic* and the changes are reversible (often known as the frictionless adiabatic process) then the process is called *isentropic.* There the pressure rise is faster than in the isothermal process and is given by the formula

$$pv^k = p_1 v_1^k = \text{constant} \quad (1.9)$$

In the above equations p is the pressure and v is the specific volume. Furthermore, one has the *equation of state,*

$$\frac{pv}{T} = R \quad (1.13)$$

in which R is the gas constant and T is thermodynamic (absolute) temperature which is related to the temperature in celsius as

$$T°K = 273.16 + t\,°C$$

While discussing the values of R and k and their inter-relationship, two more terms - specific heat at constant volume and specific heat at constant pressure - need to be introduced. *Specific heat at constant volume,* C_v is the amount of heat required to change the temperature of unit weight of a fluid through one degree celcuis when the volume remains constant. Similarly the *specific heat at constant pressure,* C_p is the amount of heat required to change the temperature of unit weight of a fluid through one degree celsius when the pressure remains unaltered. It can be shown that k, R, C_p and C_v are related as follows,

$$C_v = \frac{R}{k-1}$$

$$C_p = \frac{k}{k-1} R$$

$$\frac{C_p}{C_v} = k$$

Some average values of k and R for various gases are given in Table 14.1. A prefect gas is defined as a fluid that has constant C_p, C_v and hence k and follows Eq. 1.13.

TABLE 14.1

Average Values of k and R for various gases

Gas	k	R (m/K)
Air	1.40	29-57
Carbon monoxide	1.40	30.64
Carbon dioxide	1.30	19.50
Oxygen	1.29	26.80
Helium	1.66	215.00
Hydrogen	1.41	425.00

Since variation in the volume of gases involves consideration of temperature and heat content, the analysis of flow of fluids with appreciable volume change requires a synthesis of fluid mechanics and thermodynamics. This in turn leads to the concept of *internal energy.* The internal energy e is the energy possessed by a unit weight of fluid due to the state of molecular activity. Any net transfer of energy to the fluid producing solely an increase in the random molecular activity will represent an increase in the internal energy of the fluid. The change in the internal energy $(e_2 - e_1)$ of a unit weight of fluid depends only on the initial and the final state of fluid and does not depend on the manner in which these states are attained. In other words, the internal energy change $(e_2 - e_1)$ is solely a function of $(T_2 - T_1)$ where T_1 and T_2 are the thermodynamic (absolute) temperatures. Evidently

$$(e_2 - e_1) = C_v (T_2 - T_1)$$

When a gas expands, it will perform external work and there will be absorption of heat as well as change in the internal energy. Evidently according to the principle of conservation of energy,

$$\left\{\begin{matrix}\text{Heat absorbed}\\ \text{per unit weight}\\ \text{of gas}\end{matrix}\right\} = \left\{\begin{matrix}\text{Work done}\\ \text{per unit}\\ \text{weight of gas}\end{matrix}\right\} + \left\{\begin{matrix}\text{Increase in the}\\ \text{internal energy}\\ \text{per unit weight}\\ \text{of gas}\end{matrix}\right\}$$

$$H = W + (e_2 - e_1) \tag{14.1}$$

The statement embodied in Eq. 14.1 is known as the *First Law of Thermodynamics.*

Expressions for work done can now be obtained for isothermal as well as adiabatic processes. For isothermal process, since the temperature remains constant $(e_2 - e_1)$ is zero. Hence,

$$H = W \tag{14.2}$$

On the other hand, for the isentropic process there is no interchange of heat and hence $H = 0$ and the temperature changes. Therefore.

for isentropic process $W + (e_2 - e_1) = 0$

or

$$W = (e_1 - e_2) \tag{14.3}$$

Next, the work done by the gas during isothermal and adiabatic processes (see Fig. 14.1) can be obtained as follows.

$$W = \int_{v_1}^{v_2} p\,dv \tag{14.4}$$

But for isothermal process,

$$pv = p_1 v_1$$

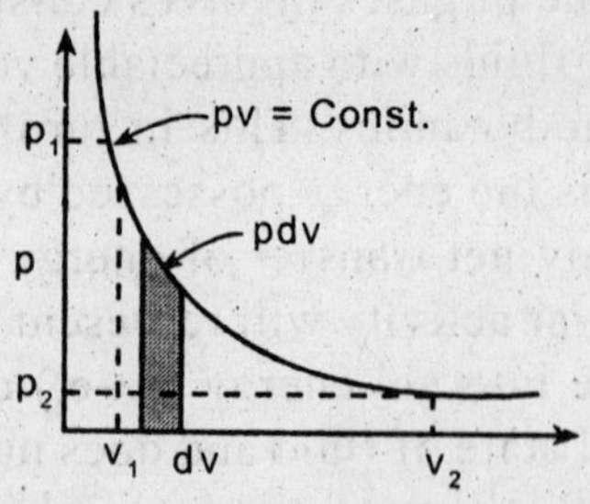

Fig. 14.1 p – v relationship

$$\therefore \quad p = \frac{p_1 v_1}{v}$$

$$\therefore \quad W = p_1 v_1 \int_{v_1}^{v_2} \frac{dv}{v} = p_1 v_1 \log_e \frac{v_2}{v_1}$$

or
$$W = RT_1 \log_e \frac{v_2}{v_1} \tag{14.5}$$

In the case of adiabatic process,

$$pv^k = p_1 v_1^k \text{ or } p = \frac{p_1 v_1^k}{v^k}$$

Hence Eq. 14.4 becomes

$$W = p_1 v_1^k \int_{v_1}^{v_2} \frac{dv}{v^k}$$

$$= \frac{p_1 v_1^k}{1-k} (v_2^{1-k} - v_1^{1-k}) \tag{14.6}$$

However
$$p_1 v_1^k = p_2 v_2^k$$

Therefore
$$W = \left(\frac{p_1 v_1 - p_2 v_2}{k-1} \right) \tag{14.7}$$

Equations 14.3, 14.5 and 14.7 give the work done per unit weight of the fluid.

Entropy of a Gas

Entropy can be defined as the measure of availability of energy for conversion into work. If ΔH is the heat absorbed by a unit weight of gas in a small time interval and if T is the thermodynamic (absolute) temperature of the gas at that instant, then the change in the entropy Δϕ is defined by the relation

$$\Delta\phi = \frac{\Delta H}{T} \tag{14.8}$$

or

$$\phi_2 - \phi_1 = \int_{T_1}^{T_2} \frac{dH}{T} \qquad (14.9)$$

In an isothermal process where temperature remains constant, it can be seen that

$$\phi_2 - \phi_1 = \frac{H}{T} = \frac{p_1 v_1 \log_e \frac{v_2}{v_1}}{JT} \qquad (14.10)$$

where J is the conversion factor for work into heat units. It is known that 4.187 joules is equivalent to 1 calory; hence J = 4.187. In an adiabatic process, since there is no change in the heat content, dH = 0; hence $(\phi_2 - \phi_1) = 0$

14.3 Propagation of Elastic Waves

In the case of compressible fluids it is possible that within a given system of fluid elements, the elements can occupy different volumes in space. In other words, a group of fluid elements can expand into a large volume without requiring a simultaneous shift to be made of all elements in the flow. But such a small displacement in fluid elements (i.e., a change in mass density) in a compressible fluid induces similar small movement in the adjacent elements or layers and therefore, a small disturbance which takes the form of a pressure wave or elastic wave travels through the medium at a certain speed. If the fluid were completely incompressible, such an adjustment of transmission of pressure wave takes place instantaneously, and hence the velocity of propagation of the elastic or pressure wave is infinite. However, since all the fluids and solids can be compressed to some extent, the velocity of pressure wave is finite. An expression for the velocity of elastic wave can be obtained as follows:

Consider an initially stationary compressible fluid in a constant-area rigid pipe, see Fig. 14.2. Suppose that with the help of some device such as a piston, a small increase in the pressure dp is established. This is achieved by moving the piston to the right at a uniform velocity u for time dt.

The resulting increase in pressure propagates through the fluid at the velocity of elastic wave C and reaches a distance Cdt in time dt. In the length Cdt, there is an increased pressure and as a result, the mass density of the fluid increases by dρ. Therefore, according to the principle of continuity,

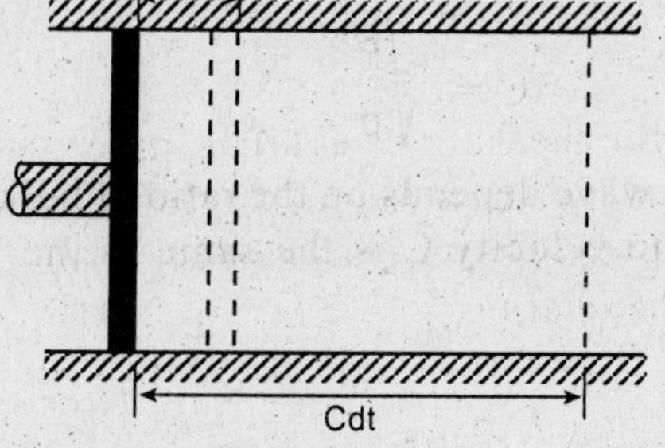

Fig. 14.2 Definition sketch

$$\rho\ A\ u\ dt = A\ C\ dt\ d\rho$$

in which A is the cross sectional area of the pipe

Or $$C = u\ \frac{\rho}{d\rho} \quad (14.11)$$

Neglecting the friction, the application of momentum equation yields

$$A\ dp\ dt\ = \rho\ A\ C\ dt\ (u - 0)$$

Or $$C = \frac{dp}{\rho u} \quad (14.12)$$

Combining Eqs. 14.11 and 14.12 the following expression can be obtained for C,

$$C^2 = \frac{dp}{d\rho} \quad (14.13)$$

It may be pointed out that this process of propagation of elastic wave, being vary rapid, can be considered to occur at constant heat content and is reversible i.e., it is an isentropic process. This is so inspite of the conditions prevalent in the flow itself.

It may be recalled that the bulk or volume modulus of elasticity of fluids E has been defined (see Chapter 1) as

$$E = -\ v\frac{dp}{dv} \quad (1.7)$$

Writing the specific volume $v = \dfrac{1}{\rho g}$, one gets

$$\rho v = \text{constant}$$

or $$vd\rho + \rho dv = 0$$

or $$\frac{v}{dv} = -\frac{\rho}{d\rho} \quad (14.14)$$

Hence combining Eq. 1.7 and 14.14, E can be expressed as

$$E = \rho\ \frac{dp}{d\rho} \quad (14.15)$$

From Eqs. 14.13 and 14.15, the expression for C becomes,

$$C = \sqrt{\frac{E}{\rho}} \quad (14.16)$$

Thus the velocity of the elastic wave depends on the ratio of bulk modulus of elasticity to the density of fluid. The elastic velocity C is the same as the velocity of sound in the fluid.

Since for isothermal process E = p, (see Chapter 1),

$$C = \sqrt{\frac{p}{\rho}} = \sqrt{gp\frac{1}{g\rho}} = \sqrt{gRT} \quad (14.17)$$

Likewise, since for isentropic process E = kp

$$C = \sqrt{\frac{kp}{\rho}} = \sqrt{kg\ RT} \quad (14.18)$$

Example 14.1

Determine the speed of sound in air at 20°C at sea level. The process of propagation of elastic wave is very rapid and hence is taken as isentropic.

$$T = 273.16 + 20 = 293.16°K$$

$$C = \sqrt{kg\ RT} = \sqrt{1.4 \times 9.81 \times 29.57 \times 293.16}$$

$$= 344.05 \text{ m/s}$$

14.4 Mach Number and its Importance

In Chapter 7 on Dimensional Analysis, a brief mention has been made about the ratio of characteristic velocity U to the velocity of sound or elastic wave C, which is designated as Mach number. Mach number can also be interpreted as the square root of the ratio of intertial force per unit volume $\rho U^2/L$ to the elastic force per unit volume E/L. As has been briefly explained in Chapter 12 on Forces on Immersed Bodies, Mach number is important in those problems in which the characteristic velocity of the flow is comparable with the velocity of elastic wave or the velocity of sound. Such occasions arise in the case of airplanes, bullets, projectiles and the tips of propellers travelling at very high speed. Mach number is also important in the case of flow of gases through orifices, nozzles and venturimeters where adiabatic acceleration takes place.

One might compare the structures of Froude number, Mach number and Weber number. It has been already mentioned that the Froude number is a ratio of the characteristic velocity to the velocity of a small gravity wave. Mach number is a ratio of the characteristic velocity to the velocity of sound or elastic wave in the medium. In the same way, Weber number can be interpreted as a ratio of the characteristic velocity to the velocity of the capillary wave.

Depending upon the value of the Mach number, the flow can be classified into the following categories:

1. *Subsonic Flow* : The Mach number anywhere in the flow lies within the range 0.4 to 1.0.
2. *Transonic Flow*: The Mach number in flow region is slightly less to slightly greater than unity.
3. *Supersonic Flow* : The Mach number in the flow region is always greater than unity but less than six.
4. *Hypersonic Flow* : The Mach number exceeds an approximate value of six.

In Chapter 12, a discussion has been presented on the transmission of pressure waves caused by the body moving in a compressible fluid. When the Mach number is less than unity, the pressure wave caused by the moving body is always ahead of the body; on the other hand, when M is greater than unity, velocity of the body is greater than the velocity of the pressure wave and as a result the body always leaves behind the pressure wave it has created. Under such circumstances all the activity is restricted in the Mach cone shown in Fig. 12.12, the angle of the cone α, known as Mach angle, being given by

$$\alpha = \sin^{-1}\frac{C}{U}$$

As another illustration of the importance of Mach number, the variation of discharge coefficient of the orifice can be discussed. If compressible fluid flows through a pipe containing an orifice plate, the forces governing the flow through the orifice will be pressure, inertia, viscous force and elastic force. As a result one would expect that the discharge coefficient C_d (which can be interpreted as Euler number) would vary with Re and M, and furthermore for large values of M, $C_d = f(M)$. Such a relationship is shown in Fig. 14.3.

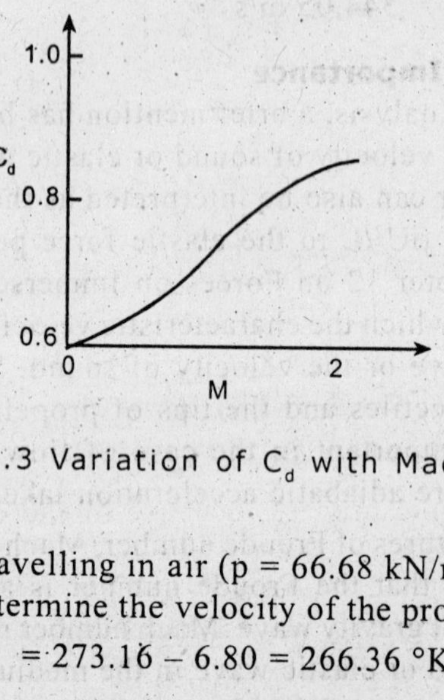

Fig. 14.3 Variation of C_d with Mach number

Example 14.2

In the case of a projectile travelling in air (p = 66.68 kN/m²) and t = – 6.8°C) the Mach angle is found to be 30°. Determine the velocity of the projectile.

$$T^\circ = 273.16 - 6.80 = 266.36\ ^\circ K$$

$$= \sqrt{kg\ RT} = \sqrt{1.4\times 9.81\times 29.57\times 266.36}$$

$$= 328.90 \text{ m/s}$$

Since $\sin\alpha = \frac{C}{U}$ ∴ $\frac{328.9}{U} = \frac{1}{2}$

Hence U = 657.8 m/s

14.5 Energy Equation for Compressible Fluids

In the discussion in the present section and in the subsequent sections, it is assumed that the flow of the compressible fluid is steady and one dimensional. Furthermore, while considering the effect of change in the cross-sectional area and of friction, it is assumed that such modifications do not alter the one dimensional character of the flow.

(a) Frictionless Flow

In the case of frictionless flow of an incompressible fluid, it was mentioned in Chapter 3 that the summation of kinetic energy, potential energy and pressure energy per unit weight or mass of the fluid remains same. This principle can be extended to frictionless flow of compressible fluid; however, one must take into account the effect of addition or subtraction of heat, and the associated changes in the internal energy of the fluid due to change in temperature. In other words, per unit weight of fluid

[kinetic energy +potential energy + pressure energy + internal energy]$_1$ = [kinetic energy + potential energy + pressure energy + internal energy]$_2$ – H

in which H is the amount of heat absorbed per unit weight of the fluid between sections 1 and 2. Or

$$\frac{U_1^2}{2g} + \frac{p_1}{\gamma_1} + z_1 + e_1 = \frac{U_2^2}{2g} + \frac{p_2}{\gamma_2} + z_2 + e_2 - H \qquad (14.19)$$

In the case of isothermal flow, because of the constancy of temperature, $e_1 = e_2$ and

$$\frac{p_1}{\gamma_1} = \frac{p_2}{\gamma_2}$$

furthermore $$H = W = RT \log_e \frac{v_2}{v_1}$$

Hence Eq. 14.19 becomes

$$(z_1 - z_2) + RT \log_e \frac{v_2}{v_1} = \frac{U_2^2}{2g} - \frac{U_1^2}{2g} \qquad (14.20)$$

Similarly in the case of isentropic process, because of the constancy of heat content, H = 0 and

$$(e_1 - e_2) = W = \frac{p_1 v_1 - p_2 v_2}{k-1} \qquad (14.7)$$

Hence for isentropic conditions, Eq. 14.19 becomes

$$(z_1 - z_2) + \frac{p_1 v_1 - p_2 v_2}{k-1} + (p_1 v_1 - p_2 v_2) = \frac{U_2^2}{2g} - \frac{U_1^2}{2g}$$

or $$(z_1 - z_2) + \frac{k}{k-1}(p_1 v_1 - p_2 v_2) = \frac{U_2^2}{2g} - \frac{U_1^2}{2g} \qquad (14.21)$$

It may further be pointed out that for the flow of gases, because of extremely small specific weight, the effect of change in elevation is very small compared to other terms and therefore the term $(z_1 - z_2)$ can be omitted from Eqs. 14.20 and 14.21.

(b) Flows with Friction

The frictional resistance to flow of compressible fluid has two effects. Firstly frictional resistance to the flow is a natural physical hindrance to flow. Secondly the energy spent in overcoming the frictional resistance is converted into heat. Part of this heat can be reutilised by the compressible fluid, causing it to expand further.

14.6 Stagnation Pressure in Compressible Flows

Consider the flow of a compressible fluid around an immersed body under frictionless adiabatic (i.e. isentropic) flow conditions. Let U_1, p_1, and ρ_1 be the velocity, pressure and mass density of the ambient flow and U_2, p_2, ρ_2 be the corresponding quantities at some other point. Hence Eq. 14.21 can be written as

$$\frac{k}{k-1}\left(\frac{p_1}{\rho_1}-\frac{p_2}{\rho_2}\right)=\frac{U_2^2-U_1^2}{2} \tag{14.22}$$

where the difference in elvation term has been dropped.

However.

$$\frac{p_1}{\rho_1^{k}}=\frac{p_2}{\rho_2^{k}} \text{ and hence } \frac{\rho_1}{\rho_2}=\left(\frac{p_1}{p_2}\right)^{\frac{-1}{k}}$$

Therefore, Eq. 14.22 can be written as

$$\frac{k}{k-1}\;\frac{p_1}{\rho_1}\left[1-\left(\frac{p_2}{p_1}\right)\left(\frac{\rho_2}{\rho_1}\right)\right]=\frac{U_2^2-U_1^2}{2} \tag{14.22 a}$$

or, since $kp_1/\rho_1 = C_1^2$ where C_1 is velocity of the pressure wave, one gets

$$\frac{U_2^2-U_1^2}{2}=\frac{C_1^2}{k-1}\left[1-\left(\frac{p_1}{p_2}\right)^{\frac{1-k}{k}}\right] \tag{14.23}$$

Equation 14.23 can be written as,

$$\frac{p_2}{p_1}=\left[1-\frac{k-1}{C_1^2}\left(\frac{U_2^2-U_1^2}{2}\right)\right]^{k/(k-1)} \tag{14.24}$$

If point 2 is situated at the stagnation point, $U_2 = 0$ and p_2 becomes the stagnation pressure p_s Hence

$$\frac{p_s}{p_1}=\left[1+\frac{k-1}{2}M_1^2\right]^{\frac{k}{k-1}} \tag{14.25}$$

When M_1 is less than unity, ½ (k – 1) M_1^2 is also less than unity, the right hand side of Eq. 14.25 can be expanded in a convergent series, as

$$\frac{p_s}{p_1} = \left(1+\frac{k}{2}M_1^{\,2}+\frac{k}{8}M_1^{\,4}+\frac{k(2-k)}{48}M_1^{\,6}+\ldots\right)$$

Further since $\quad \dfrac{p_1 k}{2}M_1^{\,2} = \dfrac{p_1 k}{2}\dfrac{U_1^{\,2}}{C_1^{\,2}} = \dfrac{p_1 k U_1^{\,2}\rho_1}{2\,kp_1} = \rho_1 U_1^{\,2}/2$

$$\frac{p_S - p_1}{\rho_1 U_1^{\,2}/2} = 1 + \frac{1}{4}M_1^{\,2} + \frac{(2-k)}{24}M_1^{\,4} + \ldots.. \quad (14.26)$$

For incompressible fluids, $(p_s - p_1)/(\rho_1 U_1^{\,2}/2)$ must be equal to unity. However, for compressible fluids it has a value greater than unity, the difference being a function of M_1. For example, when $M_1 = 0.5$,

$$(p_s - p_1)/(\rho_1 U_1^{\,2}/2) = (1 + 0.0625 + 0.003) = 1.0655$$

i.e., 6.55% greater than that for incompressible fluids. This has an important bearing on the calibration and performance of pitot tubes at high velocities.

Example 14.3

In an isentropic flow of air around an immersed body the velocity, the pressure and the mass density in the ambient flow are 140 m/s, 101.325 kN/m² and 1.226 kg/m³ respectively. If the pressure at a point on the body is 49 kN/m², determine the Mach number and temperature at that point.

For such flow it can be shown that

$$\frac{T_1}{T_2} = \left(\frac{p_1}{p_2}\right)^{(k-1)/k}$$

Therefore, $\quad \dfrac{T_1}{T_2} = \left(\dfrac{101.325}{49}\right)^{(1.4-1.0)/1.4} = 1.231$

Since $\quad \dfrac{p_1}{\rho_1 g} = RT_1;\ T_1 = \dfrac{101.325\times10^3}{9.81\times1.226\times29.57}$

$$= 284.91°K$$

Hence $\quad T_2 = \dfrac{284.91}{1.231} = 231.45°K$

$$t_2 = (231.45 - 273.16) = -41.71°C$$

Also $\quad \left(\dfrac{\rho_1}{\rho_2}\right) = \left(\dfrac{p_1}{p_2}\right)^{1/k} = (2.068)^{0.714} = 1.68$

or $\quad \rho_2 = \dfrac{1.226}{1.68} = 0.730\ \text{kg/m}^3$

Applying Eq. 14.22 (a) and substituting the values of U_1, k, p_1, ρ_1, p_2 and ρ_2, one gets,

$$\frac{U_2^{\,2} - 140^2}{2} = \frac{1.40}{0.40} \times \frac{101.325 \times 10^3}{1.226}\left(1 - \frac{1.68}{2.068}\right)$$

Hence $U_2 = 370$ m/s

Velocity of pressure wave at point 2

$$= \sqrt{1.4 \times 9.81 \times 29.57 \times 231.45}$$

$$= 306.59 \text{ m/s}$$

There fore $M_2 = \dfrac{370.0}{306.59} = 1.207$

14.7 Frictionless Adiabatic (or Isentropic) Flow Through Pipes of Varying Cross-Section

The study of flow of compressible fluid through a pipe of varying cross-section throws considerable light on the difference between compressible and incompressible flows. For a steady, one dimensional flow in a pipe

$$UA = \text{constant} \tag{14.27}$$

for incompressible flow for compressible flow Eq. 14.27 becomes

$$\rho UA = \text{constant} \tag{14.28}$$

Hence for incompressible fluids, one gets from Eq. 14.27,

$$UdA + AdU = 0$$

or

$$\frac{dA}{A} = -\frac{dU}{U} \tag{14.29}$$

Similarly, from Eq. 14.28, for the flow of compressible fluids, one can write

$$(\rho U)\, dA + Ad\,(\rho U) = 0$$

or

$$\rho UdA + \rho AdU + AUd\rho = 0 \tag{14.30}$$

Therefore, dividing all terms of Eq. 14.30 by $A\rho U$, one gets,

$$\frac{dA}{A} = -\left[\frac{dU}{U} + \frac{d\rho}{\rho}\right] \tag{14.31}$$

Furthermore, application of momentum equation to an elementary volume will yield

$$dp = -\rho UdU \tag{14.32}$$

Combining Eq. 14.31 and 14.32, one gets

$$\frac{dA}{A} = \frac{dp}{\rho U^2} - \frac{d\rho}{\rho}$$

$$= \frac{dp}{\rho U^2}\left[1 - U^2 \frac{d\rho}{dp}\right] \tag{14.33}$$

But $C^2 = \dfrac{dp}{d\rho}$ and therefore,

$$\frac{dA}{A} = \frac{dp}{\rho U^2}(1 - M^2) \tag{14.34}$$

Also $$\frac{dp}{\rho U^2} = -\frac{\rho U dU}{\rho U^2} = -\frac{dU}{U}$$

Hence $$\frac{dA}{A} = -\frac{dU}{U}(1 - M^2) \tag{14.34 a}$$

Hence Eqs. 14.29 and 14.34 give variation of dA/A for incompressible and compressible fluids respectively. As is evident from Eq. 14.34 (a) for compressible fluids the sign of dU/U will depend upon whether $(1 - M^2)$ is positive or negative i.e., on whether M is less than or greater than unity. For subsonic flows when M is less than unity, $(1 - M^2)$ is positive and hence U will increase with decrease in A. This is similar to what happens in the case of incompressible fluids. However, when M is greater than unity, $(1 - M^2)$ is negative and hence.

$$\frac{dA}{A} = -\frac{dU}{U}(M^2 - 1) \tag{14.35}$$

In other words, when Mach number exceeds unity, the velocity increases with increase in the area. Thus the subsonic flow follows the same behavior as that of incompressible fluids, however the supersonic flow behaves strangely. For this reason, a nozzle action in the case of supersonic flow is obtained by increasing the area and the diffuser action by decreasing the cross-sectional area of the pipe.

14.8 Frictionless Adiabatic Flow Through Orifices and Nozzles

The flow of a compressible fluid through an orifice or a nozzle may be regarded as a frictionless adiabatic or isentropic process if the pressure drop is appreciable. On the other hand, if the pressure drop is small, the process can be considered to be isothermal. Considering the frictionless adiabatic process energy equation gives

$$\frac{k}{k-1}\left[\frac{p_1}{\rho_1} - \frac{p_2}{\rho_2}\right] = \frac{U_2^2}{2} - \frac{U_1^2}{2}$$

see Fig. 14.4. However, U_1 is very small and can be considered to be zero. Hence

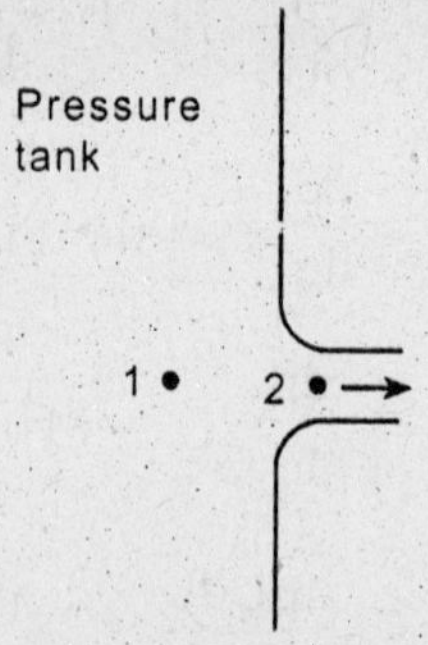

Fig. 14.4 Flow through an orifice

$$U_2 = \sqrt{\frac{2k}{k-1}\frac{p_1}{\rho_1}\left(1-\frac{p_2}{p_1}\frac{\rho_1}{\rho_2}\right)} \quad (14.36$$

However,

$$\frac{p_1}{\rho_1^{\ k}} = \frac{p_2}{\rho_2^{\ k}}$$

Hence,

$$\frac{\rho_1}{\rho_2} = \left(\frac{p_1}{p_2}\right)^{1/k} = \left(\frac{p_2}{p_1}\right)^{-1/k}$$

Substituting this value in Eq. 14.36,one gets

$$U_2 = \sqrt{\frac{2k}{k-1}\frac{p_1}{\rho_1}\left(1-n^{(k-1)/k}\right)} \quad (14.37$$

in which $p_2/p_1 = n$. If a is throat area, the weight of gas G per unit time is given by $G = aU_2/v_2$ in which v_2 is the specific volume at section 2.

or
$$G = \frac{a}{v_2}\sqrt{\frac{2k}{k-1}\frac{p_1}{\rho_1}\left(1-n^{(k-1)/k}\right)} \quad (14.38$$

or
$$G = \frac{a}{v_2}\sqrt{\frac{2kg}{k-1}\frac{p_1}{\rho_1}n^{2/k}\left(1-n^{(k-1)/k}\right)} \quad (14.39$$

It can be seen from Eq. 14.39 that for given conditions at section 1, G depends only on n i.e. on p_2/p_1. Hence for given conditions at section 1, G will be maximum when $\partial G/\partial n = ($

or
$$\frac{2}{k}\ n^{(2/k-1)} = \frac{k+1}{k}\ n^{(1/k)}$$

i.e $$n = \left(\frac{k+1}{2}\right)^{k/(1-k)} \quad \text{or} \quad \left(\frac{2}{k+1}\right)^{k/(k-1)} \qquad (14.40)$$

Assuming $k = 1.40$, G will be maximum when $n = 0.528$. For this condition it can be shown that the velocity at section 2 is

$$U_c = \sqrt{\frac{kp_c}{\rho_c}} \qquad (14.41)$$

in which the subsript c refers to the critical condition.

Example 14.4

A nozzle of throat diameter 2.5 cm is fixed in the side of a tank. The air pressure within the tank is 827.68 kN/m² and the temperature is 15° C. Determine the back pressure for maximum discharge and the maximum discharge.

The back (or downstream) pressure $= 0.528\ p_1$

$= 0.528 \times 827.68$

$= 437.02$ kN/m²

Since $\frac{p_1}{\rho_1} = g\ RT_1$ and $p_1 = 827\ 680$ N/m²

$T_1 = (273.16 + 15) = 288.16$°K

$$\rho_1 = \frac{827.680}{29.57 \times 288.16 \times 9.81}$$

$= 9.902$ kg/m³

Using Eq. 14.39 with $n = \frac{p_2}{p_1} = 0.528$ and

$$v_1 = \left(\frac{1}{9.81 \times 9.902}\right) \text{ m}^3/\text{N}$$

$$G_{max} = 0.785 \times (0.025)^2$$

$$\times \left[\frac{2 \times 1.40 \times 9.81}{0.40} \times \frac{827.680 \times 9.81 \times 9.902}{1}(0.5281.43 - 0.528^{1.714})\right]^{\frac{1}{2}}$$

$= 9.400$ N/s

14.9 Normal Shock Waves

Whenever a supersonic flow is required to be compressed, it is done so at least in part by means of a *shock wave*. In the case of one dimensional stationary shock wave, the supersonic flow at the upstream section is converted into a subsonic flow in a very short reach and such change is accompanied by a sudden rise in pressure. Shock waves can be either normal or oblique with respect to the flow direction. Shock waves occur in a diverging section of a nozzle, in the diffuser throat of supersonic wind tunnels, in pipes and in front of blunt nosed bodies. The thickness of shock waves across the discontinuity is of the order of 10^{-3} to 10^{-5} cm. Shock waves, being disturbances of large amplitude, travel at speed greater than sound waves of barely audible magnitude.

Analogous to the normal shock wave is the formation of hydraulic jump in open channel where the flow changes from supercritical to subcritical and is accompanied by change in depth and velocity of flow.

The elements of a normal shock wave can be obtained by the application of continuity equation, momentum equation and the energy equation. Let ρ_1, U_1, ρ_2 and U_2 represent the mass density and velocity before and after the normal shock, see Fig. 14.5.

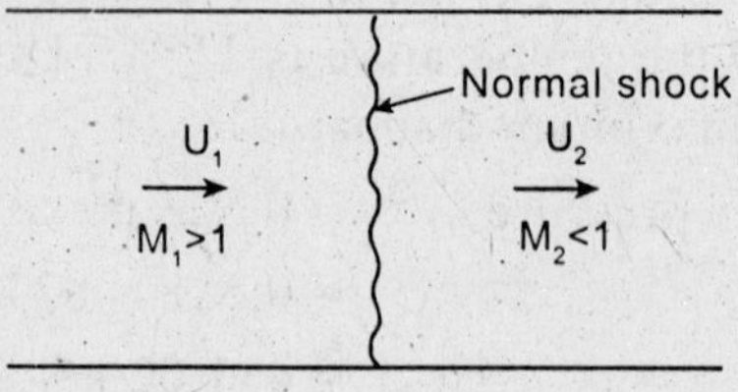

Fig. 14.5 A normal shock wave

Then according to the continuity equation, for unit area

$$\rho_1 U_1 = \rho_2 U_2$$

while the momentum equation across the shock is

$$(p_1 - p_2) = (\rho_2 U_2^2 - \rho_1 U_1^2) \qquad (14.42)$$

Similarly the energy equation between the two sections becomes,

$$\frac{U_1^2}{2} + \frac{k}{k-1}\frac{p_1}{\rho_1} = \frac{U_2^2}{2} + \frac{k}{k-1}\frac{p_2}{\rho_2} \qquad (14.43)$$

These three equations can be combined so as to express p_2/p_1, as a function of ρ_2/ρ_1, i.e.

$$\frac{p_2}{p_1} = \frac{\left(\frac{k+1}{k-1}\right)\left(\frac{\rho_2}{\rho_1}\right) - 1}{\left(\frac{k+1}{k-1}\right) - \frac{\rho_2}{\rho_1}} \qquad (14.44)$$

or

$$\frac{\rho_2}{\rho_1} = \frac{U_1}{U_2} = \frac{1 + \left(\frac{k+1}{k-1}\right)\frac{p_2}{p_1}}{\left(\frac{k+1}{k-1}\right) + \frac{p_2}{p_1}} \qquad (14.45)$$

These equations were first developed in 1870 and they are commonly known as *Rankine - Hugoniot* equations. By certain algebraic manipulations, Eqs. 14.44 and 14.45 can be written in alternative forms as

$$\left.\begin{aligned} \frac{p_2}{p_1} &= \frac{2k\,M_1^2 - (k-1)}{k+1} \\ \text{and} \quad \frac{U_1}{U_2} &= \frac{(k+1)\,M_1^2}{(k-1)\,M_1^2 + 2.0} \end{aligned}\right\} \tag{14.46}$$

in which M_1 is the Mach number just upstream of the shock wave. The corresponding equation for ratio of temperatures T_2/T_1 is

$$\frac{T_2}{T_1} = \frac{\left[(k-1)\;\;M_1^2 + 2\right]\left[2k\;\;M_1^2 - (k-1)\right]}{(k+1)^2\;\;M_1^2} \tag{14.46 a}$$

Example 14.5

If in a compression shock wave p_1 = 42.13 kN/m², t_1 = 0°C and U_1 = 1000 m/s, determine the conditions just downstream of the shock wave.

$$C_1 = \sqrt{1.40 \times 9.81 \times 29.57 \times 273.16} = 333 \text{ m/s}$$

Hence $$M_1 = \frac{U_1}{C_1} = \frac{1000}{333} = 3.001$$

Using Eq. 14.46 one gets

$$\frac{U_1}{U_2} = \frac{2.40 \times 3.001^2}{0.4 \times 3.001^2 + 2.0} = 3.86$$

or $$U_2 = 259 \text{ m/s}$$

Also, $$\frac{p_2}{p_1} = \frac{2.80 \times 3.001^2 - 0.40}{2.40} = 10.34$$

or $$p_2 = 434.64 \text{ kN/m}^2$$

From the adiabatic relation,

$$\frac{T_1}{T_2} = \left(\frac{p_1}{p_2}\right)^{\frac{k-1}{k}} = \left\{\frac{1}{10.34}\right\}^{0.40/1.40} = 0.513$$

or $$T_2 = 532.58\text{°K}$$

Hence $$t_2 = 259.42\text{°C}$$

14.10 Flow Through Converging-Diverging Nozzles

It is interesting to study frictionless flow of a compressible fluid through converging-diverging nozzle such as Laval Nozzle first introduced by the Sweedish engineer de Laval (1845-1913), see Fig. 14.6.

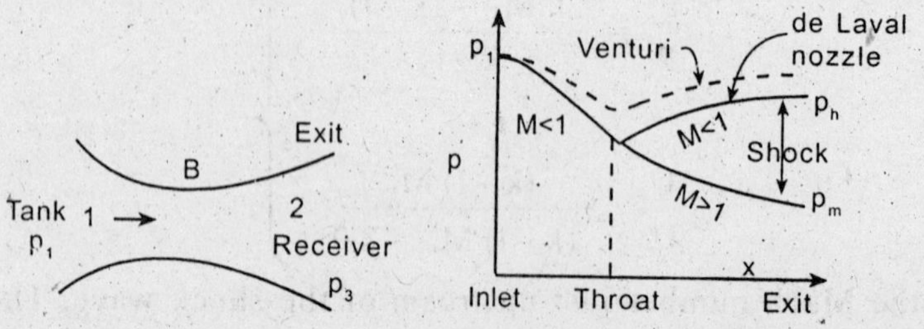

Fig. 14.6 Flow through a converging-diverging nozzle

As the receiver pressure p_3 is lowered to a pressure less than p_2, there will be flow through such a nozzle. Flow within the whole nozzle will be subsonic. The critical condition does not occur at the throat B. Such flow occurs in the case of venturimeters. As the receiver pressure is lowered further and reaches a value p_n, one gets the critical flow at B i.e., Mach number at B is unity. The flow upstream and downstream of B is still subsonic. When the exit pressure is less than p_n but greater than p_m, the flow takes place with losses because shock wave occurs in the downstream portion of the nozzle, its position depending on the nozzle shape and exit pressure. If the exit pressure is at p_m the flow is frictionless and M in the downstream section is greater than unity. If the exit pressure is less than p_m, a series of shock waves occur beyond the nozzle end.

PROBLEMS

14.1 Two cubic meters of carbon dioxide under 392.26 kN/m² pressure expand isothermally to 5.5 m³ volume. Determine the pressure of the gas under new condition.

14.2 If 3.5 m³ of a certain gas at 147 kN/m² pressure is compressed to a volume 1.75 m³ isentropically, the pressure increases to 362.84 kN/m². Determine the value of k.

14.3 If the atmospheric pressure and temperature on the ground are 101.2 kN/m² and 15°C respectively, determine the pressure at an altitude of 4880 m and the mean temperature gradient. Take k to be 1.40 and R as 29.57 m/K. (Refer Chapter 4).

14.4 Show that for an adiabatic case

$$T_1/T_2 = (\rho_1/\rho_2)^{k-1}$$

14.5 Determine the change in the internal or intrinsic energy of air if its temperature increases from 15°C to 105°C.

14.6 Air in a cylinder is allowed to expand isothermally to twice its original volume. If the weight of the air is 15.70 N and its intitial pressure and temperature are 689.4 kN/m² and 35°C, respectively determine the final pressure and external work done by the air.

14.7 Solve Problem 14.6 when the air expands adiabatically. Take k as 1.40.

14.8 At a point A in an air stream the velocity is 100 m/s, the pressure 98.1 kN/m^2 and ρ is 1.226 kg/m^3. At other point B, the pressure is 92.1 kN/m^2. Determine Mach numbers at the two points.

14.9 Compare the velocities of propagation of a pressure wave in water, benzene and ethyl alcohol at 20°C and atmospheric pressure.

14.10 If an air plane attains a flight speed of M = 2 at an altitude of 10.6 km above sea level when the temperature is – 54.3° C, what will be its speed in km/hr ?

14.11 The prototype rocket traveling at 1200 m/s velocity through air at – 20°C is to be tested in wind tunnel with air at 15°C. Determine the corresponding rocket velocity in the wind tunnel which is required to attain dynamic similarity.

14.12 An air plane is travelling through standard air (p = 101.4 kN/m^3, temp. = 15°C, ρ = 1.226 kg/m^3), at a speed of 2.70 km/s. Determine the stagnation pressure, ρ and temperature at that point.

14.13 Show that for isentropic flow,

$$\frac{\rho_s}{\rho_1} = \left\{1 + \frac{M_1^2(k-1)}{2}\right\}^{\frac{1}{(k-1)}}$$

and then show that when M_1 is small, $(\rho_s/\rho_1) \approx \frac{1}{2} M_1^2$

14.14 Air at 689.4 kN/m^2 pressure and 37.34°C flows from a tank through a converging nozzle with exit area 4.65 cm^2. Determine the exit temperature and mass rate of flow when the receiver pressure is (i) 482.48 kN/m^2 (ii) 101.0 kN/m^2.

14.15 Air at 686.46 kN/m^2 pressure, 90°C temperature and with negligible velocity enters a converging nozzle. If the exit area is 9 cm^2, determine the maximum weight discharge per second for frictionless adiabatic flow.

14.16 In Problem 14.15 determine the cross sectional area of the nozzle where the pressures are 490.3 kN/m^2 and 392.26 kN/m^2 respectively.

14.17 If in a normal compression shock wave p_1 = 49.03 kN/m^2, p_2 = 245.15 kN/m^2 and t_1 = 10°C, determine U_1, M_1, U_2, M_2 and t_2.

14.18 Starting from either equation 14.45 or 14.46 show that the maximum increase in density of air (k =1.40) across a normal shock is six times the original [i.e., show that when $p_2/p_1 \to \infty$, $(\rho_1/\rho_2) \to 6$]

14.19 In a normal shock wave in air, the upstream conditions are U_1 = 500 m/s, t_1 = 0°C and ρ_1 = 0.98 kg/m^3. Find the corresponding quantities downstream of the shock.

14.20 The temperature ratio across a normal shock wave in carbon dioxide (k = 1.30) is T_2/T_1 = 2.28. Determine the pressure, density and velocity ratios across the wave, and Mach number after the shock wave.

CHAPTER FIFTEEN

UNSTEADY FLOW

15.1 Introduction

It has been mentioned in Chapter 2 that depending on whether a certain flow characteristic such as discharge, velocity, surface elevation or pressure at a given point changes with time or not, the flow is classified as unsteady or steady flow. At a given point, the variation of the fluid property, such as density also makes the flow unsteady. In the previous chapters, attention was focused mostly on steady flows since such flows are relatively simple to analyse. However, one comes across a variety of problems which fall in the category of unsteady flows; problems concerning surge tanks, water hammer, flows through tanks with constant inflow, flood-routing, surges, etc., fall in this category. In general, the analysis of unsteady flow problems is rather complicated; however, under simplified conditions some unsteady flow problems can be easily solved. Only such problems are discussed in this chapter.

15.2 Types of Unsteady Flows

The unsteady flow problems encountered in practice can be broadly classified into four categories depending on the nature of variation of a particular variable with time. These are:

a. flows involving random and rapid fluctuations,

b. flows caused by a motion of the body at a constant velocity;

c. flows involving slow or rapid periodic variations, and

d. flows involving non-periodic changes.

Unsteady flows of the first type are those in which the quantity under consideration varies haphazardly and rapidly with time. Turbulent flows fall under this category. If the instantaneous velocity is measured at a given point in turbulent flow for various times the variation will look somewhat similar to the one shown in Fig. 10.1. Similar pattern of variation will be obtained for instantaneous pressure at a given point. Since these fluctuations are rapid and apparently do not follow any law, such flows are discussed in terms of time averaged velocities, their standard deivation, etc., as mentioned in Chapter 10. Such fluctuations are also found to occur in several hydraulic structures such as turbines, shaft spillway, and high head gates. These types of flows are analysed by using time averged quantities, their likely maximum values and treating the flows as quasi-steady.

The second type of unsteady flows results due to the translation of surge or wave in water at a constant velocity. In such cases, if attention is focused at a fixed point in the space, the flow conditions are naturally changing with time. Hence such flows are unsteady; however, the flow pattern in such flows can be transformed into one of steady flow by applying the principle of relative motion. This is achieved by applying a velocity equal in magnitude and opposite in direction to that of the body or wave, to the fluid as well as to the body or wave. This makes the body or wave stationary while the fluid will be moving in the opposite direction. The magnitude and direction of velocity at any point in space is now constant. The flow in the new system is certainly steady and hence the theory of steady flow developed in the earlier chapters is applicable.

The third type of unsteady flows comprises of variations which are either periodic or nearly so. Such oscillations or periodic variations in pressure and velocity occur in surge tanks, water hammer problems and in the water levels of reservoirs.

The fourth type of unsteady flows involve the variation in hydraulic characteristics in non-periodic manner. In other words in such problems the water level or velocity or depth at a point gradually increases or decreases. The problems of draining of a reservoir with or without inflow, flood routing, etc. fall in this category. The discussion in the present chapter will be limited to certain specific problems in the last three types of unsteady flows.

15.3 Equation of Motion for Unsteady Flow

Consideration of equation of motion for unsteady flow along a stream line yields valuable information. Since the acceleration along a stream line is $\left(\frac{\partial V_S}{\partial t} + V_S \frac{\partial V_S}{\partial t}\right)$, one can write

$$\rho \left(\frac{\partial V_S}{\partial t} + V_S \frac{\partial V_S}{\partial t}\right) = -\frac{\partial}{\partial s}(p + \gamma z) \qquad (15.1)$$

Equation 15.1 can be rewritten in the following form after dividing all the terms by γ and transposing the term of convective acceleration to the right hand side.

$$\left.\begin{aligned} \frac{1}{g}\frac{\partial V_S}{\partial t} &= -\frac{\partial}{\partial S}\left(\frac{p}{\gamma} + z + \frac{V_S^2}{2g}\right) \\ \text{or} \quad \frac{1}{g}\frac{\partial V_S}{\partial t} &= \frac{\partial H}{\partial s} \end{aligned}\right\} \qquad (15.2)$$

in which H represents the total head. Equation 15.2 shows that in the case of unsteady flow the change in velocity at any section will cause variation of total head along the direction of the flow. Equations 15.1 and 15.2 have been written for the flow along a stream line; however, if velocity over the cross-section is assumed to remain the same, and if the boundary resistance is assumed to be negligible, these equations are also applicable to pipe flows and open channel flows.

In the case of pipe flows, if the pipe cross-section remains the same along the length of pipe, the velocity head cannot change with distance. Hence the piezometric head must vary along the length of the pipe thereby changing the total head.

In case the term $\partial V_s/\partial t$ is very small, as an approximation one can neglect the term on the left band side of Eq. 15.2; hence integration of Eq. 15.2 yields H = constant along s direction at any time t. In other words, when the unsteadiness is such that $\partial V_s/\partial t$ is small, one can solve the problem by assuming the total head to be constant. Such problems are discussed in Section 15.6.

15.4 Flow Around a Body Moving Through Stationary Fluid

Consider a fixed co-ordinate frame as shown in Fig. 15.1 in a large mass of fluid which is initially at rest and let the body A move through it at a constant velocity U. If the observer focusses the attention at any point such as B (x_1, y_1), it will be seen that the velocity at B will change with time as the body moves past B. For this reason the flow is unsteady.

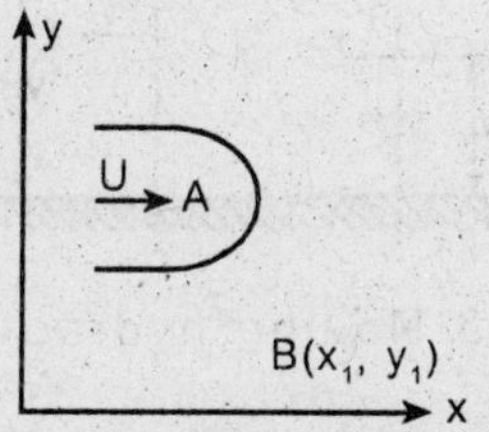

Fig. 15.1 Uniform motion of a body in an infinite fluid

This unsteady flow can be transformed into steady flow by applying a velocity U towards left to the fluid as well to the body. As a result, the body will be stationary and the fluid will flow past the body at a velocity U towards the left. The motion of the fluid will be affected by presence of the body; however, at a given point in the flow field the conditions will not change with time. Figure 15.2 shows the flow pattern when a two dimensional cylinder moves through an ideal fluid at a constant velocity U. The steady state flow pattern can be obtained by applying a velocity U to the fluid as well as to the body, in opposite direction. This is done at every point and a resultant velocity is found. One can construct the steady state pattern of flow from the knowledge of the direction of resultant velocity at every point. Typical steady flow stream lines are also shown in the figure.

This method of changing the unsteady flow into a steady flow is used in the study of moving hydraulic jumps and surges in open channels. When a hydraulic jump is moving at constant velocity U_w, in the downstream direction, it can be made stationary by applying a velocity U_w in the reverse direction to the jump and water flowing. Applying the continuity and momentum equations, a relationship can now be found between upstream and downstream velocities and depths of the hydraulic jump. This is illustrated in Example 15. 1. Analysis of surge in Chapter 13 is based on this principle.

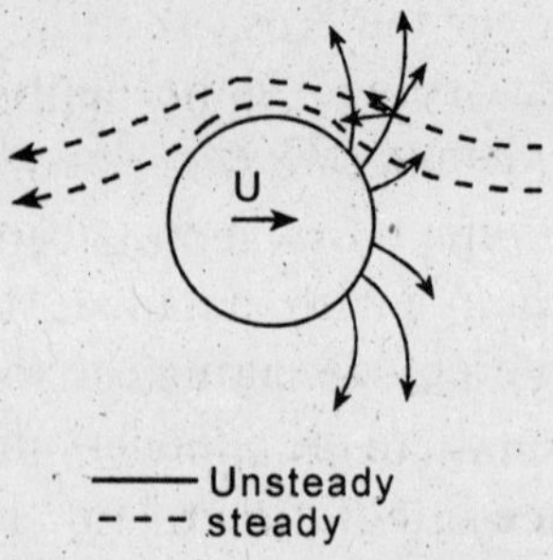

Fig. 15.2 Unsteady and steady flows around a cylinder

Example 15.1

A hydraulic jump in a rectangular channel moving in the downstream direction at a uniform velocity of 1.50 m/s has a depth of 2.50 m before the jump and 6.0 m after the jump. Determine the velocity of flow at these sections.

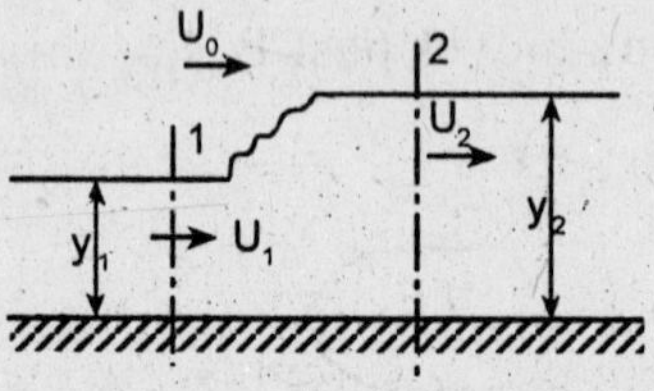

Fig. 15.3 Moving hydraulic jump

When jump is made stationary, the velocities at sections 1 and 2 will be $(U_1 - U_W)$ and $(U_2 - U_W)$ respectively.

Continuity equations gives $(U_1 - U_w)\, y_1 = (U_2 - U_w)\, y_2$ while momentum equation

gives $$q'\rho\,[(U_1 - U_w) - (U_2 - U_w)] = \frac{\gamma}{2}\,(y_2^2 - y_1^2)$$

in which $q' = y_2\,(U_2 - U_w)$. Hence substituting the known values of y_1, y_2 and U_o, one has

$$(U_1 - 1.50) \times 2.50 = (U_2 - 1.5) \times 6.00$$

or $$U_1 = (2.40\, U_2 - 2.10)$$

and $$(U_1 - U_2)\,(U_2 - 1.50) = 24.311$$

Eliminating U_1 between the last two equations, the following equation is obtained for U_2

$$1.40\, U_2^2 - 4.20\, U_2 - 21.161 = 0$$

or $$U_2 = \frac{+4.20 \pm \sqrt{4.20^2 + (4 \times 1.40 \times 21.161}}{2.80}$$

or $$U_2 = 5.667 \text{ m/s}$$

Hence $$U_1 = (2.40 \times 5.667 - 2.10) = 11.50 \text{ m/s}$$

15.5 Periodic Flows

In the category of periodic flows the two most important problems are those concerning water hammer and surge tanks. However, before water hammer problem can be discussed, one must obtain expression for the velocity of propagation of elastic waves when it is affected by elastic boundaries.

Earlier an expression has been obtained for the velocity of propagation of an elastic or pressure wave travelling in a rigid pipe where the boundary did not affect the compression or expansion (see section. 14.3). Such cases arise in the case of travel of elastic or pressure waves through infinite fluids as in aerodynamics. However, while dealing with problems concerning sudden deceleration of fluid flow through pipes one must modify the earlier analysis since elasticity of the pipe material affects the velocity of propagation of waves. As the pressure in the pipe rises, the wall material is subjected to additional stresses. These additional stresses give rise to longitudinal as well as circumferential strains. The longitudinal strains will be associated with the longitudinal displacement of the pipe wall and it is reasonable to assume that the longitudinal displacement has no influence on the propagation of waves in the fluid.

Recall that E, the volume modulus of elasticity of the fluid, has been defined as $E = -v\,(dp/dv)$ in which dv represents the change in the volume v due to change in pressure dp. When the pipe is not rigid, the change in the volume will be due to the compression of the fluid as well as the circumferential strain in the pipe; these can be designated by dv' and dv'' respectively. If K represents the resulting volume modulus of elasticity of the fluid, then

$$K = -v\frac{dp}{dv' + dv''} \tag{15.3}$$

or

$$\frac{1}{K} = -\frac{1}{v}\frac{dv'}{dp} - \frac{1}{v}\frac{dv''}{dp} \tag{15.3a}$$

The first term in Eq. 15.3 (a) evidently is (1/E) the reciprocal of volume modulus of elasticity of the fluid. The second term in the above equation can be written as follows: Because of the increase in pressure within the pipe, the circumferential stress caused will be $(2R \times 1)\,dp/(2t \times 1)$ i.e., $(R/t)\,dp$ in which R is the radius of the pipe and t is its thickness. If due to the increase in the pressure, the pipe radius increases by dR, the circumferential strain will be $(2\pi\,dR/2\pi R)$, i.e., (dR/R). Hence

Young's modulus of Elasticity

$$E_m = \frac{\text{Stress}}{\text{Strain}} = \frac{Rdp}{t}\frac{R}{dR}$$

or

$$dp = \frac{E_m\, t\, dR}{R^2} \tag{15.4}$$

The corresponding increase in the volume dv'' (per unit length) will be equal to $(2\pi R dR \times 1)$. Furthermore, the original volume v per unit length, is $(\pi R^2 \times 1)$. Substituting these values of v, dp and dv'' in the second term in Eq. 15.3 (a) one gets,

$$\frac{1}{v}\frac{dv''}{dp}=\frac{2\pi RdR\times R^2}{\pi R^2\times E_m tdR}$$

$$=\frac{2R}{t\,E_m}=\frac{D}{t\,E_{mt}}$$

Hence Eq. 15.3 (a) becomes

$$\frac{1}{K}=\frac{1}{E}+\frac{D}{t}\frac{1}{E_m}$$

or $$K=\frac{E}{1+\frac{D}{t}\frac{E}{E_m}} \qquad (13.5)$$

This shows that when the elasticity of the pipe material is taken into account, the effective volume modulus of elasticity of the fluid is smaller than the actual. The average value of E for water is 2.075×10^9 N/m² while the values of E_m for steel, cast iron and wood are 2.47×10^{11}, 1.04×10^{11} and 1.92×10^{10} N/m² respectively. The maximum velocity of an elastic or pressure values in water will be $\sqrt{2.075\times10^9/998}$ i.e., 1442 m/s. In the case of pressure waves in water in pipe lines, the velocity will naturally be smaller than 1442 m/s.

(a) Water Hammer

As the discharge flowing in a pipe is changed, pressure changes arise due to inertia of the fluid. When the valve in a pipe line carrying water is suddenly closed, a hammering sound is produced which gives an indication of sudden and large rise in the pressure within the pipe. In many cases the hammering continues with a regular periodicity unless some measure is taken to damp out the periodic motion. This phenomenon is known as *water hammer.* Water hammer is potentially destructive and especially so in long pipe lines.

If the fluid were completely incompressible and if the pipe were rigid, a simple relationship between the pressure changes and the acceleration can be obtained for the water hammer problem. Consider a horizontal pipe of cross-sectional area A and length L carrying fluid of mass density ρ. Let the velocity of this fluid be changed by closing the valve. Since the velocity in the pipe at any instant is the same and since the pipe is horizontal, Eq. 15.2 will yield,

$$-\frac{1}{\gamma}\frac{\partial p}{\partial s}=\frac{1}{g}\frac{\partial U}{\partial t}$$

or $$A\,(p_0-p)=AL\rho\,\frac{\partial U}{\partial t} \qquad (15.6)$$

in which p_o and p are the pressures at the upstream end of the pipe and just upstream of the valve. It may further be mentioned that Eq. 15.6 could have been obtained by the application of Newton's second law of motion to a mass of water ρLA.

As can be seen from this equation, when the valve is closed, $\partial U/\partial t$ is negative and hence p is greater than p_o. On the other hand, when the valve is opened, $\partial U/\partial t$ is positive and hence p is less than p_o. If the valve is closed instantaneously, Eq. 15.6 indicates that the pressure rise will be infinite. However, it has been found that in such a case the pressure rise is always finite. This discrepancy in the theoretical and observed results is due to the omission of compressibility effects from the analysis. As mentioned in Chapter 14, in the case of rapidly accelerating flows, the compressibility of fluids must be taken into account. Water hammer phenomenon is shown in Fig. 15.4.

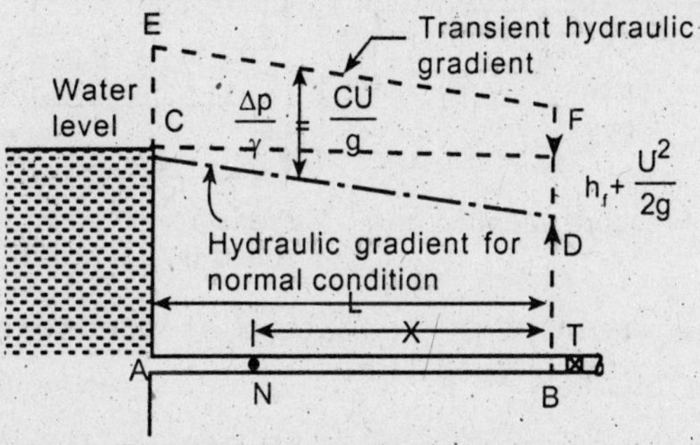

Fig. 15.4 Pressure variation due to sudden valve closure

When a pressure wave is caused in an elastic fluid due to changes in the valve opening, the wave travels with a velocity which can be computed by using Eq. 14.16. As the boundary form changes this wave is modified, reflected or both as it passes from one medium to other. In connection with an elementary discussion of water hammer, two changes in the boundary form are important. Firstly, when a solid wall comes in the way of propagation of a wave, at the wall the velocity of wave normal to it must be zero while the pressure there is free to vary. Secondly, when the pressure wave reaches a reservoir where pressure is constant, the velocity is free to vary, see Fig. 15.5.

Pressure variation due to sudden valve closure- Consider a pipe line AB (see fig. 15.4) connected to a reservoir and let there be a valve at B. When the valve is open, CD represents the piezometric gradient along AB. As soon as the valve is closed instantaneously, the fluid layer adjacent to B comes to rest and is compressed, there is a rise in pressure and the pipe surrounding the layer is stretched. Then a layer adjacent to the stationary layer comes to rest. In this manner, the pressure wave travels in the up-stream direction at a velocity C defined as $C = \sqrt{K/\rho}$. When the pressure wave reaches the end A, all the fluid in the pipe is at rest and the whole pipe is at an excess pressure. The condition is shown by the line FE. However, it is not possible to have the pressure at A greater than the static pressure. Hence the pressure at A drops down to the static pressure. A pressure gradient is thus set up in the direction BA, which causes the compressed water in the pipe line to flow back to the reservoir thus relieving the pressure. Hence a wave of rarefaction or unloading travels from A to B. When this wave reaches B, the whole fluid mass is under static pressure. However, to stop the flow of fluid towards the reservoir, pressure at B drops below static pressure by an amount equal to pressure rise at that point. This negative wave travels upstream and reaches A. However, the pressure at A must always be static. This causes a pressure gradient in the direction of AB and causes a flow. In this way, a series of pressure waves travel over the entire length back and forth. This is diagramatically shown in Fig. 15.5.

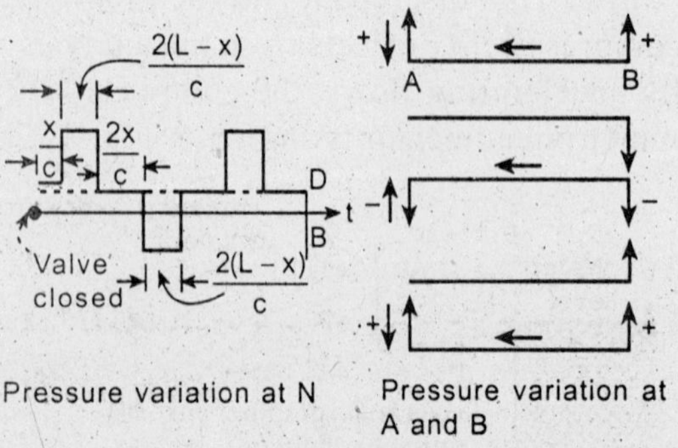

Fig. 15.5 Diagramatic presentation of pressure variation at A, B and N with time

The time required for the pressure wave to travel from B to A and back to B is

$$T = \frac{2L}{C}$$

in which L is the length AB. The variation of pressure with time at any intermediate point such as N can be easily plotted. Such variation is also shown in Fig. 15.5.

The mass of fluid in the pipe which undergoes deceleration is ρLA in which A is the cross-sectional area of the pipe. If Δp represents the rise in pressure which is caused by a change in velocity ΔU, then according to Newton's second law of motion,

$$A\,\Delta p = -\rho\,AL\,\frac{\Delta U}{\Delta t}$$

in which Δt is the time required to change the velocity of fluid mass ρ AL by ΔU. However since

$$\Delta t = \frac{L}{C}$$

one gets the following expression for Δp

$$\Delta p = -\rho L\,\frac{\Delta U}{L/C} = -\rho C\,\Delta U \qquad (15.7)$$

Thus in the case of sudden closure where $\Delta U = (0 - U)$ the rise in the pressure will be

$$\Delta p = \rho CU \qquad (15.7a)$$

When the valve is closed sufficiently rapidly so that the process of closure is completed during a time $t_c < 2L/C$, the valve will be completely closed before the pressure wave travels from B to A and back to B. In such a case the theory of sudden closure developed above and Eq. 15.7 are quite adequate. However, when the closure time t_c is greater than 2L/C the wave of rarefaction returning to the valve tends to reduce the pressure and thus prevents the attainment of the theoretical maximum. If the closure time t_c is several times larger than 2L/C, the compressibility effects no longer predominate and the pressure rise can be computed using Eq. 15.6. When the closure time is slightly greater than 2L/C, one can use the assumption that the pressure rise is reduced in the proportion of $(2L/C)(1/t_c)$.

or
$$\frac{\Delta p}{\Delta p_{max}} = \frac{2L}{C}\frac{1}{t_c}$$

in which Δp_{max} is the pressure rise for sudden closure and is given by Eq. 15.7 (a).

It may be emphasised that since sudden closure of the valve causes very large pressure within the pipe line, the valves in large pipe lines are so designed that closure time is many times greater than 2L/C. This is by far the simplest method of protecting pipes from excessive pressure. Many times air chambers of adequate size are connected to the pipe line just upstream of the valve. These prevent pressure waves of large magnitude from passing up the pipe.

In the above analysis the effect of friction has been neglected. It is true that during the passage of a pressure wave there is no loss of energy either due to expansion or compression. However, the resistance to flow at the pipe wall has two important affects. Firstly, the maximum pressure rise at the valve when friction is considered, is somewhat greater than the quantity ρCU. This is also true about any other point along the pipe length. Furthermore, friction also damps the otherwise periodic pressure fluctuation and hencc the amplitude of pressure fluctuation decreases with time.

For a simple case of a sudden closure of valve and with no friction, a solution has been obtained for maximum pressure rise. However, in other cases where the valve closure is not sudden and friction effect is to be included, one must start with the governing differential equations, namely continuity equation and momentum equation. If $h = p/\gamma + z$, and frictional resistance is assumed to be proportional to U^2, one can write these equations as

$$\frac{C^2}{g}\frac{\partial U}{\partial x} + U\frac{\partial h}{\partial x} + \frac{\partial h}{\partial t} + U\sin\theta = 0 \qquad (15.8)$$

$$g\frac{\partial h}{\partial x} + U\frac{\partial U}{\partial x} + \frac{\partial U}{\partial t} + \frac{fU|U|}{2D} = 0 \qquad (15.9)$$

Here D is the pipe diameter θ is the angle of inclination of the pipe, f is Darcy-Weisbach friction factor, C is the celerity of pressure wave and U^2 is written as $U|U|$ to provide a correct sign for friction.

Eqs. (15.8) and (15.9) are two nonlinear partial differential equations in U and h in terms of the independent variables x and t. Their solution will yield $U = U(x, t)$ and $h = h(x, t)$. However, no closed form solution of these equations is possible. These two equations can, however, be converted then into the following pair of total differential equations by certain mathematical manipulations

$$\frac{dh}{dt} + \frac{C}{g}\frac{dU}{dt} + U\sin\theta + \frac{C f U|U|}{2g D} = 0$$

$$\frac{dx}{dt} = U + C$$

and
$$\frac{dh}{dt} - \frac{C}{g}\frac{dU}{dt} + U\sin\theta - \frac{C f U|U|}{2g D} = 0$$

$$\frac{dx}{dt} = U - C$$

These are solved by the method of characteristics using finite difference scheme. With the availability of high speed computers, the solution can be obtained in a very short time, once the upstream and downstream boundary conditions are specified.

(b) Rapid Acceleration of Flow

Another phenomenon of interest is that of acceleration of flow due to sudden opening of the valve. Even though the basic consideration in the sudden closure and opening are identical, the essential difference between the two is that while in the case of sudden closure of the valve the velocity of flow reduces very rapidly and is accompanied by large pressure rise, with the sudden opening of the valve, the piezometric heads at both ends remain unchanged and the velocity of flow increases gradually. From Eq. 15.2 one can write

$$\frac{1}{g}\frac{dU}{dt} = -\frac{dH}{ds} = \frac{H_1 - H_2}{L}$$

where H_1 and H_2 are total heads at the upstream and downstream ends. Since $H_1 = h$, upstream head at the reservoir and $H_2 = \frac{U^2}{2g}$, where U is the exit velocity at tinie t, one gets

or
$$\frac{L}{gh}\frac{dU}{dt} = \left(1 - \frac{U^2}{2gh}\right)$$

or
$$\int \frac{dU}{\left(1+\frac{U}{\sqrt{2gh}}\right)\left(1-\frac{U}{\sqrt{2gh}}\right)} = \frac{gh}{L}dt$$

which yields

$$t = \frac{L}{\sqrt{2gh}} \log_e \left(\frac{1+U/U_0}{1-U/U_0} \right) \quad (5.10)$$

is which $U_0 = \sqrt{2gh}$ the ultimate equilibrium velocity. Equation 15.10 is derived with the assumptions of incompressible fluid and no f...ion. It can be seen that the time required to attain U equal to U_0 is infinity. However, U may be almost equal to U_0, say $U/U_0 = 0.95$ in a relatively short tim...

When the compressibility is taken into account yet neglecting the friction, a pressure difference γh is created at downstream end as soon as the valve is opened. The change in flow velocity required to cause this pressure difference is $U_1 = \frac{\gamma h}{\rho C} = \frac{gh}{C}$. The velocity on the upstream side of this pressure wave is zero. When the wave reaches the reservoir, the pressure there should be zero. However, the pressure there is hydrostatic and fixed, hence a wave starts moving downstream with a velocity U_2 on its upstream side and U_1 on the downstream side, U_2 being greater than U_1. The increased velocity U_2 can be shown to be twice U_1 as a first approximation. With successive passage of waves the velocity increases in steps, the relationships between the two being $U_{N+1} = 2\,U_N$; where N is the number of incremental times steps of duration 2L/C seconds. The number of time steps required to reach the maximum velocity is U_0/U_1.

Example 15.2

A 60 cm diameter steel pipe of 1.0 cm thickness and 300 m length carrying water is connected to a needle valve at the downstream end and to the reservoir at upstream end has a head of 60 m. Determine the rise in pressure if the valve is closed in 0.30 seconds and 2.0 seconds respectively.

Take $E = 2.075 \times 10^9$ N/m²

$E_m = 2.47 \times 10^{11}$ N/m²

$$K = \frac{2.075 \times 10^9}{1 + \left(\frac{60}{1} \times \frac{2.075 \times 10^9}{2.47 \times 10^{11}} \right)}$$

$$= 1.38 \times 10^9 \text{ N/m}^2$$

$$C = \sqrt{\frac{1.38 \times 10^9}{998}} = 1176 \text{ m/s}$$

$$\frac{2L}{C} = \frac{2 \times 300}{1176} = 0.51 \text{s}$$

Hence valve closure in 0.30 seconds can be considered as sudden.

$$\Delta p_{max} = \rho CU = 998 \times 1176 \times \sqrt{2\times 9.81\times 60}$$
$$= 998 \times 1176 \times 34.31$$
$$= 40\ 267\ 863\ \text{N/m}^2$$
$$= 402\ 678\ \text{kN/m}^2$$

The closure in 2.0 seconds is slow.

$$\frac{\Delta p}{\Delta p_{max}} = \frac{0.51}{2.0} \qquad \therefore \qquad \Delta p = 102\ 683\ \text{kN/m}^2$$

Example 15.3

If in Example 15.2 the valve is suddenly opened, determine how much time will be required to attain 0.90 times the equilibrium velocity. Neglect friction.

Assuming incompressible fluid

$$t = \frac{300}{34.31} \log_e \left(\frac{1+0.90}{1-0.90}\right)$$
$$= \frac{300\times 2.307}{34.31} \times \log_{10} \frac{1.90}{0.10}$$
$$= 25.79\ \text{s}$$

$$U_1 = \frac{9.81\times 60}{1176} = 0.50\ \text{m/s}$$

If fluid compressibility is taken into account, after every 0.51s, U/U_0 will change by 0.50/ 34.31 = 0.0146

$\therefore$ Number of steps required to attain $\frac{U}{U_0} = 0.90$ will be

$$\frac{0.90}{0.0146} = 61.64 \text{ or say } 62$$

$\therefore$ The time required $= 62 \times 0.51 = 31.62$ s

(c) Surge Tanks

In the case of long pipes line it is not desirable to decrease or increase the flow suddenly. When the discharge is suddenly decreased by valve closure, undesirable excessive pressures result. Similarly, if because of extra water requirements, the valve opening is suddenly increased, some time is required for the flow to adjust with the increased demand. These types of flow conditions occur in the case of hydroelectric power plants (see Fig. 15.6) where the turbines convert the potential energy of water into mechanical energy. In the hydroelectric power plants, depending on the requirements of power it is necessary either to increase or to decrease the discharge flowing through the turbines. When the demand is suddenly decreased, the entire pipe length between the reservoir and the turbines experiences increased pressures and it must be designed to withstand these pressures. Similarly, since the travel time of a pressure wave and the time required for flow establishment depend on the pipe length, it is necessary to reduce the length of the pipe line in which effects due to changes in the valve opening will be felt. This is achieved by providing a large diameter vertical open tank commonly known as the *surge tank* just upstream of the power plant.

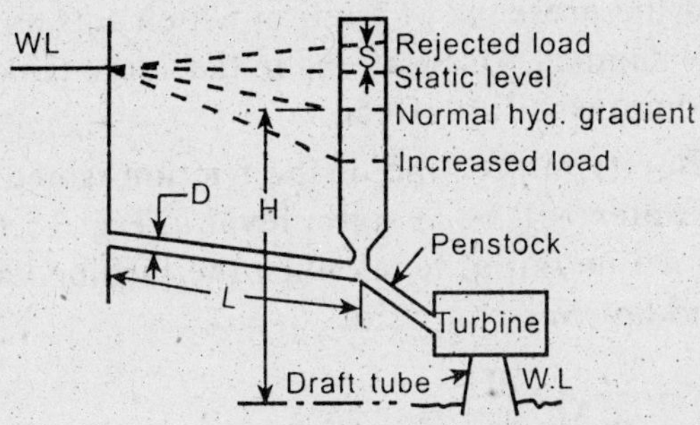

Fig. 15.6 Surge tank in a hydroelectric plant

There are various types of surge tanks out of which three are shown in Fig. 15.7. A simple surge tank acts as a reservoir connected to penstock and the water flows into and out of tank without any appreciable loss of head. It is slow in its action and requires a diameter greater than the other two types. A restricted orifice type surge tank has an orifice placed between the tank and the penstock. Such a surge tank is preferable to a simple surge tank. The other type known as differential surge tank is also shown in the figure. Surge tanks serve the following two purposes:

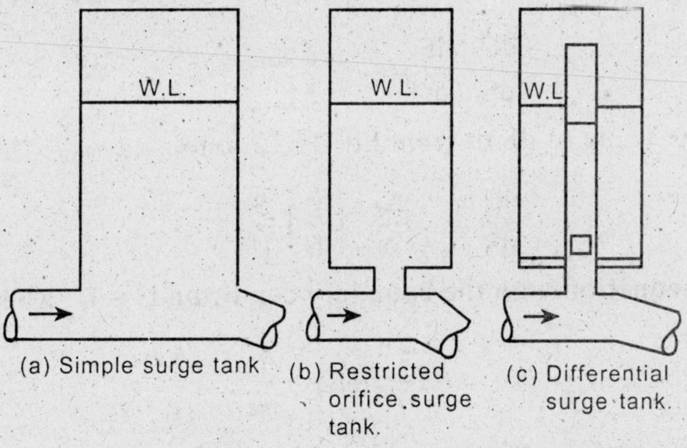

Fig. 15.7 Different types of surge tanks

1. When the power demand is suddenly increased and the valve is opened more, the surge tank supplies additional flow until the water in the pipe is accelerated. Similarly, when the valve is suddenly closed, excess flow is stored in the surge tank. In other words the surge tank acts as a balancing reservoir.

ii. The length of pipe line in which effects of the excess pressure due to sudden closure of valve will be felt is limited to the pipe length between the surge tank and the power plant.

When the discharge is suddenly decreased the water level in the surge tank rises and when the discharge is suddenly increased the water level falls below the equilibrium level. In both the cases the water level in the surge tank oscillates and produces complex unsteady flow. Because of the presence of friction which acts as a retarding force, these oscillations are eventually damped. Oscillations in the surge tank are relatively slow and are analysed neglecting compressbility effect.

Let U_0 be the initial velocity in the pipe. If the friction is neglected, initial hydraulic gradient will be zero and water will be at static level in Fig. 15.6. Water will rise in the surge tank to a level S above its initial level when the turbine valve is suddenly closed. Applying Newton's second law one can write

$$\rho AL \frac{dU}{dt} = -\gamma AS \qquad (15.11)$$

Here A is the area of the pipe and L its length between the surge tank and the reservoir. If dS represents the rise in surge tank water level in time dt, the continuity equation takes the form,

$$A_s\, dS = AU\, dt$$

or

$$\frac{dS}{dt} = \frac{AU}{A_S} \qquad (15.12)$$

in which A_s is the area of the surge tank. Equation 15.11 can be written as

$$\frac{dU}{dS}\frac{dS}{dt} = -g\frac{S}{L}$$

and substituting the value of dS/dt from Eq. 15.12, one gets

$$\frac{dU}{dS} = -\frac{A_S}{A}\left(\frac{g}{L}\right)\frac{S}{U}$$

Integration of this equation with the boundary condition $U = U_o$ when $S = 0$ yields

$$S^2 = (U_o^2 - U^2)\left(\frac{A_S}{A}\right)\left(\frac{L}{g}\right) \qquad (15.13)$$

The maximum rise in water S_{max} will occur when the valve is completely closed i.e. U = 0. Hence

$$S_{max} = U_O\sqrt{\frac{A}{A_S}\frac{L}{g}} \qquad (15.13\text{ a})$$

The continuity equation (Eq. 15.12) can also be written as

$$dt = \frac{A_S}{A}\frac{dS}{U};$$

hence
$$t = \frac{A_S}{A}\int\frac{dS}{U} = \frac{A_S}{A}\int\frac{dS}{\sqrt{U_o^{\,2} - \left(\frac{A_S}{A}\right)\left(\frac{g}{L}\right)S^2}}$$

which can be integrated to yield

$$t = \sqrt{\frac{A_S}{A}\frac{L}{g}}\ \sin^{-1}\left(\frac{S}{S_{max}}\right) \qquad (5.14)$$

The time required to reach maximum surge, t_{max}, will be obtained when $S = S_{max}$.

Hence
$$t_{max} = \frac{\pi}{2}\sqrt{\frac{A_S}{A}\frac{L}{g}} \qquad (15.14\ a)$$

Equations 15.13 (a) and 15.14 (a) give conservative estimates of S_{max}, and t_{max} actual values being smaller due to effects of friction.

When the boundary friction is taken into account, the differential equation for simple surge tank for the case of sudden closure of the valve becomes

$$\frac{d^2S}{dt^2} + \frac{f}{2D}\frac{A_S}{A}\left(\frac{dS}{dt}\right)^2 + \frac{Ag}{A_S L}S = 0 \qquad (15.15)$$

which can also be written as

$$\frac{L}{g}\frac{dU}{dt} + \frac{f\,L}{2g\,D}U\,|\,U\,| + S = 0 \qquad (15.15a)$$

since
$$A_s\,dS = AU\,dt$$

The term U^2 is written above as $U\,|\,U\,|$ in order to incorporate in the equation the fact that friction will always oppose the flow. If S is measured from reservoir level and is taken positive downwards, the above equations can be solved by finite difference scheme given below. For n^{th} computation

$$\left.\begin{aligned}
\Delta S_n &= \frac{A}{A_S}U_{n-1}\,\Delta t \\
S_n &= S_{n-1} - \Delta S_n \\
\Delta U_n &= \frac{g}{L}\left[S_n - \frac{f\,L}{2gD}(U|U|)_{n-1}\right]\Delta t \\
U_n &= U_{n-1} + \Delta U_n \\
Q_n &= A\,U_n
\end{aligned}\right\} \qquad (15.16)$$

Knowing f, L, D, A_S, initial velocity U_o and initial head loss S_o, computations become straight forward. For a typical problem Q = 140 m³/s, L = 16.5 km, diameter of surge tank = 40 m, diameter of penstock = 7.0 m, f = 0.02 and Δt=50 s, computations for 2 steps are shown in the following table and results concerning variation of Q and S with time shown in Fig. 15.8.

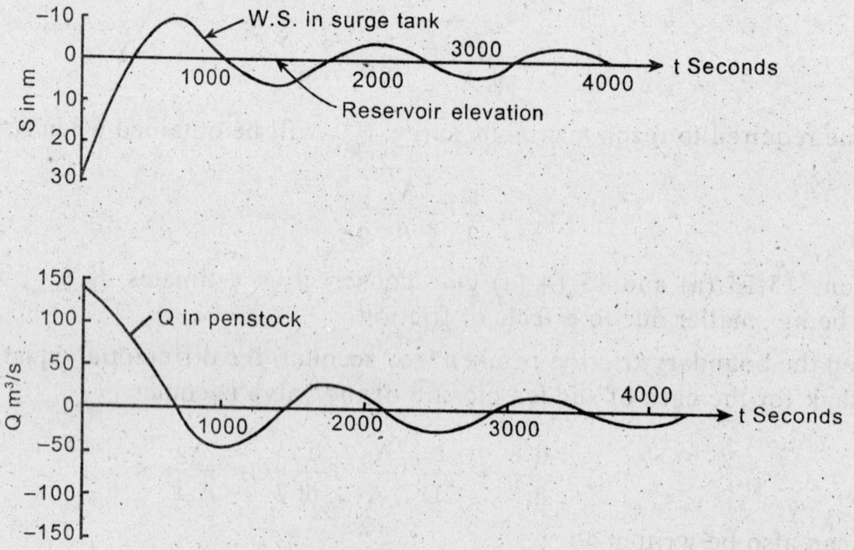

Fig. 15.8 Variation of Q and S with time

$$A = \frac{3.142 \times 49}{4} = 38.465 \text{ m}^2$$

$$A_s = \frac{3.142 \times 1600}{4} = 1256 \text{ m}^2$$

$$U_o = \frac{140}{38.465} = 3.640 \text{ m/s}$$

$$S_o = \frac{0.02 \times 16500 \times 3.64^2}{19.62 \times 7.0} = 31.83 \text{ m}$$

No	t	U m/s	ΔS m	S m	fLU²/2gD	ΔU m/s	Q m/s
	0	3.640		31.83	31.83		140
1	50	3.474	5.57	26.26	28.95	–0.166	136.6
2	100	5.236	5.32	20.94	2.516	–0.238	124.46

It can be seen from Fig. 15.8 that the amplitude of oscillations goes on decreasing with time. Here the oscillations can be seen to be almost sinusoidal; however in some cases they can be aperiodic. The minimum area of a simple surge tank necessary to damp the disturbance down in a time slightly shorter than infinity is given by $A_s = AD/fH$ where H is the steady state head on turbine. This is commonly known as *Thoma's criterion* for surge tanks. Normally the diameter of surge tank is estimated using the above criterion and increasing it by 25 percent. This ensures quick damping of oscillations.

Example 15.4.

A 30 cm diameter pipe carries water at velocity of 2.75 m/s. If the valve at the end of the pipe is suddenly closed what will be the corresponding increase in the pressure? Treat the pipe to be rigid.

Since E for water $= 2.075 \times 10^9$ N/m² and $\rho = 998$ kg/m³,

$$C = \sqrt{\frac{E}{\rho}} = \sqrt{\frac{2.074\times10^9}{998}} = 1442 \text{ m/s}$$

Hence increase in pressure Δp

$$= \rho CU$$
$$= 998 \times 1442 \times 2.75$$
$$= 3960 \times 10^3 \text{ N/m}^2$$
$$= 3960 \text{ kN/m}^2$$

Example 15.5

A 120 cm diameter steel pipe having 9 mm thickness carries water at a rate of 2.0 m³/s. Determine the increasc in the pressure if the valve at the end of 300 m long pipe is closed in 3 seconds.

Taking E_m for steel to be 2.07×10^{11} N/m² and E for water to be 2.075×10^9 N/m².

$$K = \frac{2.075\times10^9}{1+\left\{\dfrac{120\times2.075\times10^9}{0.90\times2.07\times10^{11}}\right\}}$$

$$= 0.69 \times 10^9 \text{ N/m}^2$$

Hence

$$C = \sqrt{\frac{K}{\rho}} = \sqrt{\frac{0.69\times10^9}{998}} = 830.7 \text{ m/s}$$

The time required for the pressure wave to travel from the valve to the inlet and back to valve will be

$$t = \frac{2\times3000}{830.7} = 7.223 \text{ s}$$

Since the closing time of the valve is 3 seconds, which is smaller than 7.223 second, the valve closure can be considered as sudden closure.

As, $\Delta p = \rho\, CU$

and $U = \dfrac{2.0}{0.785 \times 1.2^2} = 1.77$ m/s

∴ $\Delta p = 998 \times 830.7 \times 1.77$

$= 1470\ 399$ N/m²

$= 1470.4$ kN/m²

Example 15.6

A pipe of 2.5 m diameter connected to a reservoir has 3000 m length and a friction factor of 0.03. If the head at the entrance is 20 m, determine the time after sudden opening of the valve, for velocity to attain 0.90 times the final velocity.

$$h_f = \frac{f\,L\,U_O^2}{2g\,D} \quad \therefore\ U_O = \sqrt{\frac{2 \times 9.81 \times 2.5 \times 20}{3000 \times 0.03}}$$

or $U_O = 3.302$ m/s

$$t = \frac{LU_O}{2gH} \log_e \frac{1 + \dfrac{U}{U_O}}{1 - \dfrac{U}{U_O}}$$

$$= \frac{300 \times 3.302}{2 \times 9.81 \times 20} \log_e \frac{1 + 0.90}{1 - 0.90}$$

$= 74.33$ s

15.6 Nonperiodic Flows

As mentioned earlier, the equation which governs the unsteady flows is Eq. 15.2 and that problems of unsteady flows must be analysed using this equation. However, in several problems the term $\partial s/\partial t$ is quite small, and hence it can be taken as zero; this leads to the conclusion that when the acceleration is so small that $\partial V_s/\partial t$ can be neglected, $\partial H/\partial s = 0$ or H = constant at a given time. Below are discussed a few cases which belong to this category.

(a) Discharge through an orifice under falling head

Consider a cylindrical tank of constant cross sectional area A at the bottom of which is fitted an orifice of area a. Let h_1 represent the head over the orifice at time t equal to t_1. As the liquid flows through the orifice, the liquid level will fall and let h be the head over the orifice at time t.

If the liquid level falls through dh in time dt, continuity equation yields,

$$-\,A\,dh = C_d\, a\, V\, dt$$

The negative sign implies that with increase in time, the head over the orifice falls. If the ratio a/A is very small the velocity of efflux V will not change appreciably with time i.e. $\partial V/\partial t$ will also be small and therefore, the total head at all points will be nearly equal to elevation of free surface in the tank. Hence

$$V = \sqrt{2gh}$$

and therefore,

$$dt = \frac{-A dh}{C_d \, a \sqrt{2gh}} \tag{15.17}$$

Integration of this equation yieids

$$\int_{t_1}^{t_2} dt = \frac{-A}{C_d \, a \sqrt{2g}} \int_{h_1}^{h_2} h^{-1/2} \, dh$$

in which h_2 is the head over orifice at time t_2

$$(t_2 - t_1) = T = \frac{2A}{C_d \, a \sqrt{2g}} (h_1^{1/2} - h_2^{1/2}) \tag{15.18}$$

As long as a/A is quite small, Eq. 15.18 gives sufficiently accurate value of the time T required for the liquid surface to drop from h_1 to h_2. Similar expression can be obtained for tanks of various shapes. If the shape of the tank is such that the cross sectional area A at any elevation can be expressed as a function of elevation, then the same method can be applied, except that one must substitute for A, a term which is a function of h. If the cross sectional area A varies irregularly with h, the above integration can be performed graphically.

Example 15.7

A conical tank with its apex downwards is so shaped that the cross sectional area varies as $h^{2.5}$ where h is elevation of liquid surface above the apex. Determine the time required for water depth to reduce from 2.0 m to 0.50 m above the orifice of 3 cm diameter, given that A is 4.0 m² when h equals 2.0 m. Take C_d as 0.60.

Let $\quad A = k\, h^{2.5}$ and $A = 4.0$ m² when h = 2.0 m

$$\therefore \quad k = \frac{4.0}{2.0^{2.5}} = 0.707$$

Substituting $A = k\, h^{2.5}$ in Eq. 15.17 one gets,

$$T = \int_{t_1}^{t_2} dt = \int_{2.0}^{0.50} - \frac{k\, h^{2.5} dh}{C_d \, a \sqrt{2gh}}$$

$$= \frac{-k}{C_d \, a\sqrt{2g}} \int_{2.0}^{0.50} h^2 dh = \frac{k}{3C_d \, a\sqrt{2g}} \left[h^3\right]_{0.50}^{2.0}$$

Substituting the values of k, C_d and a, one gets

$$T = \frac{0.707 \times 10^4 (8.00 - 0.125)}{3 \times 0.60 \times (0.785 \times 9) \times \sqrt{19.62}}$$

$$= 988 \text{ s}$$

(b) Discharge through Tanks with Constant Inflow

The case of discharge from a tank through an orifice when there is a constant inflow is of particular interest since such a case leads one to the solution of problems concerning flood routing through reservoirs.

Let Q be the constant rate of inflow into a cylindrical tank of area A which is fitted with an orifice of area a at its base. Then in time dt

$$\text{Amount of inflow} = Q\,dt$$

Amount of outflow through the orifice = $C_d a \sqrt{2gh}\ dt$.

If the liquid level rises by dh during this time dt, then

$$A dh = Q\,dt - m\,h^{1/2}\,dt \tag{15.19}$$

in which $m = C_d\ a\ \sqrt{2gh}$

Therefore $dt = \dfrac{A dh}{(Q - mh^{1/2})}$

This equation can be integrated by making a substitution $x = Q - mh^{1/2}$. Hence

$$\therefore \quad h = \frac{(Q-x)^2}{m^2} \quad \text{and} \quad dh = \frac{-2(Q-x)}{m^2}\,dx$$

$$\therefore \quad dt = \frac{-2(Q-x)\,dx}{xm^2}$$

or

$$\int_{t_1}^{t_2} dt = -\frac{2A}{m^2} \int_{x_1}^{x_2} \left(\frac{Q}{x} - 1\right) dx$$

in which $x_1 = (Q - mh_1^{1/2})$ and $x_2 = (Q - mh_2^{1/2})$

This gives

$$T = (t_2 - t_1) = -\frac{2A}{m^2}\left[Q\log_e\left(\frac{Q - mh_2^{1/2}}{Q - mh_1^{1/2}}\right) - m\left(h_1^{1/2} - h_2^{1/2}\right)\right]$$

$$T = \frac{2A}{m^2}\left[m\left(h_1^{1/2} - h_2^{1/2}\right) - Q\log_e\left(\frac{Q - mh_2^{1/2}}{Q - mh_1^{1/2}}\right)\right] \tag{15.20}$$

Since the rate of inflow as well as the cross-sectional area of the tank were constant, it was possible to get an analytical expression for the period T required to change the level from h_1 to h_2. If inflow rate were to vary with time and A were to vary with the depth h, the solution would become extremely complicated. Such is indeed the case for problems concerning flood routing through reservoirs.

By constructing a dam across a stream, a large capacity reservoir is formed upstream of the dam. During the flood, water is stored in the reservoir and part of it is allowed to flow in the downstream channel through the sluices or over the spillway. As a result the peak of the flood in the downstream channel is reduced and duration of flood is increased. Since the total amount of water flowing into the reservoir during the time dt must be equal to the sum of the amounts of water flowing out during the same time and the amount stored in the reservoir, one can write

$$Q_i\, dt = Q_o dt + dS \tag{15.21}$$

in which Q_i is the inflow rate and Q_o is the rate of outflow. The storage dS can be expressed as Adh. Hence, Eq. 15.21 can be written as

$$dt = \frac{Adh}{Q_i - Q_0}$$

$$T = \int_{t_1}^{t_2} dt = \int_{h_1}^{h_2} \frac{Adh}{(Q_i - Q_0)} \tag{15.22}$$

Since A varies with h in a complex manner for the case of natural reservoir, since Q_i varies with time and Q_o varies with h, the above integration must be performed by using numerical methods.

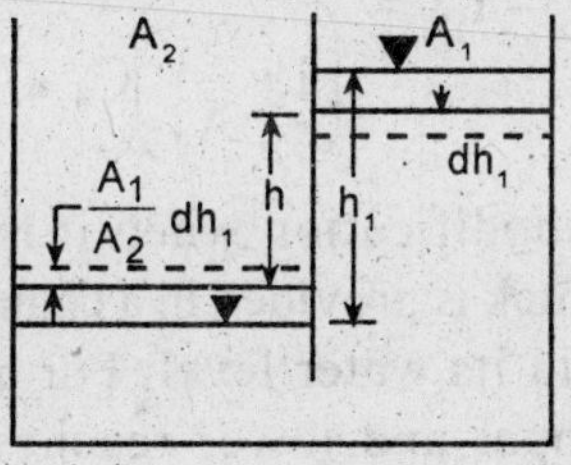

Fig. 15.9 Interconnected tanks

(c) *Interconnected Tanks*

Consider two tanks of constant cross-sectional areas, A_1 and A_2 which are interconnected by means of an opening of area a and discharge coefficient C_d, see Fig. 15.9. Let h_1 be the difference in the liquid levels in the two tanks at time t_1. Then as the liquid flows from tank 1 to tank 2, the difference between the liquid levels will reduce. Let h represent the liquid level difference at any time and dQ represent the discharge flowing into tank 2 in time dt. Then, the level in tank 1 will fall while that in the tank 2 will rise. The net difference of head after time dt will be $\left(h - dh_1 - \frac{A_1}{A_2} dh_1\right)$ i.e. $\left[h - dh_1\left(1 + \frac{A_1}{A_2}\right)\right]$,

or
$$dh = dh_1 \left(1 + \frac{A_1}{A_2}\right)$$

in which dh_1 represents drop in liquid level in tank 1 while dh represents change in h. Accordingly, continuity equation gives

$$- A_1\, dh_1 = C_d\, a\, \sqrt{2gh}\, dt$$

Substituting
$$dh_1 = \frac{dh}{\left(1 + \frac{A_1}{A_2}\right)}, \quad \text{one gets}$$

$$dt = \frac{-A_1}{\left(1 + \frac{A_1}{A_2}\right) C_d\, a \sqrt{2g}}\, h^{-1/2}\, dh$$

or
$$\int_{t_1}^{t_2} dt = \frac{-A_1}{\left(1 + \frac{A_1}{A_2}\right) C_d\, a \sqrt{2g}} \int_{h_1}^{h_2} h^{-1/2}\, dh$$

Hence

$$T = (t_2 - t_1) = \frac{2A_1 \left(h_1^{1/2} - h_2^{1/2}\right)}{\left(1 + \frac{A_1}{A_2}\right) C_d\, a \sqrt{2g}} \qquad (15.23)$$

The above equation needs slight modification when it is used for finding the time for filling the navigation lock. Navigation lock is provided in a channel which is used for navigation purpose and which has sudden drop in its water level. For a ship to travel in this reach, a chamber is provided between the upper and lower reaches of the channel, see Fig. 15.10. Assume that the water levels in the upper and lower reaches are constant. When a ship has to pass from lower reach to the upper, it is first admitted into the lock. The sluice gate 2 in the downstream is then completely closed and water is admitted into the lock chamber through the pipe system from the upstream side. When the water levels in the lock chamber and the upstream channel are the same, the sluice gate 1 is opened, the ship can then travel upstream. The procedure is reversed when the ship has to travel from upstream to the downstream reach. The ship is admitted in the lock chamber and the upstream gate is completely closed. The water in the lock chamber is allowed to flow in the downstream channel and the water level in the lock is lowered to that in the lower reach. The ship can then travel downstream. When the lock is being emptied the water level in the downstream channel does not change; hence one can substitute $A_1/A_2 = 0$ in Eq. 15.23 to find time required for lowering the water level through a given height.

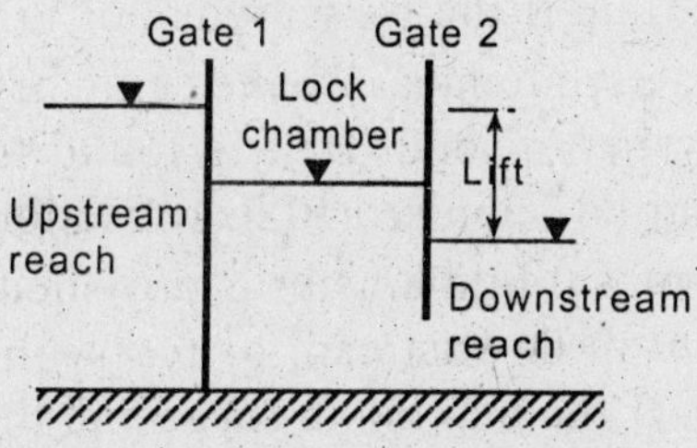

Fig. 15.10 Navigation lock

PROBLEMS

5.1 In the following cases of a moving hydraulic jump determine the missing elements

No.	y_1 m	U_1 m/s	y_2 m	U_2 m/s	U_0 m/s
1	1.00	4.60			– 1.50
2		7.60		6.10	+ 1.50

5.2 When an immersed body was towed through water in a towing tank at a constant velocity of 8.0 m/s, the velocity 1.5 m ahead of the nose of the body was found to be 3.5 m/s. What will be the difference in pressure intensity between the nose and the point under consideration? Express it in N/m².

5.3 A cylindrical body was towed at 8.0 m/s velocity through water flowing in the same direction at 2.5 m/s velocity. If the pressure difference between the nose of the body and a point some distance ahead of it is 12.55 kN/m², determine the velocity at that point.

5.4 Determine the velocity of propagation of an elastic wave in a 60 cm diameter steel pipe ($E_m = 2.07 \times 10^{11}$ N/m²) of 6 mm thickness when (i) water (ii) glycerine (iii) benzene flow through it at a temperature of 20°C.

5.5 In problem 15.4, if in each one of the given cases a discharge of 0.60 m³/s flows through the pipe, determine the pressure rise due to sudden closure of the valve.

5.6 What will be discharge of benzene flowing through a 10.0 cm diameter rigid pipe if a sudden closure of the valve produces a pressure rise of 981 kN/m²?

5.7 The velocity of water in a 60 cm diameter and 15 mm thick cast iron pipe ($E_m = 1.039 \times 10^{11}$ N/m²) is changed from 3.0 m/s to zero in 0.30 seconds by closing a valve. If the pipe length is 300 m, what will be the pressure rise? What will be the corresponding pressure rise if this closure takes place in 5 seconds and 1 second respectively?

.8 A 2.0 m diameter and 10 mm thick steel pipe carries water to a number of turbines. When the pipe is carrying 9.0 m³/s discharge, a quick acting gate is operated to stop the flow suddenly. What will be the rise in pressure due to water hammer? What will be the maximum time during which the gate can be closed while still maintaining this pressure rise if the pipe length is 4500 m? Also determine the approximate closure time if the pressure is not to exceed 981 kN/m^2.

15.9 A sonar transmitter is used to measure the depth of water in a lake. The transmitter gives out 2 impulses per second. If it is found that there is a time lag of 0.10 second between the initial impulse and its reflection, what is the depth of the lake?

15.10 A simple surge tank of 4.0 in diameter is provided for 150 cm diameter penstock and it is located 1800 m downstream of reservoir. For a discharge of 30.0 m^3/s determine the height of the maximum surge and the time required to attain it.

15.11 A rectangular tank 2.5 m wide and 7.5 m long has a 4.0 cm diameter sharp edged orifice at its bottom. What will be the time required for the water level to drop from 5.0 m to 1.5 m if the discharge coefficient for the orifice is 0.60?

15.12 Determine the time required for the reduction in the liquid level from H_1 to H_2, in a hemispherical tank of radius R with a small orifice of area 'a' at its bottom. Show that the time for completely draining the full tank is $\left(14\pi R^{5/2}/15C_d a\sqrt{2g}\right)$.

15.13 The head in a vessel with vertical sides, at an instant of opening the bottom orifice, was 4.0 m, and at closing had decreased to 2.0 m. Determine the constant head under which, in the same time, the orifice would discharge the same volume of water.

15.14 A 10 cm diameter orifice is fixed in the side of a rectangular tank of 40.0 m^2 area. While the orifice is discharging water, the water level in the tank is maintained constant by a constant inflow of 23.0 l/s. If this discharge is suddenly increased to 60.0 l/s, what will be the equilibrium head on the orifice and the time required to attain a depth of 8.0 m? Take C_d to be 0.60.

15.15 Prove that in a right angled triangular notch discharging from a tank of area A m^2, the time of lowering the water level from H_1 to H_2 m above the vertex of the notch is $T = \frac{1.25}{C_d\sqrt{2g}}\left[\frac{1}{H_2\sqrt{H_2}} - \frac{1}{H_1\sqrt{H_1}}\right]$

15.16 A tank with a water spread of 3.49×10^5 m^2 has a surplus weir 24.5 m long. Find the time in which the water will go down from 1.0 m above the crest of the weir by 30 cm, if there is no inflow into the tank. Assume C_d to be 0.60.

15.17 Two cylindrical tanks of 3.0 m and 2.0 m diameters respectively are connected by a short tube of 0.01 m^2 area and 0.60 discharge coefficient, located near the bottom. The water levels in the two tanks are 4.0 m and 2.5 m above the tube when the valve connecting the two is opened. Determine the time required for equalising the water levels.

15.18 A circular bucket with bottom diameter of 1.0 m, top diameter of 2.0 m and height 2.0 m has a hole of 10cm dia in its bottom. It is empty and immersed in a large tank of water up to its top. Determine the time required to fill it to a depth of 1.0 m.

CHAPTER SIXTEEN

TURBINES

16.1 Introduction

Fluid Machines are devices which are used for converting fluid energy into mechanical energy and vice versa. Two types of fluid machines that are of immediate interest to a hydraulic engineer are turbines and pumps. A turbine converts the energy of the fluid into mechanical energy which is then utilised in running a generator of a power plant. In the case of a hydropower scheme the fluid in question is water while in the case of steam power plant, the fluid used is steam. A pump imparts mechanical energy to the fluid and raises its pressure energy, which is then utilised either in overcoming friction or in raising fluids to higher elevation, This chapter is devoted to the discussion of turbines.

16.2 Water Wheels

The idea of using energy in water and converting it into mechanical energy was known to the mankind since long. In the earlier days this conversion was effected by passing flowing water through wheels; such wheels were known as water wheels and were used in ancient times in China, India, Egypt and later in Europe. Leonardo da Vinci (1452-1519) was the first to design and construct a water wheel. The theory of water wheels was developed in Europe by Borda, Poncelet, Bernoulli, Euler and others. The water wheels can be classified into the following categories according to the driving action of water.

(a) Overshot Wheel

Overshot wheel is driven by the weight of water and is sometimes known as gravity wheel, see Fig. 16.1 (a). This consists of a series of vanes or buckets mounted on a wheel with horizontal axle. Water is arranged to fall on them at their top with the help of a sluice gate. The pertinent data about overshot wheels are

Wheel diameter D = 3 to 20 m

Depth of shroud $\frac{(D-d)}{2} = 0.50 \text{ to } 1.0 \text{ m}$

Number of buckets z = (7 to 10) D

Periperal velocity of the buckets $v = \frac{\pi DN}{60}$

$= 1.5 \text{ to } 3.0 \text{ m/s}$

in which N is the speed of rotation in rpm and d is the inner diameter. Generally the peripheral velocity is about half the velocity V_1 of the incoming flow. The efficiency of such a wheel is about 60 to 80 percent.

(b) Breast Wheel

In the second type of the wheel known as the breast wheel, see Fig. 16.1 (b), water at atmospheric pressure strikes on the vanes attached to the wheel at or below the level of the shaft. The discharge striking the vane can be controlled by a sluice gate.

(c) Undershot Wheel

The third type of wheel, known as undershot wheel is rotated due to high velocity jet striking on a series of blades mounted on a wheel, see Fig. 16.1 (c). This wheel rotates entirely due to the impulse of water. The available energy in water is converted into kinetic energy and rotation of wheel is caused by change of momentum of the jet.

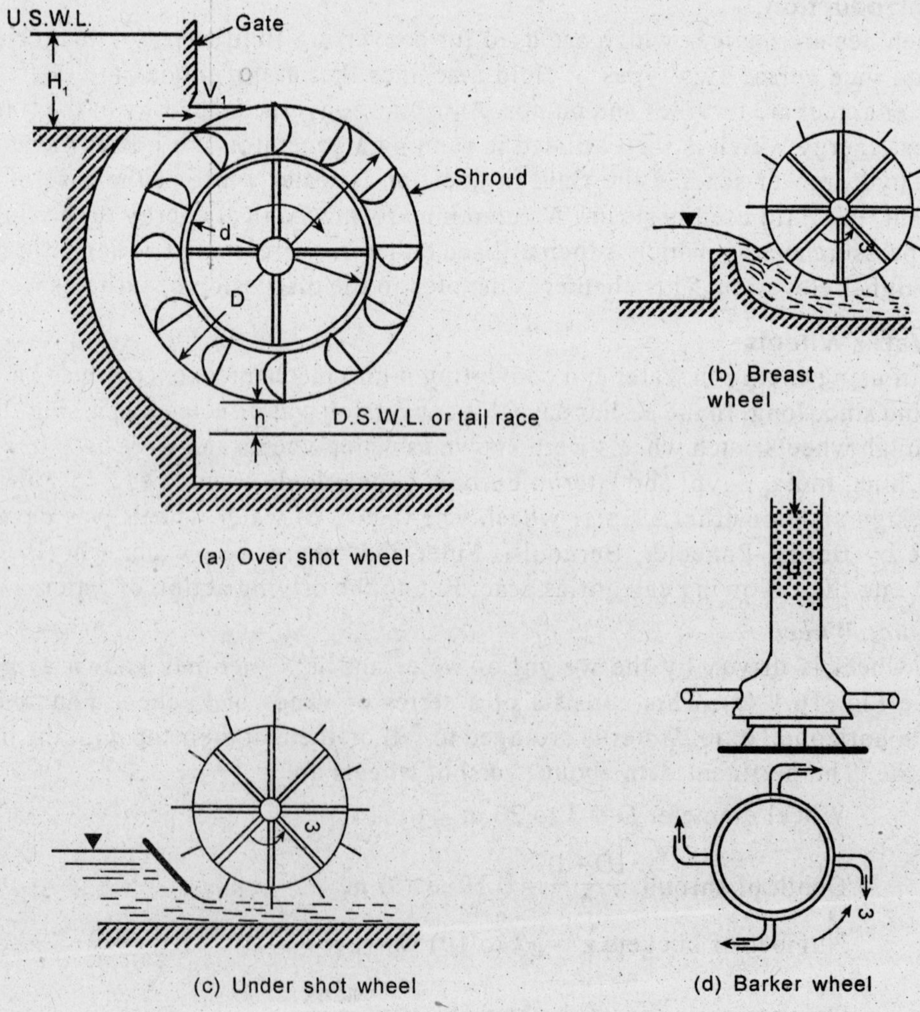

Fig. 16.1 Water wheels

(d) Barker Wheel

The fourth type of wheel, known as Barker wheel, also works on the principle of change in momentum and has considerable similarity to the lawn sprinkler. This consists of a vertical pipe carrying water in the downward direction under pressure. The pipe is mounted on bearings and has L–shaped pipes connected radially to it around its bottom, see Fig. 16.1 (d). As the water escapes through ends of the radial pipes the entire arrangement rotates in the opposite direction.

The advantage of the water wheels lies in their ruggedness, simplicity and relatively high efficiency. On the other hand, water wheels have a poor control on their operation and also have a low speed. They are further relatively heavy for the power they generate and hence more costly.

Example 16.1

A canal carrying water for the overshot wheel has a width of 1.5 m, a depth of 1.5 m and a velocity of 2.0 m/s. The total drop available is 8.0 m. If the wheel efficiency is 70 percent, determine the power developed.

$$Q = 1.5 \times 1.5 \times 2.0 = 4.50 \text{ m}^3/\text{s}$$

$$P = Q \gamma H \eta / 1000 \text{ kW}$$

$$= 4.5 \times 9787 \times 8.0 \times 0.70/1000$$

$$= 246.632 \text{ kW}$$

16.3 Classification of Turbines

Because of the inherent drawbacks of water wheels, continuous attempt was made to improve the different types of water wheels. These efforts have yielded different types of turbines. Depending on the action of water on the blades all the water turbines can be classified into two categories, namely impulse turbines and reaction turbines. In an impulse turbine, water is brought to the turbine through a penstock at the end of which is fitted a nozzle which converts energy of fluid into kinetic energy before it strikes the blades or vanes in the atmosphere. The vanes or blades or buckets of the turbine are fixed on a revolving element of the turbine, which is known as the runner. The buckets change the magnitude and direction of the velocity of water and cause rotation of the turbine. A casing provided to the impulse turbine only prevents the splashing of the water; it has no hydraulic function. This turbine is known as a free jet turbine also. Pelton wheel or Pelton turbine, named after the American Engineer Pelton (1829-1908) is an impulse turbine, see Fig. 16.2.

In the case of a reaction turbine, water enters the turbine under pressure and hence it has both pressure energy as well as kinetic energy. As the water enters the turbine under pressure, reaction turbine always runs full. It may, for some reasons, be submerged below the downstream water level (known as tail race) or may discharge into atmosphere. It must however be remembered that action in both the impulse as well as the reaction turbines depends on the change in the momentum of the fluid so that a force is exerted on the runner. Francis turbine, propeller turbine and Kaplan turbine fall under this category.

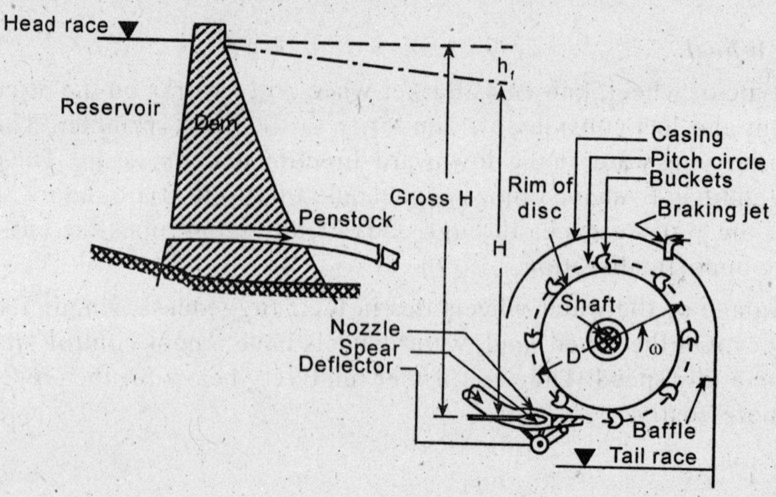

Fig. 16.2 Schematic layout of Pelton wheel

Turbines can also be classified, according to the direction of flow of water in the runner, into

- Radial flow turbines
- Axial flow turbines (e.g. Kaplan)
- Tangential flow turbines (e.g. Pelton wheel)
- Mixed (radial and axial) flow turbines

In radial flow turbine the path of water as it flows through the runner lies in a plane perpendicular to the axis of rotation of the turbine. In the outward flow turbine, water enters at the inner circumference and discharges at the outer circumference of the runner. In inward flow turbine it enters at the outer circumference of the runner and leaves at the inner circumference. Original Francis turbine was of the latter type. In the axial flow turbine water enters the turbine parallel to the shaft; Kaplan turbine is of axial flow type. In the tangential flow turbine water enters tangentially. In mixed flow turbines flow partly enters radially and partly axially.

Turbines may also differ in their relative position of the shaft. Whereas Pelton wheel shaft is usually horizontal, other turbines producing greater power normally have their shafts vertical.

Each turbine is suitable under certain conditions of discharge, head and speed. In general impulse turbines are recommended for high heads and low discharges; reaction turbines are used in the case of low heads and high rates of flow.

IMPULSE TURBINES

16.4 Pelton Wheel

The most common type of impulse turbine is Pelton wheel, the main features of which are shown in Fig. 16.2. The wheel has a series of curved split buckets mounted on the rim of the disc of the runner. A nozzle arrangement converts available high head into a uniform high velocity jet which strikes the dividing ridge of the bucket, see Fig. 16.3. The shape of the bucket is so designed as to extract the maximum possible energy from the jet. Only one jet is used in small Pelton turbines, but in larger units, more jets impinging at different points around the wheel are used. Pelton turbine is usually set with its shaft horizontal; however when more jets are used its shaft is kept vertical. Torque produced by the change in momentum causes the wheel to rotate. The speed of the turbine is kept at such a constant value that the efficiency of the turbine is maximum. This is done by providing a needle valve and also by providing a deflector outside the nozzle, as shown in Fig. 16.2, to control the quantity of water striking the jet. An auxiliary jet is provided to stop the runner within a short time after the main jet is turned off. This is known as the braking jet. The runner is situated sufficiently above the maximum tail race (or tail water level.) so that the water striking the buckets discharges under gravity under atmospheric conditions.

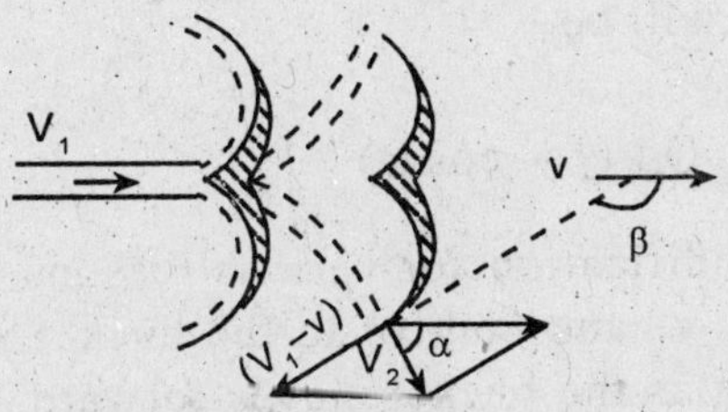

Fig. 16.3 Velocity diagram for Pelton wheel

Buckets shown in Fig. 16.4 are either hemispherical or double ellipsoidal in shape. They are made of cast iron, bronze, or steel alloyed with nickel, chromium or manganese. Small turbine runners are cast as a unit; for large turbines the buckets are cast separately and bolted to the runner. This facilitates repairs or part replacement.

16.5 Theory of Impulse Turbines

Consider a Pelton turbine rotaing at a peripheral velocity v which is at the centre of the buckets, see Fig. 16.3. The velocity of the jet impinging on the bucket is V_1. The relative velocity of the jet with respect to buckets is (V_1-v). Assuming there is no friction as water flows over the bucket, the relative velocity of jet when it leaves the bucket is also (V_1-v). Let V_2 be the absolute velocity of the jet when it leaves the bucket, which can be obtained by vectorially combining the relative velocity (V_1-v) with the peripheral velocity v. The angle between direction of impinging jet and that of relative velocity at exit is the bucket angle or deflection angle β.

Applying the momentum principle and keeping in mind that at any time one of the buckets will always be deflecting the jet, force exerted by water on the bucket in the direction of motion is

$$F_x = Q\rho\,(V_1 - V_2 \cos\alpha) \qquad (16.1)$$

in which Q is the jet discharge. However

$$V_2 \cos\alpha = v - (V_1 - v)\cos\beta$$

Substitution of this expression in Eq. 16.1 yields

$$F_x = Q\rho\,(V_1 - v)\,(1 - \cos\beta) \qquad (16.2)$$

The power transmitted to the bucket is equal to the product of force and velocity of bucket or

$$P = F_x v = Q\rho\,(V_1 - v)\,(1 - \cos\beta)\,v \qquad (16.3)$$

It can be seen that no power will be developed when V_1 equals v. The condition under which the power developed will be maximum for a given turbine and jet is obtained by differentiating P with respect to v and equating the result to zero

$$\frac{dP}{dv} = Q\rho\,(1 - \cos\beta)\,(V_1 - 2v) = 0$$

$$\therefore \quad v = \frac{V_1}{2} \qquad (16.4)$$

Thus maximum power will be developed when peripheral velocity is half the jet velocity. The maximum power P_{max} will be

$$P_{max}\; Q\rho\,(1 - \cos\beta)\,\frac{V_1^2}{4} \qquad (16.5)$$

This expression needs modification for various reasons. As the jet strikes the moving bucket the angle between V_1 and tangent to the bucket at the entry will be other than zero, and will be reducing as the bucket moves forward. Other factor is the friction on the buckets as a result of which the relative velocity of the jet at the exit will be slightly smaller than that at the entry. If the ratio of relative velocity at exit to that at entry is taken as K, the term $(1 - \cos\beta)$ in the above equations gets modified to $(1 - K\cos\beta)$. The third effect is due to the effective radius of curvature of the upper and lower parts of the bucket during its motion. Even though the actual radii are equal, the effective radii are slightly unequal. In detailed analysis these factors are taken into account. As a result tests on Pelton turbines have indicated that the best operating conditions occur when the velocity ratio $\phi = \left(\frac{v}{V_1}\right)$ is between 0 43 to 0.48.

The hydraulic efficiency of the turbine η_H is defined as the ratio of work done per second to the energy of the jet, expressed in percent; viz

$$\eta_H = \frac{Q\rho(V_1 - v)(1 - \cos\beta)\,v}{Q\rho V_1^2/2} \times 100$$

$$= 2\,\frac{v}{V_1}\left(1 - \frac{v}{V_1}\right)(1 - \cos\beta) \times 100$$

$$\therefore \quad \eta_H = 2\phi_1 (1 - \phi_1)(1 - \cos\beta) \times 100 \tag{16.6}$$

The power available at the shaft is less than $Q\rho (V_1 - v)(1 - \cos\beta)\, v$ due to mechanical losses in the bearing of the shaft and in the transmission of power. For this reason the mechanical efficiency η_M is defined as

$$\eta_M = \frac{\text{Power available at the shaft}}{Q\rho (V_1 - v)(1 - \cos\beta)\, v} \times 100 \tag{16.7}$$

The overall efficiency of the turbine η is defined as power available at the shaft to the energy of the jet, expressed in percent. Hence

$$\eta = \eta_H \, \eta_M \tag{16.8}$$

It may be mentioned that only a fraction of the power available at the shaft will be converted into electrical energy. For Pelton turbine η_M varies from 95 to 99 percent while η_H is of the order of 85 to 90 percent.

Example 16.2

A Pelton turbine having semicircular buckets and working under a head of 150 m runs at a speed of 600 rpm. If the discharge through the nozzle is 50 *l*/s, find the power available at the nozzle and the hydraulic efficiency. Take wheel diameter as 0.60 m and C_V for the nozzle as 0.97.

For semicircular buckets $\beta = 180°$.

The power available at the nozzle $= Q\gamma H$

$= 0.050 \times 9787 \times 150$

$= 73402.5$ W

or 73.403 kW

Jet velocity $\quad V_1 = C_v\sqrt{2gH} = 0.97 \times \sqrt{2 \times 9.806 \times 150}$

$= 52.611$ m/s

$$v = \frac{\pi DN}{60} = \frac{3.142 \times 0.60 \times 600}{60}$$

$= 18.852$ m/s

Also $\quad \phi_1 = \dfrac{18.852}{52.611} = 0.3583$

$\eta_H = 2 \times 0.3583\,(1 - 0.3583)\,[1 - (-1)] \times 100$

$= 91.97$ percent.

Example 16.3

A Pelton wheel develops 184 kW power under the effective head of 44 m. If the efficiency of the turbine is 82.5 percent and C_v for the nozzle is 0.98, determine the nozzle diameter.

$V_1 = 0.98\sqrt{2 \times 9.806 \times 44}$

$= 28.788$ m/s

Energy available at the nozzle

$$= \frac{184\,000}{0.825} = 223\,030 \text{ W}$$

$$\left(\frac{\pi d^2}{4} V_1 \rho\right) \frac{V_1^2}{2} = 223\,030$$

$\therefore$ $d^2 = 0.02384 \text{ m}^2$

and $d = 0.1544$ m or 15.44 cm

16.6 Pelton Wheel Parameters

Various parameters related to Pelton turbines are determined from hydraulic, mechanical as well as from the constructional considerations. The buckets are usually double ellipsoidal in shape. When the deflection angle β is 180° the deflected jet will be parallel to the striking jet and will, in theory, give maximum power for given values of Q, V_1 and v. However from practical considerations this is not possible and it is the common practice to keep β between 160° and 170°. As can be seen from Fig. 16.4 the lower portion of each bucket is cutoff. If it were not so, the bucket exactly opposite the jet would not get the full jet striking on it as some of the water will be intercepted by the lower portion of the bucket that follows. The other average dimensions of the bucket are given below:

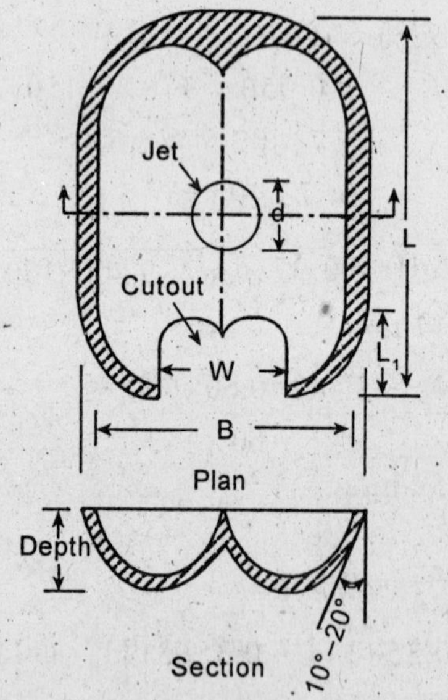

Fig. 16.4 Details of bucket

Axial width	B	= (3 to 4) d
Depth		= (0.8 to 1.2) d
Radial length	L	= (2.5 to 3.0) d
Width of cutout	W	= (1.3 to 2.0) d
Depth of cutout	L_1	= (0.30 to 0.50) d

The number of buckets is governed primarily by the following two criteria. Firstly, they should be as few in number as possible so that the frictional loss is minimum. Secondly, the number should be such that water is fully utilised and no water goes to waste. In practice the number of buckets Z is given by the following formulae which are based on data from Pelton turbines working satisfactorily.

$$\left.\begin{aligned} Z &= \frac{1}{2}\left(\frac{D}{d}\right) + 15 \\ \text{or} \quad Z &= 5.4\left(\frac{D}{d}\right)^{1/2} \end{aligned}\right\} \qquad (16.9)$$

The following table also gives the approximate number of buckets for known values of D/d.

D/d	6	8	10	15	20	25
Z	17–21	18–22	19–24	22–27	24–30	26–33

The area of the jet should be less than 0.10 times the projected area of the bucket. The diameter of the jet should not also be greater than 0.30 times the bucket width. There is also an optimum relation between the diameter of the wheel and that of the jet. The ratio D/d should be between 9 and 12. Normally a single jet is used for the wheel; but some times two jets are used to increase the power. In such a case the shaft is horizontal. In few cases when the shaft is vertical and more power is needed, more than two jets have been used but in such a case governing become a problem. Details of nozzle and spear which control the flow are shown in Fig. 16.5.

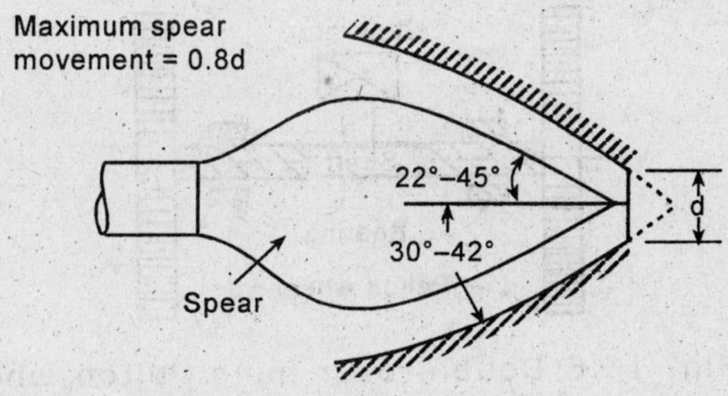

Fig. 16.5 Details of nozzle and spear

Example 16.4

A Pelton turbine running at 500 rpm produces 9325 kW of power with a head of 300 m. Assuming jet diameter to be one tenth of the wheel diameter, $C_v = 0.98$ and overall efficiency η of 85 percent, determine the jet diameter and number of jets required.

$$\frac{Q\gamma H}{1000}\eta = 9325$$

$$\therefore \quad Q = \frac{9325\times1000}{9787\times300\times0.85}$$

$$= 3.736 \text{ m}^3/\text{s}$$

$$V_1 = C_v\sqrt{2gH} = 0.98\sqrt{2\times9.806\times300} = 75.17 \text{ m/s}$$

Since $v/V_1 = 0.46$ for maximum efficiency,

$$v = 0.46 \times 75.17 = 34.578 \text{ m/s}$$

$$\text{but } \frac{\pi DN}{60} = v \therefore D = \frac{60\times34.578}{3.142\times500} = 1.321 \text{ m}$$

$$d = 0.10\,D = 0.1321 \text{ m, or } 13.21 \text{ cm}$$

Discharge through each jet

$$= 0.785 \times 0.132^2 \times 75.17 = 1.030 \text{ m}^3/\text{s}$$

$$\therefore \quad \text{Number of jets} = 3.736/1.030 = 3.63$$

Hence use four jets.

16.7 Double Over-Hung Pelton Wheel

A double over-hung Pelton wheel consists of two runners on a single shaft with the generator located in between as shown in Fig. 16.6. Such arrangement is preferred when higher speed or greater power are needed. The principles of calculation for a double over-hung Pelton wheel are the same as those for a single Pelton wheel as illustrated in Example 16.5 below.

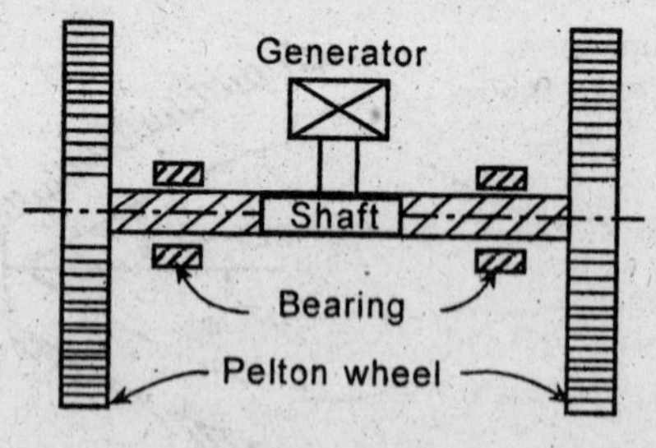

Fig. 16.6 Double over-hung Pelton wheel

Example 16.5

A double over-hung Pelton wheel produces 20 000 kW of power at 95 percent efficiency of the generator. If the effective head on the wheel is 200 in with overall efficiency of 85 percent, $C_v = 0.98$ and $\phi_1 = 0.46$, compute the wheel and jet diameters. The generator frequency is 50 Hz and number of poles is 16.

Power supplied by wheels to the generator

$$= \frac{20\,000}{0.95} = 21\,052.631 \text{ kW}$$

$$\text{Power of each wheel} = \frac{21\,052.631}{2} = 10\,526.315 \text{ kW}$$

If the wheels operate under an effective head of 200 m,

$$10\,526.315 \times 1000 = Q \times 9787 \times 200 \times 0.85$$

$$\therefore \quad Q = 6.327 \text{ m}^3\text{/s}$$

$$V_1 = 0.98\sqrt{2 \times 9.81 \times 200}$$

$$= 61.376 \text{ m/s}$$

$$\therefore \quad 6.327 = 0.785 \times d^2 \times 61.376$$

$$d^2 = 0.1313 \text{ m}^2$$

$$d = 0.3624 \text{ m or } 36.24 \text{ cm}$$

The generator frequency, pair of poles and the synchronous speed are related as

$$N = \frac{60 \times f}{\text{No. of poles}}$$

$$N = \frac{60 \times 50}{16} = 187.5 \text{ rpm}$$

$$\frac{\pi DN}{60} = v = 0.46\,V_1 = 28.233 \text{ m/s}$$

$$\therefore \quad D = \frac{28.233 \times 60}{187.5 \times 3.142}$$

$$= 2.875 \text{ m}$$

16.8 Governing of Pelton Wheels

Alternators driven by turbines have to be run at a constant speed to produce power at a given frequency, irrespective of load (i.e. power requirement). Therefore, it is necessary to run the turbine at constant speed under all loads which is accomplished by altering the input energy in conformity with the load with the help of a governor. The input energy can be altered in any one of the following ways:

i. by controlling the discharge,

ii. by deflecting the discharge,

iii. by combination of the two.

The amount of discharge coming out of the nozzle is varied by forward or backward motion of the spear inside the nozzle. Movement of the nozzle in the forward or backward direction changes the cross-sectional area and controls the flow. This arrangement is satisfactory for gradual change in discharge; however rapid closure in this way to cope with complete reduction of load causes water hammer problem and is therefore not recommended. The second way of controlling the flow striking the buckets is to deflect part or whole of the jet away from the bucket by use of a deflector the action of which is shown in Fig. 16.7. The deflector is a plate connected to an oil pressure governor by means of levers. When it is required to deflect the jet, the plate is brought into the position. Deflector control is used for coping with fluctuating loads. In a regulation using both the deflector and spear, the deflector is first used to deal with rapid change in load and then the spear is brought into position to regulate the dicharge after which the deflector is removed. This is done by using a governing arrangement based on feed back servomechanism principle. Line diagram of the governing arrangement is shown in Fig. 16.8. The arrangement works in the following way. As the load on the turbine is decreased, the centrifugal govenor moves up, thus moving the bell-crank lever towards downwards; this brings the deflector in position thereby diverting part of the jet. With the movement of bell crank lever, the roller on the cam arrangement moves up. The distributing valve also functions, thus moving the servomotor piston rod to the right. The movement of piston to the right causes spear to move in that direction thereby reducing the discharge. With the movement of the bell-crank lever, simultaneously roller is raised and also the distribution valve functions thus moving the servomotor piston to the right. This reduces the nozzle area by the forward movement of the spear. This movement of the spear rod brings the cam to the right which ultimately brings the deflector to its original position. This operation takes approximately 30 to 60 seconds.

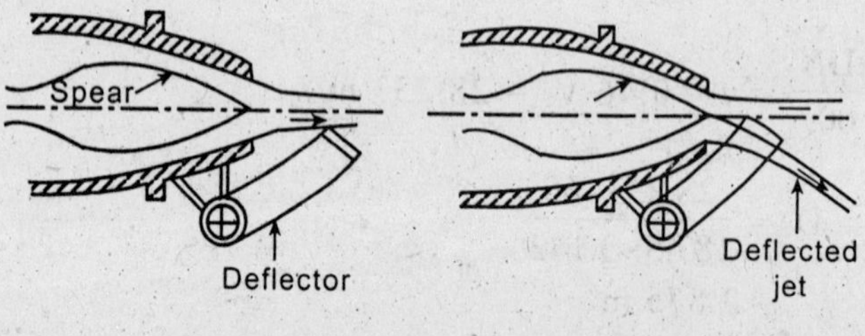

Fig. 16.7 Deflector arrangement

Runaway speed is the maximum speed, governor being disengaged, at which the turbine would run when there is no external load but operating under design head and discharge. Earlier it is shown that when $V_1 = 2.0$ v, the efficiency of the Pelton wheel is maximum. When there is no load, the speed of the wheel increases and v tends to V_1. But due to losses etc., runaway speed is slightly less than V_1. For Pelton wheel runaway speed expressed in rpm is 1.8 to 1.9 times the normal rotational speed N whereas for mixed flow turbines it is (2.0 to 2.2) N and for axial flow turbines it is (2.5 to 3.0) N.

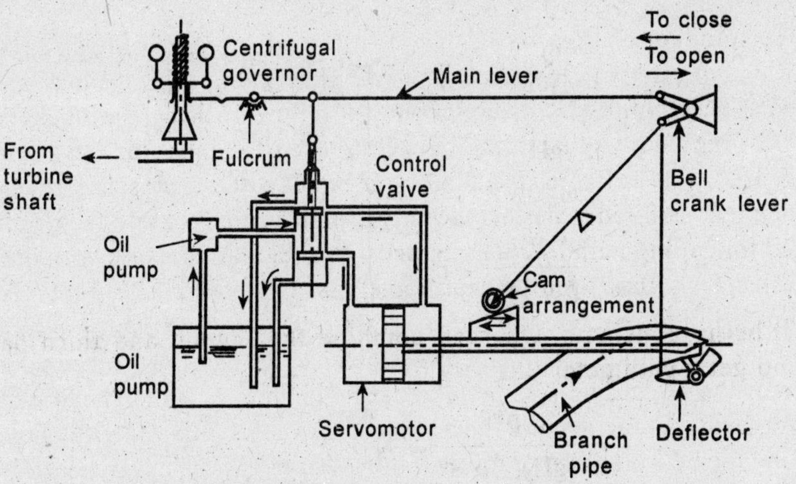

Fig. 16.8 Governing mechanism for Pelton wheel

16.9 Performance of Pelton Wheel

In order to study the performance of geometrically similar turbines in terms of relationship between head, power, efficiency, discharge and speed, one can use dimensional analysis discussed in Chapter VII. Such an analysis is also useful in predicting the performance of the prototype from the tests on the model. The power P of the turbine depends on mass density ρ and viscosity μ of the fluid, gravitational acceleration g, discharge Q., operating head H, and the turbine characteristics such as runner diameter D and speed ω (radians per second). In the above mentioned variables it is convenient to use gH as one variable giving potential energy per unit mass, since g as an individual variable does not really affect power. Viscosity μ can be omitted from the analysis, unless one is dealing with highly viscous liquids, since usually Reynolds number in the turbine is quite larger. Hence one can write

$$P = f_1 (\rho, Q, gH, D, \omega) \tag{16.10}$$

choosing D, ω, and ρ as repeating variables, one gets

$$\frac{P}{\rho\, \omega^3 D^5} = f_2\left(\frac{Q}{\omega D^3}, \frac{gH}{\omega^2 D^2}\right) \tag{16.11}$$

Similarly, efficiency η can be expressed as

$$\eta = f_3\left(\frac{Q}{\omega D^3}, \frac{gH}{\omega^2 D^2}\right) \tag{16.12}$$

For a given turbine and liquid, D, ρ and gH are constant. If ω is held constant, P will be function of Q alone. Equations 16.11 and 16.12 can be used to study the performance of a prototype turbine.

The behaviour of geometrically similar turbines operating at maximum efficiency is of interest to the designer because he can then select a proper turbine to run under given conditions of head, speed and power. When η is maximum, the following three parameters will assume constant values for geometrically similar pumps, namely

$$\left.\begin{aligned}\frac{Q}{\omega D^3} &= C_1\\ \frac{gH}{\omega^2 D^2} &= C_2\\ \frac{P}{\rho\omega^2 D^5} &= C_3\end{aligned}\right\} \tag{16.13}$$

C_1, C_2, and C_3 being constants. One can combine the second and third parameters to eliminate D and get a parameter

$$\frac{\omega P^{1/2}}{(gH)^{5/4}\rho^{1/2}} = \overline{N}_s \tag{16.14}$$

in which $\overline{N}_S$ is the *nondimensional specific speed.* Here P is expressed in watts, ω in radians per second, and ρ in kg/m³. Since ρ is 998 kg/m³ and g is 9.806 m/s² one can express the specific speed with these constants and N in place of ω. If specific speed with P expressed in kW, is designated as N_{Sk} then

$$N_{Sk} = N\,P^{1/2}/\,H^{5/4} \text{ and } N_{Sk} = 166.25\ \overline{N}_s\,.$$

Similarly if P is expressed in metric horse power and the corresponding specific speed is designated as N_{SH} then

$$N_{SH} = 1.166\ N_{Sk} = 193.85\ \overline{N}_s$$

Very often turbines are characterised by N_{SH}. In this form the specific speed can be defined as the speed of the turbine in rpm which produces 1 metric horse power when it works under a head of 1 m. From the dimensionless parameters in Eq. 16.13, one can eliminate D and express P, N and Q as, functions of H which yields

$$\frac{P}{H^{3/2}} = C_4,\ \frac{N}{H^{1/2}} = C_5 \text{ and } \frac{Q}{H^{1/2}} = C_6$$

For given D, ρ and g, C_4, C_5 and C_6 will remain constant. They are known as unit power, unit speed and unit discharge respectively. This is so because when H is unity C_4, C_5, C_6 represent power produced, speed and discharge per unit head. Usually P is expressed in metric horse power.

Machines are designed to work under a given set of conditions. Thus a turbine may be designed for a given head, discharge, rotational speed and power. However, in practice one may have to run it under conditions different from design conditions. Under such condition the user will like to know the various characteristics of the machine. This is done by collecting data from model tests or from the prototype tests. The behaviour is usually studied by preparing curves under three conditions namely constant head, constant speed and constant overall efficiency. Fig. 16.9 shows P/P_{max} versus relative speed ratio ϕ_1 curve for constant H and 100 percent gate opening for Pelton wheel. Figure 16.10

shows variation of efficiency η with percent load for constant N_s. The point to be noted is that efficiency is maximum not at 100 percent load but at smaller say 20 to 40 percent. Fig. 16.11 shows variation of unit power $P/H^{3/2}$ vs unit speed $N/H^{1/2}$ with lines of constant η and constant gate opening. From such a diagram it can be seen at a glance what the speed of the turbine should be for obtaining best efficiency for known gate opening. From such a curve maximum efficiency of the turbine for all conditions, gate opening and speed can be read. However, since speed of turbine has to be kept the same, Fig. 16.11 can be used to predict efficiency for given gate opening, load and head.

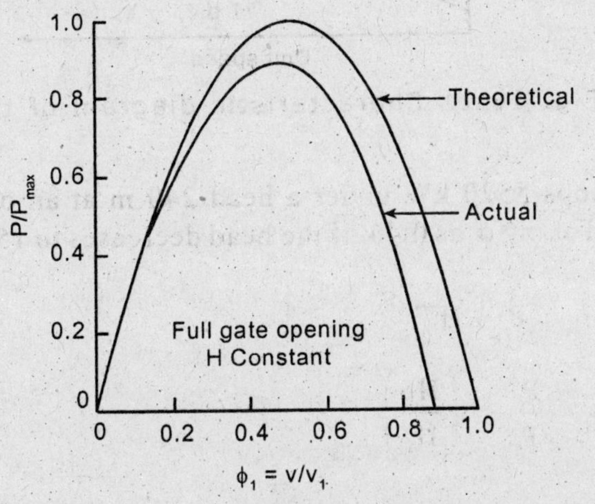

Fig. 16.9 Variation of P/Pmax with ϕ_1 for Pelton wheel

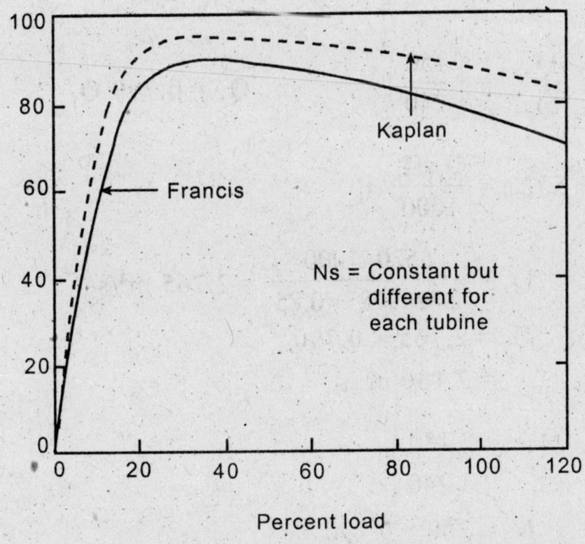

Fig. 16.10 Variation of η with percent load

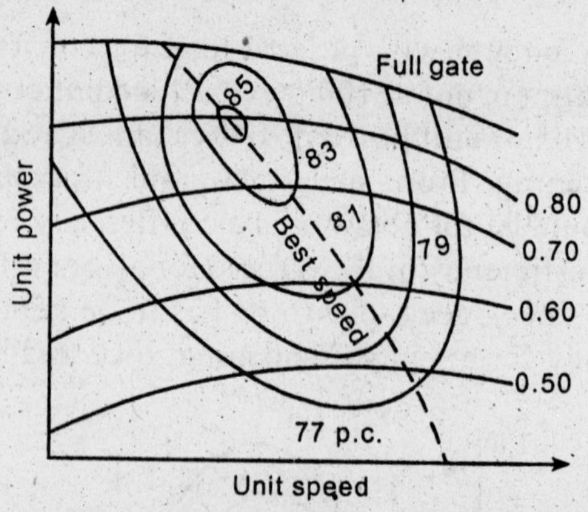

Fig. 16.11 Characteristic diagram of turbine

Example 16.6

A Pelton wheel develops 5520 kW under a head 240 m at an overall efficiency of 85 percent and 200 rpm. Taking ϕ_1 as 0.46, if the head decreases to 150 m find the discharge, power and the speed.

Since $$P \sim H^{3/2}$$

$$\frac{P_2}{P_1} = \left(\frac{H_2}{H_1}\right)^{3/2}$$

$\therefore$ $$P_2 = 5520\left(\frac{150}{240}\right)^{3/2} = 2727.464 \text{ kW}$$

Similarly $$\frac{Q_2}{Q_1} = \left(\frac{150}{240}\right)^{1/2} \qquad \therefore Q_2 = 0.790\, Q_1$$

but $$5520 = \frac{Q_1 \gamma H_1}{1000}\eta$$

$$Q_1 = \frac{5520\times1000}{240\times9787\times0.85} = 2.765 \text{ m}^3/\text{s}$$

$\therefore$ $$Q_2 = 2.765 \times 0.790$$
$$= 2.186 \text{ m}^3/\text{s}$$

$$\frac{N_2}{N_1} = \left(\frac{150}{240}\right)^{1/2}$$

$\therefore$ $$N_2 = 200 \times 0.790$$
$$= 158 \text{ rpm}$$

Example 16.7

Tests on a model turbine 30 cm in diameter give a maximum efficiency of 82 percent at 900 rpm and at 0.70 gate opening under a head of 20 m giving an output of 28 kW. A similar turbine is required to produce 370 kW at 0.70 gate opening and under a head of 25 m. Calculate its diameter and speed of rotation.

For similar turbines specific speed will be the same.

$$\therefore \quad \frac{P_p^{1/2} N_p}{H_p^{5/4}} = \frac{P_m^{1/2} N_m}{H_m^{5/4}}$$

$$\therefore \quad N_p = \frac{25^{5/4} \times 28^{1/2} \times 900}{370^{1/2} \times 20^{5/4}} = 327 \text{ rpm}$$

Since

$$\frac{H_p}{N_p^2 D_p^2} = \frac{H_m}{N_m^2 D_m^2}$$

$$\left(\frac{D_p}{D_m}\right)^2 = \left(\frac{N_m}{N_p}\right)^2 \left(\frac{H_p}{H_m}\right) = 9.469$$

$$\therefore \quad \frac{D_p}{D_m} = 3.077$$

and

$$D_p = 30 \times 3.077 = 92.31 \text{ cm}$$

REACTION TURBINES

As mentioned in Section 16.3 reaction turbines always flow full and hence under pressure, and therefore they are also known as pressure turbines. The water entering the reaction turbine has both the pressure energy as well as kinetic energy. Basically the reaction turbines consist of fixed guide blades which guide the flow to the moving vanes at a correct angle, moving blades which rotate due to reaction of striking water, the shaft to which the moving blades are fixed and a water tight casing in which are located guide blades and moving blades. Reaction turbines can be classified into

Radial flow turbines

Mixed flow turbines

Axial flow turbines

Radial flow turbines may be either radially inward flow or radially outward flow turbines. These were used in the earlier times; however because radial flow turbines have many disadvantages, they are not commonly used now. In mixed flow turbine, the flow is inward at the point of entry in the turbine, but it changes to a direction parallel to the shaft of moving blades. The modern Francis turbines fall under this category. In axial flow turbines the flow is parallel to the axis of the wheel. Kaplan turbine is all axial flow turbine; it is also called a propeller turbine.

16.10 Francis Turbine

The present day Francis turbine which is of mixed flow type i.e. radially inward entry and axial exit of flow, is the modification of earlier radially inward flow turbine developed by James Francis (1815-1892), an American Engineer. The modern Francis turbine is shown in Fig. 16.12. The water from the reservoir comes through a large sized conduit, known as penstock, made of steel. The water then enters an annular channel of spiral shape known as scroll or spiral casing which is made either of cast steel or welded rolled steel plates. Inside at the centre are the rotating vanes and water entering the scroll casing is guided to the rotating vanes through a series of guide blades. In order to distribute the water evenly between different guide blades around the circumference, the scroll casing is designed in such a way that cross-sectional area reduces uniformly from maximum at the entrance to nearly zero at the end. The spiral casing is usually provided with inspection holes and pressure gauge connections.

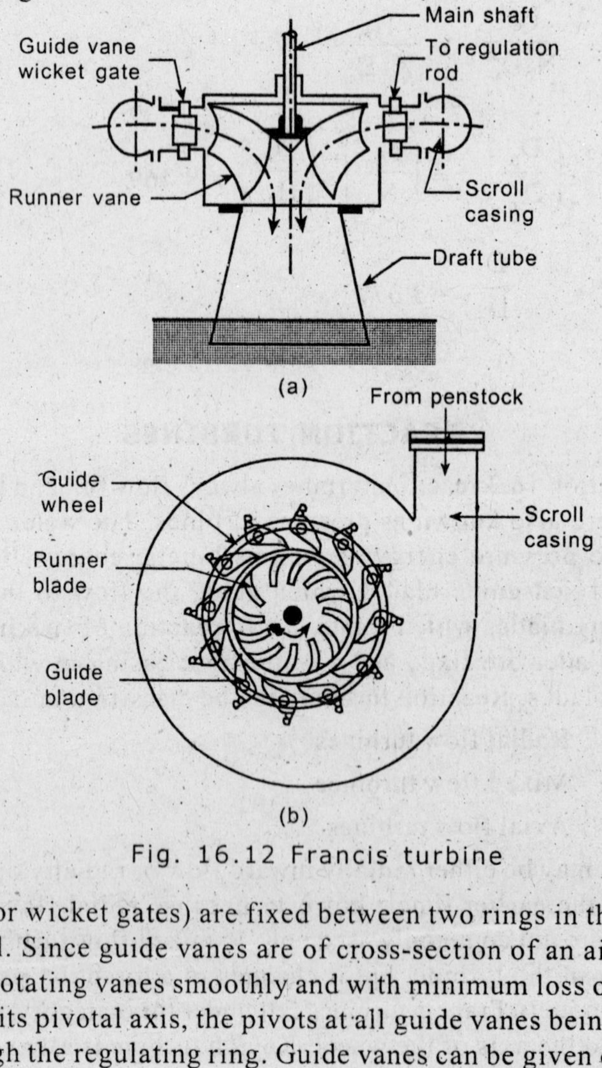

Fig. 16.12 Francis turbine

The guide vanes (or wicket gates) are fixed between two rings in the form of a wheel, known as guide wheel. Since guide vanes are of cross-section of an airfoil, water passes from scroll casing to rotating vanes smoothly and with minimum loss of head. Each guide vane can rotate about its pivotal axis, the pivots at all guide vanes being connected to two regulating rods through the regulating ring. Guide vanes can be given desired opening by rotation of regulating shaft.

The water then enters the runner vanes or rotating vanes which usually rotate about a vertical axis, however horizontal installation is not uncommon. Rotating vanes are made of cast iron, cast steel or of nonferrous metal like bronze. They can be as large as five or six meters in diameter, their number ranging from 15 to 25. The runner blades are connected to the shaft. The turbine is normally provided with a bearing. The water enters the runner blades radially inside and leaves axially after performing the work. The water then passes through the diffuser section known as *draft tube* and then discharges into the downstream pool or tail race.

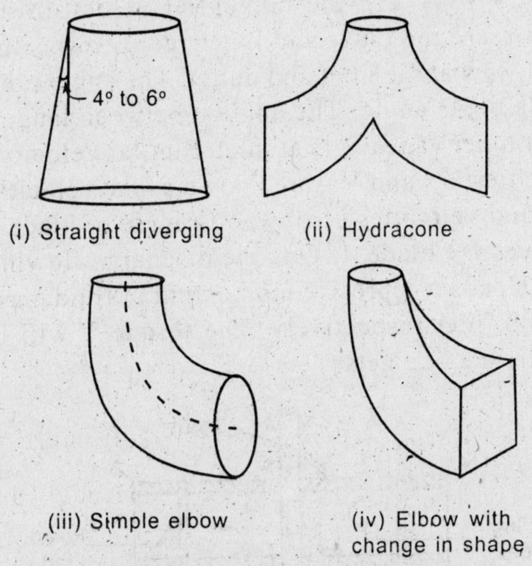

Fig. 16.13 Types of draft tubes

The draft tube which has usually a gradually increasing section connects the runner exit to the tail race. It is usually taken at least one meter below the lowest tail water level. Draft tube serves the following purposes. Firstly, because it is air tight, the draft tube enables the setting of turbine runner above the tail race, without losing the head thereby. Thus even when the turbine runner is set above the tail race, the head available is equal to the difference in water levels between the head and tail water. Secondly, the gradual increase in cross-section reduces the velocity of flow as it comes out of the draft tube. This reduces the final loss of kinetic energy thereby increasing the turbine efficiency. Since the velocity of runner exit is large, the pressure there is small and below atmospheric, thus the net working head is somewhat larger, which gives greater efficiency. Types of draft tubes commonly used in practice are shown in Fig. 16.13. Their choice depends on factors such as cost, specific speed of turbine and avoidance of excessive swirl at the exit. The straight diverging type of draft tube has the cone angle less than 10° so that the high velocity flow does not separate. Such a draft tube is preferred for turbine with low specific speed when their axis is vertical. The hydracone type helps to reduce swirl of the flow at the section. However, because of the bend action the head loss in this type of draft tube is somewhat greater than that in straight diverging diffuser. When enough space is not available, simple elbow type draft tube can be provided; however in this type of draft tube also, there is greater energy loss due to bend action. In special conditions elbow type draft tube with change in cross-sectional shape is utilised.

16.11 Velocity Triangles for Radially Inward Flow Turbine

Radially inward flow turbine is shown in Fig. 16.14. For convenience the breadths at inlet and outlet of the runner, which can be different, are shown of identical breadth b. The hydraulic relation for the inward flow turbine can be obtained by drawing velocity triangles at the inlet and outlet as shown in Fig. 16.15. If ω is the angular velocity of the runner blade, $v_1 = r_1 \omega_1$ and $v_2 = r_2 \omega_2$ are the tangential velocities at the inlet and outlet respectively. Here r_1 and r_2 are the outer and inner radius respectively. Let V_1 and V_2 be the absolute velocities of flow at the inlet and outlet. The angle α between V_1 and tangent at inlet is known as guide blade angle. The angle θ between tangent at inlet and relative velocity V_{r1} is known as runner vane angle at inlet. Similar velocity triangle can be drawn for outlet also. The velocities $V_{\omega 1}$ and $V_{\omega 2}$ are known as the velocities of swirl at inlet and outlet, V_{f1} and V_{f2} are radial velocities of flow, ϕ is angle of blade tip at exit and β is the angle at which water leaves the blade. If Q is the discharge flowing through the turbine, then $Q\rho V_2 \cos \beta$ and $Q \rho V_1 \cos \alpha$ represent momentum of fluid mass $Q \rho$ in the tangential direction at the outlet and inlet respectively. The torque T will be equal to change in moment of momentum. Hence one gets

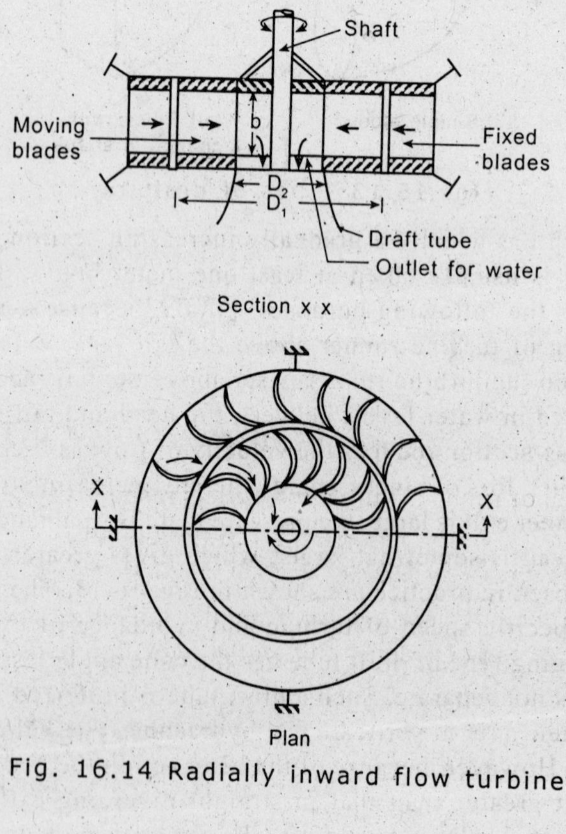

Fig. 16.14 Radially inward flow turbine

$$T = Q\rho\,(r_2 V_2 \cos\beta - r_1 V_1 \cos\alpha) \qquad (16.15)$$

Power transmitted by the fluid in the turbine runner will be

$$P = -T\omega$$
$$= Q\rho\,(r_1\omega V_1 \cos\alpha - r_2\omega V_2 \cos\beta) \qquad (16.16)$$

f H is the total head of water under which the turbine is working, $Q\gamma H$ is the energy available. Hence the hydraulic efficiency η is

$$\eta = \frac{Q\rho}{Q\gamma H}(r_1\,\omega\,V_1 \cos\alpha - r_2\omega\,V_2 \cos\beta)$$

$$= \frac{1}{gH}(r_1\,\omega\,V_1 \cos\alpha - r_2\omega\,V_2 \cos\beta) \qquad (16.17)$$

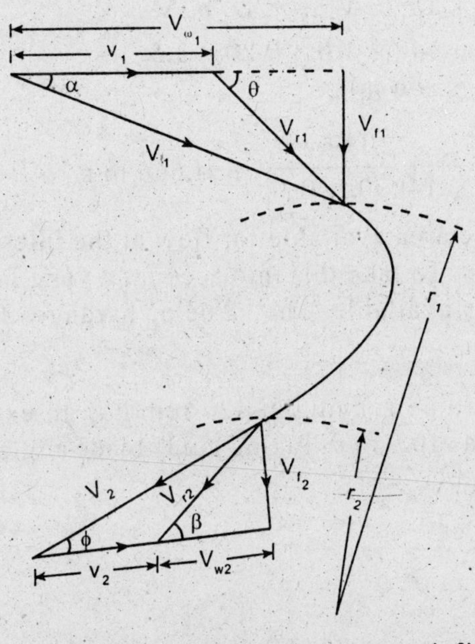

Fig. 16.15 Velocity triangles for inward flow turbine

f b_1 and b_2 are the bredths of runner at inlet and outlets respectively, continuity relation yields,

$$\pi D_1 b_1 V_{f1} = \pi D_2 b_2 V_{f2} = Q$$

Further, the total energies per unit weight of water at inlet and outlet are $(z_1 + p_1/\gamma + V_1^2/2g)$ and $(z_2 + p_2/\gamma + V_2^2/2g)$. One can now apply Bernoulli's equation between inlet and outlet and get

$$\left(z_1 + \frac{p_1}{\gamma} + \frac{V_1^2}{2g}\right) = \left(z_2 + \frac{p_2}{\gamma} + \frac{V_2^2}{2g}\right) + \frac{1}{g}(r_1\,\omega\,V_1 \cos\alpha - r_2\,\omega\,V_2 \cos\beta) + h_f \qquad (16.18)$$

where h_f is the total head loss between inlet and outlet. If H represents the available energy at section 1 and if it is assumed that water at exit of the runner contains most of the energy in form of $V_2^2/2g$, then

$$H = \frac{V_2^2}{2g} + \frac{1}{g}(v_1 V_{\omega 1} - v_2 V_{\omega 2}) + h_f$$

In most problems h_f can be neglected. If the flow at the exit is radial, $V_2 = V_{f2}$ and $V_{\omega 2} = 0$.

Example 16.8

An inward flow reaction turbine running at 250 rpm has $D_1 = 1.0$ m, $b_1 = 0.20$ m, $D_2 = 0.50$ m and $b_2 = 0.30$ m. If the water enters the wheel radially at 3.5 m/s velocity, determine the discharge and velocity of flow at the outlet. Assume vane thickness at the extremities to be negligible.

$$Q = \pi D_1 b_1 V_{f1} = \pi D_2 b_2 V_{f2}$$

$$\therefore \quad Q = 3.142 \times 1.0 \times 0.20 \times 3.5$$

$$= 2.199 \text{ m}^3/\text{s}$$

$$V_{f2} = \frac{2.199}{3.142 \times 0.5 \times 0.30} = 4.666 \text{ m/s}$$

Note: In the actual case the area available for flow at the inlet and exit will be less due to thickness of vanes. To take this into account a vane factor K can be defined as πDbK is actual area available. The value of K ranges from 0.90 to 0.95.

Example 16.9

An inward flow reaction turbine running at 420 rpm has an external diameter of 1.3 m and velocity of flow at inlet as 10.0 m/s. Taking guide blade angle at inlet as 12° determine

i. Velocity of swirl at inlet,

ii. Absolute velocity at inlet,

iii. Vane angle θ at inlet,

iv. Relative velocity at inlet.

With reference to Fig. 16.14 and Fig. 16.15

$$v_1 = \pi D_1 N/60 = 3.142 \times 1.30 \times 420/60$$

$$= 28.592 \text{ m/s}$$

Since $\quad \sin\alpha = V_{f1}/V_1$

absolute velocity $\quad V_1 = V_{f1}/\sin 12°$

$$= 10/0.2079$$

$$= 48.100 \text{ m/s}$$

Velocity of swirl at inlet

$$V_{\omega 1} = V_1 \cos 12° = 48.100 \times 0.9781$$
$$= 47.049 \text{ m/s}$$

Inlet blade angle θ can be determined from the relation

$$\tan\theta = V_{f1}/(V_{\omega 1} - V_1) = 10/(47.049 - 28.592)$$
$$= 10/18.457 = 0.541$$

$$\therefore \quad \theta = 28.45°$$

Relative velocity $V_{r1} = V_{f1}/\sin\theta = 10/\sin 28.45°$

$$= 10/0.4764 = 20.991 \text{ m/s}$$

Example 16.10

An inward flow reaction turbine carrying a discharge of 0.55 m³/s under a head of 15.25 m develops 75 kW at 375 rpm. The outer and inner diameters are 0.75 m and 0.50 m respectively while the exit velocity is 3.05 m/s. Assuming the discharge to be radial and wheel width to be constant, determine the overall and hydraulic efficiencies of the turbine and inlet angles of the guide and runner blades.

Peripheral velocity of wheel at inlet $v_1 = \pi D_1 N/60$

$$= (3.142 \times 0.75 \times 3.75)/60$$
$$= 14.728 \text{ m/s}$$

Work done by the turbine per unit weight of water is $(1/g)(r_1 \omega_1 V_1 \cos\alpha)$ i.e. $(1/g)(v_1 V_{w1})$, since at the exit V_2 is radial and hence $V_2 \cos\beta$ is zero. Also $V_2 = V_{r2} = 3.050$ m/s. Hence using Bernoulli's equation

$$\frac{14.278 \times V_{\omega 1}}{9.806} = 15.25 - \frac{3.05^2}{2 \times 9.806}$$

$$\therefore \quad V_{\omega 1} = 10.148 \text{ m/s}$$

Work done by the turbine per second $= Q\,\rho\,V_{\omega 1}\,v_1$

$$= (0.55 \times 1000 \times 10.148 \times 14.278)$$
$$= 79\,222.641 \text{ W} = 79.223 \text{ kW}$$

Available energy in kW $= (Q\gamma H)/1000$

$$= (0.55 \times 9787 \times 15.25)/1000$$
$$= 82.089 \text{ kW}$$

∴ Overall efficiency $= 75/82.089 = 0.9136 = 91.36$ percent

Hydraulic efficiency $= 79.723/82.089$

$$= 0.9712 \text{ or } 97.12 \text{ percent}$$

Further $Q = \pi D_1 b_1 V_{f1} = \pi D_2 b_2 V_{f2}$ and $b_1 = b_2$

$$\therefore \quad V_{f1} = V_{f2}\frac{D_2}{D_1} = (3.05 \times 050)/0.75$$

$= 2.033 \text{ m/s}$

Considering the velocity triangle at inlet

$$\sin\alpha = V_{f1}/V_1 \text{ and } V_1 = \sqrt{V_{f1}^2 + V_{\omega 1}^2}$$

$$\therefore \quad \sin\alpha = 2.033/\sqrt{2.033^2 + 10.148^2}$$

$$= 2.033/10.354 = 0.196$$

$$\alpha = 11.32°$$

$$\tan\theta = V_{f1}/(V_{\omega 1} - v_1) = 2.03/(10.148 - 14.278)$$

$$= -0.492$$

$$\therefore \quad \theta = 153.82°$$

Velocity triangles for radially outward flow turbines can be drawn in the same manner as that for inward flow turbine discussed earlier. In this type of turbine the guide blades are inside and rotating vanes are on the outside. In its simplest form, an outward flow reaction turbine consists of guide vanes which are fixed and which guide the flow on to rotating vanes. The water while gliding over the rotating vanes exerts a thrust on them which causes rotation. The velocity traingles for the inlet and outlet are shown in Fig. 16.16 which are self-explanatory.

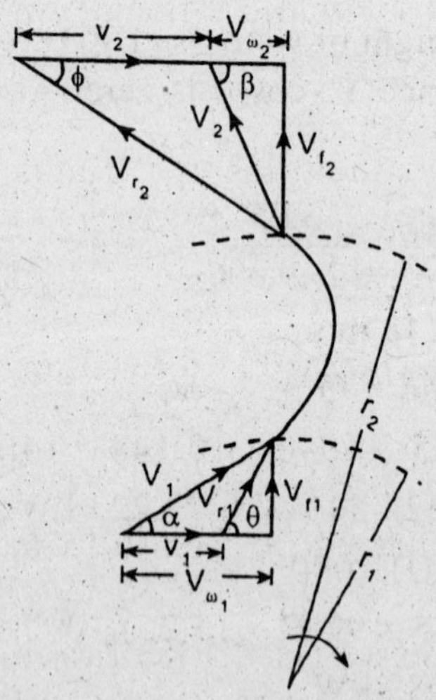

Fig. 16.16 Velocity triangles for outward flow turbine

Example 16.11

The inner and outer diameters of an outward flow turbine running at 200 rpm are 2.4 m and 3.6 m. If total head on the turbine is 40 m, and width of the wheel is constant at 0.30 m, determine the inlet and exit velocities, and velocity of swirl at inlet, if the radial discharge is 6.0 m³/s.

$$v_1 = \pi D_1 N/60$$

$$= 3.142 \times 2.4 \times 200/60 = 25.136 \text{ m/s}$$

$$Q = \pi D_1 \, b \, V_{f1}$$

$$\therefore \quad V_{f1} = 6.0/(3.142 \times 2.4 \times 0.30) = 2.652 \text{ m/s}$$

$$V_{f2} = Q / (\pi D_2 \, b)$$

$$= 6.0/(3.142 \times 3.6 \times 0.30)$$

$$= 1.768 \text{ m/s}$$

The velocity of swirl at the inlet can be determined from the relation

$$\frac{V_{\omega_1} v_1}{g} = H - \frac{V_2^2}{2g} \qquad \text{but} \qquad V_2 = V_{f2}$$

$$\therefore \quad \frac{25.136}{9.806} V_{\omega 1} = 40 - \frac{1.768^2}{2\times 9.806} = 39.841$$

$$\therefore \quad V_{\omega 1} = 15.542 \text{ m/s}$$

16.12 Francis Runner Dimensions

For given values of power P kW to be developed at head H when the turbine is running at N rpm, the following procedure can be adopted for obtaining the preliminary dimensions:

(i) Assume approximate values of hydraulic efficiency η_H and overall efficiency η. The hydraulic efficiency varies from 85 to 95 percent whereas overall efficiency ranges from 80 to 90 percent.

(ii) Since $P = Q\gamma H\eta/1000$ determine the discharge Q m^3/s.

(iii) The ratio of runner width b to the diameter D_1 designated as $n = b/D_1$ varies from 0.10 to 0.45. Assume a suitable values.

(iv) The velocity V_{f1} at the inlet is expressed as a function $\sqrt{2gH}$

$$V_{f1} = \psi_1 \sqrt{2gH}$$

in which ψ_1 is the flow ratio that varies from 0.15 to 0.35. Choose appropriate value of ψ_1 and determine V_{f1}.

v) The area at inlet can be expressed as $\pi D_1 Kb$ in which K accounts for space occupied by the thickness of runner vanes. Assuming K to be 0.95

$$V_{f1} = Q/\pi \, D_1 \, bk$$

Knowing K, $b = n\,D_1$, and V_{f1}, D_1 and then b can be determined.

vi) The peripheral velocity at inlet v_1 is expressed in terms of $\sqrt{2gH}$ as

$$v_1 = \phi_1 \sqrt{2gH}$$

where ϕ_1 is the speed ratio whose value ranges from 0.60 to 0.80, its value increasing with increase in the specific speed. Using this v_1 and $v_1 = \pi D_1 N/60$, a check on D_1 value can be made.

(vii) Assume hydraulic efficiency η_H. Since for radial discharge $\eta_H = V_{\omega 1} v_1/gH$, determine $V_{\omega 1}$.

(viii) Guide blade angle at inlet α, and vane angle at inlet θ can be determined from the relations

$$\tan\alpha = V_{f1}/V_{\omega 1}$$

$$\tan\theta = V_{f1}/(V_{\omega 1} - v_1)$$

(ix) For flow to be radial at the exit, $\beta = 90°$ and $V_{f1} = V_{f2}$, blade tip angle ϕ it the exit will be

$$\tan\phi = V_{f2}/v_2$$

and $v_2 = \pi D_2 N/60$. Assume $D_2 = 0.5D_1$ thus knowing V_2, ϕ can be computed.

(x) The number of guide blades Z_g is kept even in order to avoid vibrations due synchronous effects. The number varies from 8 to 24. The number of runner blades $Z_r = Zg \pm 1$. The thickness of runner blades ranges from 6 mm to 24 mm.

Example 16.12

Design a Francis turbine runner for the following data

$$H = 70\text{ m},\quad N = 750\text{ rpm},\quad P = 350\text{ kW}$$

Overall efficiency = 85%, hydraulic efficiency = 95%. Also take n = 0.15, $\psi_1 = 0.15$, K = 0.95. Assume the flow to be radial at exit.

$$350 = \frac{Q \times 9787 \times 70 \times 0.85}{1000}$$

This gives $Q = 0.601\text{ m}^3/\text{s}$

$$V_1 = \psi_1 \sqrt{2gH}$$

$$= 0.15\sqrt{2 \times 9.806 \times 70} = 5.559\text{ m/s}$$

but $Q/\pi\, b\, D_1 K = V_{f1}$ and $b/D_1 = 0.15$

$$0.601 = 5.559 \times 3.142 \times 0.15 \times D_1^2 \times 0.95$$

This yields $D_1^2 = 0.241$

or $D_1 = 0.491$ m say 50 cm

$\therefore$ $b = 0.15 \times 50 = 7.5$ cm

$$v_1 = \pi D_1 N/60 = 3.142 \times 0.50 \times 750/60 = 19.638\text{ m/s}$$

Since $\frac{V_{\omega_1} v_1}{gH} = \eta_H;\; V_{\omega 1} = \frac{0.95 \times 9.81 \times 70}{19.638}$

$\therefore \quad V_{\omega 1} = 33.219$ m/s

$\tan\alpha = V_{f1}/V_{\omega 1} = 5.559/33.219 = 0.1673$

$\therefore \quad \alpha = 9.50°$

$$\tan\theta = \frac{V_{f1}}{(V_{\omega 1} - v_1)} = \frac{5.559}{(33.219-19.635)} = \frac{5.559}{13.581}$$

$= 0.4093$

$\therefore \quad \theta = 22.26°$

Take $\quad D_2 = 0.50\ D_1 = 25$ cm

$\therefore \quad v_2 = 0.50 \times 19.638 = 9.819$ m/s

$\therefore \quad V_{f1} = V_{f2} = 5.559$ m/s

and $\quad \tan\phi = V_{f2}/v_2 = 5.559/9.819 = 0.5661$

$\therefore \quad \phi = 29.51°$

Use 12 guide blades and 13 runner blades.

16.13 Kaplan Turbine

Kaplan turbine developed by an Austrian engineer V. Kaplan is an axial or propeller flow reaction turbine. Here the water flows parallel to the shaft which is vertical. The essential components of the turbine are shown in Fig. 16.17. After the water enters the scroll casing, it is guided by the guide blades which are fixed but whose directions can be changed. The water then turns through 90° into the axial direction and passes through the propeller type runner and rotates it. The runner blades are attached to the hub, but they can be turned about their axes to take care of change in the load. This is done automatically through servomechanism. Thus, since both guide blades and runner blades can be adjusted, Kaplan turbine is more efficient than Francis and other turbines at part loads. In the design of Kaplan turbine the ratio of hub diameter D_o to runner outside diameter D is kept between 0.30 to 0.70 (the ratio increasing with increase in H), while the coefficient Ψ_1 relating Q to H is about 0.70 – 0.75;

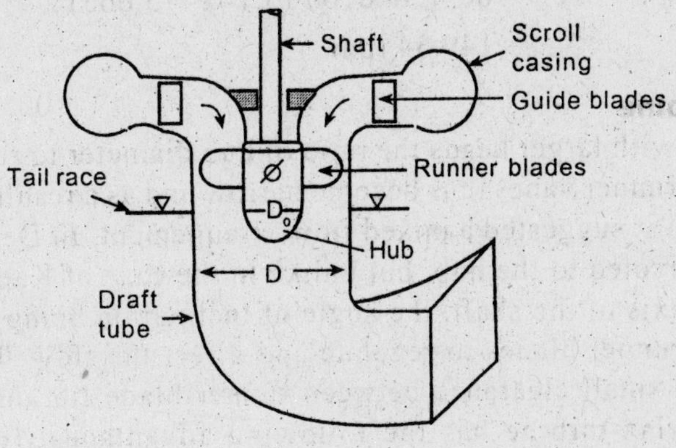

Fig. 16.17 Kaplan turbine

Hence

$$Q = \pi/4\ (D^2 - D_o^2)\ \psi_1 \sqrt{2gH}$$

The runner blades are warped and their number ranges from 3 to 6 or 8 at the maximum. They are constructed to run between 60-220 rpm and work under a maximum head of 3 to 15 m. Axial flow turbines such as Kaplan have efficiency as high as 90 percent. Where ever the head on the turbine fluctuates, the turbine gives maximum efficiency even at 25 percent of full load and upto 20 percent over load. This can be seen from Fig. 16.10.

Example 16.13

For a Kaplan turbine the following data are specified; power output P = 35 350 kW, net head = 20 m, Overall efficiency η = 86%, Velocity ratio $v/\sqrt{2gH}$ = 2. 0, ψ_1 = 0.60, and D_o/D = 0.35

Calculate the diameter of the runner and speed of the runner

$$\therefore \quad v = 2 \times \sqrt{2 \times 9.806 \times 20} = 39.610 \text{ m/s}$$

$$\text{Since} \quad \eta = \frac{P \times 1000}{Q\gamma H}$$

$$\therefore \quad Q = \frac{35350 \times 1000}{0.86 \times 9787 \times 20} = 210 \text{ m}^3/\text{s}$$

$$210 = 0.6 \times \frac{\pi}{4}\ (D^2 - 0.35^2\ D^2)\ \sqrt{2gH}$$

$$D^2 = 25.65$$

$$D = 5.065 \text{ m}$$

$$v = \frac{\pi DN}{60}$$

$$N = 60 \times 39.610 / (3.142 \times 5.065)$$

$$= 149.34 \text{ rpm}$$

16.14 Deriaz Turbine

For Kaplan turbine with larger heads the ratio of hub diameter to runner outside diameter D_o/D increases; the runner vanes thus become narrow and as a result the turbine efficiency reduces. Hence Deriaz suggested a mixed flow arrangement. In Deraiz turbine the blades of the turbine are pivoted to the hub, but unlike in the case of Kaplan turbine the blades are inclined to the axis of the shaft, the angle of inclination being 45°. Guide blades are provided ahead of runner blades to regulate and direct the flow. The shape of casing is such that there is a small clearance between runner blade tip and casing; this reduces leakage losses. Deriaz turbine has the following advantages: (i) it can be used as a pump-turbine unit; (ii) the starting torque can be reduced by adjusting the runner to shut position; (iii) inclined position of blades reduces the load on the outer trunnion journal bearing. Schematic sketch of Deriaz turbine is shown in Fig. 16.18.

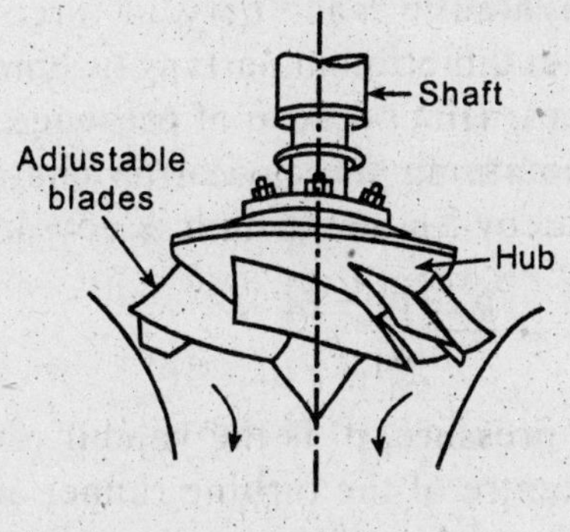

Fig. 16.18 Deriaz turbine

16.15 Governing of Reaction Turbines

The governing of the reaction turbine such as Francis turbine is achieved by closing or opening the guide blades. These are pivoted and connected to the regulating ring, see Fig. 16.19. To the regulating ring are attached two long regulating rods connected to regulating lever. The regulating lever is keyed to the regulating shaft which is turned by a servomotor piston of the oil pressure governor. When the load changes, the governing mechanism rotates the guide blades thereby controlling the flow. In the cases of Kaplan and Deriaz turbines the runner blades inclination is also adjusted through a separate servomechanism. The servomotors for regulating both the runner blades and guide blades are interconnected. In addition there is pressure regulator or a relief valve which opens when guide blades are to be closed suddenly in case of sudden loads rejection by the turbine thereby diverting the water from penstock directly to the tailrace. The function of relief valve is similar to that of deflector in Pelton wheel.

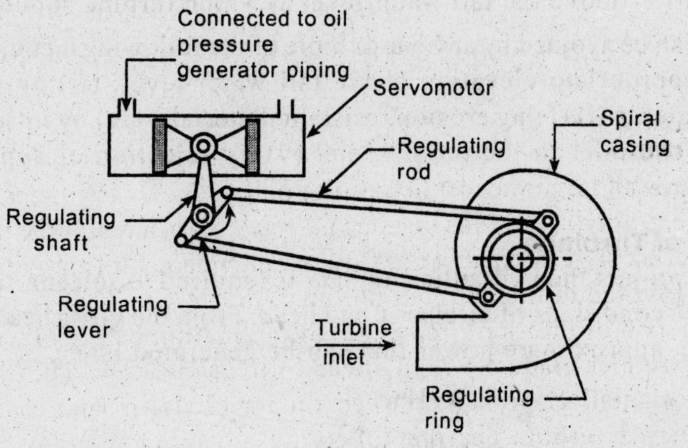

Fig. 16.19 Governing mechanism of reaction turbines

16.16 Cavitation in Turbines

An important factor in turbine running is the occurrence of cavitation. The cavitation affects the turbines or other hydraulic machinery in three ways, namely, (i) irregular collapse of vapour cavities causes vibration of parts of turbine; (ii) there is loss of material and roughening of inner surfaces; (iii) because of presence of cavities the efficiency of the turbine is reduced. For comparing the cavitation characteristics of the turbines a cavitation number σ is proposed by Thoma, which is now known as *Thoma number*,

$$\sigma = \frac{p_a - p_v - \gamma Z}{\gamma H_1} \quad (16.19)$$

in which p_a is the atmospheric pressure, p_v is the vapour pressure of the water, Z is the vertical distance between the centre of the turbine runner and tail water level and H_1 is effective or working head on the turbine. The minimum value of σ at which cavitation occurs is denoted by σ_c. Its value can be determined by noting the value of σ at which efficiency of turbine drops and vibrations and noise occur. Value of σ_c is found to be related to the specific speed N_s of the turbine. Safe values of σ_c as given by Moody for different specific speeds are presented in Table 16.1.

TABLE 16.1

Limiting values of Thoma number σ_c

	Francis turbine						Propeller turbine	
Ns	0.476	0.952	1.417	1.903	2.320	2.320	3.567	4.760
N_{SH}	92.27	184.54	274.69	368.9	449.73	449.73	691.46	922.73
σ_c	0.025	0.10	0.23	0.40	0.64	0.43	1.33	1.50

It can be seen from Eq. 16.19 that for specified values of p_a, p_v, H_1, γ and σ_c, one can obtain Z the elevation above the tail water level at which turbine should be set.

The cavitation can be avoided by any one or more of the following methods: (i) installation of turbine at an appropriate elevation above tail water level; (ii) by proper design of cavitation free runner; (iii) Using erosion resistant materials; (iv) by introduction of small quantity of air at the inlet to the turbine, and (v) by selection of appropriate specific speed of the turbine.

16.17 Selection of Turbines

In a hydroelectric project the hydraulic engineer is required to select a suitable turbine to operate under given conditions of discharge and head. From the gross head H and discharge Q available at site, approximate power that can be generated is

$$P = \frac{Q \gamma H \eta}{1000} \text{ kW}$$

in which a reasonable value of η between 80 to 95 can be assumed. The rotational speed of the generator in rpm is given by N = 60 f /p where f is the frequency of the power generated in Hz and p is the number of pairs of poles in the generator. As the generators are invariably directly coupled, the turbine speed is also N rpm. Table 16.2 gives the information regarding H, $\overline{N}_s$ the dimensionless specific speed, type of turbine and overall efficiency η. Knowing the head, the type of turbine can be selected for which $\overline{N}_s$ can be read from Table 16.2. For Francis turbines one can use $N_{SH} = 1650/\sqrt{H}$ as a guide for choosing N_{SH}. With N_{SH} or $\overline{N}_s$, H and N known, power output per unit of turbine P_t can be computed and hence the number of units required will be given by P/P_t.

For known type of turbine, H and N or ω the approximate diameter can be obtained from the relation

$$v = r\,\omega = \phi_1 \sqrt{2gH}$$

Since D = 2r. Values of ϕ_1 vary from 0.43 to 0.48 for impulse turbine, 0.60 to 0.80 for Francis turbine and 1.4 to 2.0 for propeller turbines. If the diameter is too large, more units can be adopted. It may however be mentioned that generally it is advantageous to select a turbine with higher specific speed since the size of turbine then becomes smaller. Normally small number of turbine units is preferable; however in taking the decision on number of units, the power demand fluctuations also need to be considered.

TABLE 16.2

Specific Speed, Head and Efficiency Values for Turbines

Turbine	H m	$\overline{N}_S$	N_{SH}	Max. Efficiency η
Pelton wheel (single jet)	150–300	0.05–0.10	10–20	85–90
Pelton wheel (multiple jet)	and above	0.10–0.15	20–30	82–90
		0.25 – 0.72	50–140	90 – 94
Francis turbine	50-250	0.72–1.95	140–380	94
		1.95–2.32	380–450	84-93
Propeller turbine	25 – 50	2.32 – 3.32	450–645	94
Kaplan turbine	less than 25	3.32–4.76	645–925	85-84

Example 16.14

Suggest a suitable turbine to operate under a head of 300 m with a discharge of 6.25 m^3/s. A runner speed of 200 rpm and maximum overall efficiency of 85 percent can be adopted.

$$P = \frac{6.25 \times 9787 \times 300 \times 0.85}{1000}$$

$$= 15\ 598 \text{ kW}$$

Also $$\omega = \frac{2\times3.142\times200}{60}$$

$$= 20.947 \text{ rad/s}$$

$$\overline{N}s = \frac{20.947\times(15598\times1000)^{1/2}}{(9.81\times300)^{5/4}(1000)^{1/2}}$$

$$= 0.121$$

Reference to Table 16.2 indicates that a Pelton wheel can be adopted. With value ϕ_1 = 0.45, the diameter of runner will be obtained as follows, Since

$$\frac{D\omega}{2} = \phi_1\sqrt{2gH}$$

$$D = \frac{2\times0.45(2\times9.806\times300)^{1/2}}{20.947}$$

$$= 3.30 \text{ m}$$

Example 16.15

Determine the type of the turbine required to develop 40 425 kW under a head of 120 m at 150 rpm. If the barometric pressure is 10 m of water and Thoma's cavitation number is 0.056, what should be the height of the runner above the tail race?

$$\omega = \frac{2\times3.142\times150}{60}$$

$$= 15.71 \text{ rad/s}$$

$$\overline{N}s = \frac{15.71\times(40425\times1000)^{1/2}}{(9.806\times120)^{5/4}\times(1000)^{1/2}}$$

$$= 0.458$$

For a specific speed of 0.458 and head of 120 m a Francis turbine is recommended. The height of the runner above tail race can be found from Eq. 16.19 assuming $p_v \approx 0$

$$Z = \frac{p_a - p_v}{\gamma} - \sigma_c H_1 = 10 - 0.056 \times 120$$

$$= 3.28 \text{ m}$$

PROBLEMS

6.1 The channel approaching the overshot water wheel is 2.0 m wide. The water striking the wheel has a depth of 20 cm and velocity of 3.0 m/s. If the water fall is 15.0 m determine the energy developed. Take efficiency to be 80 percent.

6.2 A Pelton wheel which operates under a head of 150 m has a velocity ratio ϕ_1 of 0.45, jet diameter of 5.0 cm, and jet deflection angle β of 160°. Using C_v as 0.95 determine the energy output of the machine. Take overall efficiency as 90 percent.

6.3 A Pelton wheel is to develop 300 kW of power under an effective head at the nozzle of 50 m. Taking the efficiency to be 85 percent and C_v for nozzle as 0.98 determine the nozzle diameter.

6.4 Each Pelton wheel at the power house delivers a maximum energy of 25 460 kW of power when working under a head of 854 m and running at 600 rpm. Taking overall efficiency to be 90 percent, determine the nozzle diameter, wheel diameter and the number of buckets (For maximum efficiency take ϕ_1= 0.45).

6.5 A Pelton wheel is required to work under a head of 100 m and to develop 308 kW at 250 rpm. Assuming an efficiency of 80 percent and C_v for nozzle as 0.98 find the diameter of the jet and the diameter of wheel.

6.6 Calculate the number of jets required and their diameter for a Pelton wheel which develops energy at the shaft equal to 11 640 kW under a head of 400 m. Other pertinent data are

speed = 600 rpm, D/d = 10.0, C_v = 0.98,

ϕ_1 = 0.46, overall efficiency = 87 percent

6.7 Design a Pelton wheel for a head of 150 m, power developed 597 kW and rotating at a speed of 360 rpm. The design includes determination of diameter of wheel, diameter of jet, width of buckets, depth of buckets, their number and number of jets. Assume any data that are required (Hint Take C_v = 0.98, η = 85 percent, ϕ_1 = 0.46).

6.8 Prove that for a singe jet Pelton wheel the specific speed is proportional to the ratio of wheel diameter to jet diameter.

6.9 A turbine producing 883 kW of power has a discharge of 3.50 m^3/s with a head of 50 m at 150 rpm speed. Find the normal speed and power under a head of 100 m.

6.10 A Pelton wheel having a semicircular bucket and working under a head of 140 m runs at 60 rpm. If the wheel diameter is 0.60 m and discharge through the nozzle is 0.05 m^3/s, determine the energy available at the nozzle and hydraulic efficiency of the wheel.

6.11 A Pelton wheel working under a head of 45 m carries a discharge of 0.8 m^3/s. The mean bucket speed is 14.0 m/s. If the jet is deflected through 165°, determine the energy produced and the efficiency.

16.12 Tests made on 1:10 scale model turbine indicate that under a head of 5.0 m the model yields a torque of 53.94 Nm when the flow is 57 l/s. What will be the mode prototype speed ratio? Find the corresponding values of torque and discharge fo the prototype.

16.13 A turbine has an output of 6400 kW when it works under a head of 20 m running at 100 rpm. What is the type of turbine? What will be its speed and power whe working at a head of 15 m?

16.14 A turbine develops 368 kW power under a head of 100 m at 200 rpm. Determine its normal speed and output under a head of 81 m.

16.15 A ventilating fan yields a flow of 7.083 m³/s of air at 1200 rpm with a power o 0.368 kW. It is found necessary to increase the capacity of the fan to twice the existing discharge value. Estimate the power and speed of the motor.

16.16 A model of a turbine 40 cm in diameter develops a power of 195 kW under a head of 3.0 m, discharge of 0.40 m³/s and at 180 rpm speed. If a geometrically similar turbine 1.2 m in diameter is to operate at the same efficiency under a head or 9.0 m, what will be its speed, power and discharge.

16.17 Absolute velocities of water entering and leaving the reaction turbine are 55.0 m/s and 5.0 m/s respectively. The other data are: $r_1 = 0.60$ m, $r_2 = 0.30$ m, $\alpha = 20°$, $\beta = 80°$, N = 400 rpm and Q = 6.5 m³/s. Find the power delivered and head utilised by the runner.

16.18 An inward flow reaction turbine has following dimensions :

$r_1 = 45$ cm $\qquad r_2 = 22.5$ cm

$b_1 = 15$ cm $\qquad b_2 = 30$ cm

If the radial velocity of flow at inlet is 3.0 m/s, determine the discharge and velocity of flow at the exit. Take K = 0.95.

16.19 An inward flow reaction turbine working under a head of 8.0 m has guide blade angle of 25° and vane angle at inlet of 105°. Assuming velocity of flow to be constant and radial discharge, determine the hydraulic efficiency of the turbine.

16.20 Show that for a turbine with radial inlet and outlet vanes, the hydraulic efficiency is given by

$$\eta_H = \frac{2}{2+\tan^2\alpha}$$

where α is the guide blade angle. Assume the velocity of flow to be constant.

16.21 An inward flow reaction turbine with radial discharge produces 147.2 kW power at an overall efficiency of 80 percent. Further, H = 8.0 m, $\phi = 0.96$, $\psi_1 = 0.36$. N = 150 rpm and hydraulic losses in the turbine are 22 percent of the available energy. Determine (i) the angle α of the guide blade at inlet (ii) vane angle θ at the inlet (iii) diameter of the wheel, and (iv) width of the wheel at inlet.

16.22 A model of a Francis turbine was tested in the laboratory to a scale of 1: 8 which gave a power of 4.0 kW at a speed of 300 rpm under a head of 2.0 m. Calculate the speed and power of the prototype when working under head of 7.0 m.

16.23 A Kaplan turbine produces 45 000 kW power at an overall efficiency of 87 percent under a head of 24 m. Taking the velocity ratio $v/\sqrt{2gH}$ as 1.8, ψ_1 as 0.70 and $D_o/D = 0.40$, calculate the diameter of the runner and its speed.

16.24 At Chambal hydroelectric scheme the available head and discharge are 55 m and 65.0 m^3/s. If turbines are to run at 180 rpm determine the type and number of units, and capacity of each unit.

16.25 Sharawati hydroelectric scheme has an available head of 443 m, and discharge of 24.0 m^3/s. If the speed of rotation prescribed is 300 rpm, determine the type of turbine, number of runners and capacity of each unit.

16.26 Select the type of turbine recommended for a hydroelectric project having $Q = 2000$ m^3/s and a head of 50 m.

16.27 The head available at a certain hydroelectric project is 300m and the available average discharge is 45.0 m^3/s. Recommend the type of turbine and number of units, if the generator has 16 pairs of poles and frequency of generated power is 50 Hz.

16.28 On a canal where the total discharge available is 250 m^3/s and net head of 9.75 m, three turbine are installed which run at 125 rpm and produce a total of 28 900 mhp. Determine the overall efficiency, the type of turbine, and its specific speed. What will be the speed ratio if the runner diameter is 3.90 m ?

16.29 A Kaplan turbine has the outer diameter D of 4.5 m and diameter of hub of 2.5 m. Under a head of 20 m, and running at 140 rpm the turbine produces 20 594 kW power. The hydraulic and overall efficiencies are 94 percent and 85 percent respectively. Find the discharge through the turbine and guide blade angle at inlet.

16.30 Following data are given for a Kaplan turbine:

Net head	=	25 m
Power developed	=	62 500 metric horse power
Overall efficiency	=	85%
Speed ratio	=	2.0
Flow ratio	=	0.6
D_o/D	=	0.40

Determine the diameter and speed of turbine.

CHAPTER SEVENTEEN

PUMPS

17.1 Introduction

Pump is a device which gives energy to the fluid thereby increasing its pressure head or kinetic energy or both. Pumps find innumerable uses in engineering. Some of the fields where pumps are used are water supply and sewage disposal, irrigation and agricultural engineering, chemical engineering, hydraulic control systems, pumped storage schemes, and transport of oil, ores, coal and other raw materials.

On the basis of the manner in which the mechanical energy is transferred to the fluid, pumps can be classified into two categories namely positive displacement pumps and rotodynamic pumps. In the case of positive displacement pumps the fluid is physically pushed or displaced from the enclosed space. The positive displacement pumps can be either of reciprocating type or of rotary type. The rotodynamic pumps increase the energy of the fluid due to kinetic energy, pressure energy and centrifugal action. The rotodynamic pumps are further classified into centrifugal (or radial) pumps, propeller (or axial) pumps and mixed flow pumps.

RECIPROCATING PUMPS

A reciprocating pump is a displacement type of machine which consists of a cylinder and a piston which moves back and forth in the cylinder. On the backward stroke of the piston, the suction valve opens and water enters into the cylinder space due to the suction created by backward stroke, see Fig. 17.1. On the forward piston stroke, the suction valve closes and delivery valve opens; the water in the cylinder is forced through the delivery pipe. Reciprocating pumps can be single acting or double acting. A double acting arrangement is shown in Fig. 17.2. In a double acting pump, water enters on both sides of the piston. When the piston moves forward, the delivery valve in the front of the piston opens and water is forced into delivery pipe A. At the same time the suction valve B on the rear opens and water enters into rear part of the cylinder. When piston moves backwards, the water is forced into delivery pipe C while at the same time suction valve D is opened. Therefore in a double acting pump relatively more uniform discharge is obtained than in a single acting pump. A reciprocating pump can also have either a single, two cylinders or more than two cylinders. In a double cylinder pump the pistons are connected to the cranks having a phase difference of 180°. Thus while the first cylinder has a forward stroke, the second executes a backward stroke.

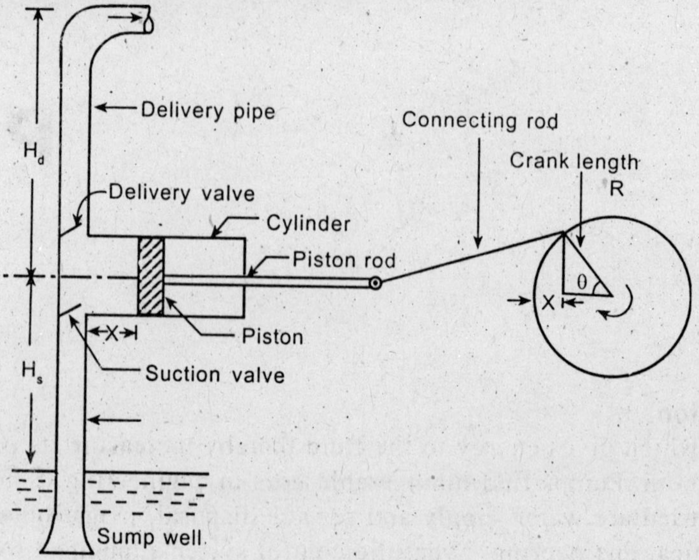

Fig. 17.1 Reciprocating pump

Therefore a double cylinder pump gives more uniform flow than the single cylinder. A double cylinder pump can be single acting or double acting. Discharge diagrams for single cylinder single acting, and single cylinder double-acting pumps are shown in Fig. 17.3.

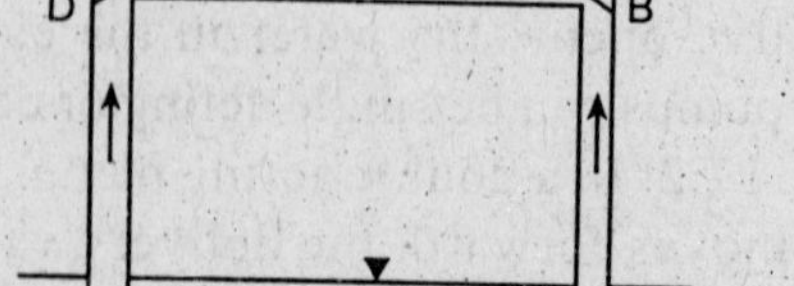

Fig. 17.2 Double acting reciprocating pump

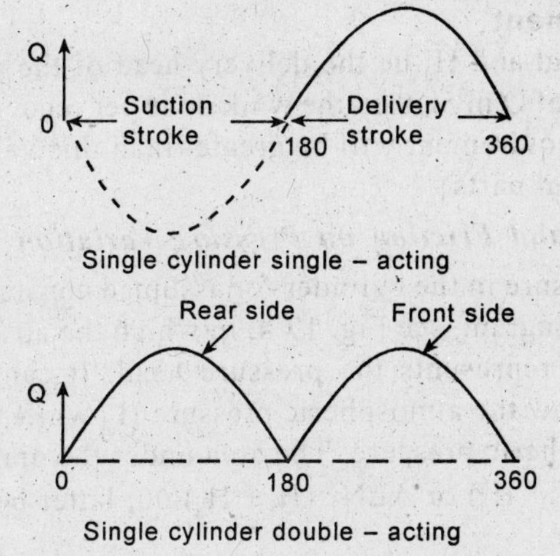

Fig. 17.3 Discharge diagrams

17.2 Discharge Relation for Reciprocating Pumps

Let A be the cross-sectional area of the piston, L be the stroke length of the piston and let N be the number of revolutions per minute of the crank of a single-acting, single-cylinder reciprocating pump. Then the theoretical discharge Q_t of the pump is

$$Q_t = \frac{ALN}{60}$$

If the cross-sectional area of the piston rod is neglected, the theoretical discharge of a single-cylinder double-acting pump is twice that of a single-cylinder single-acting pump; or

$$Q_t = \frac{2\,ALN}{60}$$

Because of the leakage through valves, glands and piston packing, and delay in closing and opening of valves, the actual discharge Q is less than theoretical discharge Q_t. The volumetric efficiency of the reciprocating pump is defined as 100 Q /Q_t and it varies from 85 to 98 percent. Another term commonly used in literature on pumps is discharge coefficient C_d which is Q/Q_t. The difference between Q_t and Q is known as the *slip of the pump* which is expressed in percent as (Q_t – Q) 100/Q_t. Usually the slip is positive. However, in some cases it is negative; this happens when the suction pipe is long, the delivery pipe is short, and the pump is running at a high speed. Because of high inertia of the suction pipe, the delivery valve opens before completion of suction stroke. Therefore some water will be pushed into the delivery pipe before the piston commences its delivery stroke. This results in actual discharge being more than the theoretical discharge and in a negative slip. Usually the slip of the pump is one to two percent.

17.3 Power Requirement

Let H_s be the suction head and H_d be the delivery head of the pump, see Fig. 17.1. If the pump carries a discharge of Q m³/s, then the work done per second will be $Q\gamma (H_s + H_d)/1000$ kW. The actual power requirement will be greater than this value because of the leakage and friction in mechanical parts.

Effect of Acceleration and Friction on Pressure Variation

Typical variation of pressure in the cylinder for assumed constant velocity of the piston is shown on the indicator diagram, see Fig. 17.4, in which the abscissa represents the stroke length and the ordinate represents the pressure head. It can be seen that the suction stroke pressure is H_s below the atmospheric pressure H_{at} while during the delivery stroke it is H_d above the atmospheric pressure. The area under the diagram is $(H_s + H_d)$ L which is proportional to $Q_t\gamma (H_s + H_d)$ or $ALN\gamma (H_s + H_d)/60$, latter being the work done by the pump in one second.

However, since the piston is driven by the rotating crank, the piston velocity is not uniform but is of simple harmonic type. It means that the piston velocity will be maximum at the centre and zero at both the ends of the cylinder. This also means that the piston will accelerate in the first half of suction stroke and decelerate in latter half. The displacement x of the piston (see Fig. 17.1) can be expressed as

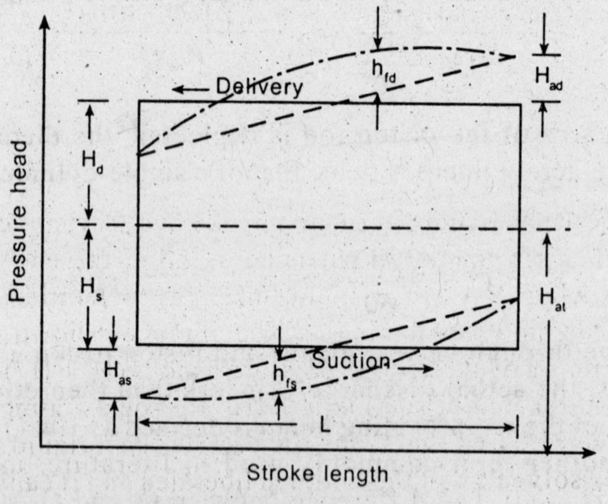

Fig. 17.4 Indicator diagram

$$x = R - R\cos\theta$$

or

$$x = R - R\cos\omega t \tag{17.1}$$

where R is crank length and ω the angular velocity of crank. Velocity of the piston U_p will be

$$U_P = \frac{dx}{dt} = R\,\omega \sin \omega t \tag{17.2}$$

whereas the acceleration will be

$$\frac{dU_p}{dt} = R\,\omega^2 \cos \omega t \tag{17.3}$$

The velocity of flow in the suction pipe U_s and that in delivery pipe U_d are related to velocity of piston U_p as

$$U_s A_s = U_p A = U_d A_d$$

where A_s and A_d are the cross-sectional areas of suction and delivery pipes. Hence

$$U_s = \frac{A}{A_s} R\,\omega \sin \omega t \tag{17.4}$$

and acceleration in the suction pipe will be $(A/A_s)\,R\,\omega^2 \cos \omega t$. If l_s is the length of the suction pipe, $(A_s\, l_s\, \rho)$ is the mass of water in the pipe and accelerating force is

$$\text{mass} \times \text{acceleration} = A_s\, l_s\, \rho \frac{A}{A_s} R\,\omega^2 \cos \omega t$$

$$= A\, l_s\, \rho\, R\,\omega^2 \cos \omega t$$

The corresponding pressure head H_{as} is

$$\frac{\text{Accelerating Force}}{\text{Area} \times \gamma} = \frac{A\, l_s\, \rho\, R\,\omega^2 \cos \omega t}{A_s\, \gamma}$$

or

$$H_{as} = \frac{l_s}{g} \frac{A}{A_s} R\,\omega^2 \cos \omega t \tag{17.5}$$

When ωt is zero i.e. at the beginning of suction stroke, the acceleration head is $l_s\, AR\,\omega^2/gA_s$, at the mid-stroke when ωt equals 90°, it is zero and at the end of the stroke when ωt equals 180° it is $-\,l_s\, AR\omega^2/gA_s$. In a similar manner acceleration head for delivery pipe can be calculated. This modifies the indicator diagram as shown in Fig. 17.4 by broken line. Thus at the beginning of suction the pressure head is $(H_s + H_{as})$ below the atmospheric pressure head while at the end of suction it is $(H_s - H_{as})$ below atmospheric pressure head. It may however be remembered that when the pressure in a liquid drops below 2.44 m of water absolute, the dissolved air in the liquid is liberated and it can break the continuity of flow. For a given pump characteristics, N can be changed to limit the acceleration head in suction pipe H_{as}, and thus limit the minimum pressure head at the beginning of suction stroke.

The effect of friction in the suction and delivery pipes can be assessed by estimating the head loss using Darcy-Weisbach equation along with expressions for U_s and U_d. The resulting expression for head loss h_{fs} and H_{fd} in the suction pipe and delivery pipe are

$$h_{fs} = \frac{f\, l_s}{2g\, D_s} \left(\frac{A}{A_s} R\,\omega \sin \omega t \right)^2 \tag{17.6}$$

$$h_{fd} = \frac{f\, l_d}{2g\, D_d}\left(\frac{A}{A_d} R\, \omega \sin \omega t\right)^2 \qquad (17.7)$$

Here D_s and D_d are diameters of the section and delivery pipes, l_s, and l_d their lengths and f is their friction factor. This gives the maximum head loss at the middle of the stroke and zero loss at the ends. Modified indicator diagram including frictional head loss is also shown in Fig. 17.4.

The maximum head loss in friction on the suction side will be at the middle of stroke, its value being

$$h = \frac{f\, l_s}{2g\, D_s}\left(\frac{A}{A_s} R\, \omega\right)^2$$

Similarly maximum head loss due to friction on delivery side is

$$h_{sdm} = \frac{f\, l_d}{2g\, D_d}\left(\frac{A}{A_d} R\, \omega\right)^2$$

The average head loss in suction and delivery pipes will be 2/3rd of the above

or $$\frac{f\, l_s}{3g\, D_s}\left(\frac{A}{A_d} R\, \omega\right)^2 \text{ and } \frac{f\, l_d}{3g\, D_d}\left(\frac{A}{A_d} R\, \omega\right)^2;$$

respectively. Hence the total work done per second will be

$$W = \frac{Q\gamma}{1000}\left[H_s + H_d + \frac{f\, l_s}{3gD_s}\left(\frac{A}{A_S} R\, \omega\right)^2 + \frac{f\, l_d}{3gD_d}\left(\frac{A}{A_d} R\, \omega\right)^2\right] \text{kW} \qquad (17.8)$$

Example 17.1

A single-acting reciprocating pump with one cylinder has the following characteristics:

Diameter of cylinder	20 cm
Stroke length	40 cm
Discharge	6.00 *l*/s
Suction head	4.0 m
Delivery head	20.0 m
Speed	30.0 rpm

Find the theoretical discharge, slip of the pump and energy required to drive the pump.

$$\text{Theoretical discharge} = \frac{ALN}{60} = \frac{0.785 \times 0.2^2 \times 0.40 \times 30}{60}$$

$= 0.006\ 28\ m^3/s$

$= 6.28\ l/s$

$\therefore$ Slip of the pump $= \dfrac{(6.28-6.00)}{6.28} \times 100$

$= 4.46$ percent

Energy required $= \dfrac{Q\gamma(H_s + H_d)}{1000} = \dfrac{0.006 \times 9787 \times 24}{1000}$

$= 1.409$ kW

Example 17.2

A single cylinder single-acting reciprocating pump running at 30 rpm has a stroke length of 40 cm. and piston diameter of 20 cm. The suction head is 3.0 m, suction length of pipe 6.0 m and its diameter 10 cm. Take f = 0.02 and determine the absolute pressure on the piston at the beginning, middle and end of suction stroke (Assume H_{at} = 10.3 m of water)

$A = 0.785 \times 0.20^2 = 0.0314\ m^2$

$A_s = 0.785 \times 0.\ 10^2 = 0.007\ 85\ m^2$

Radius of crank = ½ stroke length

= 0.20 m

Angular velocity $\omega = \dfrac{2\pi N}{60} = \dfrac{2 \times 3.142 \times 30}{60} = 3.142$ rad/s

Acceleration head at the beginning and end

$$\therefore \quad H_{as} = \frac{l_s}{g}\frac{A}{A_s} R\omega^2 = \frac{60}{9.806} \times \frac{0.0314}{0.007\ 85} \times 0.2 \times 3.142^2$$

$= 4.83$ m

The friction head at middle of suction stroke

$$= \frac{f\,l_s}{2gD_s}\left(\frac{A}{A_s} R\,\omega\right)^2$$

$$\therefore \quad h_{fs} = \frac{0.02 \times 6.0}{2 \times 9.806 \times 0.10}\left(\frac{0.0314 \times 0.2 \times 3.142}{0.007\ 85}\right)^2$$

$= 0.386$ m

$\therefore$ Absolute pressure at the beginning of suction stroke

$= H_{at} - H_s - H_{as} = 10.300 - 3.000 - 4.830$

$= 2.47$ m

Absolute pressure at the middle = $(H_{at} - H_s - H_{fs})$

$$= 10.300 - 4.830 - 0.386 = 5.084 \text{ m}$$

Absolute pressure at the end of suction stroke

$$(H_{at} - H_s + H_{as}) = 10.30 - 3.0 + 4.83 \text{ m} = 12.13 \text{ m}$$

17.4 Air Vessels

Air vessel is a closed chamber connected on the suction or delivery side (or both) of the pump as shown in Fig.17.5. Purpose of fitting air vessels to the reciprocating pump is to obtain a more uniform flow. The function of air vessel on the delivery side can be explained as follows. During the forward stroke of piston, water is forced into delivery pipe. Some water enters the air vessel and compresses the air there. During the backward stroke, the delivery is closed and thus no water is discharged from the cylinder. However, during this stroke, the water stored in vessel is released and flow is maintained in the discharge pipe. In a similar fashion the function of air vessel on suction side can be explained. In pipe lengths between the cylinder and air vessel, the velocity will be varying. Hence to reduce acceleration head, air vessels are always located close to the cylinder. If l_{sa} and l_{da} the lengths of suction and delivery pipes upto the air vessels are small, the acceleration or retardation head on the suction side H_{sa} or delivery side H_{da} will be smaller. Therefore absolute pressure head on suction side will be larger. As a consequence of this there is less danger of cavitation.

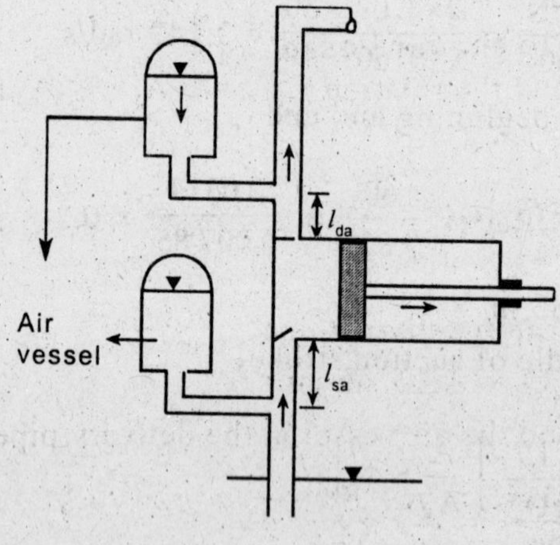

Fig. 17.5 Air vessels in a reciprocating pump

Volume of air vessels on suction and delivery sides of a reciprocating pump depends on the volume of water entering the piston per second, speed of rotation and the lengths of suction and delivery pipes respectively. These volumes are about 0.4 to 0.6 times volume entering the pump per cycle for air vessel on delivery side and 0.2 to 0.3 times for air vessel on suction side.

One can determine the saving in the work done due to fitting of an air vessel. Consider the case when there is no air vessel either on suction side or on delivery side.

Work done in one stroke

$$\frac{LA\gamma}{1000}\left\{H_s + \frac{f\,l_s}{3gD_s}\left(\frac{A}{A_s}R\,\omega\right)^2 + H_d + \frac{f\,l_s}{3gD_d}\left(\frac{A}{A_d}R\,\omega\right)^2\right\}\text{kW} \qquad (17.9)$$

When the air vessel is provided on the suction side at a distance l_{sa} from the cylinder, see Fig. 17.5, it is only in this length that the velocity will vary. In the length $(l_s - l_{sa})$ the velocity will be constant.

Hence work done per stroke on suction side will be

$$\frac{LA\gamma}{1000}\left[H_s + \frac{f(l_s - l_{as})}{2gD_s}\overline{U}_s^2 + \frac{f\,l_{sa}}{3gD_s}\left(\frac{A}{A_s}R\,\omega\right)^2\right]\text{kW} \qquad (17.10)$$

where $\overline{U}_s$ = average velocity in suction pipe. Similarly work done per stroke on delivery side will be

$$\frac{LA\gamma}{1000}\left[H_d + \frac{f(l_d - l_{da})\overline{U}_d^2}{2gD_d} + \frac{f\,l_{da}}{3gD_d}\left(\frac{A}{A_d}R\,\omega\right)^2\right]\text{kW} \qquad (17.11)$$

One can find the saving in the work done per storke using Eqs. 17.9, 17.10 and 17.11.

17.5 Discharge Variation in the Air Vessel

It can be seen from Eq. 17.2 and the relation $U_pA = U_sA_s = U_dA_d$ that the velocity in the delivery pipe is

$$U_d = \left(\frac{A}{A_d}\right)U_p = \frac{A}{A_d}R\,\omega\,\sin\omega t$$

∴ Discharge from the cylinder into delivery pipe

$$Q_d = A_dU_d = AR\omega\,\sin\omega t$$

The velocity of water beyond the air vessel in the delivery pipe is

$$U_d = \frac{ALN}{60A_d} = \frac{A}{A_d}\,\frac{R\omega}{\pi}$$

Since $\quad L = 2R \quad$ and $\quad N = \dfrac{60\omega}{2\pi}$

∴ Discharge in the delivery pipe beyond air vessel is

$$Q = A\,\overline{U}_d = \frac{AR\omega}{\pi}$$

Hence discharge into air vessel $Q_a = (Q_d - Q)$

$$= \left(AR\omega \sin \omega t - \frac{AR\omega}{\pi} \right)$$

or $$Q_a = AR\,\omega \left(\sin\theta - \frac{1}{\pi} \right) \qquad (17.12.)$$

Since $\frac{1}{\pi} = 0.3183$, the corresponding θ value for sin θ = 0.3183 is 18.56°. This means that if the quantity in the bracket is +ve, water will flow into the air vessel and if it is negative, the discharge will take place from air vessel to the pipe When the air vessel is fixed on the suction side, the air vessel will discharge when $\left(\sin\theta - \frac{1}{\pi} \right)$ is +ve and will take in discharge when it is negative.

In the same manner one can show that corresponding expression for single cylinder double acting pump is

$$Q_a = AR\omega \left(\sin\theta - \frac{2}{\pi} \right) \qquad (17.12a)$$

Example 17.3

A single acting single cylinder reciprocating pump has the following details:

Suction diameter	D_d	=	7.50 cm
Delivery diameter	D_s	=	7.50 cm
Length of suction pipe	l_s	=	3.5 m
Length of delivery pipe	l_d	=	13.5 m
Suction head	H_s	=	2.5 m
Delivery head	H_d	=	9.0 m
Piston diameter	D	=	12.5 cm
Stroke length	L	=	50 cm. (∴ R = L/2 = 25 cm)
	f	=	0.02

Neglecting the slip and assuming a suitable value for minimum permissible pressure, calculate the maximum permissible speed and energy required to drive the pump if an air vessel is provided on the delivery side close to the pump axis.

$$A = 0.785 \times 0.125^2 = 0.0123 \text{ m}^2$$

$$A_s = A_d = 0.785 \times 0.075^2 = 0.004\,42 \text{ m}^2$$

Assume permissible absolute pressure head $H_{min} = 2.60$ m

$$H_{min} = H_{at} - (H_s + H_{as})$$

$$H_{as} = 9.76 - 2.6 - 2.5$$

$$= 4.66 \text{ m}$$

(Atmospheric pressure head is taken as 9.76 m. of water).

But

$$H_{as} = \frac{l_s}{g} \frac{A}{A_s} R\,\omega^2$$

$$\therefore \quad \omega^2 = \frac{H_{as} g A_s}{l_s A R}$$

$$= \frac{4.66 \times 9.806 \times 0.00442}{3.50 \times 0.0123 \times 0.25}$$

$$= 18.77 \text{ (rad/s)}^2 \quad \therefore \quad \omega = 4.33 \text{ rad/s}$$

$$N = \frac{60\omega}{2\pi} = \frac{60 \times 4.33}{2 \times 3.142} = 41.37 \text{ rpm}$$

$$Q = \frac{ALN}{60} = \frac{0.0123 \times 0.50 \times 41.37}{60}$$

$$= 0.004\,24 \text{ m}^3\text{/s} \quad \text{or} \quad 4.24 \ l\text{/s}$$

Maximum head loss on suction. side is

$$h_{fsm} = \frac{f\,l_s}{2gD_s}\left(\frac{A}{A_s} R\,\omega\right)^2$$

$$= \frac{0.02 \times 3.5}{19.62 \times .075}\left\{\frac{0.0123}{0.00442} \times 0.25 \times 4.33\right\}^2$$

$$= 0.432 \text{ m}$$

∴ Average head loss in suction pipe = 2/3 × 0.432 = 0.288 m

Because of the presence of air vessel, the velocity in the delivery pipe will be steady and its value will be

$$\overline{U}_d = \frac{Q}{A_d} = \frac{0.004\,24}{0.004\,62} = 0.959 \text{ m/s}$$

∴ Frictional head loss in delivery pipe is equal to

$$\frac{f\,l_d}{2gD_d}\,\overline{U}_d^2 = \frac{0.02 \times 13.5 \times 0.959^2}{19.62 \times 0.075} = 0.169 \text{ m}$$

∴ Work done per second

$= Q\gamma\,(H_s + H_d + \text{head loss in suction pipe} + \text{head loss in delivery pipe})$

$= 0.00424 \times 9787 \times (2.5 + 9.0 + 0.288 + 0.169)/1000$ kW

$= 0.496$ kW

Example 17.4

A single-acting single-cylinder reciprocating pump is provided with an air vessel on the delivery side. The piston diameter is 30.5 cm while the piston stroke is 61.0 cm. The delivery pipe of 17.5 cm diameter is 61 m long. Determine the energy saved in overcoming friction in the delcevery pipe if f = 0.04 and N = 120 rpm.

Without the air vessel

$$h_{fd} = \frac{f\,l_d}{3gD_d}\left(\frac{A}{A_d}R\omega\right)^2$$

$$R = 0.61/2 = 0.305 \text{ m}$$

$$\omega = \frac{2\pi N}{60} = \frac{2\times3.142\times120}{60} = 12.568 \text{ rad/s}$$

$$A/A_d = (0.305/0.175)^2 = 3.038$$

$$h_{fd} = \frac{0.04\times61}{3\times9.806\times0.175}(3.038\times0.305\times12.568)^2$$

$$= 64.25 \text{ m}$$

When the air vessel is fitted on the delivery side the velocity in the delivery pipe will be uniform

$$\overline{U}_d = Q/Ad$$

$$= \frac{ALN}{60A_d} = \frac{3.038\times0.61\times120}{60} = 3.706 \text{ m/s}$$

$$(h_{fd})_i = \frac{0.04\times61}{2\times9.806\times0.175}\times3.706^2$$

$$= 9.760 \text{ m}$$

∴ Work saved $= Q\gamma\,(64.25 - 9.76)$

$$= \frac{(0.785\times0.305^2)\times0.61}{1000}\times\frac{120}{60}\times9787\,(54.49) \text{ kW}$$

$$= 47.511 \text{ kW}$$

To find the maximum permissible speed of a reciprocating pump fitted with air vessel, one must limit the separation head

$$H_{sep} = H_{at} - [H_s + H_{as} \text{ for } l_{ps} + h_f \text{ for } (l_s - l_{sa})]$$

Example 17.5

A single-cylinder single-acting reciprocating pump is installed 3.5 m above the water level in the sump. The suction pipe is 20 cm in diameter and 10 m in length. The piston is of 30 cm. diameter and 50 cm stroke. Determine (i) the speed at which separation may take place at the beginning of suction stroke, and (ii) change in the speed of the pump if an air vessel is fitted on the suction side 2.5 m above the sump water level. Take H_{at} = 10.3 m. f = 0.05 and separation to occur at 2.5 m of water absolute.

$$D_s = 0.2 \text{ m}$$

$$\therefore \quad A_s = 0.785 \times 0.2^2 = 0.031\ 42 \text{ m}^2$$

$$l_s = 10 \text{ m}, \ l_{sa} = 7.5 \text{ m}$$

$$A = 0.785 \times 0.3^2 = 0.0707 \text{ m}^2$$

$$L = 0.5 \text{ m} \quad \therefore \quad R = 0.50/2 = 0.25 \text{ m}$$

When air vessel is not provided

$$H_{sep} = H - (H_s + H_{as})$$

$$H_{as} = H_{at} - H_s - H_{sep} = 10.3 - 3.5 - 2.5$$

$$= 4.3 \text{ m}$$

But

$$H_{as} = \frac{l_s}{g}\frac{A}{A_s}R\omega^2$$

$$\therefore \quad \omega^2 = \frac{4.3 \times 9.806}{10} \times \left(\frac{0.03142}{0.0707}\right)\frac{1}{0.25}$$

$$= 7.499$$

$$\therefore \quad \omega = 2.738 \text{ rad/s}$$

or

$$N = \frac{60\omega}{2\pi} = 26.15 \text{ rpm}$$

When air vessel is provided on the suction side, the speed can be computed in the following way.

Suction pipe length l_{sa} between cylinder and air vessel

$$= 10 \times \frac{2.5}{3.5} = 7.14 \text{ m}$$

$(l_a - l_{sa})$ the remaining length = 10 – 7.14 = 2.86 m

$$\overline{U}_s = \frac{ALN}{60}\frac{1}{A_s} = \left(\frac{0.30}{0.20}\right)^2 \times \frac{0.50 \times \omega}{2\pi}$$

$$= 0.179\ \omega$$

$$\therefore \quad h_{fs} = \frac{0.04 \times 7.14 \times (0.179\,\omega)^2}{2 \times 9.806 \times 0.20}$$

$$= 0.0023\ \omega^2$$

The acceleration head in the suction pipe will be

$$H_{as} = \frac{(l_s - l_{sa})}{g}\left(\frac{A}{A_s}\right) R\,\omega^2$$

$$= \frac{2.86}{9.806}\left(\frac{0.30}{0.20}\right)^2 \times 0.25\ \omega^2$$

$$= 0.164\ \omega^2$$

$$\therefore \quad H_{sep} = H - (H_s + h_{fs} + H_{as})$$

$$2.5 = 10.3 - (3.50 + 0.0023\ \omega^2 + 0.164\ \omega^2)$$

$$\therefore \quad 0.1663\ \omega^2 = 4.3$$

or $$\omega = 5.08 \text{ rad/s}$$

and $$N = \frac{60 \times 5.08}{2 \times 3.142} = 48.5 \text{ rpm}$$

Therefore the change in speed due to provision of air vessel is an increase of (48.50 – 26.15) or 22.35 rpm.

17.6 Other Pumps of Displacement Type

The reciprocating pump described earlier is a positive displacement type where the motion is linear. Another pump of this type is the plunger pump in which the piston of the reciprocating pump is replaced by a plunger. Plunger pump develops high pressure and is used for rough work or when water contains sand etc. These can be single-acting or double-acting.

The other type of displacement pumps are rotary pumps, in which the motion is rotary. An external gear pump of this type is shown in Fig. 17.6, which has two gear wheels. One gear wheel is connected to the driving shaft while the other gear wheel serves as an idle wheel. The liquid is entrained between the teeth and the casing and is carried from suction to delivery side. The theoretical volume of liquid displaced per revolution is equal to the sum of volumes of liquid enclosed between teeth and casing. If a is the area enclosed between two adjacent teeth and casing, *l* is the axial length of teeth and z is number of teeth in each gear wheel,

$$\text{volume displaced in the revolution} = a\,l\,z$$

$$\therefore \quad Q = \frac{al\,zN}{60}$$

Fig. 17.6 Rotary pump

where N is number of revolutions per minute. Gear pumps are used for hydraulic systems with oil. Other pumps falling in this category are internal gear pump, screw pump and vane pump.

One of the important characteristics of rotary displacement pumps is that the discharge is nearly uniform. Secondly the percent slip in well designed rotary pumps is less than five. The efficiency of these pumps varies from 65 to 90 percent. Highly viscous liquid gives smaller efficiency.

ROTODYNAMIC PUMPS

As mentioned earlier the most commonly used rotodynamic pump is the centrifugal pump in which the water enters parallel to the shaft and flows radially outwards. In fact, it is the reverse of radially inward flow reaction turbine.

17.7 Description of Centrifugal Pumps

Various parts of a centrifugal pump are described below:

(a) Impeller

It is a wheel or set of vanes attached to the shaft. The shaft is rotated from the outside using an electric motor or a diesel engine. The rotation of the vanes in the liquid imparts energy to the liquid present around the impeller enclosed in the casing. The impeller consists of two disks called shrouds one of which is fixed to the hub and the other is fixed to the former on curved vanes, see Fig. 17.7 (a). The material of the impeller depends upon the nature of liquid to be pumped. For pumping clear water a cast steel impeller is commonly used; for pumping chemicals which are likely to cause corrosion, impellers made of nonferrous metals such as gunmetal or stainless steel are used. When two shrouds are used in this way, it is called enclosed impeller. Enclosed impellers are used for pumping clear water and other clear liquids of low viscosity.

Semi-open impellers have only one shroud on the backside, see Fig. 17.7 (b) while open impellers do not have any shroud, see Fig. 17.7 (c). Semi-open and open impeller pumps are used for very viscous liquids or liquids carrying sand and other particulate matter in suspension.

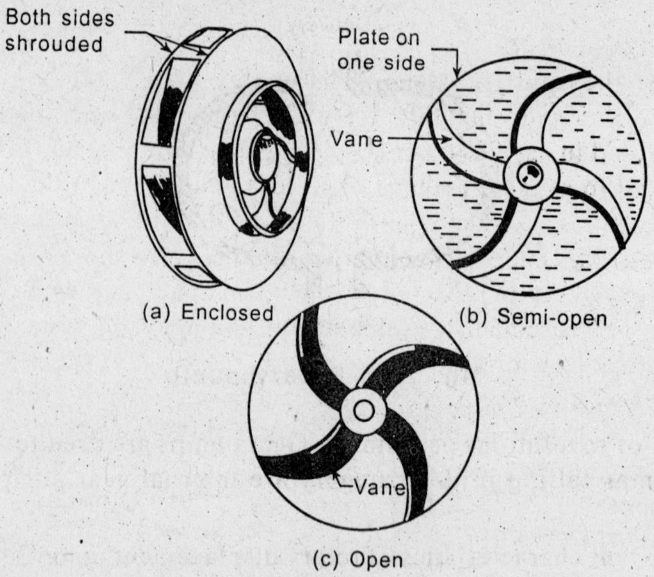

Fig. 17.7 Types of impellers

The vanes or blades of the impeller can either be straight, ending radially, bending backwards or bending forward, see Fig. 17.8. The number of blades varies from six to twelve.

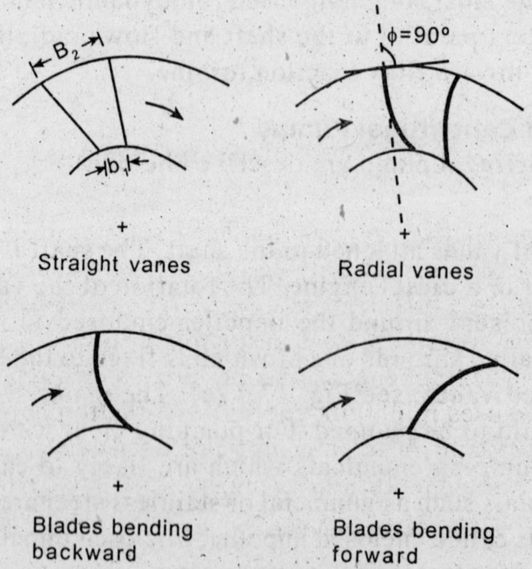

Fig. 17.8 Types of vanes

(b) Pump Casing

The impeller of the centrifugal pump is enclosed in what is known as a casing. Arrangements for water entering into the casing (suction) and for leaving the casing (delivery) are provided in each casing. The casing also contains facilities for stuffing box and packing material to prevent leakage of water outside. When the liquid is given high velocity upto the tip of blades due to their rotating action, it is given enough kinetic energy and rotation. Some of this energy is converted into pressure energy because of the casing by the time the water enters the discharge pipe. The efficiency of this conversion of the kinetic energy into pressure energy is dependent on the shape of casing and is achieved by providing a volute or a diffuser type casing, see Fig. 17.9. In a volute casing the cross-sectional area of the passage gradually increases toward the delivery pipe. This gradual increase is such that inspite of increasing flow towards the delivery pipe, the velocity remains constant. If a simple circular casing were provided, the energy loss would have been more.

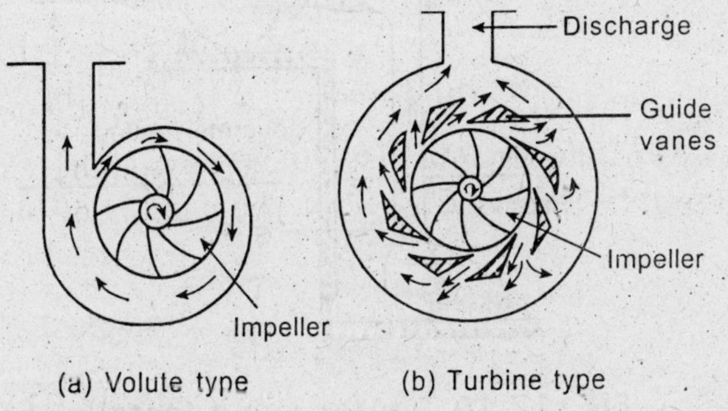

Fig. 17.9 Types of casings

As water flows from suction towards delivery side the pressure increases gradually. Another type of casing that can be provided is diffuser casing in which, after the water leaves the blades, it enters a diffuser casing which consists of a series of guide vanes in which the flow passage increases; as a result the velocity decreases and the pressure correspondingly increases. The guide vanes are so designed that the water leaves tangentially and thus causes minimum energy loss due to change of direction. Thus the major conversion of velocity head into pressure head takes place in the diffuser ring. Such casings are also known as turbine casings.

(c) Priming Valve, Foot Valve, Reducer

The centrifugal pump assembly has a priming valve since centrifugal pumps need to be completely filled with liquid from the suction side upto the pump thereby removing air out of the casing. This process is known as priming. A small valve is provided for this purpose. A foot valve is provided on the submerged end of suction pipe so that the water does not escape while priming the pump. A screen provided at the entrance to the suction pipe prevents entry of solid material into the pump.

Normally suction pipe diameter is large so that for a given discharge the velocity in the pipe is small and so also the energy loss. For minimising the head loss the suction pipe is kept as straight as possible and any elbows used are of large radius. Since suction pipe is of larger diameter a reducer is used between suction pipe and the pump.

When starting a centrifugal pump, It is first primed with delivery valve closed; then this valve is gradually opened as the pump is started. A typical pump installation is shown in Fig. 17.10.

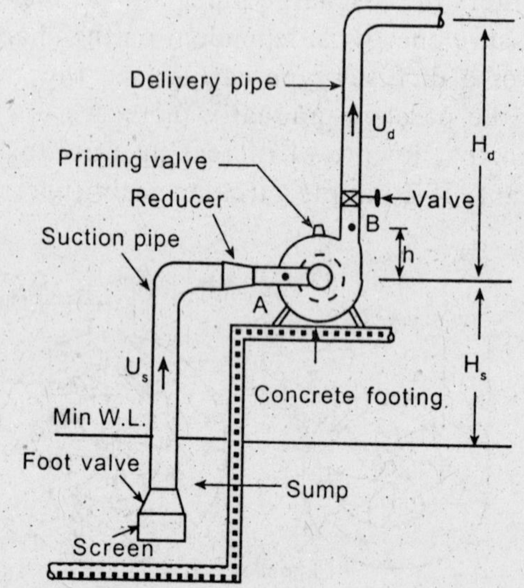

Fig. 17.10 Typical pump installation

17.8 Classification of Centrifugal Pumps

Centrifugal pumps can be classified into volute pump, and diffuser or turbine pumps as shown in Fig. 17.9. This classification is based on the type of casing used for the pumps. Pumps can also be classified according to the number of stages. For small heads a single impeller is used. When large head is to be developed one can use two stage or multistage pump in which two or more impellers are used in series, the discharge from one impeller being fed into suction of the next impeller. These impellers are usually housed in the same casing. The centrifugal pumps can also be classified according to the position of shaft, into pumps with horizontal shaft and pumps with vertical shaft, the former being the most common position. Again pumps can be classified into single suction and double suction pumps depending on whether the pump has one sided or double sided suction.

17.9 Velocity Diagrams

The analysis of velocity diagrams for a centrifugal pump is exactly similar to that for turbine as can be seen from the following example.

Example 17.6

A centrifugal pump with an impeller of 50 cm outside and 25 cm inside diameter runs at 950 rpm. The vanes are set back at an angle of 35° to the outer rim. If the radial velocity of water through the impeller is constant at 2.0 m/s, determine the angle of the vane at the inlet, and velocity and direction of water at the outlet.

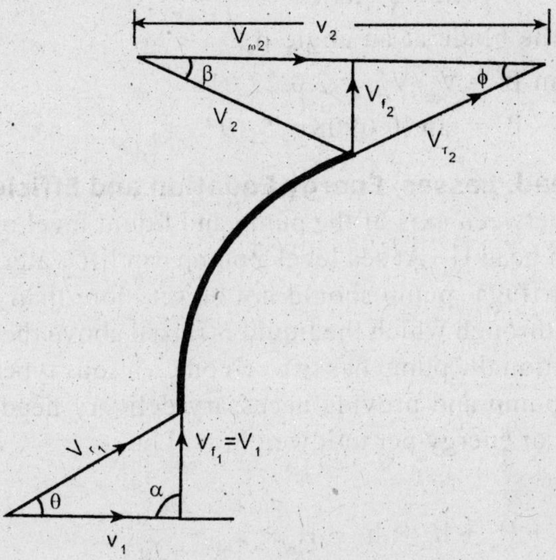

Fig. 17.11 Velocity diagram

Tangential velocity, at inlet

$$v_1 = \frac{\pi D_1 N}{60}$$

$$= 3.142 \times 0.25 \times 950/60$$

$$= 12.437 \text{ m/s}$$

$$\tan \theta = V_{f1}/v_1 = 2.0/12.437$$

$$= 0.1608$$

$$\therefore \quad \theta = \tan^{-1} 0.1608 = 9.136°$$

If V_2 is the absolute velocity of water at the outlet, it can be determined in the following way.

$$v_2 = \pi D_2 N/60$$

$$= 3.142 \times 0.50 \times 950/60$$

$$= 24.874 \text{ m/s}$$

Velocity of swirl $\quad V_{\omega 2} = v_2 - \dfrac{V_{f2}}{\tan \varphi}$ where $\phi = 35°$

$$= 24.874 - \frac{2.0}{0.7002} = 22.018 \text{ m/s}$$

$$\therefore \quad V_2 = \sqrt{V_{f2}^{\ 2} + V_{\omega 2}^{\ 2}} = \sqrt{2.0^2 + 22.018^2}$$

$$= 22.063 \text{ m/s}$$

Since the water leaves the blade at an angle β,

$$\tan \beta = V_{f2}/V_{\omega 2} = 2.0/22.018$$

$$\therefore \quad \beta = \tan^{-1} 0.0908 = 5.19°$$

17.10 Manometric Head, Losses, Energy Equation and Efficiencies

The difference of level between axis of the pump and liquid level on suction side is called the suction lift or suction head H_s. At sea level a pump can lift water upto a height 10.35 m. However actually a centrifugal pump should not be set more than 7.5 m above the water supply level. The height through which the liquid is raised above the pump axis is known as delivery head H_d. In addition the pump has to overcome various types of losses taking place in the pipes and in the pump and provide necessary delivery head. Hence the total head supplied by the pump H, or energy per unit weight will be

$$H = h_e + H_s + h_{fs} + h_l + H_d + h_{fd} + \frac{U_d^2}{2g} \qquad (17.12)$$

in which

h_e = entrance loss of head

h_{fs} = frictional loss of head in suction pipe

h_{fd} = frictional loss of head in delivery pipe

h_l = head loss in the impeller and casing

The head loss at the entrance is small and is usually neglected. Further, impeller losses and losses in casing are not considered; in such case the total head is the effective head or dynamic head H_m

$$H_m = H_s + h_{fs} + H_d + h_{fd} + \frac{U_d^2}{2g} \qquad (17.\ 13)$$

This is known as the *manometric head* H_m. If two piezometers are connected one just upstream of entrance to the pump and other just after the delivery end of the pump, such as A and B in Fig, 17.10, Bernoulli's equation can be written in the form

$$\frac{p_A}{\gamma} + \frac{U_s^2}{2g} = \frac{p_B}{\gamma} + h + h_l + \frac{U_d^2}{2g} - H \qquad (7.14)$$

or

$$\left(\frac{p_B}{\gamma} + h\right) - \frac{p_A}{\gamma} = \frac{U_s^2}{2g} - \frac{U_d^2}{2g} + (H - h_l) \qquad (17.15)$$

The left hand side represents the manometric head difference between point B and A and this will he equal to $(H-h_l)$ if U_s is equal to U_d.

The total losses occurring in a centrifugal pump can be grouped under the following heads. Frictional and form losses occur in the pump and pump line system. The frictional loss in the pump takes place on the blades and casing walls whereas the form loss takes place at the entrance and exit to the pump and the flow expands between vanes and casing. The friction loss also takes place in suction and delivery pipes and form loss takes place in the bends and valves.

Mechanical friction takes place in the bearings and glands. Leakage loss is loss of energy caused by high velocity liquid escaping as leakage through glands.

The expression for energy imparted to the fluid by rotating vanes can be derived in the same manner as done for the reaction turbine. If V_1 is the velocity with which the liquid enters the impeller and V_2 is the velocity with which it leaves the impeller and if r_1 and r_2 are the inner and outer radii of the impeller vane, then the torque exerted by the impeller on the liquid is

$$T = Q\,\rho\,(V_2\,r_2 \cos\beta - V_1\,r_1 \cos\theta) \qquad (17.16)$$

in which β and θ are the angles made by the absolute velocities V_2 and V_1 with tangent to the impeller at outer side and inside respectively, Q being the discharge through the pump. Since work done equals Tω,

$$\text{Work done per second} = Q\rho\,\omega(V_2\,r_2 \cos\beta - V_1\,r_1 \cos\theta)$$

$$= Q\rho\left(V_{\omega 2}v_2 - V_{\omega 1}v_1\right) \qquad (17.17)$$

Where $V_{\omega 2}$ and $V_{\omega 1}$ are velocities of swirl at outlet and inlet respectively. Work done per unit weight of liquid will be

$$\frac{T\omega}{Q\gamma} = \frac{1}{g}\,(V_{\omega 2}\,v_2 - V_{\omega 1}\,v_2) \qquad (17.18)$$

If the liquid enters radially $V_{\omega 1} = 0$ and Eq. (17.18) becomes

Theoretical head developed (Also known as Euler head)

$$= \left(\frac{1}{g}V_{\omega 2}v_2\right) \qquad (17.19)$$

Four types of efficiencies are commonly used in describing the performance of the pump.

Manometric efficiency η_{mo} is defined as the ratio of manometric head H_m to the theoretical head developed: or

$$\eta_{mo} = H_m/(V_{w2}\,v_2\,/g) \times 100$$

Mechanical efficiency η_m is the ratio of available head at the impeller to the energy given to impeller by the prime mover. This accounts for energy loss in packings, glands bearings, and on shrouds. Its value ranges from 95 to 98 percent.

Volumetric efficiency η_v gives idea about the leakage of liquid through the pump and is defined as the ratio of actual discharge at pump outlet to total discharge flowing through the impeller. Hence

$$\eta_v = \left(\frac{Q}{Q+q}\right) \times 100 \quad (17.21)$$

where q is the leakage discharge; η_v is about 97 – 98 percent.

Overall efficiency η_o is the ratio of work done by the pump to energy supplied to the pump by the prime mover. It can be easily seen that

$$\eta_o = \eta_{mo}\ \eta_m\ \eta_v \quad (17.22)$$

Example 17.7

A centrifugal pump running at 1500 rpm against a head of 25 m carries 125 *l*/s discharge of water. It the impeller diameter at the outlet is 25 cm, the width there is 5.0 cm and vanc angle at outlet ϕ is 42°, determine the manometric efficiency.

Velocity diagram, Fig. 17-11 gives the following:

$$v_2 = \pi\, D_2\, N/60 = \frac{3.142\times0.25\times1500}{60}$$

$$= 19.638 \text{ m/s}$$

Since $\quad Q = \pi D_2\, V_{f2}\, b_2$

$$0.125 = 3.142 \times 0.25 \times 0.05 \times V_{f2}$$

$\therefore \quad V_{f2} = 3.183$ m/s

Since $\quad \tan\phi = V_{f2}/(v_2 - V_{w2})$ and $\phi = 42°$

$$(v_2 - V_{\omega2}) = \frac{3.183}{0.9004} = 3.535$$

$\therefore \quad V_{\omega2} = 19.638 - 3.535 = 16.103$ m/s

$$\eta_{mo} = \frac{gH_m}{V_{\omega2}v_2} = \frac{9.806\times25}{16.103\times19.638}$$

$$= 0.7755 \quad \text{or} \quad 77.55 \text{ percent}$$

Example 17.8

A centrifugal pump having an overall efficiency of 75 percent delivers a discharge of 0.03 m^3 /s at a height of 18 m through 90 m long delivery pipe of 10 cm diameter. If its friction factor is 0.048, calculate the energy required to drive the pump. Assume friction loss in suction pipe to be negligible

$$H_s + H_d = 18 \text{ m}$$

Manometric head $H_m = H_s + H_d + h_{fd} + \frac{U_d^2}{2g}$

$$U_d = \frac{0.03}{0.785\times0.10^2} = 3.822 \text{ m/s}$$

$$\therefore \quad h_{fd} = \frac{0.048\times90\times3.822^2}{2\times9.806\times0.10} = 32.164 \text{ m}$$

$$\frac{U_d^2}{2g} = \frac{3.822^2}{2\times9.806} = 0.745 \text{ m}$$

$$\therefore \quad H_m = 18.000 + 32.164 + 0.745 = 50.909 \text{ m}$$

$$\eta_o = Q\gamma H_m/(\text{energy required to drive the pump})$$

$$\therefore \quad \text{Energy} = \frac{0.030\times9787\times50.909}{0.75} = 19\,930 \text{ W or } 19.93 \text{ kW}$$

Example 17.9

Show that the pressure rise in an impeller of a centrifugal pump is given by

$$(V_{f_1}^{\,2} + v_2^{\,2} - V_{f_2}^{\,2} \operatorname{cosec}^2 \phi) / 2g$$

Apply Bernoulli's equation between entrance and exit of the impeller; assuming that their elevations are the same and that there is no energy loss between them, one gets

$$\frac{p_1}{\gamma} + \frac{V_1^2}{2g} = \frac{p_2}{\gamma} + \frac{V_2^2}{2g} - \text{work done by impeller per unit weight of fluid}$$

$$\frac{p_2 - p_1}{\gamma} = \frac{V_1^2}{2g} - \frac{V_2^2}{2g} + \frac{V_{\omega2}\, v_2}{g}$$

Since entry is radial $V_1 = V_{f_1}$ and $V_{\omega_2} = v_2 - V_{f_2} \cot \phi$

Further $V_2^{\,2} = V_{f_2}^{\,2} + V_{\omega2}^{\,2}$

$$= V_{f_2}^{\,2} + (v_2 - V_{f_2} \cot \phi)^2$$

$$\therefore \quad V_2^{\,2} = V_{f_2}^{\,2} (1 + \cot^2 \phi) + v_2^{\,2} - v_2 V_{f_2} \cot \phi$$

$$= V_{f_2}^{\,2} \operatorname{cosec}^2 \phi + v_2^{\,2} - 2\, v_2 V_{f_2} \cot \phi$$

Substituting these values of $V_1^{\,2}$. $V_2^{\,2}$ and $V_{\omega2}$ in the expression for $(p_2 - p_1)/\gamma$ one gets

$$\left(\frac{p_2 - p_1}{\gamma}\right) = \frac{V_{f1}^{\,2}}{2g} - \frac{V_{f_2}^{\,2} \operatorname{cosec}^2 \phi + v_2^2 - 2\, v_2\, V_{f2} \operatorname{cosec} \phi)}{2g} + \frac{(v_2 - V_{f2} \cot \phi)(2\, v_2)}{2g}$$

$$= \frac{1}{2g}\left(V_{f1}^2 + v_2^2 - V_{f2}^2 \operatorname{cosec}^2 \phi\right)$$

17.11 Axial and Mixed Flow Pumps

Axial flow pumps resemble a reversed propeller turbine. Essential features of such a pump are shown in Fig. 17.12. These pumps generally operate with vertical shaft. Two sets of guide blades are provided one each in suction and delivery pipe. In between them is a set of propeller vanes fixed on the boss attached to the shaft. Axial flow pumps are well suited for pumping large discharge upto a head of 9 to 12 m. Axial flow pumps run at higher speed than the radial (i.e. centrifugal) pumps; their specific speed is therefore higher. Since at high speed there is a danger of cavitation, the suction head H_s is kept low. These pumps are used for land drainage, flood control, storm water disposal, irrigation, etc. When the pump works under variable head, its efficiency goes down at part or overloads. Therefore, in some cases adjustable vanes are used The specific speed of axial flow pumps varies from $NH_m^{\frac{3}{4}}/Q^{\frac{1}{2}} = 4000$ to 8000.

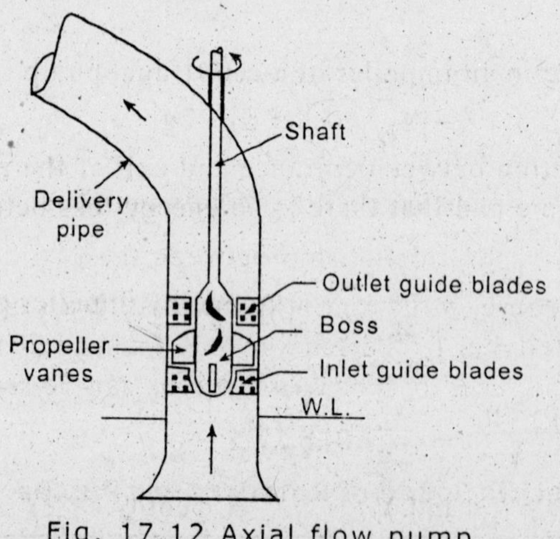

Fig. 17.12 Axial flow pump

In mixed flow pumps the water flows through the impeller axially as well as radially. These pumps are used for high discharge and relatively low suction heads. The specific speed for mixed flow turbines varies from 3900 to 7750.

17.12. Similitude in Pumps

As in the case of pumps, one can consider the power P and efficiency η as dependent variables whereas the discharge Q, head (gH), characteristic diameter D, angular velocity ω and mass density of liquid ρ can be taken as independent variables. One can then write

$$\eta \text{ or } P = f(Q, \rho, gH, D, \omega) \tag{17.23}$$

By performing dimensional analysis one gets

$$\eta \text{ or } \frac{P}{\rho\omega^3 D^5} = f\left(\frac{Q}{\omega D^3}, \frac{gH}{\omega^2 D^2}\right) \tag{17.24}$$

If $Q/\omega D^3$ and $gH/\omega^2 D^2$ are kept the same for model and prototype which are geometrically similar, η or $P/\rho\omega^3 D^5$ will also remain same between the two. Thus performance of the prototype can be predicted from the model. From the above three dimensionless parameters one can also get (after replacing ω by N)

$$\left.\begin{aligned} \frac{DN}{H^{1/2}} &= C_1 \\ \frac{Q}{D^2 H^{1/2}} &= C_2 \\ \frac{P}{D^2 H^{3/2}} &= C_3 \\ \frac{NQ^{1/2}}{H^{3/4}} &= C_4 \end{aligned}\right\} \tag{17.24}$$

This shows that for a given pump. i.e. given D, $H \sim N^2$, $Q \sim H^{1/2}$ and $P \sim H^{3/2}$.

The term $NQ^{1/2}/H^{3/4}$ is the specific speed N_s in a dimensional form. Its dimensionless form is $\overline{N}_s = (\omega Q^{1/2})/(gH)^{3/4}$, the relationship between the two being $\overline{N}_s = 0.0189\ N_s$. Sometimes N_s is defined with Q in l/s and H in m; in such a case specific speed is the speed of the pump which delivers 1 l/s discharge under a head of 1 m. The type of pump and corresponding specific speed are closely related as can be seen from Table 17.1.

TABLE 17.1

Specific Speed of Rotodynamic Pumps

Type of pump	N_s	$\overline{N}_s$
Centrifugal: Low speed	less than 10	less than 0.189
Medium speed	10-20	0.189 - 0.378
High speed	20-80	0.378 - 1.512
Mixed flow pumps	80- 100	1.512 - 1.890
Axial flow pumps	greater than 100	greater than 1.89

(Note Here N_s is with Q in m^3/s)

Example 17.10

A centrifugal pump having 15 cm diameter impeller discharges 0.04 m³/s at a speed of 1500 rpm against a head of 5 m. Determine the corresponding speed and head for a geometrically similar pump of impeller diameter 30.0 cm when it discharges 0.80 m³/s.

$$\frac{Q_1}{N_1 D_1^3} = \frac{Q_2}{N_2 D_2^3}$$

$$N_2 = \frac{0.80}{0.040}\left(\frac{15}{30.0}\right)^3 \times 1500 = 3750 \text{ rpm}$$

$$\frac{D_1 N_1}{H_1^{1/2}} = \frac{D_2 N_2}{H_2^{1/2}}$$

$$\left(\frac{H_2}{H_1}\right) = \left(\frac{D_2}{D_1}\right)^2 \left(\frac{N_2}{N_1}\right)^2 \text{; or } \quad H_2 = 125 \text{ m}$$

Example 17.11

A centrifugal pump model with impeller diameter of 21.5 cm gives best efficiency while running at 1060 rpm at a discharge of 0.114 m³/s under a head of 5 m. It then needs 8 kW energy. The prototype is required to deliver 9.42 m³/s under a head of 5.4 m. Determine the impeller diameter, speed of prototype and energy required.

Since $$\frac{Q_1}{D_1^2 H_1^{1/2}} = \frac{Q_2}{D_2^2 H_2^{1/2}}$$

$$\therefore \quad D_2^{\,2} = \frac{9.42}{0.114} \times (21.5)^2 \times \left(\frac{5}{5.4}\right)^{1/2} = 36\ 754.55$$

$$D_2 = 191.71 \text{ cm, or } 1.917 \text{ m}$$

Since $$\frac{D_1 N_1}{H_1^{1/2}} = \frac{D_2 N_2}{H_2^{1/2}}$$

$$N_2 = N_1 \left(\frac{H_2}{H_1}\right)^{1/2} \left(\frac{D_1}{D_2}\right) = \left(\frac{5.4}{5}\right)^{\frac{1}{2}} \left(\frac{21.5}{191.71}\right) \times 1060$$

$$= 128.39 \text{ rpm}$$

Also $$\frac{P_1}{D_1^2 H_1^{3/2}} = \frac{P_2}{D_2^2 H_2^{3/2}}$$

$$\therefore \quad P_2 = P_1 \left(\frac{D_2}{D_1}\right)^2 \left(\frac{H_2}{H_1}\right)^{3/2}$$

$$\therefore \quad P_2 = 8 \times \left(\frac{191.71}{21.5}\right)^2 \left(\frac{5.4}{5}\right)^{3/2}$$

$$= 713.90 \text{ kW}$$

17.13 Characteristic Curves for Centrifugal Pumps

As in the case of turbines the characteristic curves of a pump show graphically its behaviour and performance under various conditions of operation. These curves are obtained from the actual tests conducted in the laboratory in which the pump is run at the design speed and variation of manometric head, input power, and efficiency η_o are studied as the discharge is varied. Such curves in the nondimensional form are shown in Fig. 17.13 in which $\frac{\eta_o}{\eta_{oo}}$, $\frac{P}{P_o}$ and $\frac{H_m}{H_{mo}}$ are plotted against Q/Q_o. Here η_{oo}, P_o, H_{mo} and Q_o are the values of overall efficiency, energy and manometic head at the design discharge Q_o. The curves predict performance of the pump if it is run at any other discharge. It should be kept in mind that these curves depend on the other design details of the impeller such as geometry, diameter, vane angles, etc.

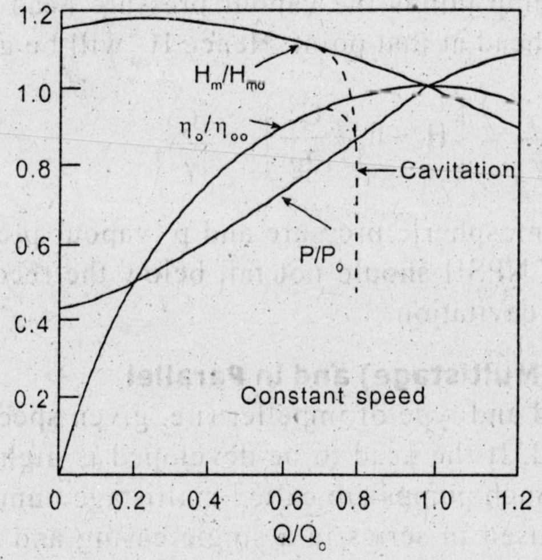

Fig. 17.13 Characteristic curves for a centrifugal pump

By running the pump at various speeds one can prepare H_m v_s Q curves at different speeds. At each point on the curve η_o can be marked and then curves of constant η_o can be prepared. Typical constant speed and efficiency curves are shown in Fig. 17.14. Such curves enable one to determine the range of operation of the pump to get the given efficiency.

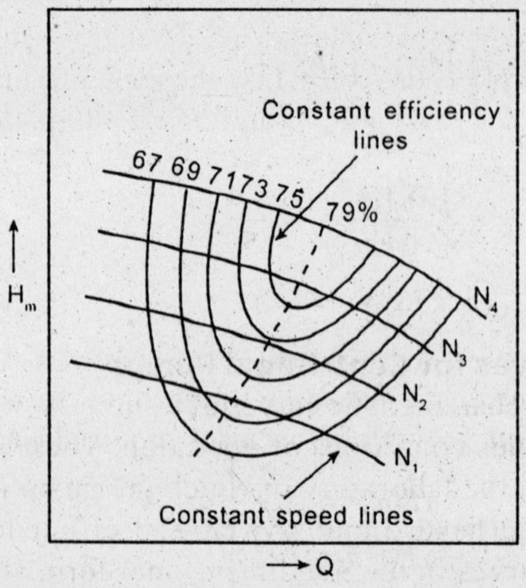

Fig. 17.14 Constant speed and efficiency curves

If a valve is placed in the suction side one can throttle it and reduce the pressure at the reducer. Upto a certain limit of closure of this valve, the pump performance is unaffected. However, if the valve is further throttled, it effectively increases the suction lift and causes cavitation. The head and efficiency drop down as indicated in Fig. 17.13. The *net positive suction head* H_{sp} (often mentioned as NPSH) is defined as the absolute pressure head at the inlet to the pump minus the vapour pressure head corresponding to liquid temperature plus velocity head at that point. Hence H_{sp} will be given by

$$H_{sp} = \frac{p_{at}}{\gamma} - \left(H_s + h_s + \frac{U_s^2}{2g} \right) - \frac{p_v}{\gamma}$$

in which p_{at} is absolute atmospheric pressure and p_v vapour pressure of liquid at given temperature. The value of NPSH should not fall below the recommended value so that pump can operate without cavitation.

17.14 Pumps in Series (Multistage) and in Parallel

For given discharge, speed and type of impeller (i.e. given specific speed N_s) the pump can develop a certain head. If the head to be developed is higher, one must use two or more impellers in series. Such pumps are called multistage pumps. In multistage pumps identical impellers are housed in series in a single casing and the delivery of the first impeller is connected to the suction of the next. In such a case the total head developed H is the sum of heads developed by individual impellers H_i; or

$$H = \sum_{i=1}^{n} H_i$$

where n is the number of impellers

If the head to be developed is not very large, but discharge requirement is large, one can use two or more pumps in parallel. In such a case these pumps are arranged in parallel and connected externally. If Q_i is the discharge in individual pump, the total discharge will be

$$Q = \sum_{f=1}^{n} Q_i$$

Example 17.12

A centrifugal pump is required to deliver 0.10 m³/s discharge of water against a head of 180 m. If the pump unit running at 1450 rpm at 75 percent overall efficiency has the specific speed N_s equal to 20, determine the number of units required and their arrangement.

$$20 = \frac{1500 \times (0.10)^{1/2}}{(H/0.75)^{0.75}}$$

$$\therefore \quad H = 65.0 \text{ m}$$

$$\therefore \quad 180/65 = 2.769$$

$$\therefore \quad n = 3.0$$

Hence three pumps should be connected in series

Example 17.13

A centrifugal pump with specific speed of 40 and running at 1500 rpm is to be used for delivering 0.90 m³/s of water at a head at 35 m. Assuming an overall efficiency of 75 percent, determine the number of units and their arrangement.

$$40 = \frac{1500 \times Q^{0.50}}{(35/0.75)^{0.75}}$$

$$\therefore \quad Q^{0.50} = 0.476 \text{ m}^3/\text{s}$$

or $$Q = 0.2267 \text{ m}^3/\text{s}$$

$$\therefore \quad \text{number of units required in parallel} = \frac{0.90}{0.2267} = 4$$

17.15 Preliminary Design of Centrifugal Pumps

In the preliminary design of centrifugal pump, it is assumed that the required discharge Q, head H_m and the rotational speed N or ω are known. The actual lift should not be more than approximately 40-45 m for one impeller. If the actual lift is greater than this, multistage pump consisting of two or more impellers in series should be used. Basic steps in the design are as follows.

(i) Compute specific speed $N_s = NQ^{1/2}/H^{3/4}$. If this is within the limit of 80, only one impeller is used. If it is larger because Q is large, use two or more impellers in parallel.

(ii) $v_2 = \phi_2 \sqrt{2gH_m}$ where ϕ_2 value lies between 0.95 and 1.40. Choose higher value of ϕ_2 for higher specific speed and determine v_2. The coefficient ϕ_2 is known as the speed ratio.

(iii) Since $v_2 = \dfrac{\pi D_2 N}{60}$, knowing v_2 and N, D_2 can be determined.

(iv) The ratio D_1/D_2 for the impeller varies from 0.30 to 0.70; as manometric head decrease so does D_1/D_2. Choose an appropriate value of D_1/D_2 and find D_1.

(v) V_f is generally the same at inlet and exit, and its value is given by

$$V_f = \psi \cdot \sqrt{2gH_m}$$

Value of ψ varies from 0.10 to 0.25.

(vi) The product D b where b is width between vanes remains constant, if the vane thickness is neglected. Otherwise one can write

$$(\pi D_1 - Z t_1)\, b_1 = (\pi D_2 - Z t_2)\, b_2$$

where Z is the number of blades and t_1 and t_2 are the thicknesses of vanes, at inlet and exit respectively

(vii) The number of vanes depends on the pump size. Smaller pumps have fewer vanes. The number of vanes varies from six to twelve.

(viii) The angles θ and ϕ vary between 12° and 30°.

(ix) The suction pipe should be of slightly larger diameter than the delivery pipe.

17.16 Selection of Rotodynamic Pumps

The selection of rotodynamic pump depends upon the discharge, head and speed values. For these values one can determine the specific speed and the type of rotodynamic pump can be determined referring to Table 17.1. The specific speed gives head developed by one pump. If this is low, two stage or multistage pump can be used. If specific speed is high two or more pump can be used in parallel. The type of pump impeller depends upon the nature of the liquid to be pumped. If it is clear liquid, a shrouded impeller is recommended; for solid-liquid mixtures unshrouded or propeller type impeller is preferred. For very viscous liquids positive displacement type pumps are recommended.

17.17 Pump Intakes and Sump

For satisfactory performance of the pump it is essential that a proper intake is provided. A satisfactory intake reduces the entrance loss to minimum, ensures that the flow as it enters the suction pipe is axial and prevents entry of air into the suction pipe through formation of vortices.

Entrance loss is minimized and smooth axial flow is facilitated by providing a bellmouth at the entrance to the suction pipe. Dimensions of bellmouth are shown in Fig. 17.15. Also shown in this figure is the recommended setting of bellmouth.

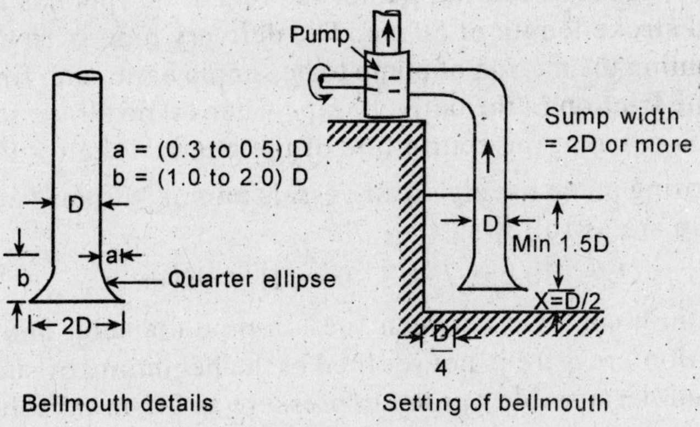

Fig. 17.15 Pump intake

A good sump design should satisfy certain conditions. The volume of water in the sump should be adequate so that sudden starting of the pump does not lower the water level appreciably causing flow condition susceptible to vortex formation. The approach velocity in the sump should be about 0.30 m/s and it should be uniform across the sump width. Large scale secondary flow or swirling flow in the sump should be avoided by avoiding abrupt expansion in sump and large stagnation zones. As far as possible, pump intake should be located in the direction of approach flow; this avoids formation of swirl. If there are more than one intake in the same sump, the intakes should be separated by divide walls so that interference effect is eliminated. On the whole the emphasis is on avoiding formation of swirl and air entraining vortices since they reduce the efficiency of the pump and can cause severe vibrations and cavitation.

PROBLEMS

17.1. A single-acting single cylinder reciprocating pump has the following characteristics:

$H_s = 3.5$m, $D_s = 20$cm, $l_s = 10$m

Cylinder diameter = 30cm, L = 50cm

Determine the speed at which the pump be run when cavitation pressure may occur at the beginning of suction stroke. Atmospheric pressure head is 10.3 m and permissible minimum pressure head is 2.5m of water absolute.

17.2. A double acting reciprocating pump has a piston area of 1000 cm^2 and a stroke length of 30cm. If the pump is discharging 40 *l*/s of water at 45 rpm against a total head of 10 m, find slip of the pump and power required to drive the pump.

17.3. A single acting reciprocating pump has plunger diameter of 20 cm and stroke length of 30 cm. The other details are:

$D_s = 10$ cm, $l_s = 8$ m, $H_s = 4.0$ m, N = 40 rpm

$H_{at} = 10.3$ m, f = 0.02

Determine the pressure head at the beginning, in the middle and at the end of suction stroke.

17.4 A single acting reciprocating pump, running at 60 rpm has a plunger diameter of 25 cm, and stroke length of 50 cm. The delivery pipe is 10 cm diameter and 50 m long. Assuming the motion of pump to be simple harmonic, find the energy required to overcome friction in the delivery pipe when (i) no air vessel is fitted, (ii) a large air vessel is fitted at the centre line of the pump. Take f = 0.02,

17.5 A reciprocating pump having no air vessels runs at 36 rpm. The other characteristics of the pump are as follows:

$$L = 30 \text{ cm}, l_s = 7.30 \text{ m}, H_s = 40 \text{ m}$$

Find the minimum ratio between suction pipe diameter and plunger diameter so that cavitation pressure is not reached at the beginning of suction stroke. Take H_{at} = 10.0m and permissible minimum pressure as 2.5 m (absolute) of water.

17.6 Starting from the basic principles, show that the work saved against friction in the delivery pipe of a single acting reciprocating pump by the fitting an air vessel is 84.8 percent.

17.7 A double acting reciprocating pump has the following characteristics.

Speed	= 90 rpm
Cylinder diameter	= 10 cm
Stroke length	= 25 cm
Suction pipe diameter	= 10 cm
Suction pipe length	= 5.0 m

Determine the maximum permissible lift if separation occurs at 2.0 m of water absolute and there are no air vessels.

17.8 Determine the work saved in overcoming friction if large air vessels are fitted near the suction and delivery sides of a reciprocating pump with following details:

Cylinder diameter = 20 cm	Length of delivery pipe = 50 m
Stroke length = 35 cm	Diameter of suction pipe = 15 cm
Speed = 60 rpm	Length of suction pipe = 8 m
Diameter of delivery pipe = 10 cm	f = 0.04 for both pipes.

17.9 A single acting reciprocating pump has a piston area of 0.14 m^2 and stroke of 30 cm. The area of delivery pipe is 0.021 m^2 and water is lifted through a height of 12.5 m. If the pump runs at 60 rpm and the actual discharge is 0.04 m^3/s, determine the discharge coefficient and power required to drive the pump.

17.10 Water is raised to a height of 20 m by single acting reciprocating pump having a cylinder of 15 cm, diameter and stroke length 40 cm. If the pump runs at 60 rpm find the theoretical discharge and power required.

17.11 A double acting reciprocating pump has a bore of 17.5 cm and a stroke of 35 cm. The suction pipe, which is fitted with an air vessel, is 15 cm in diameter. Determine the crank angle at which there will be no flow of water to or from the vessel Take N = 150 rpm and assume the plunger to have simple harmonic motion.

17.12 A double acting reciprocating pump has the cylinder diameter of 25 cm and a stroke of 50 cm. The suction pipe diameter is 10 cm and it is fitted with an air vessel. Determine the discharge into or from the air vessel at crank angles of 30° and 120° with inner dead centre. Take the speed of pump as 120 rpm.

17.13 A centrifugal pump having impeller diameter of 25cm and 50 cm at inlet and outlet respectively, runs at 900rpm. The vanes are set back at angle of 30° to the outer rim. If the velocity of flow through the impeller is constant at 2.0 m/s, determine the vane angle at inlet and the velocity of flow and its direction at outlet.

17.14 A centrifugal pump running at 700 rpm under a head of 29 m carries a discharge of 0.125 m^3/s. The other pertinent parameters of the pump are $D_1 = 30$ cm, $D_2 = 60$ cm, area of flow = 0.065 m^2. Vanes are set back at an angle of 45°. If the water enters the impeller radially, determine the manometric efficiency and the vane angle at the inlet.

17.15 A centrifugal pump running at 1000 rpm delivers water against a head of 14.5m. The vanes are curved backwards at an angle of 30° with its periphery. If impeller diameter at the outlet is 30 cm and outlet width of 5 cm, determine the discharge. Take the manometric efficiency as 95 percent.

17.16 A centrifugal pump having an overall efficiency of 75 percent delivers 0.030 m^3/s of water to a height of 20 m through 90 m length of 10 cm diameter pipe. Taking the friction factor for the pipe to be 0.03 calculate the power required to drive the pipe.

17.17 A centrifugal pump lifts 0.014 m^3/s of water from a depth of 35 m. If the rating of the pump motor is 6.0 kW, determine the overall efficiency of the pump.

17.18 For a centrifugal pump with impeller of outside diameter 30 cm and outlet width 2.0 cm, the following data are given.

Suction head H_s = 2.5 m

Delivery head H_d = 28.0 m

Diameter of suction and delivery pipe = 12 cm.

Friction loss in suction pipe = 1.0 m

Friction loss in delivery pipe = 7.5 m

Speed = 1500 rpm

Vane angle at outlet (set back) = 35°

Manometric efficiency = 80 percent

Mechanical efficiency = 75 percent

Determine the discharge and energy required to drive the pump.

17.19 A pump impeller of 30 cm diameter is surrounded by a concentric cylindrical chamber of 50 cm. diameter. The impeller discharges water with a velocity having its radial and tangential components as 2.5 m/s and 13.0 m/s. Assuming the flow in the chamber to be of free vortex type, determine the components of velocity of water at the exit of the chamber and rise in the pressure. (Assume no energy loss and take $b_1 = b_2$).

17.20 It is required to deliver 0.25 m³/s of water to a height of 200 m using pumps of overall efficiency of 80 percent. If pumps running at 1500 rpm and with specific speed N_s of 30 are to be used, determine the number of pumps and their arrangement.

17.21 A discharge of 1.0 m³/s is to be pumped to 40m height using centrifugal pumps of specific speed N_s of 50 running at 1500 rpm at overall efficiency of 75 percent. Determine the number and arrangement of pumps.

17.22 Centrifugal pump designed to work against a head of 22 m is tested in the laboratory using 1:5 scale model. At 500 rpm the model has the maximum efficiency and consumes 10 kW developing a head of 7.0 m. At what speed should the prototype be run to give the same efficiency and how much power will it consume?

17.23 Determine the speed of a full size propeller pump one meter in diameter to deliver 1.5 m³/s of water, given that the scale model of this pump with 20 cm diameter gave best efficiency when pumping 0.10 m³/s against a head of 4.0 m. at 2000 rpm.

17.24 A centrifugal pump delivers 0.05 m³/s water at a total head of 24 m at 80 percent manometric efficiency. The impeller runs at 1500 rpm and yields a constant velocity of flow of 2.4 m/s. If $D_2/D_1 = 2.0$ for the impeller and vanes are curved back at an angle of 30° to tangent at exit, determine the blade angle of the inlet and energy required to drive the pump.

17.25 Show that the minimum starting speed for a centrifugal pump is given by the relation

$$\frac{V_2^2 - V_1^2}{2g} = \eta_{mo} \frac{V_{\omega 2} V_2}{g}$$

CHAPTER EIGHTEEN

MISCELLANEOUS DEVICES

18.1 Introduction

The previous two chapters have been devoted to dealing with turbines and pumps in which either the potential or kinetic energy of water is converted into mechanical energy or mechanical energy is converted into kinetic or potential energy. There are some such machines which use the liquid (oil or water) as a medium for transmission of power or pressure. These machines, which work on principles of hydrostatics, are discussed below.

18.2 Hydraulic Lift

Hydraulic lift (see Fig.18.1) consists of a cage which is secured to the top of a vertical ram sliding in fixed vertical cylinder. Water from the delivery pipe enters the bottom of the cylinder and works underside of the sliding ram. As a result the ram moves upwards along with the cage thereby carrying persons or load to higher elevations. The total load carried is evidently given by $W = p\pi D^2/4$ in which W is the weight of external load and sliding cylinder of diameter D and p is the impressed pressure.

18.3 Hydraulic Press

Hydraulic press is a simple device by which one can lift larger loads by applying a comparatively much smaller force. Its principle is illustrated in Example 4.1 and Fig 4.2. If a is the area of plunger and A that of the ram, then the force F is related to load W as

$$p = \frac{F}{a} = \frac{W}{A}$$

according to Pascal's law. Of course due to frictional resistance between the ram and outside cylinder the actual load carried will be smaller than W. If volumes of liquid displaced by the plunger and ram are equal, one gets the following relationship,

(total displacement of plunger) × a = (total displacement of ram) × A

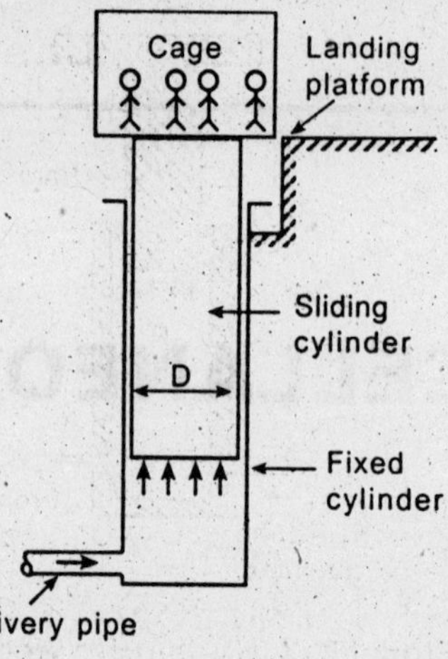

Fig. 18.1 Hydraulic lift

The mechanical advantage of the system is A/a. This can be increased further by applying force on the plunger by means of a lever. Hydraulic press is used to press squeezable materials into smaller size e.g. preparation of moulds of bakelite, cotton bales, tablets, pressing of sheet metal etc.

18.4 Hydraulic Accumulator

Hydraulic accumulator stores energy in the form of pressure energy to be made available whenever it is required. It consists of a cylinder A and the plunger R which is also known as sliding ram, see Fig. 18.2. Sometimes the ram is loaded with weights, othertimes a container fixed to the ram is loaded with heavy material. One side of the cylinder is connected to the press pump while the other side is connected to the hydraulic machine.

When the press pump works the ram is lifted up. When the ram reaches the maximum height, the bypass valve V allows the liquid to flow back to the pump sump. By lifting the ram with the weight, energy is stored in the accumulator. During the period of maximum work the machine will draw energy from the accumulator and the ram will come down. If A is the area of the base of the ram and H is the maximum lift, then AH is the volume of the accumulator. If p is the pressure intensity of the water supplied, then pA will be equal to W, and pAH will be the work done in lifting the ram. This energy will be stored in the accumulator. Hence

$$\text{Energy stored} = pAH$$
$$= p \times \text{volume of accumulator}$$

This is also known as the capacity of accumulator which is equal to the potential energy of the lifted ram.

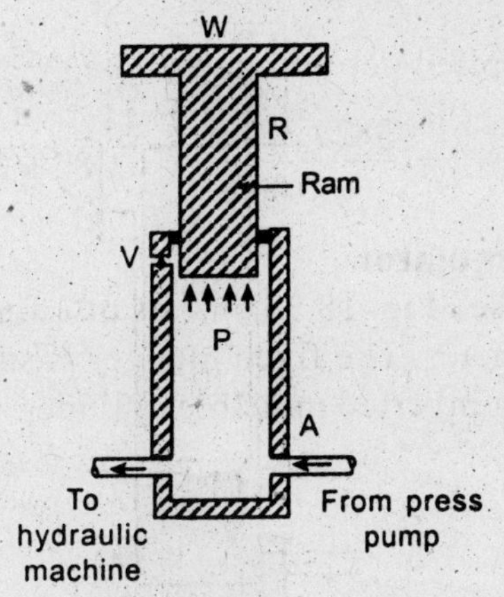

Fig. 18.2 Hydraulic accumulator

Example 18.1

An accumulator has a ram of 30 cm diameter and an effective stroke of 6.0 m. It is loaded with a total weight of 400 kN. If the friction of the ram amounts to five percent of the total load, determine the energy delivered to the hydraulic machine if the ram falls steadily through its full stroke in 2 minutes while during the same time the pump delivers 0.50 m^3 per minute.

Work is supplied to the machine by the pump as well as the accumulator.

Work supplied by accumulator ram per minute

$$= \frac{400\ 000 \times 0.95 \times 6}{2}$$

$$= 1140\ 000 \text{ Nm}$$

Pressure intensity in the accumulator $= \dfrac{400 \times 0.95}{0.785 \times 0.30^2}$

$$= 5378.627 \text{ kN/m}^2$$

Head H due to this pressure

$$= \frac{5378.627}{9.787} = 549.569 \text{ m}$$

∴ Work supplied by the pump per minute

$$= (0.5 \times 9787) \times 549.569$$

$$= 2689\ 315.9 \text{ Nm}$$

Total work supplied to the machine in one minute

$$= 1140\ 000 + 2689\ 315.9$$

$$= 3829\ 315.9 \text{ Nm}$$

∴ Energy i.e. work supplied per minute wili be

$$= \frac{3829\ 315.9}{60 \times 1000} = 63.82 \text{ kW}$$

18.5 Differential Accumulator

Differential accumulator, see Fig. 18.3 consists of a fixed vertical plunger with a central vertical hole of small diameter. The fixed plunger is surrounded by a brass sleeve which is further surrounded by an inverted movable cylinder.

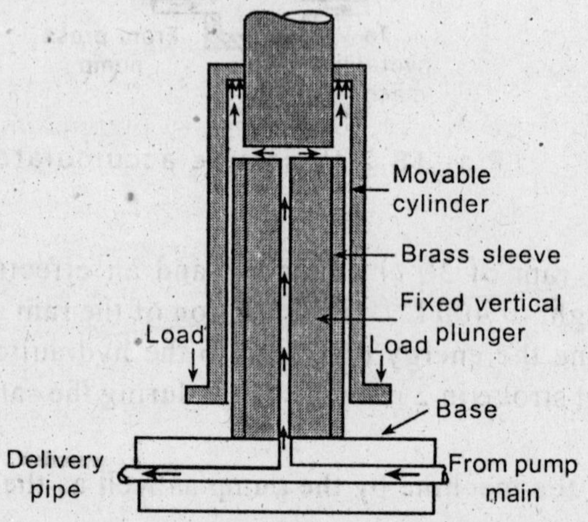

Fig. 18.3 Differential accumulator

The water coming from the pump main moves up through the vertical tube and exerts an upward pressure on the annular area of the base of loaded cylinder. This annular area is equal to the horizontal cross-sectional area of brass sleeve. The advantage of this type of accumulator is that water can be stored at a high pressure by a comparatively smaller load on the movable cylinder. Here, W = pa where a is the annular area and W is the weight of the loaded cylinder. Energy stored in accumulator is WH or paH.

Example 18.2

Weight of the loaded moving cylinder of a differential accumulator is 40 kN. The diameters of the larger and smaller parts of the ram are 15 cm and 14 cm respectively. Neglecting the friction, find the pressure of water in the accumulator. If the stroke of accumulator is 4.0 m which is executed in one minute, determine the power supplied by the accumulator.

$$a = 0.785\ (0.15^2 - 0.14^2) = 0.785 \times 0.0029$$

$$= 0.0023 \text{ m}^2$$

$$W = p.a$$

$$\therefore \quad p = \frac{40}{0.0023} = 173\ 91.3 \text{ kN/m}^2$$

$$\text{Power supplied} = \frac{WH}{t} = \frac{40 \times 4}{60} = 2.667 \text{ kW}$$

18.6 Hydraulic Ram

Hydraulic ram is a device by which small quantities of water can be pumped to higher levels from available large quantity of water at lower heads. Its principle of working is as follows. When the flowing liquid is suddenly brought to rest, the change in the momentum of the mass of the liquid causes a sudden rise in the pressure. This increased pressure is utilised to raise a portion of liquid to higher levels, see Fig. 18.4.

The water from tank A begins to flow through the supply pipe P into the valve chamber. The waste water valve C is open and the water flows through it to waste. However, through the dynamic pressure of water coming into the chamber, the valve C is closed when the dynamic pressure is greater than the weight of valve C. Because of this closure, the water flowing through pipe P into chamber suddenly comes to rest thereby increasing the pressure there. This increase in pressure opens the valve F and water rushes into air vessel D and compressing the air there. The increased air pressure in the air vessel forces water into the tank B. When the momentum of water in the chamber is destroyed the valve F is closed and valve C opens; as a result water starts flowing from tank A to valve chamber and the process repeats. Valves C and F may act due to weight or spring.

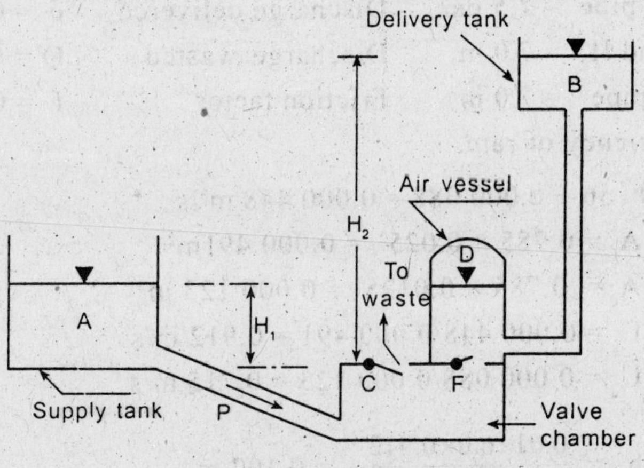

Fig. 18.4 Hydraulic ram

If q is the discharge supplied by ram, Q is the discharge wasted, h_{fs} and h_{fd} are the frictional head losses in supply and delivery pipes then the work done per second is $\gamma q\,(H_2 + h_{fd})$ while work supplied per second is $\gamma(Q + q)\,(H_1 - h_{fs})$. Hence efficiency η is given by

$$\eta = \frac{\gamma q(H_2 + h_{fd})}{(Q+q)(H_1 - h_{fs})\gamma}$$

If the friction is neglected the corresponding expression for η becomes

$$\eta = \frac{\gamma q H_2}{(Q+q)H_1\gamma}$$

Lowest head at which the ram works is about 1m while the delivery head varies from 6 to 12 m. Also q is about 0.1 to 0.05 times (Q + q).

The overall efficiency of hydraulic ram is as large as 80 percent and water can be raised to 50 times the height of fall if adequate quantity of water is wasted. Hydraulic ram has several advantages, No fuel is required for prime mover. It requires no lubrication and packing and hence almost no maintenance. It works almost continuously and has high efficiency.

Example 18.3

Details of hydraulic ram are given below.

Supply head H_1	= 3.0 m		
Length of supply pipe	= 6.0 m	Diameter of delivery pipe = 1.25 cm	
Diameter of supply pipe	= 2.5 cm	Discharge delivered	q = 0.000 088 m^3/s
Lift or delivery head H_2	= 7.0 m	Discharge wasted	Q = 0.000 36 m^3/s
Length of delivery pipe	= 7.0 m	Friction factor	f = 0.01

Determine the efficiency of ram.

Total discharge = 0.000 36 + 0.000 088 = 0.000 448 m^3/s

Area of supply pipe $A_s = 0.785 \times 0.025^2 = 0.000\,491 m^2$

Area of delivery pipe $A_d = 0.785 \times 0.0125^2 = 0.000\,123\ m^2$

$\therefore$ $U_s = 0.000\,448/0.000\,491 = 0.912$ m/s

$U_d = 0.000\,088/0.000\,123 = 0.715$ m/s

$$h_{fs} = \frac{0.01\times6.0\times0.912^2}{2\times9.806\times0.025} = 0.102\ m$$

$$h_{fd} = \frac{0.01\times7.0\times0.715^2}{2\times9.806\times0.0125} = 0.145\ m$$

$$\eta = \frac{0.000088\times(7.0+0.145)}{0.000448\times(3.0-0.102)} = 0.4842$$

= 48.42 percent

18.7 Hydraulic Intensifier

Hydraulic intensifier increases the intensity of pressure of given liquid with the help of low pressure liquid of large quantity. Hydraulic intensifier is shown in Fig. 18.5.

The moving cylinder C slides between fixed cylinder A and the fixed ram R. The cylinder C of diameter D is supplied with a liquid whose pressure is to be increased. High pressure liquid comes out of the bottom of the fixed ram R. Initially the cylinder C is at its lowest position. The fixed cylinder A is fed by the liquid of low pressure intensity p. Valves V_2 and V_4 are kept closed and V_3 is opened. Hence low pressure liquid enters inside the moving cylinder C. In the mean time valve V_1 is opened; therefore low pressure liquid from fixed cylinder is discharged to exhaust and the sliding cylinder moves upwards. Eventually the sliding cylinder moves to its top most position and inside of the cylinder C gets filled with low pressure liquid. At this time valves V_2 and V_4 are opened and valves V_1 and V_3 are closed. Low pressure liquid entering through valve V_4 exerts a downward force on the sliding cylinder. The sliding cylinder moves downward; the pressure of liquid between it is raised and high pressure liquid is supplied to the driven machine.

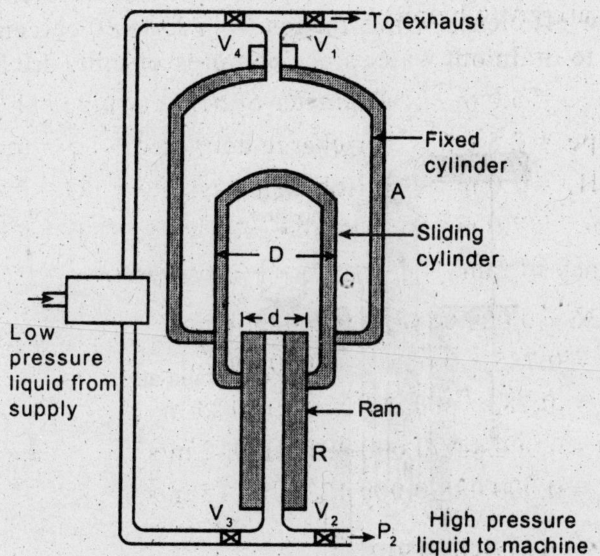

Fig. 18.5 Hydraulic intensifier

If A_1 and A_2 are the cross-sectional areas of the sliding and fixed cylinders respectively, and p_1 and p_2 are the low pressure and high pressures respectively.

$$P_1 A_1(1 - k) = \frac{p_2 A_2}{(1-k)}$$

in which k is the fractional pressure loss at each of the packings of the intensifier. Hence

$$p_2 = \frac{p_1 A_1}{A_2} (1 - k)^2$$

or

$$p_2 = \frac{p_1 D^2}{d^2} (1 - k)^2$$

were d is the diameter of ram. This is the single cylinder intensifier. For continuous supply of high pressure a double cylinder intensifier is used.

18.8 Air-Lift Pump and Jet Pump

Air-lift pump is a simple pumping device consisting of no moving parts, see Fig. 18.6. A compressor unit located on the ground surface supplies compressed air through the air pipe whose nozzle is located H_1 m below the water surface. Covering the nozzle is the discharge pipe. When air rushes through the nozzle and mixes it with water in the discharge pipe, the apparent density of this column decreases. As this column of water has to balance against a weight of water column of height H_1 it rises up in discharge pipe. If large quantity of air is introduced. the water will rush out through discharge end located H_2 m above water surface. For efficient working of air-lift pump, H_2/H_1 should be between 1 and 4. The main advantages of air-lift pump is that it has no moving parts which can wear out and therefore it is ideally suited for carrying sediment-water mixtures. However its disadvantage is its low efficiency which ranges from 25 to 30 percent. Air-lift pumps are often used in mines to drain out water since compressor units are already available there.

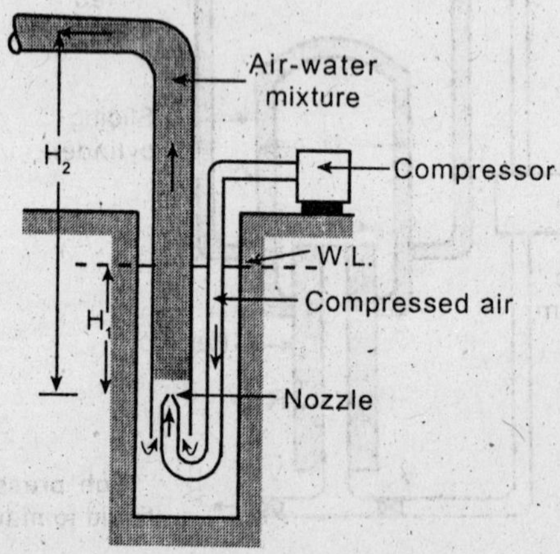

Fig. 18.6 Air-lift pump

A jet pump is a combination of normal radial flow pump with a jet nozzle at the suction end as shown in Fig. 18.7. As usual the pump is primed and started. Part of the water from delivery side is diverted and allowed to flow through nozzle at high velocity. Alternately water can be supplied to the nozzle from supply reservoir. The high velocity jet through the nozzle causes a pressure drop there which in turn causes water to enter from pump well into suction pipe. In effect the pump is able to lift water with greater suction heads as large as 6 m. Such pumps are used in mining and for pumping oil. The efficiency of a jet pump is defined as

$$\eta = \frac{Q_s (H_s - H_d)}{Q_l (H_l - H_d)}$$

where Q_l is the discharge through the nozzle, Q_s is the discharge through suction pipe. H_l is the pressure head on the delivery side, H_s is the suction head and H_d is the delivery head.

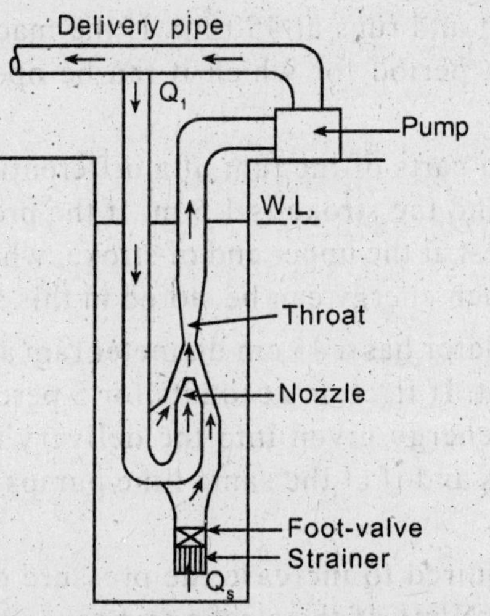

Fig. 18.7 Jet pump

PROBLEMS

18.1 A hydraulic lift raises a total load of 100 kN through a height of 15 m once in every 60 seconds. Determine the energy required to drive the pump.

18.2 A hydraulic press has a ram of 50 cm diameter and a plunger of 5 cm diameter. What force is required on the handle to lift a load of 8000 N if the leverage is 1: 10.

18.3 Determine the energy required for motor to drive the plunger of a hydraulic press lifting 10 kN to a height of 1m in 10 minutes, the diameters of the cylinder and plunger being 15 cm and 2.5 cm respectively. Plunger stroke is 30 cm. Find also the number of strokes required by the plunger.

18.4 An accumulator has a ram of 15 cm diameter and a lift of 6 m. If water is supplied at a pressure of 2200 kN/m² determine the necessary load on the ram and capacity of accumulator. Take friction equal to 5 percent of load on the ram.

18.5 What additional weight must be placed on the ram so that it can develop a pressure of 4000 kN/m² if the weight of 30 cm diameter ram of the accumulator is 40 000 N.

18.6 Following details of accumulator are given:

Diameter of ram	= 30 cm
Height of ram	= 3.0 cm
Gross weight of ram	= 343.5 kN

The accumulator is fed through a 4.80 m long 10 cm diameter pipe. The three stroke reciprocating pump supplying the liquid has the plunger diameter of 4.5 cm, stroke 35 cm, slip 3 percent and runs at 45 rpm. If the machine absorbs 36.8 kW power, calculate the longest period for which it ran be operated continuously. Take f = 0.032.

18.7 Diameters of the two parts of the ram of a differential accumulator are 15 cm and 14 cm respectively and the stroke is 1.5 m. If the pressure of water is 9800 kN/m^2 when the load is at rest at the upper end of stroke, what will be the weight of loaded cylinder and how much energy can be stored in this accumulator?

18.8 A hydraulic accumulator has a 45 cm diameter ram and 7.0 m lift. It is loaded with 1300 kN total weight. If friction accounts for 5 percent of the total weight on the ram, determine the energy given into the delivery main if the accumulator falls steadily in 3 minutes and if at the same time pumps are supplying 0.45 m^3/min to the accumulator.

18.9 An intensifier is required to increase the pressure of water from 4200 kN/m^2 on the main to 18 000 kN/m^2. If the stroke and capacity of the intensifier are 1.2 m and 0.0144 m^3 respectively, determine the diameter of the ram.

18.10 A jet pump fitted 2 m above the suction reservoir and 18 m below the supply reservoir lifts water through a total height of 2.5 m. Determine the efficiency of the jet pump. Determine the efficiency of the pump if it delivers 7.6 *l*/s water while using 2.5 *l*/s water from supply reservoir.

APPENDIX - I

GENERAL QUESTIONS

(Note : For multiple choice questions, choose the correct answer)

Chapter 1

1. List a few examples of fluid flow phenomena encountered in daily life.
2. List two flow phenomena each, in every day life, in which (i) the flow is laminar, (ii) the flow is turbulent, and (iii) surface tension plays an important role.
3. Mention which fluid property is important in the following cases: (i) travel of a bullet through air, (ii) flow of heavy oil through pipe, (iii) water jet issuing from the fire hose, (iv) formation of soap bubbles, (iv) flow of water through a nozzle.
4. Why does viscosity of a gas increase with increase in temperature ?
5. List the following fluids in the decreasing order of their dynamic and kinematic viscosities: Mercury, Air, Water, Ethyl Alcohol, Kerosene, and Benzene.
6. Why can a pin, which is heavier than water, float on water surface?
7. List the following substances in the decreasing order of their compressibility: water, steel, and air.
8. Will the resistance in air be more than resistance in water for a body in motion at a given velocity ? Explain your answer.
9. Is air more viscous than water in terms of kinematic viscosity? Why?
10. A Newtonian fluid is that for which

(i) $\tau = \mu \left(\dfrac{\partial u}{\partial y}\right)^m$, $m \neq 1$ (ii) $\tau = \tau_c + \mu \dfrac{\partial u}{\partial y}$

(iii) $\tau = \mu \dfrac{\partial u}{\partial y}$ (iv) $\tau = \tau_c + \mu \left(\dfrac{\partial u}{\partial y}\right)^m$, $m \neq 1$

11. Dimensions of dynamic viscosity are

(i) L^2/T (ii) Ns^2/m (iii) kg/m s (iv) kg s/m

12. Kinematic viscosity of water at 20°C is

(i) 10^{-8} m²/s (ii) 10^{-6} m²/s

(iii) 10^{-5} m²/s (iv) 10^{-3} m²/s

Chapter 2

13. Give one example each where path lines, streak lines and stream lines are the same and are different.

14. Classify the flow in a rotating arm lawn-sprinkler as (i) steady or unsteady, (ii) uniform or non-uniform. Give reasons.

15. Give one example each in which (ii) convective tangential, (ii) convective normal, (iii) local tangential, and (iv) convective tangential and normal accelerations are present.

16. What boundary conditions must be satisfied by an enclosed two dimensional irrotational flow? What will be the corresponding conditions for enclosed, two dimensional, rotational flow?

17. Why is it more difficult to draw a flownet for steady flow over a spillway than for two dimensional contraction?

18. You are standing on the bank of a çanal. A surge of height 0.50 m is travelling in the downstream direction at a speed of 4.0 m/s. Is the flow steady or unsteady ?

19. Site examples where streamlining is done to avoid separation.

20. If ϕ_1 and ϕ_2 are solutions of Laplace equation,

(i) $\phi_1 + 3\phi_2$ (ii) ϕ_1/ϕ_2 (iii) $\phi_1^2 + \phi_2^2$

is a solution of Laplace equation.

21. An unsteady flow can be transformed into steady flow case

(i) If a body is moving at a constant velocity in an infinite fluid.

(ii) If a body is moving at it variable vêlocity in an infinite fluid.

(iii) None of the above.

22 Flow of a real fluid such as air or water can be treated as irrotational if

(i) Reynolds number is small; (ii) Froude number is large;

(iii) Flow is rapidly converging; (iv) Flow is rapidly diverging;

23 Flow net can be drawn if

(i) Flow is laminar; (ii) Fluid is ideal; (iii) Flow is unsteady

24. Stream function exists

(i) for laminar flow only; (ii) for flow of ideal fluids only;

(iii) none of the above

25. Which of the following statements are true for 2-dimensional irrotational flow of an incompressible fluid?

(i) $\frac{\partial u}{\partial y} - \frac{\partial v}{\partial x} = 0$ (ii) $\frac{\partial u}{\partial x} - \frac{\partial v}{\partial y} = 0$

(iii) $\frac{\partial u}{\partial x} + \frac{\partial v}{\partial y} = 0$ (iv) $\frac{\partial^2 u}{\partial x^2} + \frac{\partial^2 u}{\partial y^2} = 0$

26. Stream line, streak line and path line will coincide if

(i) flow is unsteady; (ii) flow is steady;

(iii) flow is laminar; (iv) flow is unsteady but direction of flow does not change.

Chapter 3

27. Express qualitatively energy equation for compressible fluid involving temperature changes.

28. Why is pressure head an energy?

29. Under what conditions will the energy between two sections (i) increase, (ii) decrease, (iii) remain constant ? Give one example of each.

30. Why does fluid head concept lose its significance in the case of gases?

31. Justify the statement that for confined, steady, irrotational flow through two dimensional boundary form each point is characterised by a constant value of Euler's number.

32. Suggest an arrangement to measure a pressure of 50 kN/m^2 in an air-chamber.

33. How will you measure a pressure difference of 33 N/m^2?

34. Why is it necessary to calibrate in place the flow measuring devices such as orifice meter, bend meter, and venturimeter?

35. Suggest a method, drawing necessary sketches, for calibrating an orifice meter in a 10cm diameter pipe.

36. Euler's equations of motion represent

(i) Energy balance in different directions

(ii) Force balance in different directions.

(iii) Momentum balance in different directions.

37. The equation $\frac{p}{\gamma} + z + \frac{V^2}{2g}$ = constant in the whole flow field implies the following assumptions:

(i) flow is incompressible (ii) flow is frictionless

(iii) flow is rotational (iv) flow is irrotational

(v) flow is steady (vi) flow is along a stream line.

38. For uniform velocity distribution in a pipe
    (i) α is greater than β (ii) β is greater than α
    (iii) α is equal to β. (iv) $\alpha = \beta = 1$

39. The energy correction factor is unity for
    (i) laminar flow (ii) turbulent flow
    (iii) irrotational flow (iv) u (y) = constant.

Chapter 4

40. Give examples of hydrostatic and nonhydrostatic pressure distributions.

41. Hydrostatic pressure variation exists if
    (i) p = constant (ii) $p - \gamma y$ = constant
    (iii) $p + \gamma y$ = constant (iv) $p \sim e^{(-\gamma_o/p_o)y}$

42. In an isothermal atmosphere.
    (i) pressure decreases exponentially with elevation
    (ii) pressure decreases linearly with elevation
    (iii) None of the above.

43. Buoyant force is equal to
    (i) volume of liquid displaced (ii) weight of liquid displaced
    (iii) resultant force acting on the body

44. Centre of pressure is
    (i) at the centroid of area (ii) at the centre of buoyancy
    (iii) always above the centroid (iv) always below the centroid.

45. In a forced vortex
    (i) $V \sim \frac{1}{r}$ (ii) $V \sim r^n$ (iii) $V \sim r$

Chapter 5

46. How will you decide whether a given two dimensional orifice in the side of a tank acts as a small or a large orifice ?

47. For the case of a sharp crested weir describe physically why and how viscosity and surface tension will affect its C_d.

48. If air is pumped underneath the nappe of a sharp crested weir so that the pressure there is greater than atmospheric, what will be is effect on head for given Q?

49. Fluid always flows from
    (i) higher pressure to lower pressure

(ii) higher piezometric head to lower piezometric head

(iii) higher total energy to lower total energy.

50. Which of the following statements are true in a free vortex ?

(i) $V \sim r$

(ii) total energy is constant

(iii) pressure variation in the vertical is hydrostatic

(iv) pressure variation in the vertical is non-hydrostatic

(v) $V \sim \frac{1}{r}$,

(vi) flow is rotational.

51. As a circular jet of water comes vertically downwards,

(i) its diameter remains constant

(ii) its diameter increases in the downward direction

(iii) its diameter decreases in the downward direction.

Chapter 6

52. What will be the effect of large momentum correction factor at section 2 in sudden expansion on the energy loss and pressure there ?

53. In a sudden expansion in a pipe

(i) total energy line rises in the downstream direction,

(ii) the pressure continuously decreases,

(iii) piezometric head line rises in the downstream direction,

(iv) there is a greater frictional resistance.

54. Following assumptions are made in the derivation of momentum Eq. 6.9:

(i) frictionless fluid, (ii) steady flow,

(iii) compressible flulid, (iv) velocity constant over the end sections,

(v) no gravity force.

55. What fluid mechanics principles are involved in the dynamics of rockets?

56. Is the derivation of equation for head loss in a sudden expansion in pipes valid for laminar flow?

Chapter 7

57. List the variables which may affect the mixing efficiency a domestic mixer.

58. What variables will govern the condition of incipient motion of sediment in an alluvial channel?

59. Form a dimensionless parameter from Reynolds number and Euler number which does not involve velocity. What is its physical significance?

60. State whether Re or Fr law of modelling will be used for studying (i) hydraulic jump, (ii) atmospheric diffusion, (iii) flow of heavy oils over a plate, (v) flow configuration in harbours.

61. Dimensionless parameter obtained from d (diameter), γ_s (specific weight), ρ (mass density) and ν kinematic viscosity, is

(i) $\frac{\gamma_S \rho}{d^3 \nu}$ (ii) $\frac{\gamma_S d^2}{\rho \nu}$ (iii) $\frac{\gamma_S \nu}{\rho d^2}$ (iv) $\frac{\gamma_S d^3}{\rho \nu^2}$

62. For a model built according to equality of Froude number, the velocity scale will be

(i) $\sqrt{Er/\rho r}$ (ii) $l_r^{1/2}\ gr^{1/2}$ (iii) $\mu_r/\rho_r l_r$

63. While performing dimensional analysis of fluid-statics problem one should use

(i) F, M, L (ii) F, L, T (iii) M, L, T (iv) F, L

as the primary units.

64. Reynolds number equality is essential if

(i) there is a free surface,

(ii) Reynolds number is large,

(iii) Reynolds number is small,

(iv) if there is a large acceleration or deceleration.

65. $(\Delta p)\ L/\mu U$ is a ratio of

(i) inertial force to viscous force per unit volume

(ii) pressure force to viscous force per, unit volume

(iii) pressure force to inertial force per unit volume

66. Dimensionless parameter obtained from τ_o, d and $\Delta\gamma_s$ is

(i) $\frac{\tau_o}{\Delta\gamma_S d^3}$ (ii) $\frac{\tau_o d^2}{\Delta\gamma_S}$ (iii) $\frac{\tau_o}{\Delta\gamma_S d}$

Chapter 8

67. What are the distinguishing characteristics between laminar and turbulent flows?

68. Describe the consequences if river flows were laminar.

69. What is the significance of Reynolds experiment?

70. Why does Hagen-Poiseuille's equation for Δp does not involve fluid density?

71. Flow through porous material becomes turbulent if Ud/ν is greater than

(i) 300 (ii) 3×10^5 (iii) 1.0 (iv) 10 (v) 300

72. Match appropriate critical Reynolds number with each phenomenon:

Transition from Laminar to turbulent flow in

pipes 5×10^5

boundary layer	0.10
porous material	2300

73. What is the mechanism by which laminar flow changes into turbulent?
74. How does capillary tube model for flow through porous material differ from drag model?
75. Is it possible to obtain laminar flow in a pipe at Reynolds numbers greater than 2300? Why?
76. Compare flow of blood through veins with flow of a viscous liquid in a capillary tube, highlighting the similarities and differences.

Chapter 9

77. Give examples of boundary layer formation in flow phenomena in every life.
78. Obtain an expression for energy thickness of boundary layer δ^{**}.
79. Give two examples where separation may be advantageous.
80. What is the difference between laminar boundary layer and laminar sub-layer?
81. List the similarities and dissimilarities between c_f, C_f and f.
82. A flat plate is held perpendicular to the boundary past which occurs boundary layer flow. Draw detailed flow pattern indicating the nature of flow.
83. Which of the following velocity distributions u/U satisfy the boundary conditions for laminar flow along a flat plate?

    (i) $\frac{u}{U} = e^{\eta}$, (ii) $\frac{u}{U} = 2\eta - \eta^3$, (iii) $\frac{u}{U} = \eta$, (iv) $\frac{u}{U} = \cos\frac{\pi\eta}{2}$

    where $\eta = y/\delta$
84. Separation is caused by
    (i) an adverse pressure gradient,
    (ii) boundary layer thickness reducing to zero,
    (iii) laminar flow changing to turbulent flow.

Chapter 10

85. Draw a sketch showing velocity distribution in a pipe at Reynolds number of 100, 2000, 20000 and 2×10^5.
86. Compare μ with eddy viscosity η.
87. Prandtl's mixing length is
    (i) useful for computing laminar flow problems
    (ii) dependent on shear stress,
    (iii) universal constant,
    (iv) is a function of distance from the boundary.

88. Give two examples each where the turbulence is advantageous and disadvantageous.

89. In what way does turbulent flow in a rough pipe differ from that in a smooth pipe?

90. Why does the equation $f = 64\mu/UD\rho$ for laminar flow does not indicate that the resistance depends on the density?

91. Will the friction factor for a commercial pipe carrying water always remain the same with time?

92. The boundary of smoke plume coming out of the chimney is initially smooth, however after a certain distance it becomes wavy. Why does this happen?

Chapter 11

93. Draw hydraulic grade line and total energy line for flow in a pipe line on the upstream and downstream side of a valve that is provided in the pipe line.

94. List the similarities and dissimilarities between a pipe network and an electrical network.

95. For turbulent flow in a hydrodynamically smooth pipe with Reynolds number less than 10^5, obtain values of r and n in $h_f = r\,Q^n$.

96. How is secondary flow developed in a pipe bend ?

97. How is the flow energy dissipated when a pipe discharges into a large pool of water?

Chapter 12

98. Is perfect streamlining necessary far cars or trucks? Give reasons for your answer.

99. What type of drag predominates in (i) a mist droplet falling in air, (ii) parachute, (iii) fish moving in the water, (iv) an air bubble in honey, (v) wind flowing past a sign board.

100. Below are given a set of C_D values and a set of body shapes. Match the two.

Body Shape	C_D
Airfoil	1.90
Cylindrical chimney (Re ≈ 10^6)	0.05
Parachute	0.35
Plate held perpendicular to flow	400
Tiny mist droplet	1.33

101. Which fluid mechanics principles concerning drag and lift are involved in the games of cricket and table-tennis? Explain.

102. Clearly differentiate between friction drag and deformation drag.

103. What is a wake ? What type of flow prevails in a wake ? Give three examples where wake is formed. Draw wake flow pattern downstream of a 2 – D cylinder.

104. Why is there a sudden reduction in C_D of a sphere at Re = 3 × 10^5 ?

105. Explain the effect of turbulence on C_D – Re relationship for a cylinder.

Chapter 13

106. What is the difference between total head and specific head ?

107. Why is the study of regimes of flow in alluvial streams important ?

108. Define critical depth in as many as you can.

109. Is it possible to know whether the flow in a stream is subcritical or supercritical by dropping a stone in it? Explain.

110. Draw all the twelve surface profiles, name them and show their end conditions.

111. Compare Mannings n values of channels with (i) ply wood bottom, (ii) 10 cm gravel bed (iii) duned bed.

112. Write continuity, momentum and energy equations for a hydraulic jump forming on a channel bed with positive step. Assume that the jump is just complete at the step.

113. Examine what types of surges can be formed in the upstream and downstream channels by moving the gate up or down.

114. Why are canal head-works preferably located on the outside of a river bend?

115. Analyse the flow condition downstream of a free over fall.

116. Compare flow in sudden expansions in a pipe and in an open channel.

117. Under what conditions friction blocks should bc provided in a stilling basin?

Chapter 14

118. Differentiate between isentropic and adiabatic flows.

119. Compare the characteristics of hydraulic jump and shock wave.

120. Compare the structure of Froude, Mach and Weber numbers.

121. Give a few examples of fluid flow where the compressibility of fluid has to be taken into account.

122. C_p and C_v are related as

(i) $k = C_p/C_v$ (ii) $k = C_p C_v$ (iii) $k = C_v/C_p$ (iv) $C_p = Cv^K$.

123. An isentropic process is always

(i) reversible and isothermal

(ii) irreversible and isothermal

(iii) reversible and adiabatic

124. A normal shock wave is analogous to
   (i) open channel flow with $F_r < 1.0$
   (ii) a small amplitude wave in open channels
   (iii) hydraulic jump

Chapter 15

125. How does friction affect the pressure variation in water hammer phenomenon ?
126. Will a pressure wave travel faster in water or air?
127. What are the functions of a surge tank ?
128. Why is compressibility not considered in the analysis of surge tanks ?
129. Draw a sketch to illustrate the variation of velocity with time when the valve in a pipe line is suddenly opened.

Chapter 16

130. What is the difference between an impulse turbine and it reaction turbine ?
131. Why is the Pelton bucket provided with a notch ? Does it affect the efficiency of the turbine ?
132. What are the functions of draft tube ?
133. How is specific speed of a turbine defined ? What is it utility ?
134. Using dimensional analysis show how power, discharge and speed of a turbine are related to discharge.
135. What information is needed to make a proper choice of a turbine ?
136. If the head on a turbine is halved what would be the corresponding change in power produced ?
137. Why are the blades of Francis runner odd in number and the number of guide vanes as even ? What is runway speed of a reaction turbine ?

Chapter 17

138. How are pumps classified ?
139. Why is the suction height of a pump limited ?
140. Why is the speed of a reciprocating pump smaller than that of a centrifugal pump?
141. What functions do air vessels on the suction side and the delivery side serve ?
142. What kind of the impeller would you select for pump required to handle (i) water, (ii) sediment – water mixture, (iii) molasses ?
143. State the effect of change in speed of a centrifugal pump on discharge, power and head.
144. The model of a pump required for pumping a very viscous liquid is to be tested. Are the similarity laws given in Chapter 17 adequate for this ?

Chapter 18

145. Explain the working and utility of the following devices :

(i) hydraulic lift,

(ii) hydraulic press,

(iii) hydraulic accumulator,

(iv) differential accumulator,

(v) hydraulic ram, and

(vi) hydraulic intensifier.

APPENDIX II

VISCOSITY OF COMMON LIQUIDS

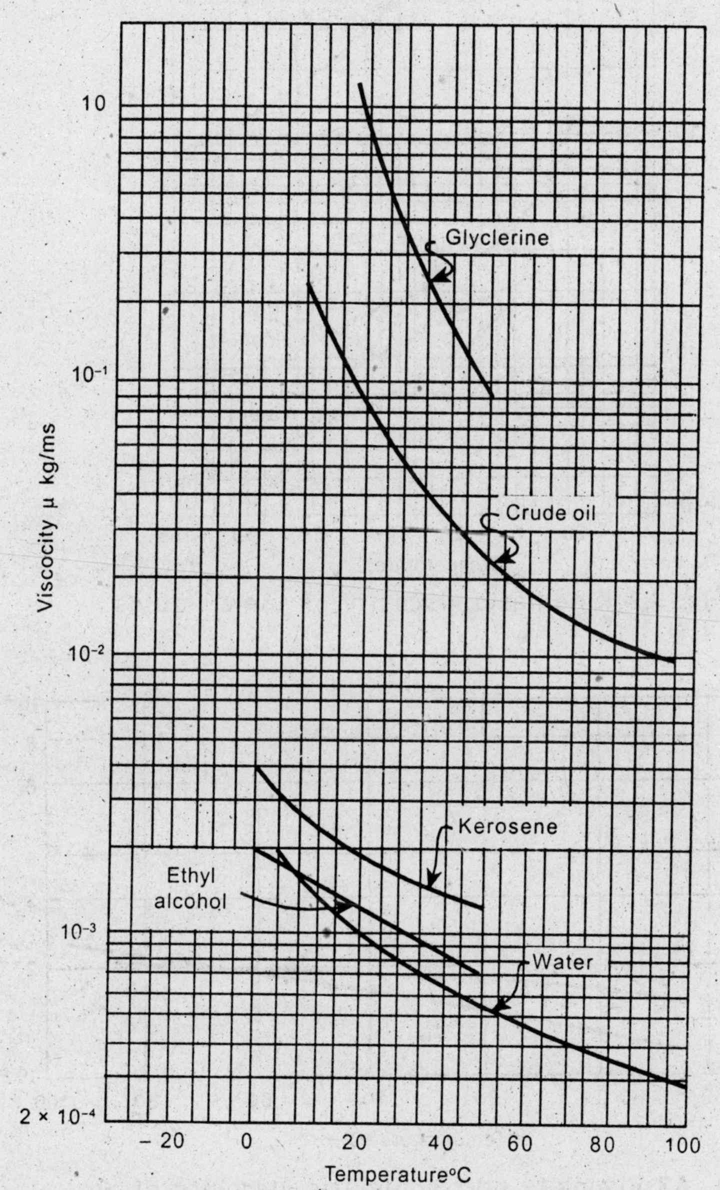

Fig. A1 Viscosity of some common fluids

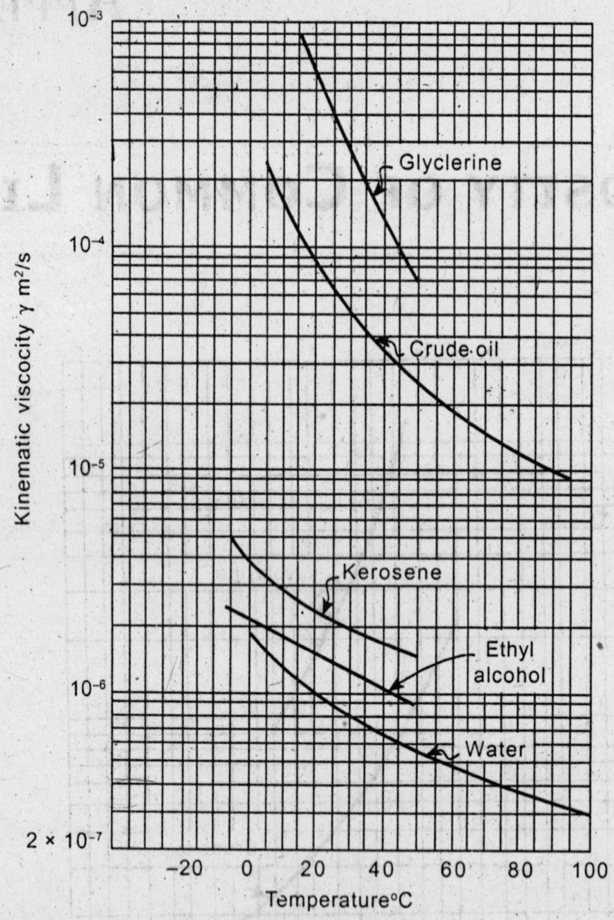

Fig. A2 Kinematic viscosity of some liquids

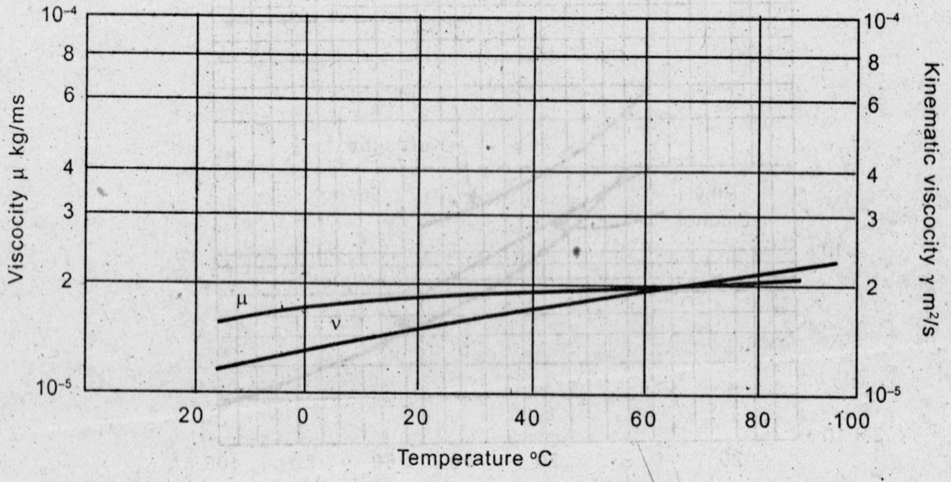

Fig. A3 Viscosity and Kinematic viscosity of air

INDEX

D

T

APPENDIX - III

The varied flow function

$$F(u, N) = \int_0^u \frac{du}{1 - u^N}$$ with constant of integration adjusted so that F(O, N) = 0 and F(∞, N) = 0.

u \ N	2.50	3.0	3.33	4.00	u \ N	2.50	3.0	3.33	4.00
0.00	0.000	0.000	0.000	0.000	0.63	0.700	0.676	0.66	0.652
0.02	0.020	0.020	0.020	0.020	0.64	0.716	0.690	0.679	0.664
0.04	0.040	0.040	0.040	0.040	0.65	0.46	0.703	0.692	0.676
0.06	0.060	0.060	0.060	0.060	0.66	0.72	0.717	0.705	0.688
0.08	0.080	0.080	0.080	0.080	0.67	0.76	0.731	0.718	0.701
0.10	0.100	0.100	0.100	0.100	0.68	0.777	0.746	0.732	0.713
0.12	0.120	0.120	0.120	0.120	0.69	0.795	0.761	0.746	0.726
0.14	0.140	0.140	0.140	0.140	0.70	0.811	0.776	0.760	0.739
0.16	0.161	0.160	0.160	0.160	0.71	0.828	0.791	0.775	0.752
0.18	0.181	0.180	0.180	0.180	0.72	0.845	0.807	0.790	0.766
0.20	0.201	0.200	0.200	0.200	0.73	0.863	0.823	0.805	0.780
0.22	0.222	0.221	0.220	0.220	0.74	0.881	0840	0.821	0.794
0.24	0.243	0.41	0.240	0.240	0.75	0.900	0.857	0.837	0.808
0.26	0.263	0.261	0.261	0.260	0.76	0.919	0.874	0.852	0.823
0.28	0.284	0.282	0.281	0.280	0.77	0.40	0.892	0.870	0.838
0.30	0.305	0.302	0.301	0.300	0.78	0.962	0.911	0.887	0.854
0.32	0.326	0.323	0.322	0.321	0.79	0.985	0.930	0.905	0.870
0.34	0.347	0.343	0.342	0.341	0.80	1.008	0.950	0.924	0.887
0.36	0.368	0.364	0.363	0.361	0.81	1.032	0.971	0.943	0.904
0.38	0.391	0.385	0.383	0.381	0.82	1.057	0.993	0.963	0.922
0.40	0.413	0.407	0.404	0402	0.83	1.083	1.016	0.985	0.940
0.42	0.435	0.428	0.425	0.423	0.84	1.110	1.040	1.007	0.960
0.44	0.458	0.450	0.447	0.447	0.85	1.139	1.065	1.030	0.980
0.46	0.481	0.472	0.469	0.464	0.96	1.171	1.092	1.055	1.002
0.48	0.504	0.494	0.490	0.485	0.87	1.205	1.120	1.081	1.025
0.50	0.528	0.517	0.512	0.506	0.88	1.241	1.151	1.109	1.049
0.52	0.553	0.540	0.533	0.528	0.89	1.279	1.183	1.139	1.075
0.54	0.578	0.563	0.557	0.550	0.90	1.319	1.218	1.172	1.103
0.56	0.604	0.587	0.580	0.572	0.91	1.362	1.257	1.206	1.133
0.58	0.631	0.612	0.604	0.594	0.92	1.400	1.300	1.246	1.166
0.60	0.658	0.637	0.628	0.617	0.93	1.455	1.348	1.290	1.204
0.61	0.673	0.650	0.641	0.628	0.94	1.520	1.403	1.340	1.246
0.62	0.686	0.663	0.653	0.640	0.950	1.605	1.467	1.398	1.296

u \ N	2.50	3.0	3.33	4.00
0.960	1.703	1.545	1.468	1.355
0.970	1.823	1.644	1.559	1.431
0.975	1.899	1.707	1.615	1.478
0.980	1996	1.783	1.684	1.536
0.985	2.111	1.880	1.772	1.610
0.990	2.273	2.017	1.895	1.714
0.995	2.550	2.250	2.106	1.889
0.999	3.195	2.788	2.590	2.293
1.000	/	∞	∞	∞
1.001	2.786	2.814	1.907	1.508
1.005	2.144	1.649	1.425	1.107
1.010	1.867	1.419	1.218	0.936
1.015	1.705	1.286	1.099	0.836
1.020	1.602	1.191	1.014	0.766
1.03	1.436	1.060	0.896	0.688
1.04	1.321	0.967	0.813	0.600
1.05	1.242	0.896	0.749	0.548
1.06	1.166	0.838	0.697	0.506
1.07	1.111	0.790	0.651	0.471
1.08	1.059	0.749	0.618	0.441
1.09	1.012	0.713	0.586	0.415
1.10	0.973	0.681	0.558	0.392
1.11	0.939	0.652	0.532	0.372
0.12	0.907	0.626	0.509	0.354
1.13	0.878	0.602	0.488	0.337
1.14	0.851	0.581	0.479	0.322
1.15	0.824	0.561	0.452	0.308
1.16	0.802	0.542	0.436	0.295
1.17	0.782	0.25	0.421	0.283
1.18	0.760	0.509	0.406	0.272
1.19	0.740	0.494	0.393	0.262
1.20	0.723	0.480	0.381	0.252
1.22	0.692	0.454	0.358	0.235
1.24	0.666	0.431	0.338	0.219
1.26	0.633	0.410	0.320	0.205
1.28	0.609	0.391	0.303	0.193
1.30	0.587	0.373	0.289	0.181
1.32	0.568	0.357	0.275	0.171
1.34	0.549	0.342	0.262	0.162

u \ N	2.50	3.0	3.33	4.00
1.36	0.531	0.329	0.251	0.153
1.38	0.513	0.316	0.239	0.145
1.40	0.496	0.304	0.229	0.138
1.42	0.481	0.293	0.220	0.131
1.44	0.467	0.282	0.211	0.125
1.46	0.455	0.272	0.203	0.119
1.48	0.444	0.263	0.196	0.113
1.50	0.432	0.255	0.1888	0.108
1.55	0.405	0.235	0.172	0.097
1.60	0.380	0.218	0.158	0.087
1.65	0.359	0.203	0.145	0.079
1.70	0.340	0.189	0.135	0.072
1.75	0.322	0.177	0.125	0.65
1.80	0.308	0.166	0.116	0.60
1.85	0.293	0.156	0.108	0.55
1.90	0.279	0.147	0.102	0.050
1.95	0.268	0.139	0.095	0.046
2.00	0.257	0.132	0.089	0.043
2.10	0.238	0.119	0.079	0.037
2.20	0.220	0.107	0.071	0.032
2.3	0.204	0.098	0.064	0.028
2.4	0.190	0.089	0.057	0.024
2.5	0.179	0.082	0.052	0.022
2.6	0.169	0.076	0.048	0.019
2.7	0.160	0.070	0.043	0.017
2.8	0.150	0.065	0.040	0.015
2.9	0.142	0.060	0.037	0.014
3.0	0.135	0.056	0.034	0.012
3.5	0.106	0.041	0.024	0.008
4.0	0.087	0.031	0.017	0.005
4.5	0.072	0.025	0.013	0.004
5.0	0.062	0.019	0.010	0.003
6.0	0.048	0.014	0.007	0.002
7.0	0.038	0.010	0.005	0.001
8.0	0.031	0.008	0.004	0.001
9.0	0.027	0.006	0.003	0.000
10.0	0.022	0.005	0.002	0.000
20.0	0.051	0.002	0.001	0.000

Answers to Problems

1.1 10.10 kN/m^3
0.99×10^{-4} m^3/N

1.2 7840.446 N/m^3

1.3 250.0 kN/m^2

1.4 9.98×10^{-4} kg/m s

1.5 0.000 1293 m^3/N

1.7 0.0882 st
0.0882×10^{-4} m^2/s
0.0075 N s/m^2

1.8 1.480×10^{-5} m^2/s

1.9 0.575 N/m^2
0.316 N/m^2

1.10 6.38×10^{-4} m^2/s

1.11 0.9807 N s/m^2

1.12 2.275×10^{-3} N s/m^2

1.13 1.375×10^{-3} N s/m^2

1.14 $2.3\,47 \times 10^{8}$ N/m^2

1.15 $E = \rho \dfrac{dp}{d\rho}$

1.16 0.288 kN/m^2

1.17 680 kN/m^2
340 kN/m^2
680 kN/m^2

1.18 3321.52 kN/m^2

1.19 897.27 kN/m^2

1.20 1.73 mm

1.21 0.002 mm

1.22 $h = \dfrac{2\sigma \cos\theta}{t\gamma}$

1.23 1078 kg/m^3

1.24 2.5 m

1.25 0.278

1.26 0.10×10^{-4} J

2.1 Unsteady
Nonuniform
Unsteady nonuniform
Nonuniform
Unsteady

2.2 0.045 m^3/s, 45.0 l/s

2.3 20.0 cm/s
30.0 l/s

2.4 6.062 l/sm

2.5 (i) Yes
(ii) Yes
(iii) No

2.6 (i) $w = -6xz - 2xz^2 + f(x, y, t)$
(ii) $w = -4xz - 2yz - \dfrac{2}{3} z^3 + (x, y, t)$

2.9 $3x^2 - y^3 = -113$

2.10 5.372 m/s

2.11 8.44 m/s

2.12 6.38 m/s

2.13 31.24 m/s^2
47.68 m/s^2
$a_x = 0.05\ 42/(0.30-0.15x)^2$

2.14 76.25 cm/s^2
357.60 cm/s^2

2.15 1.962

2.16 24

2.17 13.8 m/s^2

2.18 – A

2.19 $\psi = -y^2/4 + \text{const.}$
Yes

2.22 (i) Yes
(ii) Yes
(iii) Yes
(iv) Yes

2.23 8.65
$\tan^{-1}\left(\frac{1}{\sqrt{2}}\right)$

2.24 7.211
$\tan^{-1}\left(\frac{2}{3}\right)$

2.25 $\phi = -V(x \cos\theta + y \sin\theta) + C$
$\psi = V(x \sin\theta - y \cos\theta) + C$

2.26 $\psi = 2Axy + C$

2.27 2A

2.28 (– 9, – 3)
(– 9, – 9)
12 units

2.29 $2\pi A$, zero

2.30 $\left(1, \frac{4}{3}\right)$

3.1 35.593 kN/m^2

3.2 50.783 kN/m^2

3.3 101.551.7 N/m^2
99 344.9 N/m^2

3.4 0.159 m^3/s
6.25 m/s
176.859 kN/m^2

3.7 1 .133

3.8 2.00
1.10
2.00

3.9 0.277 m^3/s

3.10 80.477 kW

3.11 8.211 kN/m^2
31.74 kN/m^2

3.13 92.281 kN/m^2

3.16 3.52 m
From X to Y

3.17 1.653 m/s

3.18 201.73 kN/m^2

3.19 1.128

3.20 0.137 m^3/s

4.1 407139 N/m^2
407.139 kN/m^2
4.07 139 bars

4.2 0.4086 kN
0.073 55 kW

4.3 33.340 kN/m^2

4.4 25.446 kN/m^2
125.446 kN/m^2
106.434 kN/m^2
206.434 kN/m^2

4.5 77.632 kN/m^2
80.199 kN/m^2

4.6 19.755 kN/m^2

4.7 0.762 m

4.8 28.921 kN/m^2

4.9 – 32.835 kN/m^2

4.10 0.252 m

4.11 1.0

4.12 0.925 kN/m^2

4.13	0.428 mm
4.14	22.974 kN/m²
4.15	244.67 N 68.51 N
4.16	4404.150 kN/m² 20 m below w.s.
4.17	34.573 kN 4.514 m
4.19	49.698 kN 2.88 m
4.20	53.420 3.148
4.21	244.33 kN 8.6°
4.23	8.743 kN/m³
4.24	0.2288 m
4.25	0.34 m
4.27	$\frac{D}{\sqrt{8(1-S)S}}$
4.28	0.25 m 1.50 m above base
4.29	84.042 kN 164.26 kN
4.30	0.816 m/s² 9.807 kN/m². 19.614 kN/m²
4.31	– 799.24 N/m² (gauge) 22.898 kN/m² (gauge
4.33	17.358 kN/m²
4.35	32.852 kN/m² 6.77 m 105.911 kN/m²
4.36	0.41 m³ 1.275 m
4.37	100 rpm
5.2	156.90 N/m²
5.3	380.66 kN/m²
5.4	13.88 kN/m²
5.5	0.644
5.6	67.72 kN/m²
5.7	6.44 cm 5450 N/m²
5.8	321.03 kN/m²
5.9	0.98
5.10	1.15 m
5.11	23.55 cm
5.12	265 cm²
5.13	1.039 m³/s 1.283 m/s
5.15	1.0 m
5.16	0.0885 m³/s 8.0 m
5.17	32.75 *l*/s 7.56 m. 9.12 m
5.18	1.065
5.19	2.83 m
5.20	0.125 m³/s m
5.21	7.79 m³/s
5.22	116.0 m³/s
5.23	9.22 m³/s
5.25	0.99 m
5.26	12.22 m³/s
5.28	2.19 m
5.29	3.92 m³ /s 4.38 m³/s
5.30	E*l*. 101.84
5.31	14.7 *l*/s
5.32	45.4 m
5.33	120 m/s 113.85 kN/m²
5.34	4.52 m /s 2.58 m/s
5.35	Two pipes of 4.0 cm dia
6.1	36.540 kN
6.2	1818.5 N

6.3 $\overleftarrow{11.307 \text{ kN}}$
1.538 kN ↑
7°46′

6.4 $\overleftarrow{87.1 \text{ kN}}$
26.04 ↑ kN

6.5 $\overleftarrow{3035.6 \text{ N}}$
2140.5 ↑ N
35°11′

6.7 1.333
28/27
1.333
1.333

6.8 $\overleftarrow{22\,373 \text{ kN}}$
81.543 ↑ kN

6.9 3.43

6.10 $\overleftarrow{286.07 \text{ kN}}$

6.11 206.54 kN/m² (gauge)

6.12 1232.71 m/s

6.13 0.537 N

6.14 $\overrightarrow{10\,199 \text{ N}}$
3893 ↓ N

6.15 2540 N

6.16 19.6 l/s

6.17 1765 N
8.850 kW

6.18 $\overrightarrow{200 \text{ N}}$
345.2 ↓ N

6.19 $\overleftarrow{698.35 \text{ N}}$
187.12 ↑ N
5.18 m/s
6.98 kW

6.20 588.75 N
2.944 kW
37.5 percent

6.21 $\overrightarrow{95.315 \text{ N}}$
21.13 ↓ N
1.144 kW

6.22 886.22 N
4.927 kW
71.46%

6.23 1.367 N m
48.336 rad/s

7.1 $\tau = 0.0021\ \rho\ U^2 R^{-1/3}$

7.2 (i) $\dfrac{U}{\sqrt{gl}}$ (ii) $\dfrac{\rho U^2 l}{\sigma}$

(iii) $\dfrac{U}{\sqrt{E/\rho}}$ (iv) $U\sqrt{t/\nu}$

(v) $Q\rho\ /\ l\mu$ (vi) $\Delta p\ /\ \rho U^2$

(vii) $\nu t\ /\ l^2$ (viii) $\dfrac{\Delta p l}{\mu U}$

(ix) $\dfrac{\tau}{\mu du/dy}$ (x) $\Delta p\ /\ \gamma l$

7.3 (i) yes (ii) no (iii) yes
(iv) yes (v) yes.

7.4 first equation

7.5 $y = \text{Const.}\ (q^2/g)^{1/3}$

7.6 $P = \text{Const.}\ (Q\gamma\ H)$

7.7 $\dfrac{Q}{d^2\sqrt{\Delta p/\rho}} = f\ (D/d)$

7.8 $\delta/x = f(Ux\ \rho/\mu)$

7.9 $\delta' = \text{Const.}\ \dfrac{\mu}{\tau_0^{1/2}\rho^{1/2}}$

7.10 $\dfrac{u}{u_*} = f\left(\dfrac{u_* y}{\nu}\right)$

7.11 $\dfrac{P}{\rho\omega^3 D^5} = f\left(\dfrac{Q}{\omega D^3}\right)$

7.12 $\dfrac{y^2\rho(du/dy)}{\mu}$

7.13 $p = \text{Const.}\ (\rho\omega^2 r^2)$

7.14 $\dfrac{T}{\mu\omega R^3} = f\left(\dfrac{y}{R}\right)$

7.15 $\dfrac{\tau_0}{\Delta\gamma s d} = f\left(\dfrac{d^3\Delta\gamma s\rho}{\mu^2}\right)$

7.16 $\dfrac{q}{H\sqrt{gH}} = f\left(\dfrac{W}{H}, \dfrac{\rho g H^2}{\sigma}, \dfrac{g^{1/2}H^{3/2}}{\nu}\right)$

7.18 $\eta = f\left(\dfrac{Q}{\omega D^3}, \dfrac{\rho\omega D^2}{\mu}\right)$

7.19 $f\left(\dfrac{Q}{ND^3}, \dfrac{d^2 N\rho}{\mu}, \dfrac{\gamma}{\rho d N^2}, \dfrac{\rho d^3 N^2}{\sigma}\right) = 0$

.20 $\dfrac{F}{l^2\rho U^2} = f\left(\dfrac{\rho U l}{\mu}, \dfrac{U}{\sqrt{gl}}\right)$

.21 $\dfrac{\Delta p}{\rho U^2} = f\left(\dfrac{d}{D}, \dfrac{Ud\rho}{\mu}\right)$

.22 $\dfrac{F}{l^2\rho U^2} = f\left(\dfrac{\rho U l}{\mu}, \dfrac{U}{\sqrt{E/\rho}}\right)$

.24 $\dfrac{W}{\gamma D^3} = f\left(\dfrac{\sigma}{\gamma D^2}\right)$

.25 $\dfrac{p_s}{\rho_0 U_0^2} = f\left(\dfrac{U}{\sqrt{E/\rho_0}}\right)$

7.26 $\dfrac{y}{\sqrt[3]{q^2/g}} = f\left(x\Big/\sqrt[3]{q^2/g}\right)$

7.27 $h/D = f\ (L/D,\ U^2/gD)$

7.28 $\dfrac{nD}{U} = f\ (UD\rho/\mu)$

7.29 $Q_r = Lrhr^{3/2}$

7.30 (i) $L_r = Er/\rho r$

(ii) $L_r = \sqrt{\sigma_r/\rho_r}$

(iii) $L_r = (\mu_r/\rho_r)^{2/3}$

7.31 1.0 m/s

7.32 6.40 km/hr

7.33 119.65 kN/m², 68.0 *l*/s

7.34 0.8 m

1.67 m

0.22 m

0.387 m³/s

7.35 3.4×10^{-2} st

7.36 120 kN

7.38 485 s

7.39 18 atmospheres

7.40 $\sqrt{E_r/\rho_r}$, $E_r/\rho_r\ l_r$

8.1 300 35.6 N/m²

8.2 0.990 N s/m²

8.3 0.0916 *l*/s

7.159 N/m²

3.142 N m/s

8.4 13.12 cm

8.5 25.5 cm

1.884 kW

8.7 0.084 cm

8.8 15 053 N/m²

3.68 m/s

488

8.9 0.772 N s/m²

8.10 0.230 N s/m²

8.11 0.64×10^{-2} N s/m²

8.12 9.95×10^{-3} poise

8.13 28.13 cc/min

8.14 25.92 kN/m²
450.0 kN/m²

8.15 $\frac{2}{9}\ \frac{UD\rho}{\mu}$

8.16 100.2 kN/m³
4.0 m/s

8.17 $\frac{h_f}{L} = \frac{U^2}{2g}\frac{1}{R_e}$

8.19 3.993 N m.

8.20 1623 kN/m²

8.21 29.5 cm/s

8.22 2.00; 1.33

8.23 2.5 cm/s

9.1 2.13 cm, 0.576 cm

9.3 Turbulent after 0.167 m
Laminar
Turbulent after 0.0735 m

9.4 1.35 cm
1.51 cm

9.5 2.408, 0.803

9.6 8.913 N
1.585 N/m²

9.7 0.00520

9.8 11.82 W

9.9 1.42×10^7
5.90 m/s
45.70 N/m²
38.06 N/m²

9.10 2.618

9.11 17.804 kN
6.339 kN

9.12 Smooth
Transition

9.13 2.34 mm

9.14 3.093
7.50 m

9.15 (i) $\frac{1}{2}, \frac{1}{6}$ (ii) $\frac{3}{8}, \frac{39}{280}$

9.16 $\frac{\sqrt{8\alpha_1\beta_1}}{R_{eL}^{1/2}}$

9.17 $\frac{5.836}{R_{ex}^{1/2}}, \frac{0.686}{R_{ex}^{1/2}}, \frac{1.372}{R_{eL}^{1/2}}$

9.18 $\frac{\delta}{x} = \frac{0.37}{R_{ex}^{1/5}}$

$c_f = \frac{0.0576}{R_{ex}^{1/5}}$

10.1 13.037 m/s
0.0138 m²/s²
0.009

10.3 0.223

10.4 1475 *l*/m

10.5 3.37 mm
42.56 N/m²
0.0395
2.94 m/s

10.6 0.140 m³/s
5.835 W

10.7 1.68, 3.05

10.8 0.0615 mm

10.9 17.97 m/s

10.10 35.2 *l*/s
0.0475
3.76 mm

10.11 0.0576 m/s

10.12 1.412 m/s

10.13 10.64 cm

10.14 9.94 cm

10.15 2417.28 kW

10.16 39.0 *l*/s

10.17 1.16 mm

10.18 (i) 4 mm
(ii) 0.667 mm

10.19 $\frac{C}{C_a} = e^{-\omega(y-a)/Ds}$

10.20 0.465 mm, 25.5 *l*/s, 583 *l*/s

11.1 22.113 m
3.605 m

11.2 42.6 *l*/s

11.3 100 D_2(In addition to length required for expansion)

11.4 142.645 kN/m^2

11.5 0.138 m
2.00 m

11.6 69.80 *l*/s

11.7 53.99 *l*/s

11.8 9 cm dia pipe will carry more discharge

11.9 60. 7 *l*/s

11.10 63.39 kW

11.11 0.033
1.31 mm

11.12 16.70 cm

11.13 14.30 m
25.17 kW

11.15 1.60 m^3/s

11.16 33.6 mm

11.17 3.807 cm

11.18 9.19 kW

11.19 148.5 *l*/s
3.54 m

11.20 25.34 m

11.21 65.57 *l*/s
5.877 m (abs)
6.124 m (abs)

11.23 30.70, 84.0 *l*/s
168.0 *l*/s, 297.0 *l*/s

11.24 42.28 *l*/s

11.25 7.99 *l*/s
22.01 *l*/s

11.26 32.1 *l*/s

11.27 46.7 cm

11.28 49.3 *l*/s
25.0 *l*/s
24.3 *l*/s

11.29 5.37 m below A

11.30

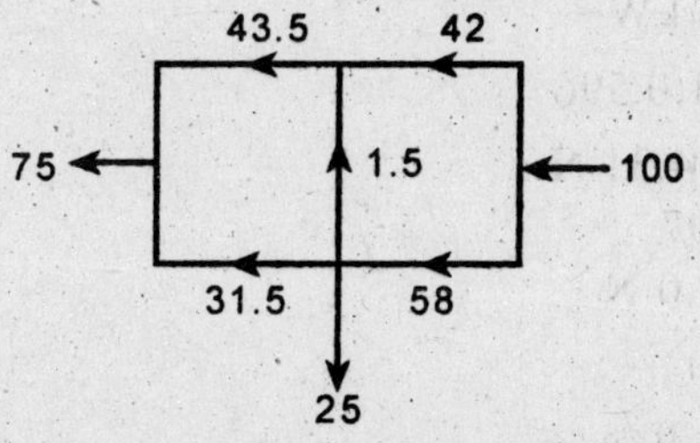

11.31

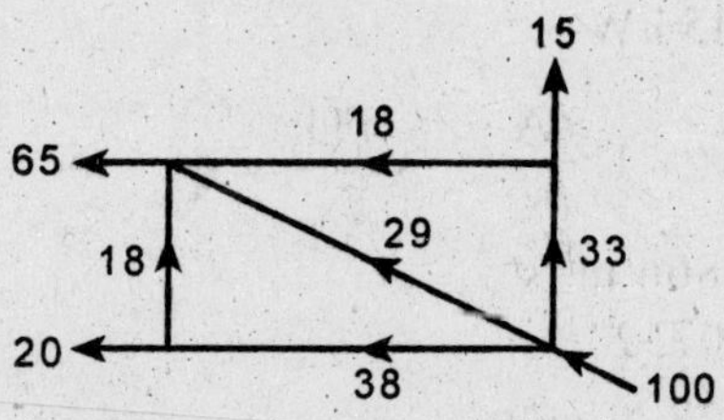

11.32

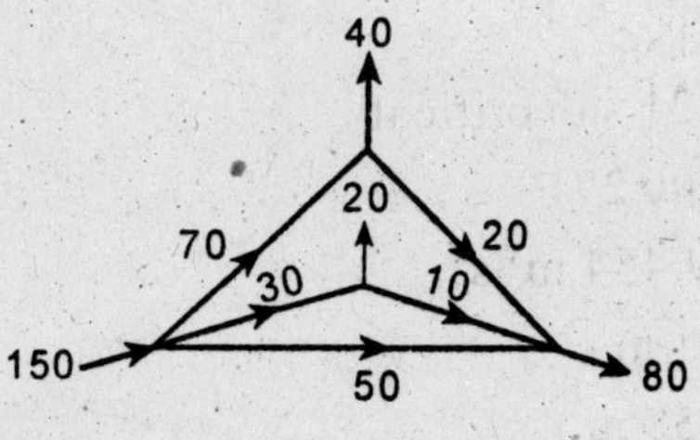

12.1 0.41

12.2 1122.75 N/m

12.3 0.353 m/s

12.4 218

12.5 264 250 N m

12.6 2.92 St

12.7 98.13 N

12.8 1112.4 N

12.9 16.1 kW

12.10 7262 N m^3

12.11 49.36 m^2/s
− 51.7° and 231.7°
4926.1 kN
9.87

12.12 382 rpm

12.13 0.323

12.14 143 167 N
3977 kW

12.15 0.381,0.596

12.16 31454.31 N
0.0107
1398.0 N

12.17 0.210
17.5 m^2/s
1.915°

12.18 1145 kW

13.1 $\frac{\partial A}{\partial t} + U\frac{\partial A}{\partial x} + A\frac{\partial U}{\partial x} = q$

13.5 0.7866 m^3/s

13.6 0.00732

13.7 7.528 N/m^2

13.8 83.68 *l*/s

13,9 0.0184
56.21 sub critical

13.11 0.000 291

13.12 319.454 m^3/s

13.13 1.31 m

13.14 1.758 m

13.16 69.707 m^3/s

13.17 869.0 m^3/s

13.19 0.382 N/m^2

13.20 Ripple and dune,
Plane bed and standing waves,
Antidunes

13.23 5.0 cm

13.24 54.25 m^3/s
0.000 61

13.25 0.003 43
5.754 m^3/s m

13.26 5.933 m
4.800 m
0.000 7578

13.32 $\alpha = (n + 1)^3/n^2\,(n + 3)$
$\beta = (n+1)^2/n(n+2)$

13.33 1.30 m
1.775 m
1.05 m

13.34 1.462 m^3/s m
Turbulent
Rapid
0.936 m, 2.744 m^3
0.602 m
0.735 m

13.35 0.663 m

13.36 0. 841 m

13.38 1.022 m
0.001 05

13.40 1.10 m
1.65 m
3.20 m

13.41 $\left(P\frac{\partial A}{\partial y_0} - A\frac{\partial P}{\partial y_0}\right)\Big/P^2 = 0$

13.44 3.33 m

13.45 30.5 cm
2.27 m

13.46 7.17 m^3/s

13.47 1.62 m
0.913 m
1.375 m

13.48 0.97 m drop

13.50 2.335 m^3/s

13.52 On the central floor M_3 curve followed by a hydraulic jump, then M_2; S_2 on the last slope

13.53 M_2, 290.88 m
S_2, 80.0 m
13.54 M_1 curve, 3.85 m
13.56 210 m
13.58 640 m
13.62 Jump followed by S_1 curve on the first slope
13.64 (i) 6.45 m/s, 1.29 m³/s m, 1.07 m/s and 1.04 m
(ii) 0. 188 m, 13.30 m/s, 2.50 m³/s m and 6.60 m
(iii) 1.28 m, 39.06 m/s 19.33 m and 2.59 m/s
13.65 1.076 m, 0.843 m
13.70 265 m from spillway, 280 m
13.71 7.67 m/s
– 2.33 m/s
13.72 0.31 m
5.60 m/s
13.73 14.2 m/s, 15.4 m/s
13.74 14.02 m, 4.68 m/s
13.75 0.018, 66
14.1 142.64 kN/m²
14.2 1.304
14.3 54.15 kN/m²
9.65°C per 1000 m
14.5 6653.25 N m/N
14.6 344.70 N m
993 44 N m
14.7 261.23 kN/m²
86 617.6 N m
14.9 1442 m/s
1097 m/s
1190 m/s
14.11 1280 m/s
14.12 152.87 kN/m²
1.644 kg/m³
50.87°C
14.15 12.86 N/s
14.17 712.13
2.10
252.7
0.567
215.3°C
14.19 268.50 m/s
116.03 °C
1.827 kg/m³
14.20 10.05, 4.404, 0.227.

15.1 2.30 m, 1.15 m/s
2.45 m, 3.25 m
15.2 10.125 kN/m²
15.3 2.99 m/s
15.4 1018 m/s
1060 m/s
890 m/s
15.5 2156.9 kN/m²
2853.5 kN/m²
1624.9 kN/m²
15.6 8.1 *l*/s
15.7 3216.0 kN/m²
180.0 kN/m²
1800.0 kN/m²
15.8 2380.33 kN/m²
26.2 s
15.9 71.75m
15.10 86.28 m
56.75 s
15.11 3.24 hr
15.13 2.912 m
15.14 8.271 m
9. 225 hr
15.16 0.893 hr
15.17 200 s
15.18 104 s
16.1 140.933 kW
16.2 115 908 kW

16.3 17.3 cm

16.4 18.44 cm
1.817 cm
20

16.5 11.70 cm; 1.50 m

16.6 4

16.7 1.304 m
10.68 cm
53.0 cm
13.0 cm
21
singlejet

16.9 212 rpm
2497.5 kW

16.10 68.509 kW
94.3 percent

16.11 332.25 kW
98.15 percent

16.12 3.162
5.395×10^5 Nm
18.025 m^3/s

16.13 Francis
36.60 rpm
4156.92 kW

16.14 180 rpm
268.27 kW

16.15 2.944 kW
2400 rpm

16.16 103.92 rpm
9118.45 kW
0.235 m^3/s

16.17 8373.4 kW
131.625 m

16.18 1.209 m^3/s
3.0 m/s

16.19 8.8 m/s
91.17 percent

16.21 41.92°
147.08°
1.531 m
10.83 cm

16.22 70.156 rpm
1676.26 kW

16.23 4.682 kW
159.31 rpm

16.24 Francis
3 units
25 MW

16.25 Pelton
2 units
90 MW

16.26 Francis

16.28 89.1%
Kaplan
712
1.846

16.29 119.56 m^3/s
62.8°

16.30 5.022 m
168.41 rpm

17.1 26.20 rpm

17.2 11.10 percent
4.40 kW

17.3 1.46 m
6.01 m
11.14 m

17.4 7.869 kW
1.170 kW

17.5 0.673

17.7 2.68 m

17.8 1.225 kW

17.9 0.952
4.894 kW

17.10 5.30 *l*/s
1.037 kW

17.11 39.53°

17.12 – 0.0211 m^3/s
(to the air vessel)
+ 0.0354 m^3/s
(from the air vessel)

17.13	9.63°
	20.20m/s
	5.68°
17.14	64.45 percent
	9.92°
17.15	0.168 m^3/s
17.16	15.70 kW
17.17	79.93 percent
17.18	0.0432 m^3/s
	21.985 kW
17.19	7.8 m/s
	1.5 m/s
	5.717 m
17.20	4 units in series
17.21	3 units in parallel
17.22	177.28 rpm
	1392.90 kW
17.23	240 rpm
17.24	13.92°
	14.68 kW
18.1	25.0 kW
18.2	8.0 N
18.3	0.0167 kW
	120
18.4	50 074 kN
	280 132.50 Nm
18.5	242.6 kN
18.6	35.9 s
18.7	22.54 kN
	338 100 Nm
18.8	106 437.01 Nm
18.9	25.59 cm
18.10	29.14 percent

REFERENCES

1.	Prandtl, L.	Essentials of Fluid Dynar. ics.	Blackie and Sons Ltd., 1952.
2.	Vallentine, H.R.	Applied Hydrodynamics.	Butterworth and Co. Ltd., 1959.
3.	Streeter, V.L.	Fluid Dynamics.	McGraw Hill Book Co., 1948.
4.	Rouse, H.	Elementary Mechanics of Fluid.	John Wiley and Sons Inc., 1946.
5.	Shames, I.H.	Mechanics of Fluid.	McGraw Hill Book Company Inc., 1962.
6.	Olson, R.M.	Essentials of Engineering Fluid Mechanics.	International Text Book Company. 1961.
7.	Sobhagya Mal.	Effect of Shape on the Discharge Coefficient of Sharp Edged Orifice Plates.	M.E. Thesis, Roorkee University, 1965.
8.	Streeter, V.L.	Fluid Mechanics.	McGraw Hill Book Company Inc., 1958
9.	Pao, R.H.F.	Fluid Mechanics.	John Willey and Sons Inc., 1961.
10.	Albertson. M.L., Dai Y.B, Jensen, and H. Rouse.	Diffusion of Submerged Jets.	Trans. ASCE, Vol. 115, 1950.
11.	Francis, J.R.D. A	Text Book of Fluid Mechanics Engineering Students.	Edward Arnold Publishers Ltd., for London, 1958.
12.	Vennard.J.K.	Elementary Fluid Mechanics.	John Wiley and Sons Inc., 1962.
13.	Rouse, H. (Editor)	Engineering Hydraulics.	John Wiley and Sons Inc., 1950.
14.	Rouse, H.	Fluid Mechanics for Hydraulic Engineers.	Dover Publications Inc., 1961.
15.	Langhaar, H.L.	Dimensional Analysis and Theory of Models.	John Wiley and Sons Inc., 1954.
16.	Schlichting. H.	Boundary Layer Theory.	McGraw Hill Book Company Inc. 1955.
17.	Bakhmeteff, B.	The Mechanics of Turbulent Flow.	Princeton University Press, 1941.
18.	Malaika, J.	Flow in Noncircular Conduits.	Proc. ASCE Journal of Hydraulics Division, Nov. 1962.

19.	Woodward, S.M. and Posey, C.J.	Hydraulics of Steady Flow in Open Channels.	John Wiley and Son Inc., 1941.
20.	Bakhmeteff, B.	Hydraulics of Open Channels.	McGraw Hill Book Company Inc., 1932.
21.	Ven Te Chow.	Open Channel Hydraulics.	McGraw Hill Book Company Inc., 1959.
22.	Davis, C.V.	Handbook of Applied Hydraulics.	McGraw Hill Book Company Inc., 1952.
23.	Yuan, S.Y.	Foundations of Fluid Mechanics.	Prentice Hall of India, Private Ltd., 1969.
24.	Eskinazi, S.	Fluid Mechanics and Thermodynamics of Our Environment.	Academic Press, New York., 1975.
25.	Jain A.K.	Accurate Explicit Equation for Friction Factor. Technical Note.	Proc ASCE, JHD Div., May 1976
26.	Hoerner S.F.	Fluid Dynamic Drag.	Midland Park, New Jersey (U.S.A.) 1965
27.	Hwang, L. and E.M Laursen	Shear Measurement Technique for Rough surfaces.	Proc. ASCE, JHD, Vol. 89, No.Hy – 2.